PURE AND APPLIED MATHEMATICS

A Series of Texts and Monographs

Edited by: R. COURANT • L. BERS • J. J. STOKER

Vol. I: **Supersonic Flow and Shock Waves**
By R. Courant and K. O. Friedrichs

Vol. II: **Nonlinear Vibrations in Mechanical and Electrical Systems**
By J. J. Stoker

Vol. III: **Dirichlet's Principle, Conformal Mapping, and Minimal Surfaces**
By R. Courant

Vol. IV: **Water Waves**
By J. J. Stoker

Vol. V: **Integral Equations**
By F. G. Tricomi

Vol. VI: **Differential Equations: Geometric Theory**
By Solomon Lefschetz

Vol. VII: **Linear Operators**
By Nelson Dunford and Jacob T. Schwartz.

Vol. VIII: **Modern Geometrical Optics**
By Max Herzberger

Vol. IX: **Orthogonal Expansions**
By G. Sansone

Additional volumes in preparation

PURE AND APPLIED MATHEMATICS
A Series of Texts and Monographs

Edited by: R. COURANT • L. BERS • J. J. STOKER

VOLUME VIII

MODERN GEOMETRICAL OPTICS

MAX HERZBERGER
RESEARCH LABORATORIES, EASTMAN KODAK COMPANY
ROCHESTER, NEW YORK

19 58

INTERSCIENCE PUBLISHERS, INC., NEW YORK
INTERSCIENCE PUBLISHERS LTD., LONDON

Library of Congress Catalog Card Number 58-9218

INTERSCIENCE PUBLISHERS, INC.
250 FIFTH AVENUE, NEW YORK 1, N.Y.

For Great Britain and Northern Ireland:
INTERSCIENCE PUBLISHERS LTD.
88/90 CHANCERY LANE, LONDON W.C. 2, ENGLAND

PRINTED IN THE NETHERLANDS

To my friends

H. BOEGEHOLD AND T. T. SMITH

the two living men
whose contributions to the field
of modern optics
have been
most precious to me

Preface

This book is the result of more than fourteen years' continuous labor. I am submitting the material now for publication, not because I feel that it represents the ideas in perfected form, but because there has to be an end of revising and supplementing if the book is to reach its readers.

One problem, which led to frequent rewriting, was the choice of the method of presentation. The best way to write the book would have been to start with the law of Fermat, or the equivalent Formula (14.4), and derive from it all the laws systematically. This would lead to an esthetically more pleasing treatment, but one that would require a considerable amount of mathematical knowledge on the part of the reader.

Those who most need a thorough knowledge of the theory of optics are the designers of optical lenses. I have a great admiration for the achievements of commercial designers, but lens design is still more an art than a science and, unfortunately, the acquaintance of the average designer with higher mathematics is limited. Since I hope that, in addition to setting forth a consistent theoretical system, this book will be of use in the practical design of optical instruments, it was necessary to accomplish the desired results with a minimum of mathematical technique. Moreover, the mathematical methods that are used are explained in detail in an appendix prepared by my colleague, Dr. Erich Marchand. I have limited the problems to those which can be treated by these methods.

The aim of the book is nothing less than to develop a mathematical model of an optical system that is complex enough so that all the characteristics of the geometrical optical image can be obtained from it and at the same time simple enough to be intelligible. It may be mentioned that the same model might also be used as a basis for calculating the diffraction image, since it gives the phase relationships in the exit pupil, but this is outside the scope of this book.

Part I concerns the problem of tracing rays through an optical system. Much of the extensive literature on this subject is now obsolete; the particular type of formulae used always depends on the computational tools at the disposal of the designer, and while the manuscript was in preparation, methods of computation that reduce many fold the time required for tracing a ray came into widespread use. The formulae in this book were developed to be suitable for high-speed electronic computers. To these formulae are added independent controls that are carried along in order to check the correctness of the machine operations.

Part II gives the first-order approximation theory (Gaussian optics), for which a new tool, the so-called Gaussian brackets, is introduced. This new tool enables us to investigate the effect of a variation of system data on the constructional elements of the system (focal length, back focus, magnification, etc.). We can thereby compute an approximate system (a system of thin lenses separated by finite distances) which has, in the realm of Gaussian optics, the desired specifications and is also corrected for Petzval sum and longitudinal and lateral color aberrations.

The ideas of Hamilton are derived in Part III as well as other laws of optical image formation. Special emphasis is laid on the study of the different *types* of imagery.

Concentric systems are taken up in Part IV, and it is shown that, for this limited field, a complete mathematical treatment can be given so that all optical systems with specified characteristics can be specified by the system data. If it were possible to extend the methods of this chapter to systems with rotational symmetry, the problem of lens design would change from an art to a science.

Part V emphasizes the specific form which the methods and general laws of Part III assume in systems with symmetry of rotation. A general theorem (22.5) of many applications enables us to investigate the limitations of optical image formation.

In Part VI most of the results of Allvar Gullstrand's work are derived by the method developed in this book. This gives rise to an approximation theory for normal systems along a principal ray.

The results are used in Part VII to develop a new image-error theory that combines third- and fifth-order aberrations for the neighborhood of the axis.

Finally, in Part VIII we develop a mathematical model of an optical system. The results of tracing a few rays, both meridional and skew, from several object points are fitted to a fifth-order formula equivalent to the theory discussed in Part VI. This formula is then used as an interpolation formula to calculate the intersection points of a large number of rays with one or more image planes. The rays are evenly spaced over the exit pupil, and therefore the plots of the intersection points, called spot diagrams, give a record of the distribution of light over the selected image planes. These spot diagrams are treated as vector sums of simple diagrams, and they serve as a new tool in lens design, giving a record of the behavior of all rays from each of the selected object points.

The last chapter indicates how the methods can be applied to the case of inhomogeneous media. The mathematical techniques are developed in an appendix, while other appendices give numerical examples and some remarks on the history of geometrical optics. The book ends with an extensive bibliography of source material.

Some of the mathematical tools used in this book are worthy of special mention. The treatment is simplified by considerations of symmetry. The introduction of the concept of the diapoint (the intersection of the image ray with the plane that passes through the object point and the axis of symmetry) also results in a simplification. The treatment of the chromatic aberrations is facilitated by using dispersion formulae that are linear functions of the indices.

A future edition of this book should contain some of the integral laws of optical systems, so important for energy considerations, a more detailed study of the dependence of image errors on the system data, and difference formulae for ray tracing. A chapter should also be added on the evaluation of the image of lines and objects of nonuniform density. In recent years much interest has been aroused in this field, and the many papers now being published will undoubtedly further the development of our science.

I want to thank Dr. Fred Perrin and Dr. Erich Marchand for

their help in the difficult task of editing and proofreading this book; Miss Nancy McClure for her help in preparing the index; Miss Helene Donnelly and Miss McClure for preparing and checking the numerical examples; Mr. James Watts for the preparation of the difficult optical drawings; as well as Mr. Stephen Insalaco, who prepared the drawings for Chapter 12.

I am greatly indebted to my publisher for his patience and to him and the printer for their painstaking care in setting in type such difficult material.

Finally, I want to thank the Eastman Kodak Company, who not only gave me the time to write this book, but put all their many facilities at my disposal.

Rochester, New York M. H.
March 1, 1958

Contents

Part VI. Approximation Theory for Normal Systems

Part VII. Third- and Fifth-Order Image-Error Theory

Part VIII. Interpolation Theory of the Optical Image

Part IX. Optics in General Media

Part X. Appendix

PART I. RAY-TRACING

CHAPTER ONE

The Laws of Refraction and Reflection

Geometrical optics is based on two simple physical assumptions. The first has to do with the behavior of light within a given medium and the other with its behavior in passing from one medium to another.

The velocity of light depends on the medium through which the light passes. Since optical systems are commonly used in air, we may take the velocity in air as the standard and call it c; if the velocity in another medium is designated v, the ratio c/v is defined as the *refractive index* of the second medium with respect to air. The index with respect to vacuum would be only slightly different, since the index of air with respect to free space is only 1.0003.

Except in free space, the velocity of light and therefore the refractive index of the medium varies with wavelength λ, by which is meant the wavelength in space or, practically, in air. This variation of index with wavelength, known as *dispersion*, is negligible for air but is great enough to be very serious for the materials used in optical systems. Unless the contrary is stated or implied, the light will be assumed to be *monochromatic*, which means that the refractive index of a given medium is constant.

If the refractive index is independent of the location of the point under consideration in the medium, the latter is said to be *homogeneous*; if the index is independent of the direction of travel of the light through the point, the medium is said to be *isotropic*. Except when the contrary is stated, all media will be assumed to be both homogeneous and isotropic.

The first basic assumption of geometrical optics is that, in a homogeneous, isotropic medium, light of a given wavelength travels in straight lines called *rays*. The second basic assumption is the law of refraction and reflection. Light rays change their direction in passing from one homogeneous, isotropic medium to another of different refractive index. The surface separating two such media will be assumed to be smooth, that is, it will be considered to be continuous with a continuously varying tangential plane. At such a surface, a light ray is generally split into two parts, one being *refracted* into the second medium and the other being *reflected* backwards into the first medium.

The laws relating to reflection and refraction have a long and interesting history.

The law of reflection—that the angle of reflection equals the angle of incidence—appears as early as 300 B.C. in the "Catoptrics" of *Euclid*. This is very probably the first book on optics, although there is some doubt of its authenticity.

Around 60 B.C., Hero of Alexandria "derived" the law of reflection from a minimum principle: "The light path is the shortest way between two of its points." It is interesting that he draws only planes and convex mirrors to prove his point, and not concave mirrors, for which the principle does not always apply.

The phenomenon of refraction was also known to the Greeks. There is a famous passage in *Plato's* "Timaios" in which Plato tries to prove the unreliability of our perceptions by demonstrating that a stick submerged in water seems to be shorter than in air, whereas, by withdrawing it, one can immediately see that its length has not changed.

Ptolemy of Alexandria (A.D. 150) tried to find the law of refraction by measuring the angle between the incident and the refracted rays for combinations of air and glass, air and water, and water and glass at 10 intervals for the incident angle. *Boegehold* has shown that all his values may not have been observed because they obey too accurately a second-order interpolation formula.

Witelo (Vitellius), about 1270, edited a ten-volume "Handbook on Optics" containing tables for the combinations studied by Ptolemy. The values in these tables certainly could not have been obtained experimentally because some of them go beyond the angle of total reflection. These erroneous tables were unfortunate for *Kepler* when he studied the phenomenon of refraction, about 1610. His account of his numerous unsuccessful attempts to find the law of refraction is worth reading. Eventually he reduced the problem to one of finding a surface which refracts a parallel bundle of rays so that they come to a focus (cf. Chapter 5). He investigated a hyperbolic surface of rotation and obtained the right answer, but dismissed it on the grounds that it did not lead to Witelo's values.

The credit for discovering the law of refraction must be divided between the Dutch physicist *Snell* (Snellius, 1591–1626) and the French mathematician, physicist, and philosopher *Descartes*. Unfortunately, Snell's book that was said to have contained the law was destroyed by fire, so that Descartes' "Dioptrique" (1637) is the first extant publication containing the refraction law. Descartes has been posthumously attacked by I. Voss, who claimed that Descartes had seen Snell's book before its publication. Possibly; but recent studies of some of Descartes' letters by H. Boegehold indicate that Descartes probably knew the law of refraction before his visit to Leyden, where he first became acquainted with Snell.

The *law of refraction*, as discovered by Snell and Descartes, may be stated as follows:

The incident ray and the refracted ray lie in a plane that contains the normal to the refracting surface at the point of incidence (the incidence normal), and the directions of the two rays are related by the equation

$$n \sin i = n' \sin i', \tag{1.1}$$

where n and n' are the refractive indices of the first and second media respectively, i is the angle between the incident ray and

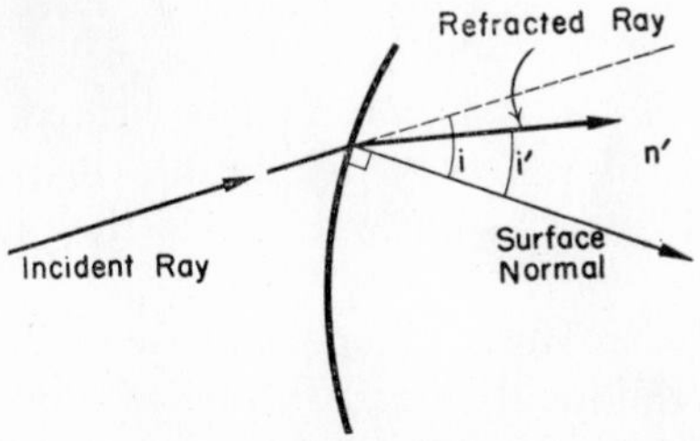

Fig. 1.1. Refraction.

the surface normal (Fig. 1.1), and i', the angle between the refracted ray and the normal. The light will always be assumed to travel from left to right in the drawings (except in certain cases of reflection, to be considered later) and the surface normals will always be drawn from left to right. The positive direction of a ray will always be taken as the direction in which the light travels. Then i will be defined as the angle between the direction of the incidence normal and the positive direction of the incident ray, and i' will be defined correspondingly with respect to the refracted ray. Since two intersecting lines form four angles, we shall assume that $0 \leqq i \leqq \pi$. There is no lack of generality if we assume that $\sin i$ and $\sin i'$ are positive since the calculation formulae involve only the squares of these quantities. (One exception will be made to obtain the traditional formula for meridional rays from our development.)

It should be noted that Equation (1.1) has two solutions, the sum of the two being 180° or π. Only one makes sense physically, however, because the refracted ray must enter the *second* medium. The ambiguity is avoided if one adds to Equation (1.1) the condition that both $\cos i$ and $\cos i'$ shall have the same sign in the case of refraction.

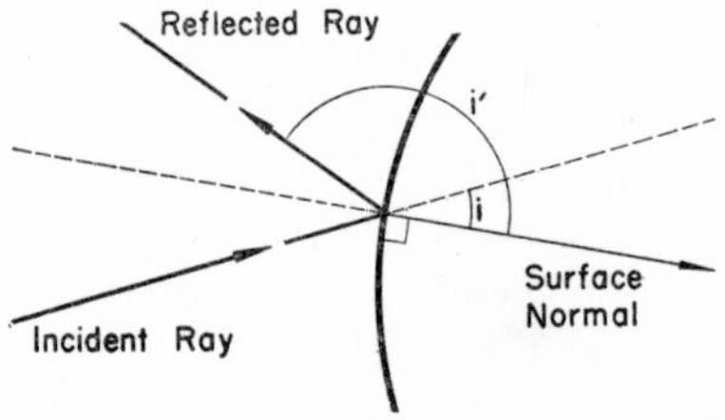

Fig. 1.2. Reflection.

The complete *law of reflection* can be stated as follows: The incident ray and the reflected ray lie in a plane containing the incidence normal, and this normal bisects the angle between the two rays.

This law can be treated as a special case of the refraction law. The direction of the incident ray will be assumed to be from left to right in the drawings, whereas the reflected ray will go from right to left after one or an odd number of reflections. If we set $n = n'$ in Equation (1.1), we obtain

$$\sin i = \sin i'. \tag{1.2}$$

This equation again has two possible solutions, namely, $i' = i$ and $i' = \pi - i$, but only the second solution makes sense physically since the reflected ray must return into the *same* medium as the incident ray. This requirement can be expressed mathematically by demanding that the cosine change its sign, or that simultaneously (Fig. 1.2)

$$\sin i' = \sin i \tag{1.3}$$

and

$$\cos i' = -\cos i,$$

whence

$$i' = \pi - i. \tag{1.4}$$

The author considers that this treatment of the law of reflection is more logical than the widely used convention of postulating a negative refractive index in the case of reflection, since a negative index could have no physical significance.

The case of *normal incidence,* when $i = 0$, gives $i' = 0$ for the refracted ray from Equation (1.1) and $i' = \pi$ for the reflected ray from Equations (1.2) and (1.3). The reflected and the refracted rays therefore lie along the direction of the surface normal.

When a ray goes from an optically dense medium into a less dense medium, $n > n'$ and Equation (1.1) shows that $\sin i'$ may then become greater than unity. This is mathematically impossible, so, for incidence angles greater than i_c as defined by

$$\sin i_c = n'/n, \tag{1.5}$$

no light is refracted and all the incident light is reflected. The angle i_c is called the *critical angle,* and any ray with a greater angle of incidence is *totally reflected.* This phenomenon was discovered by Kepler.

The laws of refraction and reflection are the only physical laws required for geometrical optics. All that follows can be considered to be simply an evaluation of their consequences.

The two parts of the law of refraction—relating to (*a*) the magnitude and (*b*) the coplanarity of angles i and i'—can be combined into a single formula in vector notation.* This is the simplest form for analyzing optical problems.

* The fundamental operations of vector analysis are outlined in the Appendix.

Let $\vec{s}$ be a vector in the direction of the entering ray, its length being equal to the refractive index n of the first medium. Let $\vec{s}'$ be a vector in the direction of the refracted ray, its length being equal to the refractive index n' of the second medium. Let the direction of $\vec{s}$ and $\vec{s}'$ be positive when the vectors point to the right and let $\vec{o}$ be a vector of unit length normal to the refracting surface at the point of incidence and drawn to the right (Fig. 1.3). Then the complete law of refraction can be written as

$$\vec{s} \times \vec{o} = \vec{s}' \times \vec{o} = \vec{j}, \tag{1.6}$$

where the symbol "$\times$" designates the cross or vector product.

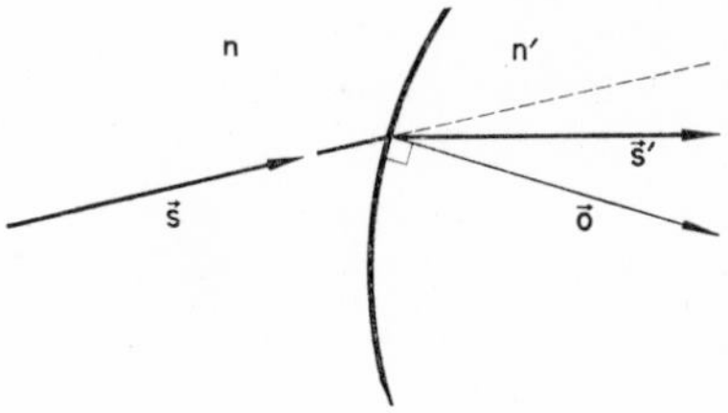

Fig. 1.3. Refraction (vector description).

That this equation represents both parts of the refraction law can be easily seen. The product $\vec{s} \times \vec{o}$ represents a vector normal to the plane of incidence while $\vec{s}' \times \vec{o}$ represents a vector normal to the plane of refraction. The equation states that the two planes coincide, thus fulfilling the first part of the law. Furthermore, the magnitude of $\vec{s}' \times \vec{o}$ is equal to the value of $n \sin i$ and the magnitude of $\vec{s}' \times \vec{o}$ is equal to $n' \sin i'$, and thus the equality of the vector products in Equation (1.6) gives the equation

$$n \sin i = n' \sin i'. \tag{1.7}$$

But this is merely a restatement of Equation (1.1) and thus Equation (1.6) fulfills the second part of the refraction law.

The problem involved in applying the refraction law is to find $\vec{s}$ when $\vec{s}$ and $\vec{o}$ are given. Now (1.6) can be written

$$(\vec{s}' - \vec{s}) \times \vec{o} = 0, \tag{1.8}$$

which means that the vector $(\vec{s}' - \vec{s})$ lies along the direction of $\vec{o}$ since the sine of the angle between $(\vec{s}' - \vec{s})$ and $\vec{o}$ must equal zero. That being the case, it must be possible to multiply the unit vector $\vec{o}$ by some scalar Γ to obtain $(\vec{s}' - \vec{s})$, or

$$\vec{s}' - \vec{s} = \Gamma\,\vec{o}. \tag{1.9}$$

The quantity Γ is frequently called the *astigmatic constant* in the literature because it was first found in connection with the formulae for tracing astigmatism along a ray (*cf.* Chapter 25). We prefer to call it the *deviation constant.*

By the rules of scalar multiplication, it follows from Equation (1.9) that

$$\Gamma = \vec{o}\vec{s}' - \vec{o}\vec{s} = n' \cos i' - n \cos i. \tag{1.10}$$

Introducing the refraction law,

$$\begin{aligned}\vec{o}\vec{s}' &= n' \cos i' = \sqrt{n'^2 - n'^2 \sin^2 i'}\\ &= \sqrt{n'^2 - n^2 \sin^2 i} = \sqrt{n'^2 - n^2 + n^2 \cos^2 i}\\ &= \sqrt{n'^2 - n^2 + (\vec{o}\vec{s})^2},\end{aligned} \tag{1.11}$$

where the sign of the root is positive in the case of refraction. Therefore

$$\Gamma = \sqrt{n'^2 - n^2 + (\vec{o}\vec{s})^2} - \vec{o}\vec{s}. \tag{1.12}$$

With Γ found, the direction of the refracted ray can be determined from Equation (1.9) to be

$$\vec{s}' = \vec{s} + \Gamma\,\vec{o}. \tag{1.13}$$

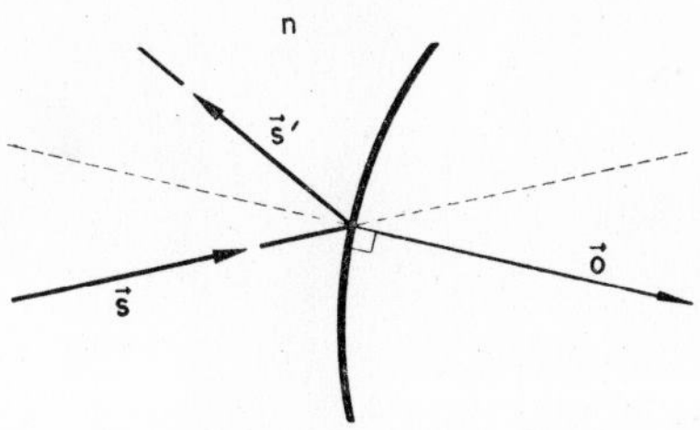

Fig. 1.4. Reflection (vector description).

In the case of *reflection* (Fig. 1.4), Equation (1.10) combined with (1.3) gives

$$\Gamma = -2n \cos i = -2(\vec{o}\vec{s}), \tag{1.14}$$

and substitution in (1.9) then gives

$$\vec{s}' = \vec{s} - 2(\vec{o}\vec{s})\vec{o}. \tag{1.15}$$

The fundamental ray-tracing formulae are thus Equations (1.12) and (1.13) for refraction and (1.15) for reflection.

CHAPTER TWO

Tracing a Ray through a Spherical Surface

The general problem of ray-tracing can be described as follows: We choose a coordinate origin O. The object ray is then given by one of its points, characterized by the directed quantity OA, that is, vector $\vec{a}$ with coordinates (x, y, z) in an arbitrary given Cartesian coordinate system, and the direction vector $\vec{s}$ in the positive direction of the ray with coordinates (ξ, η, ζ) having the length n, n being the refractive index of the medium.

The first problem is to find a value l such that*

$$\vec{a}^* = \vec{a} + l\,\vec{s} \tag{2.1}$$

is the vector from O to the intersection point with the refracting surface. Having calculated the coordinates (x^*, y^*, z^*) of $\vec{a}^*$, we must next calculate the coordinates (α, β, γ) of the unit vector $\vec{o}$ in the direction of the incidence normal. The refraction (reflection) law gives us then, according to the first chapter, the direction vector along the refracted (reflected) ray as

$$\vec{s}' = \vec{s} + \Gamma\,\vec{o}. \tag{2.2}$$

The refracted (reflected) ray is now given by the vector from the origin to one of its points, namely $\vec{a}^*$, and its direction vector $\vec{s}'$. Thus we can continue the procedure, calculating the intersection point with the second surface and so on. Having thus traced the ray from the object point to its intersection point with the last surface $\vec{a}^*$, we can finally calculate in the same way the intersection point with the fixed plane or surface on which we want to investigate the image.

Throughout this book, the object and the image rays will each usually be given by one of its points (vectors $\vec{a}$ or $\vec{a}'$, respectively) and the direction vector $\vec{s}$ or $\vec{s}'$ of length n or n' along the ray. To

* Here nl is the distance between the two points.

have a convenient name, we will call $\vec{a}$ the *initial point*, and $\vec{a}'$, the *terminal point*. Until now, for refraction or reflection at a single surface, we have taken the terminal point as the point of intersection with the surface. This may be slightly modified in the cases in which the optical system has certain symmetry properties, because, in these instances, it may be more convenient to give the refracted (reflected) ray by a different terminal point so as to eliminate the explicit calculation of the point of intersection with the refracting surface.

The Single Refracting (Reflecting) Sphere

In tracing a ray though a single *sphere* it seems appropriate to choose the coordinate origin at the center of the sphere. In this case, the vector $\vec{a}^*$ from the origin to the point of intersection lies along the direction of the surface normal. Thus we can write

$$\vec{a}^* = -r\vec{o}. \tag{2.3}$$

The minus sign in this formula comes from the tradition in optics that the radius is counted from the surface towards the center. Ordinarily the surface separating two media may be assumed to consist of only a small part of the mathematical surface, a sphere in this case. The sign of r can then be used to distinguish the two shells of the sphere from each other.

In all the drawings in this book, we shall assume that light enters the first surface coming from left to right. This direction of the light rays is changed only after an odd number of reflections, as mentioned in Chapter 1. This suggests giving to the radius of a surface which is convex against the original light direction (that is, where the center lies to the right of the surface) a positive sign, and to the radius of a surface which is concave towards the original light direction (that is, where the center lies to the left of the surface) a negative sign.

These sign conventions having been understood, our basic ray-tracing formulae become

$$\begin{aligned} \vec{a} + l\vec{s} &= \vec{a}^* \\ \vec{s}' &= \vec{s} - \phi\,\vec{a}^*, \end{aligned} \tag{2.4}$$

where ϕ is an abbreviation for Γ/r.

A general point on the refracted (reflected) ray is given by

$$\vec{a}' = \vec{a}^* + l' \, \vec{s}' \tag{2.5}$$

with arbitrary l'.

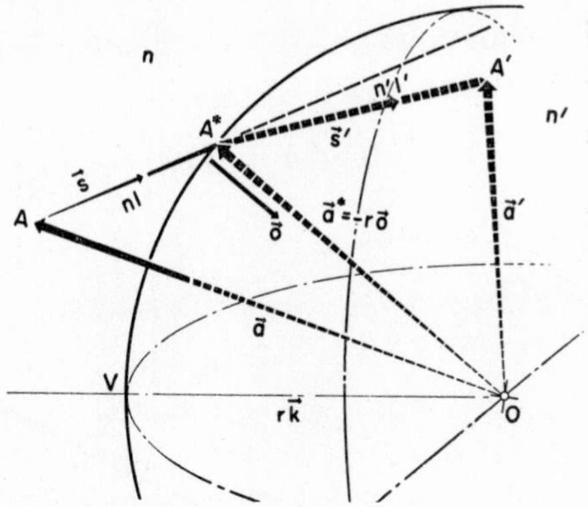

Fig. 2.1. Refraction at a single sphere, origin at center.

Combining the three equations we obtain, eliminating $\vec{a}^*$

$$\vec{a}' = \vec{a}\,(1 - l'\,\phi) + \vec{s}\,(l + l' - ll'\phi)$$
$$\vec{s}' = -\,\vec{a}\,\phi + \vec{s}\,(1 - l\,\phi). \tag{2.6}$$

Choosing the arbitrary point and therefore l' so that the coefficient of $\vec{s}$ vanishes, that is, setting

$$l' = \frac{l}{l\phi - 1} \tag{2.6a}$$

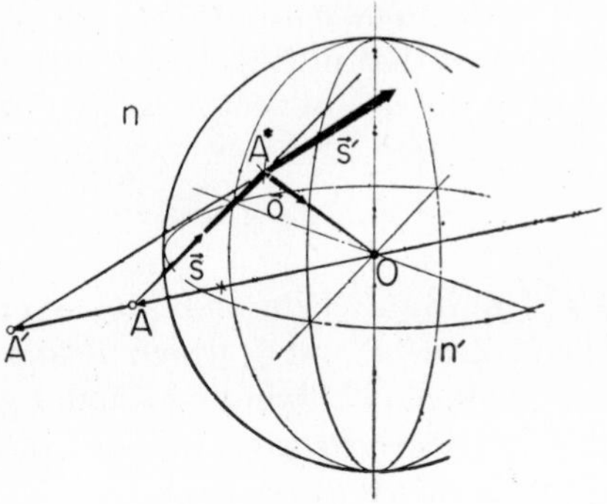

Fig. 2.2. Diapoint trace for refraction at a single sphere.

and abbreviating

$$m = 1 - l' \phi = \frac{1}{1 - l\phi} , \tag{2.7}$$

we establish the equations

$$\begin{aligned} \vec{a}' &= m\,\vec{a} \\ \vec{s}' &= -\,\phi\,\vec{a} + (1/m)\,\vec{s}. \end{aligned} \tag{2.8}$$

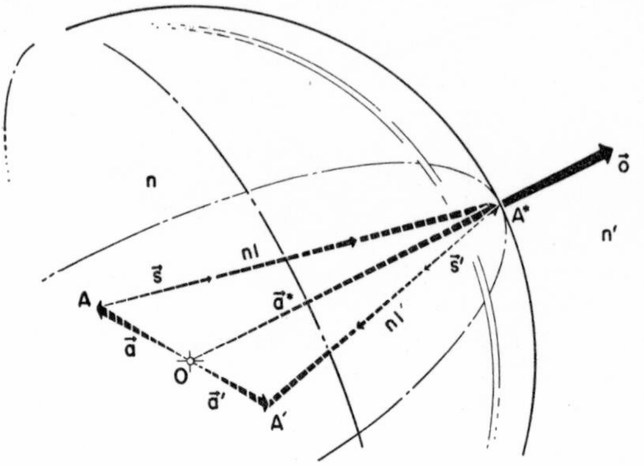

Fig. 2.3. Diapoint trace for reflection at a single sphere.

The terminal point thus chosen has the quality that the initial point (vector $\vec{a}$), origin, and terminal point (vector $\vec{a}'$) lie on a straight line. We call the point A' thus determined the *diapoint* of A, and we call m the *diamagnification.*

Equations (2.6) show that in tracing a ray through a spherical surface, there exists an invariant vector $\vec{J}$. We find from (2.4) and (2.5) that

$$\vec{a}' \times \vec{s}' = \vec{a}^* \times \vec{s}' = \vec{a}^* \times \vec{s} = \vec{a} \times \vec{s} = \vec{J}. \tag{2.9}$$

From Equations (2.6) it may be noted, moreover, that the plane of $\vec{a}$ and $\vec{s}$ contains vectors $\vec{a}'$ and $\vec{s}'$, which means that the tracing of a ray through a sphere is a two-dimensional problem.

These are all results derived from the fact that the refracting surface is a sphere. However, to trace a ray, we must still solve the following problem: Given the vectors $\vec{a}$ and $\vec{s}$ by their coordinates (x, y, z), (ξ, η, ζ), respectively, we want to find l, ϕ, and m as functions of these coordinates.

From the symmetry of the problem we may conclude that l, ϕ, and m are functions only of the symmetric functions of $\vec{a}$ and $\vec{s}$:

$$\begin{aligned} \vec{a}^2 &= x^2 + y^2 + z^2 = 2U \\ \vec{a}\vec{s} &= x\,\xi + y\,\eta + z\,\zeta = V. \end{aligned} \tag{2.10}$$

Multiplying Equations (2.4) scalarly by $\vec{s}$ and $\vec{a}^*$, respectively, and taking into account that

$$\begin{aligned} \vec{s}^2 &= n^2 \\ \vec{a}^{*2} &= r^2 \end{aligned} \tag{2.11}$$

we obtain

$$\begin{aligned} n^2 l &= \vec{a}^*\vec{s} - \vec{a}\vec{s} \\ r^2\phi &= \vec{a}^*\vec{s} - \vec{a}^*\vec{s}'. \end{aligned} \tag{2.12}$$

The expressions $\vec{a}^*\vec{s}$ and $\vec{a}\vec{s}$ are obtained from Equation (2.9) and the resulting vector equations:

$$\begin{aligned} \vec{J}^2 = (\vec{a} \times \vec{s})^2 &= \vec{a}^2\vec{s}^2 - (\vec{a}\vec{s})^2 = 2Un^2 - V^2 \\ = (\vec{a}^* \times \vec{s})^2 &= \vec{a}^{*2}\vec{s}^2 - (\vec{a}^*\vec{s})^2 = r^2n^2 - (\vec{a}^*\vec{s})^2 \\ = (\vec{a}^* \times \vec{s}')^2 &= \vec{a}^{*2}\vec{s}'^2 - (\vec{a}^*\vec{s}')^2 = r^2n'^2 - (\vec{a}^*\vec{s}')^2, \end{aligned} \tag{2.13}$$

from which we derive (for the case of refraction)

$$\begin{aligned} \vec{a}^*\vec{s} &= -r\sqrt{n^2 - \frac{1}{r^2}(2Un^2 - V^2)} \\ \vec{a}^*\vec{s}' &= -r\sqrt{n'^2 - \frac{1}{r^2}(2Un^2 - V^2)}. \end{aligned} \tag{2.14}$$

The minus sign in (2.14) is the result of the definition of r given in (2.3). By using this definition Equations (2.14) give (with the correct sign)

$$\begin{aligned} -\frac{1}{r}\,\vec{a}^*\vec{s} &= Q = \sqrt{n^2 - (1/r^2)\,\vec{J}^2} \\ -\frac{1}{r}\,\vec{a}^*\vec{s}' &= Q' = \sqrt{n'^2 - (1/r^2)\,\vec{J}^2}, \end{aligned} \tag{2.15}$$

where

$$\vec{J}^2 = (\vec{a} \times \vec{s})^2 = 2Un^2 - V^2.$$

Notice that the roots in Equations (2.14) and (2.15) are defined as positive for the case of refraction. For reflection, however, because of (1.3) we have

$$Q' = -Q = -\frac{1}{r}\vec{a}*\vec{s}' = -\sqrt{n^2 - (1/r^2)\vec{J}^2} = (1/r)\,\vec{a}*\vec{s}.$$

Inserting this into (2.12) we find

$$\begin{aligned} l &= -(1/n^2)(rQ + V) \\ \phi &= (1/r)(Q' - Q) \end{aligned} \tag{2.16}$$

and considering (2.7)

$$m = \frac{1}{1 - l\phi} = \frac{n^2}{QQ' + (1/r^2)\vec{J}^2 + (1/r^2)(Q' - Q)V}. \tag{2.17}$$

Having calculated m and ϕ, one finds the coordinates of $\vec{a}'$ and $\vec{s}'$ by Equations (2.8). A good check is obtained by remembering from (2.9) that

$$\vec{a}' \times \vec{s}' = \vec{a} \times \vec{s}$$

and from the definition of $\vec{s}'$, that

$$\vec{s}'^2 = n'^2. \tag{2.18}$$

We recapitulate the formulae:
Given

$$\vec{a}\,(x, y, z) \qquad \vec{s}\,(\xi, \eta, \zeta),$$

we compute

$$\begin{aligned} U &= \tfrac{1}{2}(x^2 + y^2 + z^2), \quad V = x\xi + y\eta + z\zeta \\ \vec{J}^2 &= 2\,Un^2 - V^2 \\ Q &= \sqrt{n^2 - (1/r^2)\vec{J}^2} \\ Q' &= \sqrt{n'^2 - (1/r^2)\vec{J}^2} \text{ for refraction} \end{aligned}$$

$$(\text{For reflection } Q' = -Q) \tag{2.19}$$

$$m = 1/(1 - l\phi)$$

$$\begin{aligned} x' &= mx & \xi' &= -\phi x + (1/m)\,\xi \\ y' &= my & \eta' &= -\phi y + (1/m)\,\eta \\ z' &= mz & \zeta' &= -\phi z + (1/m)\,\zeta. \end{aligned}$$

The checks are given by

$$\begin{aligned} x'\eta' - y'\xi' &= x\eta - y\xi \\ x'\zeta' - z'\xi' &= x\zeta - z\xi \\ y'\zeta' - z'\eta' &= y\zeta - z\eta \\ \xi'^2 + \eta'^2 + \zeta'^2 &= n'^2. \end{aligned} \tag{2.20}$$

These are the basic formulae for tracing a ray through a spherical surface. However, in the case of the trace through a single spherical surface or a set of concentric spheres (see Chapter 3), the problem can be very much simplified with respect to actual numerical calculation by choosing a system of coordinates in a suitable way.

We have selected the coordinate origin at the center. Due to the central symmetry it is possible to choose the axis freely. We do so by assuming the z-axis as going through the object point.

Moreover, Equations (2.8) show that the plane through object point $\vec{a}$ and ray $\vec{s}$, that is, the plane of incidence, contains the refracted ray. This suggests making this one of the coordinate

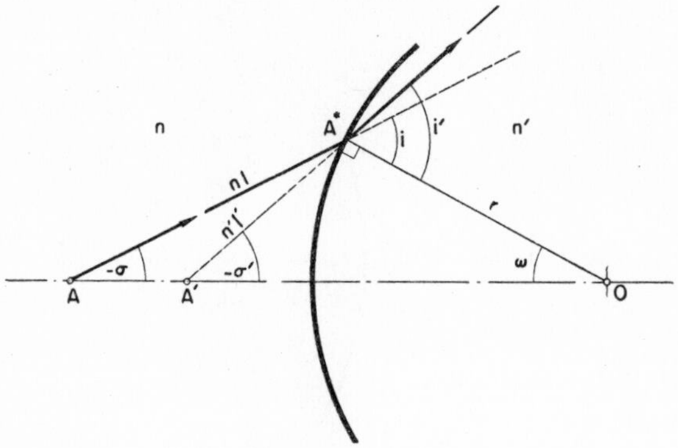

Fig. 2.4. Trigonometrical trace through a single sphere.

planes, for instance the yz-plane. Then the coordinates of $\vec{a}$, $\vec{s}$, $\vec{a}'$, $\vec{s}'$, and $\vec{J}$ become

$$\vec{a} : (0, 0, z) \qquad\qquad \vec{a}' : (0, 0, z')$$
$$\vec{s} : (0, \eta, \zeta) \qquad\qquad \vec{s}' : (0, \eta', \zeta')$$
$$\vec{J} : (-z\eta, 0, 0) = (-z'\eta', 0, 0). \tag{2.21}$$

The formulae given in Equation (2.9) suggest the introduction of auxiliary angles. Let σ, σ' be the angles which the incident and refracted rays, respectively, form with the z-axis. To comply with the sign convention used in optical literature, we set

$$\eta = -n \sin \sigma \qquad \eta' = -n' \sin \sigma'$$
$$\zeta = n \cos \sigma \qquad \zeta' = n' \cos \sigma'. \tag{2.22}$$

Moreover, we introduce the angles i, i' between the ray and the incidence normal. Then

$$nz \sin \sigma = nr \sin i = n'r \sin i' = n'z' \sin \sigma' = p. \tag{2.23}$$

Figure 2.4 shows that

$$\sigma + i = \sigma' + i' = \omega, \tag{2.24}$$

where ω is the angle which the incidence normal forms with the axis.

Equations (2.23) and (2.24) permit the tracing of the ray.

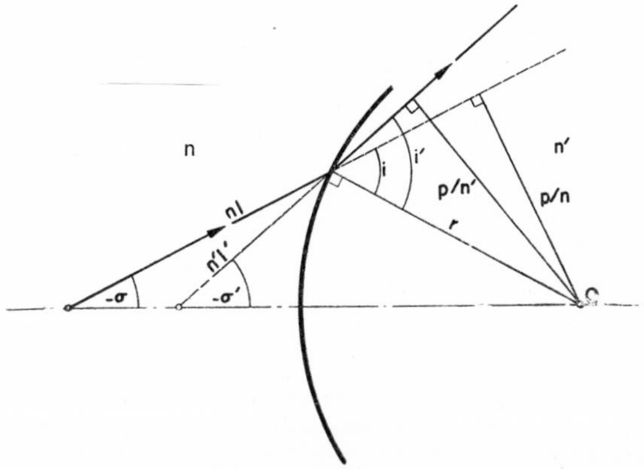

Fig. 2.5. Geometrical meaning of the invariant p.

Given z and σ we compute i and i' from (2.23), then σ' from (2.24), and finally z' from (2.23). Thus, for *refraction,*

$$\begin{aligned} p &= nz \sin \sigma & \sin i' &= p/n'r \\ \sin i &= p/nr & z' &= p/(n' \sin \sigma'). \\ \sigma' &= \sigma + i - i' \end{aligned} \tag{2.25}$$

Figure 2.5 shows the geometrical meaning of p. It is equal to the optical length of the perpendicular dropped from the center to the object ray and this is equal to the optical length of the perpendicular dropped from the center to the image ray.

If we want to compute l and ϕ for theoretical reasons, (2.15) and (2.16) in conjunction with (2.23) give

$$\begin{aligned} l &= -\frac{1}{n}(r \cos i + z \cos \sigma) = -\frac{p}{n^2}(\cot i + \cot \sigma) \\ &= -\frac{z \sin \omega}{n \sin i} = -\frac{r \sin \omega}{n \sin \sigma} \end{aligned} \tag{2.26}$$

$$\phi = \frac{1}{r}(n' \cos i' - n \cos i) = \frac{nn'}{p} \sin (i - i') = \frac{nn'}{p} \sin (\sigma' - \sigma).$$

In the case of *reflection* Formulae (2.25) become

$$\begin{aligned} p &= nz \sin \sigma & \sin i &= p/nr \\ \sigma' &= \sigma + 2i - \pi & z' &= p/(n' \sin \sigma') \end{aligned} \tag{2.25a}$$

and (2.26) gives

$$nl = -z(\sin \omega/\sin i) \qquad \phi = -(2n/r) \cos i \tag{2.26a}$$

since $i' = \pi - i$.

Equations (2.25) teach us that in general z' is a function of the object distance z and the inclination σ. It is of interest that distances exist for which z' is independent of σ. In this case, all the object rays from a point at distance z come to a focus at the point at the distance z'. In this case we shall say that the object point is *sharply* imaged. It will be shown that, on the z-axis, three object points exist which are sharply imaged. We shall show in a later chapter that these are the only axis points sharply imaged by a sphere.

Because of the central symmetry of the problem, we can state that, whenever one axial point at a distance z is sharply imaged, all the points of the sphere of radius $-z$ around the center must be sharply imaged at the same time.

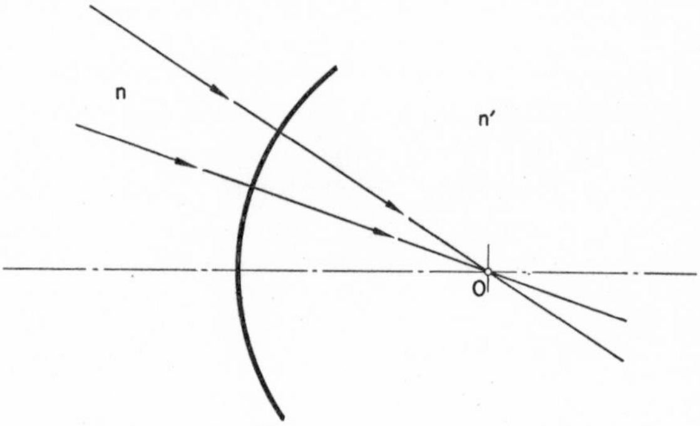

Fig. 2.6. Center of a sphere imaged on itself.

(*a*) *The Center*

From (2.25) and (2.26) we see that $z = 0$ leads to $p = i = i' = 0$

$$z' = 0 \qquad \sigma' = \sigma$$
$$l = -r/n \qquad \phi = (n' - n)/r \qquad m = n/n' \qquad (2.27)$$

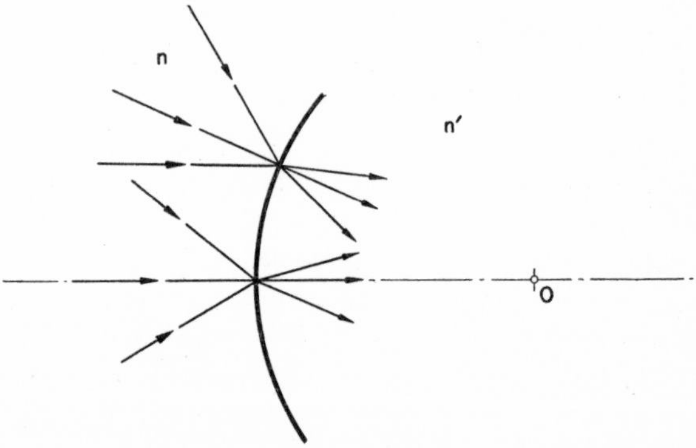

Fig. 2.7. Any point of a sphere imaged on itself.

or, in words, the center is imaged upon itself. The rays through the center are unrefracted ($\sigma' = \sigma$). The diamagnification is given by (2.7) as equal to n/n'.

(b) The Refracting Surface

Again using (2.25) and (2.26) we obtain

$$\begin{aligned} & z = -r, \quad i = -\sigma, \quad i' = -\sigma' \\ & z' = -r \\ & l = 0, \phi = \frac{1}{r}(n' \cos \sigma' - n \cos \sigma) \qquad (2.28) \\ & m = 1\,. \end{aligned}$$

The minus sign in the first line of (2.28) comes from the fact that z is measured from the center while r is measured from the vertex. We learn from (2.28) that the refracting surface is imaged on itself with a diamagnification equal to unity.

(c) The Aplanatic Surfaces

We assume an axial object point at the distance $z = (n'/n)r$ and find by again using (2.25) and (2.26),

$$\begin{aligned} & z = (n'/n)\, r \quad \sigma = i' \quad \sigma' = i \\ & z' = (n/n')\, r \quad m = n^2/n'^2. \qquad (2.29) \end{aligned}$$

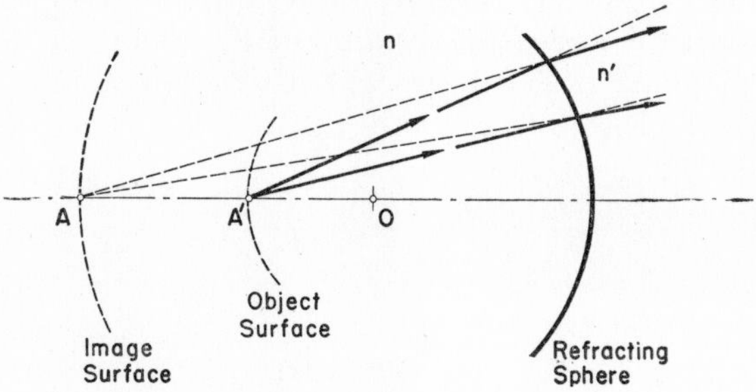

Fig. 2.8. Aplanatic surfaces of a sphere.

This shows that points of the sphere with a radius of $R = -(n'/n)r$ are imaged sharply upon the points of a sphere with a radius $R' = -(n/n')r$, if R and R' are measured from the respective vertices. These spheres are called the *aplanatic surfaces* of a sphere.

This is one of the few examples in optics where all the rays from a point come to a sharp focus. As such it forms a useful tool for optical design. There is, unfortunately, a slight drawback. As Equation (2.29) shows, the object and image surfaces lie on the same side of the refracting surface. We call an image *real* if the image point is accessible to the actual light rays; we call it *virtual* if the rays emerge from the system diverging, as if they come from a common focus. In the same way we can speak of a virtual *object*.

In the case in which the *image* of the aplanatic surface is virtual, that is, inaccessible, the situation is like that of the image in a plane mirror, in which case the image can be seen, but we cannot put a camera in back of the mirror at the plane of the image and take a picture.

The reader may convince himself that in the case of reflection the aplanatic spheres coincide with the reflecting surface.

In conclusion let us remark that, with respect to refraction and reflection, a special group of rays exists, those for which $\vec{J} = O$. In this case $\vec{s}, \vec{a}, \vec{s}', \vec{a}', \vec{a}^*$ all have the same direction, namely, the direction of the line connecting the object and the center. These rays are unrefracted. We call their common direction the *pseudoaxis*. For them the definition of the diapoint as the point of intersection of the image ray with the axis loses its meaning. However, the formal definition given in Equation (2.7) leads to a well-defined value of l', which can be used to define a diapoint also in this case. Let us set ($\sigma = 0$) in Equation (2.25). We find from (2.26) and $\sigma = i = i' = \sigma' = 0$

$$l = -\frac{1}{n}(r+z) \qquad m = \frac{1}{1-l\phi} = \frac{1}{\dfrac{n'}{n} + \dfrac{z}{n}\,\dfrac{n'-n}{r}} \tag{2.30}$$

$$\phi = \frac{n'-n}{r} \qquad z' = mz.$$

The point given by (2.30) is called the *paraxial diapoint* or *focus*. From (2.30) we can derive for it the equation

$$\frac{1}{n'z'} - \frac{1}{nz} = -\left(\frac{1}{n'} - \frac{1}{n}\right)\frac{1}{r}, \quad m = \frac{z'}{z}, \tag{2.31}$$

and for reflection

$$l = -\frac{1}{n}(r+z), \quad \phi = -\frac{2n}{r}, \quad m = \frac{-1}{1+(2z/r)}, \quad \frac{1}{z'} + \frac{1}{z} = -\frac{2}{r}. \tag{2.31a}$$

CHAPTER THREE

Tracing a Ray through a Set of Concentric Surfaces

We shall now consider an optical system consisting of a number of refracting and reflecting spherical surfaces having a common center. We designate the quantities which belong to the *vth* surface by the index ν, and the quantities before and after refraction are distinguished by primes to denote the latter quantities.

Taking the origin at the common center, we obtain from (2.8) the consecutive equations

$$\begin{aligned} \vec{a}_{\nu+1} &= m_\nu \, \vec{a}_\nu \\ \vec{s}_{\nu+1} &= -\phi_\nu \, \vec{a}_\nu + (1/m_\nu) \, \vec{s}_\nu \end{aligned} \qquad (3.1)$$

where

$$\vec{a}_\nu' = \vec{a}_{\nu+1} \text{ and } \vec{s}_\nu' = \vec{s}_{\nu+1} \, .$$

All these equations can be combined into an equation similar to the one for a single surface,

$$\begin{aligned} \vec{a}' &= m \, \vec{a} \\ \vec{s}' &= -\phi \, \vec{a} + (1/m) \, \vec{s}. \end{aligned} \qquad (3.2)$$

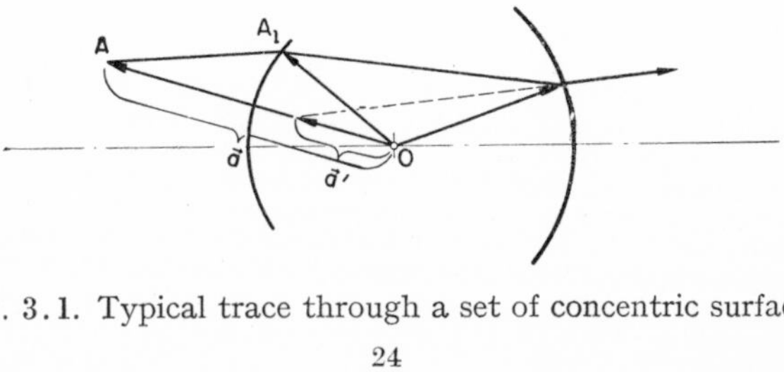

Fig. 3.1. Typical trace through a set of concentric surfaces.

The quantity m, the diamagnification of the system, is evidently equal to the product of the individual magnifications:

$$m = m_1 m_2 \ldots m_k, \tag{3.3}$$

whereas one finds that

$$m \phi = \sum_{\nu=1}^{k} m_\nu \phi_\nu (m_1 m_2 \ldots m_{\nu-1})^2. \tag{3.4}$$

Again we can simplify our computations by the introduction of trigonometric functions. We choose the z-axis in the direction of $\vec{a}$. We then obtain

$$\begin{gathered} nz \sin \sigma = n_\nu r_\nu \sin i_\nu = n_{\nu+1} r_\nu \sin i_\nu' = n'z' \sin \sigma' = p \\ \sigma' + \Sigma i_\nu' = \sigma + \Sigma i_\nu. \end{gathered} \tag{3.5}$$

Again the optical length p of the perpendicular from the center to the ray is invariant, so we can trace the ray in the following way: Given z and σ, we compute in order

$$\begin{aligned} p &= nz \sin \sigma \\ \sin i_\nu &= p/n_\nu r_\nu \\ \sin i_\nu' &= p/n_{\nu+1} r_\nu \\ \sigma' &= \sigma + \Sigma i_\nu - \Sigma i_\nu' \\ z' &= p/(n' \sin \sigma'). \end{aligned} \tag{3.6}$$

Thus the ray-trace through a system of concentric surfaces is given. In case of reflection at the *νth* surface we have to insert

$$i_\nu' = \pi - i_\nu. \tag{3.7}$$

In a later chapter we shall investigate the systems for which a point can be sharply imaged. Here we shall only investigate what happens if the ray is a pseudoaxis, that is, if

$$\vec{J} = \vec{a} \times \vec{s} = \vec{a}' \times \vec{s}' \tag{3.8}$$

vanishes. We find from (2.31) that

$$\frac{1}{n'z'} - \frac{1}{nz} = -\Sigma\left(\frac{1}{n'_\nu} - \frac{1}{n_\nu}\right)\frac{1}{r_\nu}, \quad m = \frac{z'}{z}. \tag{3.9}$$

We shall, however, conclude this chapter by giving three examples of concentric systems which image a point sharply.

(*a*) Let us assume we have three media with indices n_1, n_2, n_3, such that

$$n_2^2 = n_1 n_3 \tag{3.10}$$

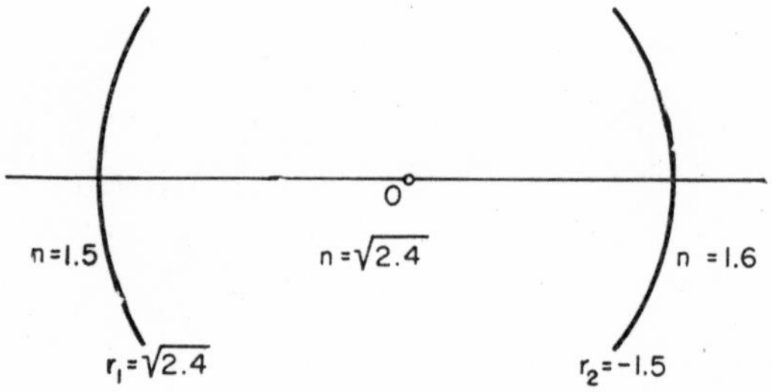

Fig. 3.2. System imaging all points of space sharply.

and two refracting surfaces having radii r_1, r_2 with

$$r_2 = -\frac{n_1}{n_2} r_1 = -\frac{n_2}{n_3} r_1 . \tag{3.11}$$

Equations (3.5) then give

$$\begin{aligned} n_1 z \sin \sigma = n_1 r_1 \sin i_1 = n_2 r_1 \sin i_1' = n_2 r_2 \sin i_2 \\ = n_3 r_2 \sin i_2' = n_3 z' \sin \sigma' \end{aligned} \tag{3.12}$$

$$\sigma + i_1 + i_2 = \sigma' + i_1' + i_2',$$

which leads to

$$\begin{aligned} i_2 &= -i_1 \\ i_2' &= -i_1' \\ \sigma' &= \sigma \end{aligned} \tag{3.13}$$

and therefore finally to

$$z' = \frac{n_1}{n_3} z, \quad m = \frac{n_1}{n_3} . \tag{3.14}$$

Equations (3.14) show that the system thus obtained images every point in space sharply and it images every point in space with the same magnification $m = n_1/n_3$. The optical distances of every object point and its image point from the center are the same, a special case of a general law obtained in Chapter 14.

Aside from a plane mirror, this is the simplest system which images all points of space sharply. Such a system we shall call a *spatial* system, and in a later chapter we shall give a method for finding all concentric spatial systems.

(*b*) Consider a lens with two radii such that $r_2 = (-n_1/n_2)r_1$. We have

$$\begin{aligned} n_1 z \sin\sigma = n_1 r_1 \sin i_1 = n_2 r_1 \sin i_1' &= n_2 r_2 \sin i_2 \\ = n_3 r_2 \sin i_2' &= n_3 z' \sin\sigma' \end{aligned}$$

$$\sigma + i_1 + i_2 = \sigma' + i_1' + i_2', \quad i_1 = -i_2$$

or

$$\sigma = \sigma' + i_1' + i_2'. \tag{3.15}$$

If we choose the object point so that

$$n_1 z = n_2 r_1 \quad (\sigma = i_1'),$$

we find

$$n_3 z' = -n_3 r_2 \quad (\sigma' = -i_2'),$$

that is,

$$z = \frac{n_2}{n_1} r_1, \quad z' = -r_2 = \frac{n_1}{n_2} r_1, \quad m = \frac{n_1^2}{n_2^2}. \tag{3.16}$$

On the other hand, if we choose the object point so that

$$n_1 z = n_3 r_2 \qquad (\sigma = i_2'),$$

we find

$$n_3 z' = -n_2 r_1 \qquad (\sigma' = -i_1'),$$

that is,

$$z = \frac{n_3}{n_1} r_2 = -\frac{n_3}{n_2} r_1, \quad z' = -\frac{n_2}{n_3} r_1, \quad m = \frac{n_2^2}{n_3^2}. \tag{3.17}$$

We see that the lens with radii r_1 and $r_2 = (-n_1/n_2)r_1$ images two spheres sharply, namely, the sphere with the radius $R = (-n_2/n_1)r_1$, upon the sphere with radius $R = (-n_1/n_2)r_1$ and the sphere with radius $R = (n_3/n_2)\, r_1$ upon the points of the sphere with radius $R = (n_2/n_3)\, r_1$.

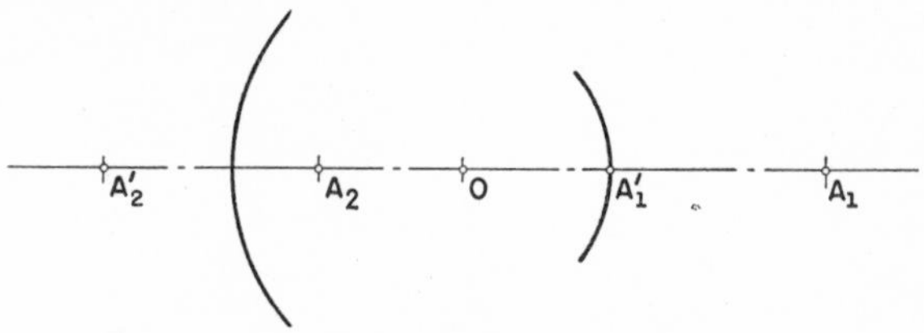

Fig. 3.3. System imaging two spheres sharply.

The lens is a two-surface imaging system and the product of the diamagnifications equals

$$m_1 m_2 = n_1^2/n_3^2.$$

This, we shall find later, is a general law for the image-formation in concentric systems. If the system images one point sharply (aside from the center), it images two spheres sharply and with diamagnifications whose product is equal to the ratio of the squares of the indices of the object and image spaces.

(c) *The mirror lens.* Let us consider a lens whose second surface is silvered so that light is reflected back through the first surface, that is, a lens in which the first and third radii are identical. The ray-tracing equations (3.5) then become

$$\begin{aligned} n_1 z \sin \sigma = n_1 r_1 \sin i_1 = n_2 r_1 \sin i_1' = n_2 r_2 \sin i_2 = n_2 r_2 \sin i_2' \\ = n_2 r_1 \sin i_3 = n_1 r_1 \sin i_3' = n_1 z' \sin \sigma' \qquad (3.18) \\ \sigma + i_1 + i_2 + i_3 = \sigma' + i_1' + i_2' + i_3'. \end{aligned}$$

From the first equation it follows that

$$\begin{aligned} i_2' &= \pi - i_2 \\ i_3 &= \pi - i_1' \qquad (3.19) \\ i_3' &= \pi - i_1 \end{aligned}$$

or

$$\sigma' + \pi - \sigma + 2i_1' = 2i_1 + 2i_2.$$

These are the equations of a mirror lens. Let us assume $n_1 = 1$, that is, the lens being in air. Let us write $n_2 = n$ and choose

$$r_2 = -(1/n)r_1. \tag{3.20}$$

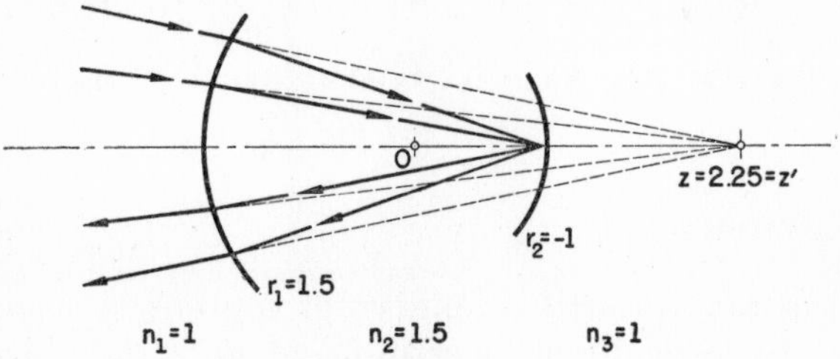

Fig. 3.4. Mirror lens.

An examination of Formulae (3.18) shows that, if Equation (3.20) is fulfilled, the axis object point given by $z = nr_1$ is imaged sharply upon the image point given by $z' = nr_1$ and with the diamagnification *unity*. This is then the only axis point (except for the center) which is imaged sharply, a fact which is, however, consistent with the general law mentioned above. In this case we have to consider the object sphere as being imaged doubly upon itself, in which case the product of the diamagnifications will again be seen to be equal to *unity*.

CHAPTER FOUR

Tracing a Ray through a Surface or System of Surfaces with an Axis of Rotational Symmetry

General Remarks

Tracing a ray through a number of concentric systems was found to be practically a linear problem since the object point and all its diapoints lie on a straight line through the center. We took the center as origin and the line just described as one of the axes. The invariance of $\vec{a} \times \vec{s}$ then gave the ray-tracing formulae.

In a system with symmetry of rotation about an axis, it will be convenient to choose the origin on the axis of symmetry and to take this line as the z-axis (unit vector $\vec{k}$). We shall then prove that we can transform the three-dimensional tracing problem into a two-dimensional one by projecting the vectors into a plane perpendicular to the axis.

It is found that, in a rotation-symmetric system, instead of an invariant vector, we have only an invariant scalar, namely, the projection of $(\vec{a} \times \vec{s})$ along the z-axis, that is, we can prove from the basic tracing formulae that

$$[\vec{a}\vec{s}\vec{k}] = [\vec{a}'\vec{s}'\vec{k}] = J. \tag{4.1}$$

The quantity J is called the *skewness* of the ray.

We shall first describe the general procedure for tracing a ray through a single surface that is rotationally symmetric and then investigate the trace through special types of surfaces, such as planes, spheres, second-order surfaces, and general surfaces having symmetry of rotation.

It will be convenient to choose the various positions of the origin on the axis in the ray-tracing process. This is especially helpful in systems having several surfaces. We consider an origin at the vertex of each of the consecutive surfaces, the *vertex* being defined as the point at which the axis intersects the surface. The distances between consecutive vertices are called the *thicknesses* of the lens and are designated by d_i.

In systems with symmetry of rotation, there are three types of rays:

(*a*) *The axis.* This single ray intersects all surfaces in the direction of the surface normal and is therefore refracted (or reflected) in its own direction.

(*b*) *Meridional rays.* A ray lying in a plane through the object point and the axis is called *meridional,* and the corresponding plane is called a *meridional* (or *meridian*) plane. Since, because of rotation-symmetry, the incidence normal intersects the axis, that is, is in the meridian plane, the refracted (or reflected) ray also lies in the meridian plane. For meridional rays we frequently find simplified tracing formulae, which is one reason why lens designers sometimes are satisfied to consider only the meridional rays, a custom which will be shown to be unsatisfactory. The meridional rays are those for which the invariant scalar J in (4.1) vanishes.

(*c*) *Skew rays.* Rays that do not lie in the meridional plane are called *skew* rays. The intersection points of the skew rays with the meridional plane (a plane through a given object-point and the axis) we shall call the *diapoints,* a definition which agrees with the one given for concentric systems in the preceding chapter.

Let us now assume the object ray to be given by one of its points, vector $\vec{a}$ (from an arbitrary origin on the axis) and the direction vector $\vec{s}$. Let $\vec{a}^*$ be the vector to a refracting (or reflecting) surface, and $\vec{s}'$ the direction vector after refraction. The tracing formulae then are

$$\begin{aligned} \vec{a}^* &= \vec{a} + l\vec{s} \\ \vec{s}' &= \vec{s} + \Gamma\vec{o}, \end{aligned} \tag{4.2}$$

where l and Γ have to be computed. We have found for Γ [Eq. (1.12)]

$$\Gamma = \vec{s}'\vec{o} - \vec{s}\vec{o} = \sqrt{n'^2 - n^2 + (\vec{s}\vec{o})^2} - \vec{s}\vec{o}. \tag{4.3}$$

The computation of l or the equivalent quantity l/ζ will be considered next. If the initial point lies on the plane $z = 0$, as we shall assume for the most part in this chapter, and if the equation of the surface is

$$F(u^*, z) = 0$$

with

$$2u^* = x^{*2} + y^{*2}, \tag{4.4}$$

we then have

$$\begin{aligned} x^* &= x + l\xi & \qquad x^* &= x + z\xi/\zeta \\ y^* &= y + l\eta \quad \text{or} & y^* &= y + z\eta/\zeta\,. \\ z &= l\zeta \end{aligned} \tag{4.5}$$

We shall now rewrite the basic equations in order to separate the vector equations into two parts, (1) a two-dimensional vector equation, the vectors of which are perpendicular to the axis, and (2) the equation involving the projections along the axis. The vectors perpendicular to the z-axis, that is, having their z-component zero, will be designated by capital letters.

Equation (4.5) suggests either

(*a*) the use of two vectors $\vec{A}$ with coordinates $(x, y, 0)$ and $\vec{T}$ with coordinates $\left(\Xi = \frac{\xi}{\zeta}, H = \frac{\eta}{\zeta}, 0\right)$, or

(*b*) the use of two vectors $\vec{P}$ with coordinates $(X = x\zeta, Y = y\zeta, O)$ and $\vec{S}$ with coordinates $(\xi, \eta, 0)$, giving

$$\begin{aligned} \vec{a} &= \vec{A} = (1/\zeta)\,\vec{P} \\ \vec{s} &= \vec{S} + \zeta\vec{k} = \zeta(\vec{T}+\vec{k}). \end{aligned} \tag{4.6}$$

Both designations will be used advantageously in different parts of the book. Equations (4.5) can then be written in either of the forms

$$\begin{aligned} \vec{A}^* &= \vec{A} + zT, \\ \vec{P}^* &= \vec{P} + z\vec{S}. \end{aligned} \tag{4.7}$$

For the ray-tracing problems, the use of $\vec{S}$ and $\vec{P}$ will be seen to be most convenient. In a system having rotational symmetry, the normal vector at the point of incidence intersects the axis. Thus we can write

$$\begin{aligned} -r_s\vec{\sigma} &= \vec{A}^* - (t-z)\vec{k} \\ -\zeta r_s\vec{\sigma} &= \vec{P}^* - (t-z)\zeta\vec{k}, \end{aligned} \tag{4.8}$$

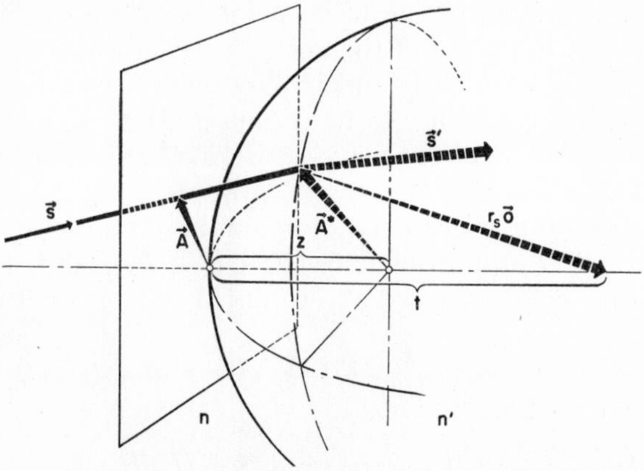

Fig. 4.1. Geometrical quantities used in general skew-ray trace.

where r_s, the *sagittal radius of curvature*, is the distance along the surface normal from the incidence point to the point of intersection with the axis. The latter point is called the *sagittal center of curvature* of the surface. The quantity t is the distance, on the axis, from the vertex to the sagittal center of curvature. In Chapter 2 the normal vector $\vec{o}$ was defined so that it has a positive z-component. Thus in (4.8) r_s and $(t-z)$ must have the same sign, which is in accordance with the sign of a radius of a sphere, assumed as positive or negative according as the surface at the point of incidence is convex or concave respectively, that is, according as the sagittal center lies to the right or left of the vertex. In most cases, the curvature at the incidence point has the same sign as at the vertex.

To compute z, we proceed generally as follows: Let the surface be given in the form

$$F(u^*,z) = 0, \quad 2u^* = x^{*2}+y^{*2}. \tag{4.9}$$

Squaring (4.7) we find

$$\vec{P}^{*2} = 2u^*\zeta^2 = \vec{P}^2 + 2z\vec{P}\vec{S} + z^2\vec{S}^2, \tag{4.10}$$

after which (4.8) and (4.10) permit the computation of z either in closed form or approximately, depending on the degree of F. The equation thus obtained may formally have more than one solution for z. However, if the initial point is chosen on the vertex plane, that is, the plane of the vertex perpendicular to the axis, as we shall suggest doing, and if the origin of coordinates is at the vertex, the value of z to be chosen must be the one having the smallest numerical value and satisfying both Equations (4.9) and (4.10).

Having found z, we can compute t and r_s as follows: The incidence normal is proportional to (F_{x^*}, F_{y^*}, F_z), and, therefore, abbreviating $x^{*2} + y^{*2} = 2 u^*$, we find $\vec{o}$ proportional to

$$F_{u^*} \vec{A}^* + F_z \vec{k}.$$

Comparison with (4.8) gives

$$t - z = - F_z / F_{u^*}, \quad r_s{}^2 = \vec{A}^{*2} + (F_z/F_{u^*})^2$$
$$= 2u^* + (F_z/F_{u^*})^2. \qquad (4.11)$$

In the special case where F_{u^*} vanishes, evidently $\vec{o}$ becomes identical with $\vec{k}$, and the center of curvature goes to infinity, that is, the normal becomes parallel to the z-axis.

It remains to compute $\vec{s}'$ (or $\vec{S}'$). Remembering that

$$\vec{s} = \vec{S} + \zeta \vec{k}, \quad \vec{s}' = \vec{S}' + \zeta' \vec{k} \qquad (4.12)$$

and the refraction law, Equation (1.9)

$$\vec{s}' - \vec{s} = \Gamma \vec{o}, \qquad (4.13)$$

we find, with the help of (4.6), (4.7), and (4.8),

$$\vec{S}' - \vec{S} = - \psi (\vec{P} + z\vec{S})$$
$$\zeta' - \zeta = + \psi \zeta (t - z), \qquad (4.14)$$

where ψ is defined by

$$\psi = \Gamma / \zeta r_s. \qquad (4.15)$$

The refracted ray may be given by the direction vector $\vec{S}'$ and the position vector $\vec{P}*' = \vec{A}^* \zeta'$ of the incidence point. It will be found convenient to compute the vector $\vec{P}' = \vec{A}' \zeta'$ for the intersection point $(\vec{a}' = \vec{A}')$ of the image ray with the vertex plane. From

$$\vec{a}' = \vec{a} + \frac{z}{\zeta} \vec{s} - \frac{z}{\zeta'} s' \qquad (4.16)$$

we find, by using (4.14),

$$\vec{P}' = \vec{A}'\zeta' = (\vec{P}+z\vec{S})\,[1+\psi(t-z)]-z\vec{S}'$$
$$= (\vec{P}+z\vec{S})\,[1+\psi(t-z)]-z\vec{S}+z\psi\,(\vec{P}+z\vec{S}), \qquad (4.16a)$$

which gives

$$\vec{P}'-\vec{P} = \psi t\,(\vec{P}+z\vec{S})$$
$$\vec{S}'-\vec{S} = -\psi\,(\vec{P}+z\vec{S}). \qquad (4.17)$$

We still have to compute ψ. From (4.8), (4.15), and (1.12) we obtain

$$\psi = \frac{\Gamma}{\zeta r_s} = \frac{1}{\zeta r_s}\left[\sqrt{n'^2 - n^2 + (\vec{o}\vec{s})^2} - \vec{o}\vec{s}\right] = \frac{q'-q}{\zeta^2 r_s^{\,2}} \qquad (4.18)$$

with

$$q = \zeta r_s\,(\vec{o}\vec{s}) = -\,(\vec{P}+z\vec{S})\,\vec{S}+(t-z)\,\zeta^2$$
$$q'^2 = (n'^2-n^2)\zeta^2 r_s^{\,2} + q^2, \text{ for refraction,} \qquad (4.19)$$

and for reflection $q' = -q$.

To recapitulate the ray-tracing formulae, we first find z as the numerically smallest root of

$$F\,(u^*, z) = 0$$
$$2u^*\,(n^2-\vec{S}^2) = \vec{P}^2+2\vec{P}\vec{S}z + \vec{S}^2 z^2. \qquad (4.20)$$

We then compute

$$t = z - F_z/F_{u^*}$$
$$R = \zeta^2 r_s^{\,2} = \vec{P}^2 + 2\vec{P}\vec{S}z + \vec{S}^2 z^2 + (F_z/F_{u^*})^2\,(n^2-\vec{S}^2)$$
$$q = -\,(\vec{P}+z\vec{S})\vec{S} + (t-z)\,(n^2-\vec{S}^2)$$
$$q'^2 = (n'^2-n^2)R + q^2, \text{ for refraction} \qquad (4.21)$$
$$(\text{for reflection } q' = -q)$$
$$\psi = (q'-q)/R$$

and

$$\vec{P}' - \vec{P} = t\,\psi\,(\vec{P} + z\vec{S})$$
$$\vec{S}' - \vec{S} = -\,\psi\,(\vec{P} + z\vec{S}). \qquad (4.22)$$

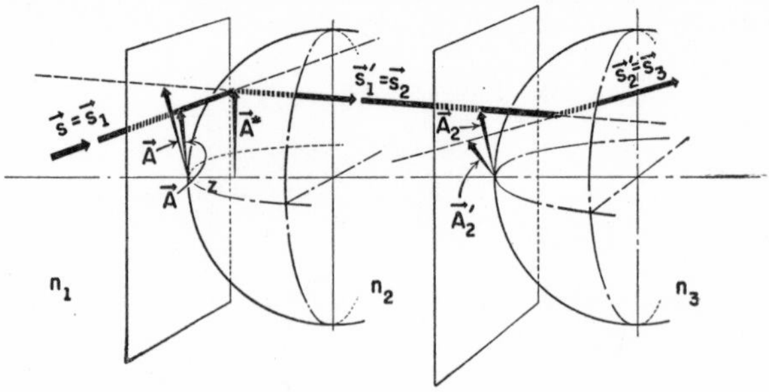

Fig. 4.2. Skew-ray trace through several surfaces.

Going to the second surface, we find

$$\vec{P}_2 = \vec{P}' + d\vec{S}'$$
$$\vec{S}_2 = \vec{S}', \tag{4.23}$$

which gives the starting data for the second surface, d being the distance between the two consecutive vertices.

Equation (4.14) gives us an important check. The reader will notice that ζ^2 was eliminated in (4.20) to (4.22). The two relations [cf. (4.14)]

$$\zeta' = \zeta\,[1 + \psi\,(t - z)]$$
$$\vec{S}'^2 = n'^2 - \zeta'^2 \tag{4.24}$$

may be used as a check.

Moreover, from the basic equation

$$[\vec{a}'\vec{s}'\vec{k}] = [\vec{a}\vec{s}\vec{k}]$$

or from Equations (4.22) and (4.24) it is easily shown that

$$\frac{1}{\zeta'}\,(\vec{P}' \times \vec{S}') = \frac{1}{\zeta}\,(\vec{P} \times \vec{S})$$

or

$$\vec{P}' \times \vec{S}' = [1 + \psi\,(t - z)]\,(\vec{P} \times \vec{S}), \tag{4.25}$$

which can serve as another independent check.

Arbitrary points on the object and image rays can be specified by giving their horizontal distances s and s' from the vertex plane:

$$\vec{\tilde{P}} = \vec{P} + s\vec{S}, \quad \vec{\tilde{P}}' = \vec{P}' + s'\vec{S}'$$

(s and s' are distances and are not to be confused with the direction vector $\vec{s}$). Abbreviating Equation (4.22) as

$$\begin{aligned} \vec{P}' &= \varkappa\vec{P} + \lambda\vec{S} \\ \vec{S}' &= \mu\vec{P} + \nu\vec{S} \end{aligned} \quad \text{with} \quad \begin{aligned} \varkappa &= 1 + \psi t & \lambda &= z\psi t \\ \mu &= -\psi & \nu &= 1 - \psi z \end{aligned} \tag{4.26}$$

and with

$$\varkappa\nu - \mu\lambda = 1 + \psi(t - z),$$

we find

$$\begin{aligned} \vec{\tilde{P}}' &= \tilde{\varkappa}\vec{\tilde{P}} + \tilde{\lambda}\vec{S} \\ \vec{S}' &= \tilde{\mu}\vec{\tilde{P}} + \tilde{\nu}\vec{S} \end{aligned} \tag{4.27}$$

with

$$\begin{aligned} \tilde{\varkappa} &= \varkappa + \mu s' & \tilde{\lambda} &= \lambda + \nu s' - \varkappa s - \mu s s' \\ \tilde{\mu} &= \mu & \tilde{\nu} &= \nu - \mu s. \end{aligned} \tag{4.28}$$

Assuming s to be arbitrary and choosing s' so that $\tilde{\lambda}$ vanishes, we obtain

$$s' = \frac{-\lambda + \varkappa s}{\nu - \mu s} = \frac{-z\psi t + (1 + \psi t)s}{1 - \psi z + \psi s} \tag{4.29}$$

and consequently

$$\begin{aligned} \vec{\tilde{P}}' &= \frac{\varkappa\nu - \mu\lambda}{\nu - \mu s}\vec{\tilde{P}} = \frac{1 + \psi(t - z)}{1 - \psi z + \psi s}\vec{\tilde{P}} \\ \vec{S}' &= \mu\vec{\tilde{P}} + (\nu - \mu s)\vec{S} = -\psi\vec{\tilde{P}} + (1 - \psi z + \psi s)\vec{S}. \end{aligned} \tag{4.30}$$

It is obvious that if $\vec{P}$ and $\vec{P}'$ are parallel, $\vec{A}$ and $\vec{A}'$ must be parallel too, that is, the point defined by Equation (4.29) is the *diapoint* of the initial point, which means, for a skew ray, the point at which the image ray intersects the meridional plane through the initial point and the axis.

Formulae (4.29) and (4.30) can be used to give a definition of the diapoint for meridional rays where the above geometric definition breaks down, since the object and image rays lie entirely in the meridional plane. If a point of the object ray has a vertex distance s, its diapoint is defined as the point lying on the image ray having s' given by Equation (4.29).

This concept can be used to simplify the trace of a meridional ray. A meridional ray intersects the axis on the object and image sides at the distances s and s', respectively, so that

$$\vec{P} + s\vec{S} = 0, \quad \vec{P}' + s'\vec{S}' = 0. \tag{4.31}$$

We then find from Equations (4.29) and (4.30) (with $\tilde{\vec{P}} = 0$)

$$\begin{aligned} \vec{S}' &= (1 - \psi z + \psi s)\,\vec{S} \\ s' &= \frac{-\,z\psi t + (1 + \psi t)s}{1 - \psi z + \psi s}. \end{aligned} \tag{4.32}$$

If the incident ray is parallel to the axis, we must let $s \to \infty$, $\vec{P} = \tilde{\vec{P}}$, and $\vec{S} = 0$ in Equations (4.29) and (4.30), which gives

$$\begin{aligned} s' &= (1/\psi) + t \\ \vec{S}' &= -\,\psi\vec{P}. \end{aligned} \tag{4.33}$$

On the other hand, if s is chosen such that

$$s = z - (1/\psi), \tag{4.34}$$

Equation (4.32) gives $\vec{S}' = 0$.

These two points are called the image and object side *diafocal points*, respectively. Equation (4.22) gives in the second case ($\vec{S}' = 0$):

$$\vec{P}' = \vec{P} + t\vec{S} \tag{4.35}$$

and in the case of $\vec{S} = 0$

$$\begin{aligned} \vec{P}' &= (1 + \psi t)\,\vec{P} \\ \vec{S}' &= -\,\psi\vec{P}. \end{aligned} \tag{4.36}$$

We conclude this chapter by considering the so-called *paraxial* trace of a ray. Here it is assumed that second-order terms in x, y, ξ, and η are negligible—a condition which is approximately fulfilled for rays sufficiently near the axis. For a paraxial ray, therefore, it is assumed that

$$\vec{P}^2 = \vec{P}\vec{S} = \vec{S}^2 = 0, \quad \zeta^2 = n^2, \quad u^* = 0, \tag{4.37}$$

the last of these being evident from Equation (4.10). If (4.9) represents the vertex equation of the surface, it follows that, for a paraxial ray, where $u^* = 0$, we have

$$z \to 0. \tag{4.38}$$

From Equation (4.11) it is seen that

$$t = -F_z/F_{u*} = r_s\,(z \to 0) = r_o \tag{4.39}$$

in the paraxial case. The limiting value for r_s, for $z = 0$, is evidently the vertex radius of curvature.

For a paraxial ray-trace, Formulae (4.21) and (4.22) reduce to

$$t = -F_z/F_{u*} = r_o, \quad z = 0$$

$$R = r_o^2 n^2, \quad q = r_o n^2, \quad q' = r_o n n', \quad \psi = \frac{n' - n}{r_o n} \tag{4.40}$$

$$\vec{P}' = (n'/n)\vec{P} \qquad \text{or} \qquad \vec{A}' = \vec{A}$$

$$\vec{S}' = \vec{S} - \frac{n' - n}{r_o n}\vec{P} \qquad\qquad \vec{S}' = \vec{S} - \frac{n' - n}{r_o}\vec{A},$$

which, for $F_{u*} \to 0$, $t = r_o \to \infty$, become

$$\begin{matrix} \vec{P} = (n'/n)\,\vec{P} & \text{or} & \vec{A}' = \vec{A} \\ \vec{S}' = \vec{S} & & \vec{S}' = \vec{S}. \end{matrix} \tag{4.41}$$

CHAPTER FIVE

Ray-Tracing through Special Surfaces

We shall now apply the method of Chapter 4 to derive ray-tracing formulae for special surfaces. Let us first consider the surfaces of second order that are rotationally symmetric. Let x^*, y^*, z be the coordinates of the surface point, and let the surface equation be given in the form

$$F(u^*, z) = z + \tfrac{1}{2} BCz^2 - Bu^* = 0 \text{ with } 2u^* = x^{*2} + y^{*2}. \qquad (5.1)$$

Analysis will show that the constant B in (5.1) is equal to the vertex curvature of the surface,* and $B = 0$ gives the equation of a plane. The constant C, on the other hand, can be considered as the form coefficient of the surface. Setting $C = 0$ gives a paraboloid, $C < 0$ an ellipsoid, $C > 0$ a hyperboloid, and $C = -1$, a sphere (a special type of ellipsoid). In every case the z-axis is an axis of rotational symmetry.

To verify these facts in detail, we observe that $B = 0$ gives the equation

$$z = 0 \qquad (5.2)$$

of a plane, whereas $C = 0$ gives

$$z = Bu^*, \qquad (5.3)$$

the well-known vertex equation of a paraboloid, and for $C \neq 0$, we obtain from Equation (5.1) the standard equation

$$\frac{\left(z + \dfrac{1}{BC}\right)^2}{\left(\dfrac{1}{BC}\right)^2} + \frac{2u^*}{-\dfrac{1}{B^2C}} = 1\,, \qquad (5.4)$$

* For small z the surface is approximated by $z = Bu^* = \frac{1}{2}B(x^{*2} + y^{*2})$, which represents a sphere of radius $1/B$ with vertex at the origin.

which is an ellipsoid if $C < 0$, a hyperboloid if $C > 0$, and a sphere if $C = -1$.

The z-coordinate (vertex distance) s_F of the focus of the paraboloid (5.3) is given by

$$Bs_F = \tfrac{1}{2}, \tag{5.5}$$

and correspondingly the positions of the two foci of an ellipsoid (for the case $-1 < C < 0$) or of a hyperboloid ($C > 0$) given by (5.4) are found by

$$Bs_F = -(1/C)\,(1 \pm \sqrt{1+C}). \tag{5.6}$$

Introducing the abbreviation e for the positive root in (5.6), we write these as

$$Bs_F = \frac{1}{1 \mp e}, \tag{5.7}$$

where $e = 1$ for the paraboloid, $e < 1$ for the ellipsoid, $e > 1$ for the hyperboloid, and $e = 0$ for the sphere (for which the two foci coincide with the center).

We shall now apply to Equation (5.1) the general ray-tracing formulae of Chapter 4. We find from (5.1)

$$F_{u*} = -B, \quad F_z = 1 + CBz, \tag{5.8}$$

and therefore (4.11) gives

$$\begin{aligned} Bt &= 1 + (C+1)\,Bz \\ B^2 r_s{}^2 &= 2u^*B + B^2\,(t-z)^2 = 2Bz + CB^2z^2 + B^2\,(t-z)^2 \\ &= B^2t^2 - Bz\,(Bt-1). \end{aligned} \tag{5.9}$$

In order to find z we must compute it [*cf.* (4.9) and (4.10)] from

$$2z\zeta^2 + BCz^2\zeta^2 = 2u^*\,B\zeta^2 = B\,(\vec{P}+z\vec{S})^2$$

i.e. $$B^2z^2(\vec{S}^2-C\zeta^2) + 2Bz\,(B\vec{P}\vec{S}-\zeta^2) + B^2\vec{P}^2 = 0, \tag{5.10}$$

which leads (after multiplication by $\vec{S}^2 - C\zeta^2$) to

$$[Bz(\vec{S}^2-C\zeta^2) + B\vec{P}\vec{S}-\zeta^2]^2 = (B\vec{P}\vec{S}-\zeta^2)^2 - B^2\vec{P}^2(\vec{S}^2-C\zeta^2). \tag{5.10a}$$

From (4.19) and (5.9) we find

$$\bar{q} = Bq = B\zeta r_s (\vec{\sigma}\vec{s}) = -B(\vec{P}+z\vec{S})\vec{S} + \zeta^2 (1+CBz). \quad (5.11)$$

Comparing the right side of (5.11) and the left side of (5.10a), we finally find

$$\bar{q}^2 = (B\vec{P}\vec{S} - n^2 + \vec{S}^2)^2 - B^2\vec{P}^2 [\vec{S}^2 - C(n^2 - \vec{S}^2)]$$

$$z = \frac{-(\bar{q} + B\vec{P}\vec{S} - n^2 + \vec{S}^2)}{B[\vec{S}^2 - C(n^2 - \vec{S}^2)]} = \frac{B\vec{P}^2}{\bar{q} - B\vec{P}\vec{S} + n^2 - \vec{S}^2}, \quad (5.12)$$

where $\bar{q}$ is to be taken as the positive root of (5.12) since B and r_s in (5.11) have the same sign for second-order surfaces. The second form for z is obtained by factoring $\bar{q}^2 - (\vec{P}\vec{S}B - n^2 - \vec{S}^2)^2$ in the first formula of (5.12). It is of special value since z remains determined when $B \to 0$, that is, for surfaces with weak vertex curvature. Having found z, Bt, and $\bar{q}$ we can compute $\bar{R}$, $\bar{q}'$, $\bar{\psi}$, and the tracing equations (4.22).

The calculation can be simplified slightly by writing $Bt = \bar{t}$, etc. We then have, collecting the results in the order of calculation,

$$\begin{aligned}
\zeta^2 &= n^2 - \vec{S}^2 \\
\bar{q}^2 &= (B\vec{P}\vec{S} - \zeta^2)^2 - B^2\vec{P}^2 (\vec{S}^2 - C\zeta^2) \\
z &= \frac{B\vec{P}^2}{\bar{q} - B\vec{P}\vec{S} + \zeta^2} \\
\bar{t} &= 1 + Bz(C+1), \quad \bar{R} = \bar{t}^2 - Bz(\bar{t} - 1) \\
\bar{q}'^2 &= (n'^2 - n^2)\bar{R}\zeta^2 + \bar{q}^2, \quad \bar{q}' > 0 \quad (\bar{q}' = -\bar{q} \text{ for reflection}) \\
\bar{\psi} &= \frac{\bar{q}' - \bar{q}}{\bar{R}\zeta^2} \qquad\qquad (5.13) \\
\vec{P}' - \vec{P} &= \bar{t}\bar{\psi}(\vec{P} + z\vec{S}) \\
\vec{S}' - \vec{S} &= -B\bar{\psi}(\vec{P} + z\vec{S}).
\end{aligned}$$

We shall now derive the formulae which confirm the well-known focal qualities of second-order surfaces for which $C + 1 > 0$. Surfaces with $C < -1$ have no focus (in the geometrical sense) on the axis of rotation and therefore no points which are sharply imaged in the optical sense.

Introducing e (the eccentricity of the second-order surface) as the positive square root of $C + 1$, we have

$$e^2 - 1 = C, \quad e > 0. \tag{5.14}$$

Our theorem states that the meridional rays passing through the axis point with the vertex distance given by $Bs = 1/(1 - e)$ are reflected at the second-order surface so that the reflected rays pass through the point at the vertex distance given by $Bs' = 1/(1 + e)$. Likewise, the rays passing through the point of vertex distance given by $Bs = 1/(1+e)$ are reflected so as to pass through a point given by $Bs' = 1/(1-e)$.

In the first case, we obtain from (4.31)

$$\begin{aligned} \vec{P} &= -\frac{1}{B}\,\frac{1}{1-e}\,\vec{S} \\ \vec{P}^2 &= \frac{1}{B^2}\,\frac{1}{(1-e)^2}\,\vec{S}^2 \\ \vec{P}\vec{S} &= -\frac{1}{B}\,\frac{1}{1-e}\,\vec{S}^2 \end{aligned} \tag{5.15}$$

and from (5.13)

$$\begin{aligned} &\bar{q} = n\zeta \qquad\qquad Bz = \frac{n-\zeta}{(1-e)\,(n-e\zeta)} \\ &\bar{t} = \frac{n - e\zeta - ne\,(1-e)}{(1-e)\,(n-e\zeta)} \\ &\bar{R} = \frac{n}{(n-e\zeta)^2}\,(n - 2e\zeta + ne^2), \quad \bar{\psi} = \frac{-\,2\,(n-e\zeta)^2}{\zeta\,(n - 2e\zeta + ne^2)}. \end{aligned} \tag{5.16}$$

These results inserted into (4.29) lead to

$$Bs' = 1/(1 + e). \tag{5.17}$$

Likewise, changing e to $-e$ in (5.15) and (5.16) shows that the rays passing through the *second* focal point are reflected so that they converge towards the *first*. For a parabola ($C = 0$, $e = 1$), one of the focal points is at infinity, that is, a parallel bundle is reflected towards the single finite focus ($Bs' = 1/2$), and the rays aiming toward the finite focus are reflected so that the emerging rays are parallel to the system axis.

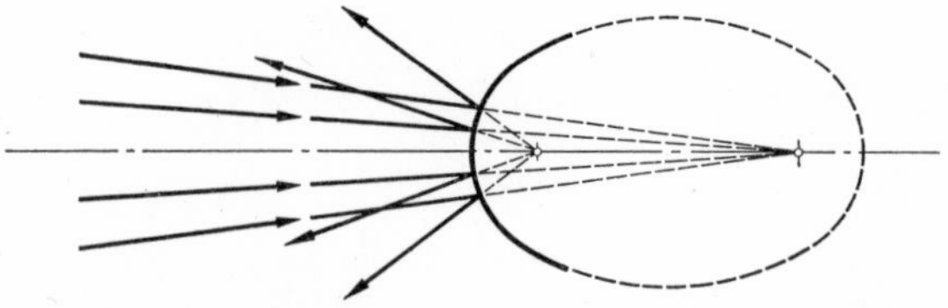

Fig. 5.1. Reflection property of ellipsoidal mirror (first case).

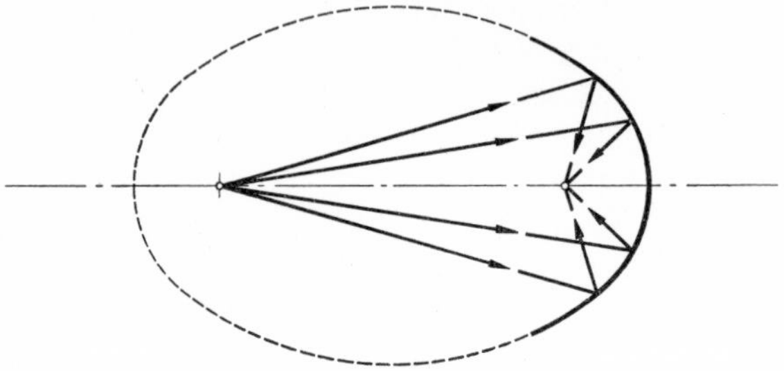

Fig. 5.2. Reflection property of ellipsoidal mirror (second case).

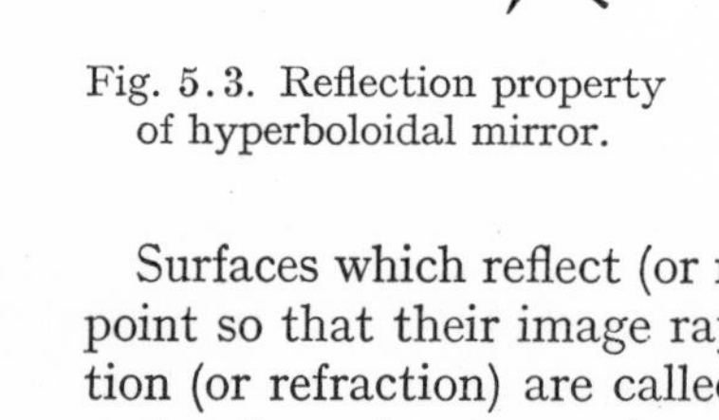

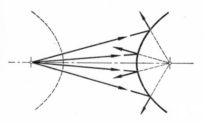

Fig. 5.3. Reflection property of hyperboloidal mirror.

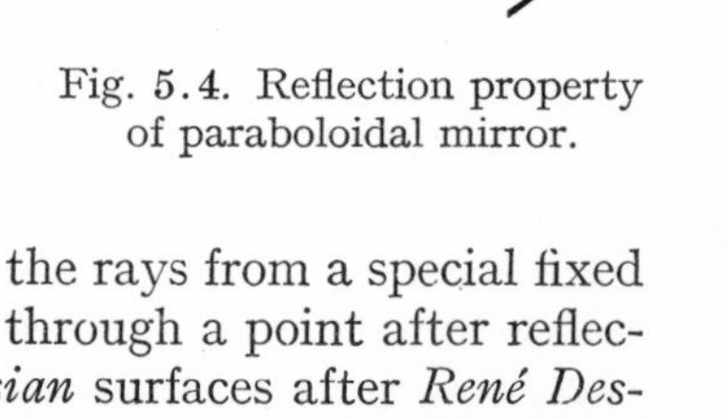

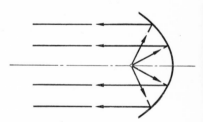

Fig. 5.4. Reflection property of paraboloidal mirror.

Surfaces which reflect (or refract) the rays from a special fixed point so that their image rays pass through a point after reflection (or refraction) are called *Cartesian* surfaces after *René Descartes*. Second-order surfaces, with the exception of spheres (for which the aplanatic points are always sharply imaged), are, in general, not Cartesian surfaces for *refraction*. Only ellipsoids and hyperboloids of rotation for which the eccentricity has the special values

$$e = n'/n \quad \text{or} \quad e = n/n' \tag{5.18}$$

form Cartesian surfaces for refraction also.

With the first choice (where the surface is an ellipsoid for $n' < n$ and a hyperboloid for $n' > n$) the rays passing through the focal point given by $Bs = 1/(1 - e)$ emerge parallel to the axis. To show this we proceed as in (5.15) and (5.16), the same expressions obtained there for $\bar{q}$, z, $\bar{t}$, and $\bar{R}$ being valid also for the present case. From (5.13) we obtain, however,

$$\bar{q}'^2 = (n'^2 - n^2)\,\bar{R}\zeta^2 + \bar{q}^2 = \frac{n^2 n'^2 \zeta^2 (\zeta - n')^2}{(n^2 - n'\zeta)^2}. \tag{5.19}$$

Remembering that $\bar{q}' > 0$, we are therefore led to

$$\bar{q}' = \frac{nn'\zeta(\zeta - n')}{n^2 - n'\zeta}, \quad \bar{\psi} = \frac{\bar{q}' - \bar{q}}{\bar{R}\zeta^2} = \frac{n'\zeta - n^2}{n\zeta}, \quad s' = \infty, \tag{5.20}$$

which proves the point.

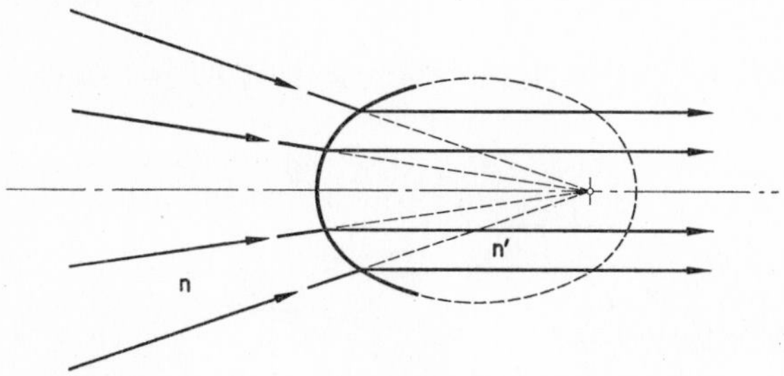

Fig. 5.5. Refraction property of ellipsoidal surface (first case).

In the same way it is found that, in the second case ($e = n/n'$), a bundle of rays parallel to the axis is focused at the point given by $Bs' = 1/(1 - e)$. The proof, following Formulae (5.13) and (4.33), proceeds as follows:

$$\vec{S} = 0, \quad C = e^2 - 1, \quad e = n/n'$$
$$\bar{q}^2 = n^2 [n^2 + B^2 \vec{P}^2 (e^2 - 1)]$$

$$z = \frac{\bar{q} - n^2}{Bn^2(e^2 - 1)}, \quad \bar{t} = \frac{e^2\bar{q} - n^2}{n^2(e^2 - 1)}, \quad \bar{R} = 1 + \frac{e^2B^2\vec{P}^2}{n^2} \tag{5.21}$$

$$\bar{q}' = n^2/e, \quad \bar{\psi} = \frac{n^2 - e\bar{q}}{e(n^2 + e^2B^2\vec{P}^2)}, \quad Bs' = \frac{1}{\bar{\psi}} + \bar{t} = \frac{1}{1-e}.$$

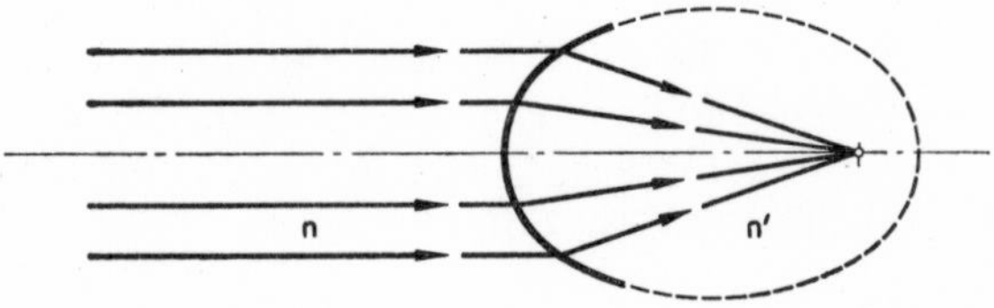

Fig. 5.6. Refraction property of ellipsoidal surface (second case).

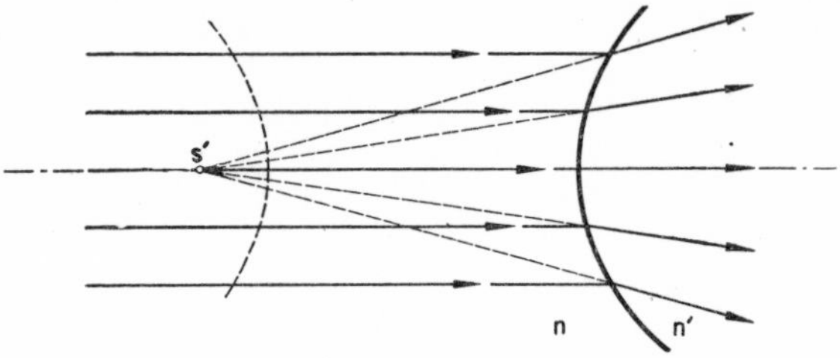

Fig. 5.7. Refraction property of hyperboloidal surface (first case).

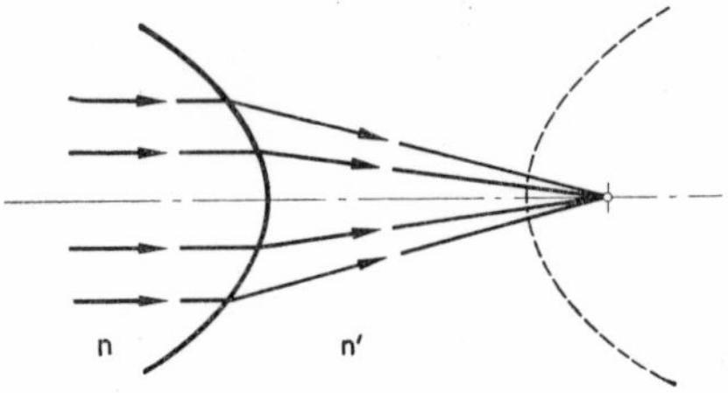

Fig. 5.8. Refraction property of hyperboloidal surface (second case).

It is left to the reader to verify that these surfaces do not have the refractive Cartesian property for the rays through the focus given by $Bs = 1/(1 + e)$.

We next consider the ray-tracing formulae as they are applied to each particular type of surface.

(*a*) *Tracing Rays through a Plane*

When $B = 0$, Equation (5.1) represents a plane:

$$z = 0. \tag{5.22}$$

In this case, Formulae (5.13) lead to

$$\begin{aligned}
&\bar{q} = \zeta^2, \quad z = 0, \quad \bar{t} = 1, \quad \bar{R} = 1 \\
&\bar{q}'^2 = \bar{q}\,(n'^2 - n^2 + \bar{q}) \text{ for refraction} \\
&(\text{for reflection } \bar{q}' = -\,\bar{q}) \\
&\bar{\psi} = \frac{\bar{q}' - \bar{q}}{\zeta^2}, \quad 1 + \bar{\psi} = \bar{q}'/\bar{q} \\
&\vec{P}' = (\bar{q}'/\bar{q})\,\vec{P} \\
&\vec{S}' = \vec{S}.
\end{aligned} \tag{5.23}$$

For the case of reflection, where $\bar{\psi} = -2$, Equation (4.32) gives

$$s' = \frac{(1 + \bar{\psi})s}{1 + B\bar{\psi}s} = -\,s. \tag{5.24}$$

Thus the plane reflecting surface (called a *plane mirror*) gives a sharp image of every point of the axis and, therefore, since any

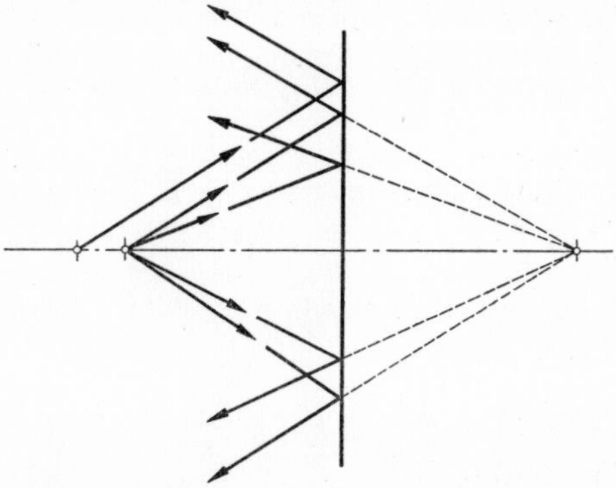

Fig. 5.9. Reflection at a plane mirror.

normal to the plane can be considered as an axis, a sharp image of any point of space. The negative sign in (5.24) shows that, if the object is in front of the mirror (a real object), the image point is behind the mirror (a virtual image) and *vice versa.*

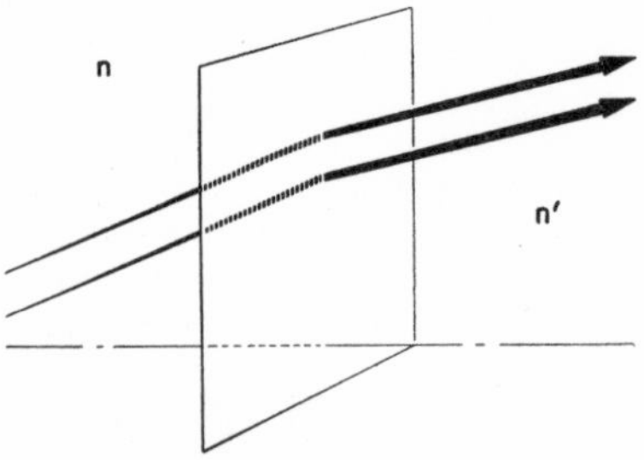

Fig. 5.10. Refraction at a plane surface.

For a *refracting* plane, the points of the refracting plane ($s = 0$) are sharply imaged upon themselves ($s' = 0$). A parallel bundle of rays is imaged into a parallel bundle of rays. This follows from the relations

$$\vec{S}' = \vec{S}, \quad \zeta'^2 = n'^2 - \vec{S}'^2 = n'^2 - \vec{S}^2, \tag{5.25}$$

showing that the direction of the image ray is dependent only on the direction and not on the position of the object ray.

(b) *The Plane-Parallel Plate*

For a pair of parallel refracting planes with air as the first and third media, we have

$$\begin{aligned} &\vec{S}_1 = \vec{S}_2 = \vec{S}_3, \quad n_1 = n_3 = 1 \\ &\zeta_3^2 = 1 - \vec{S}_3^2 = 1 - \vec{S}_1^2 = \zeta_1^2, \quad \zeta_3 = \zeta_1, \end{aligned} \tag{5.26}$$

showing that every image ray is parallel to its object ray. The tracing equations are

$$\begin{aligned} &\vec{P}_2 = \vec{P}_1 + d\vec{S}_2 = \vec{P}_1 + d\vec{S}_1 \\ &\vec{S}_3 = \vec{S}_1, \end{aligned} \tag{5.27}$$

d being the thickness of the plate. The horizontal shift is easily calculated by

$$c = d(1 - \zeta_1/\zeta_2) = d(1 - \bar{q}_1/\bar{q}'_1), \tag{5.28}$$

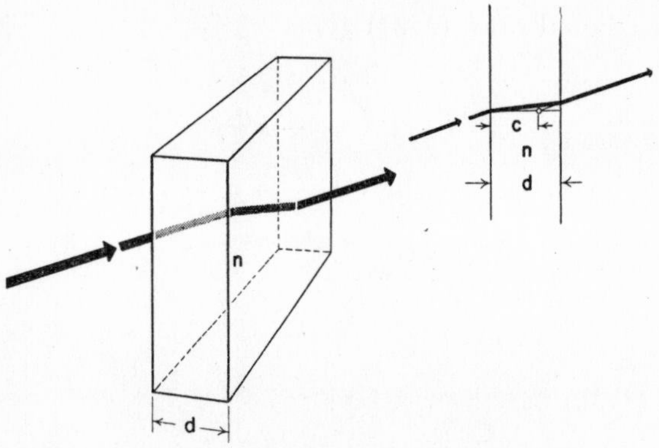

Fig. 5.11. Refraction at a plane-parallel plate.

with

$$\bar{q}_1 = \zeta_1^2, \quad \bar{q}_1'^2 = \bar{q}_1 (n_2^2 - 1 + \bar{q}_1). \tag{5.29}$$

(c) The Refracting Sphere, Vertex Trace

For a sphere we have $C = -1$, $e = 0$. The quantity $B = \varrho = 1/r$ is the curvature of the sphere, positive if the sphere is convex, negative if it is concave towards the direction of the light incident on the system. In the case of the sphere we have from (5.13)

$$\begin{aligned}
\bar{q}^2 &= (B\vec{P}\vec{S} - \zeta^2)^2 - n^2 B^2 \vec{P}^2, \quad \bar{q} > 0 \\
z &= \frac{B\vec{P}^2}{\bar{q} - B\vec{P}\vec{S} + \zeta^2}, \quad \bar{t} = 1, \bar{R} = 1 \\
\bar{q}'^2 &= (n'^2 - n^2)\zeta^2 + \bar{q}^2, \quad \bar{q}' > 0 \\
\bar{\psi} &= \frac{\bar{q}' - \bar{q}}{\zeta^2} \\
\vec{P}' - \vec{P} &= \bar{\psi}(\vec{P} + z\vec{S}) \\
\vec{S}' - \vec{S} &= -B\bar{\psi}(\vec{P} + z\vec{S}).
\end{aligned} \tag{5.30}$$

For transition to the next surface we have, as always,

$$\begin{aligned}
\vec{P}_2 &= \vec{P}' + d\vec{S}' \\
\vec{S}_2 &= \vec{S}' \\
\zeta_2^2 &= n_2^2 - \vec{S}_2^2.
\end{aligned} \tag{5.31}$$

For meridional rays, (4.31) gives

$$\vec{P}^2 = s^2\vec{S}^2$$
$$\vec{P}\vec{S} = -\, s\vec{S}^2, \tag{5.32}$$

so that we have, by introduction of $\bar{s} = Bs$, $\bar{s}' = Bs'$ in (5.30),

$$\bar{q}^2 = [n^2\bar{s} - \zeta^2(\bar{s} - 1)]^2 - n^2\bar{s}^2(n^2 - \zeta^2)$$
$$Bz = \frac{n^2\bar{s} - \zeta^2(\bar{s} - 1) - \bar{q}}{n^2}, \quad \bar{\psi} = \frac{\bar{q}' - \bar{q}}{\zeta^2}, \quad \bar{t} = 1. \tag{5.33}$$

Formula (4.32) may be written

$$\bar{s}' = \frac{\bar{s} + \bar{t}\bar{\psi}(\bar{s} - Bz)}{1 + \bar{\psi}(\bar{s} - Bz)}, \tag{5.34}$$

and consequently, by substitution of (5.33), we obtain

$$\bar{s}' = \frac{[\bar{q} + \zeta^2(\bar{s} - 1)]\,[\bar{q}' - \zeta^2(\bar{s} - 1)] + n^2\zeta^2\bar{s}(\bar{s} - 1)}{[\bar{q} + \zeta^2(\bar{s} - 1)]\,[\bar{q}' - \zeta^2(\bar{s} - 1)] + n^2\zeta^2(\bar{s} - 1)^2}. \tag{5.35}$$

If $\bar{s} - 1 = 0$ or $s = r$, we see at once that

$$\bar{s}' = 1, \quad s' = r, \tag{5.36}$$

showing that the center of the sphere is sharply imaged upon itself.

If we set $\bar{q} + \zeta^2\,(\bar{s} - 1) = 0$, using (5.33) and (5.35), we are led to

$$s = 0 = s', \quad \bar{q} = \zeta^2, \tag{5.37}$$

showing that the vertex is sharply imaged upon itself. Setting $\bar{q}' - \zeta^2\,(\bar{s} - 1) = 0$ leads with the help of (5.30) and (5.33) to

$$\bar{q}' = \zeta^2 n/n', \quad \bar{s} - 1 = n'/n. \tag{5.38}$$

Keeping in mind that $\bar{q}' > 0$, we get

$$\bar{s} = \frac{n + n'}{n} \qquad s = \frac{n + n'}{n}\,r$$
$$\bar{s}' = \frac{n + n'}{n'} \qquad s' = \frac{n + n'}{n'}\,r, \tag{5.39}$$

which indicates the imaging of one of the aplanatic spheres upon the other.

(d) The Paraboloid

Here we have $C = 0$, $e = 1$, and Formulae (5.13) give

$$\begin{aligned}
\bar{q}^2 &= (B\vec{P}\vec{S} - \zeta^2)^2 - B^2\vec{P}^2\vec{S}^2, \quad \zeta^2 = n^2 - \vec{S}^2 \\
z &= -\frac{\bar{q} + B\vec{P}\vec{S} - \zeta^2}{B\vec{S}^2} = \frac{B\vec{P}^2}{\bar{q} - B\vec{P}\vec{S} + \zeta^2} \\
\bar{t} &= 1 + Bz, \quad \bar{R} = 1 + 2Bz \qquad (5.40) \\
\bar{q}'^2 &= (n'^2 - n^2)\bar{R}\zeta^2 + \bar{q}^2, \quad \bar{\psi} = (\bar{q}' - \bar{q})/\bar{R}\zeta^2 \\
\vec{P}' - \vec{P} &= \bar{t}\bar{\psi}\,(\vec{P} + z\vec{S}) \\
\vec{S}' - \vec{S} &= -B\bar{\psi}\,(\vec{P} + z\vec{S}).
\end{aligned}$$

As noted before, since $e = 1$, one of the two focal points is at infinity. The paraboloid reflector, which reflects the light from a point source to infinity (that is, in a parallel beam) is of great practical use in searchlights. It can be enclosed by a plane-parallel plate, which does not change the path of rays parallel to the axis.

(e) The Ellipsoid and Hyperboloid

For the ellipsoid, we have $C < 0$, $e < 1$, and for the hyperboloid, $C > 0$, $e > 1$. Here the general formulae (5.13) are used. The two foci, in either case, are given by

$$Bs_1 = 1/(1 - e), \quad Bs_2 = 1/(1 + e). \qquad (5.41)$$

For ellipsoids ($e < 1$), s_1 and s_2 have the same sign, and for hyperboloids ($e > 1$) they have opposite signs. This means that, for a reflecting ellipsoid, the foci are either both real or both virtual, whereas for a reflecting hyperboloid one focus is real and one virtual.

For refraction at an ellipsoid or hyperboloid, we found that a parallel bundle is sharply imaged with

$$e = n/n', \quad Bs' = 1/(1 - e). \qquad (5.42)$$

The image point is evidently real or virtual according to whether

B is positive or negative, that is, whether the surface is convex or concave.

The ellipsoidal surface for which $C < -1$ does not have the focal properties described above. However, the calculation formulae (5.13) remain valid.

(*f*) *The Luboshez Lens*

In connection with the foregoing results, it is of interest to observe that two spherical surfaces can be combined to make a Cartesian lens. The most important practical application is the following lens on which B. Luboshez has a patent. The same idea, however, has been used in microscope design. If an object point is located at the center of the first sphere and at the aplanatic point of the second, the point is sharply imaged with a constant magnification n_3^2/n_2^2.

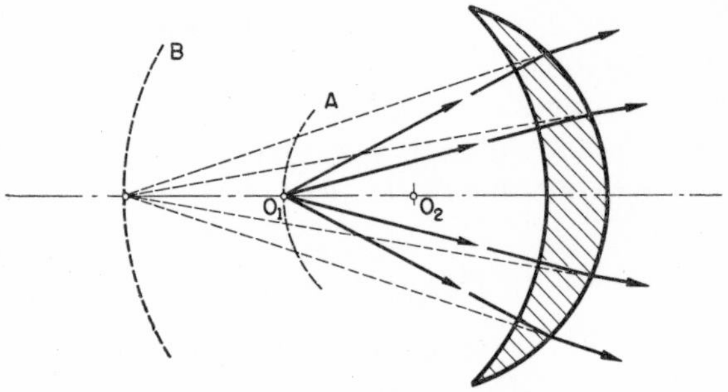

Fig. 5.12. Luboshez lens.

The ray-tracing formulae given in this chapter have been given in a form which is well suited to the special requirements of machine computation. By assuming an origin at the vertex and by suitable definitions for the quantities to be calculated, it was possible (1) to hold down the size of the numbers to be computed, (2) to use the same basic formulae for planes, spheres, and any second-order surfaces, and (3) to remove the calculation difficulties arising when long radii are present.

Consider, for example, the formula

$$z = -\frac{\bar{q} + B\vec{P}\vec{S} - \zeta^2}{B(\vec{S}^2 - C\zeta^2)} = \frac{B\vec{P}^2}{\bar{q} - B\vec{P}\vec{S} + \zeta^2}. \tag{5.43}$$

The first form for z becomes indeterminate for a long radius ($B \to 0$) since $\bar{q} - \zeta^2 \to 0$. However, the second formula gives at once $z \to 0$. Similarly

$$\bar{\psi} = \frac{\bar{q}' - \bar{q}}{\bar{R}\zeta^2} = \frac{\psi}{B}, \quad \bar{t} = 1 + Bz(C+1) = Bt$$

$$\vec{P}' - \vec{P} = \frac{t\psi}{B}(\vec{P} + z\vec{S}) = \bar{t}\bar{\psi}(\vec{P} + z\vec{S}) \qquad (5.44)$$

involves an indeterminacy if $t\psi$ is to be computed, whereas $\bar{\psi}$ approaches a finite value and $\bar{t} \to 1$ as $B \to 0$.

Before turning to unsymmetric surfaces, we apply Formulae (5.13) to the case of rays near the axis. Here we assume $\vec{S}^2 = \vec{P}\vec{S} = \vec{P}^2 = 0$, that is, that second-degree terms in ξ, η, x, y may be neglected. We then find

$$\zeta = n, \quad \bar{t} = 1, \quad \bar{\psi} = \frac{n' - n}{n}$$

$$\bar{q} = n^2, \quad \bar{R} = 1$$

$$z = 0, \quad \bar{q}' = nn' \ (\bar{q}' = -n^2 \text{ for reflection}) \qquad (5.45)$$

$$\vec{P}' = (n'/n)\,\vec{P}$$

$$\vec{S}' = \vec{S} - \frac{n' - n}{n} B\vec{P}.$$

It may be noted that C does not occur in these formulae, which, therefore, are the same for an ellipsoid, paraboloid, or hyperboloid as for a sphere, provided the vertex curvature B is the same. For a plane ($B = 0$), the last two of Equations (5.45) reduce to

$$\begin{array}{llll} \vec{P}' = (n'/n)\vec{P} & x' = x & \xi' = \xi & \zeta = n \\ \vec{S}' = \vec{S} & y' = y & \eta' = \eta & \zeta' = n'. \end{array} \qquad (5.46)$$

We next give a few examples of second-order surfaces which do not have rotational symmetry. Consider, for example, a circular cylinder lying along the y-axis and having the equation

$$F = z - \tfrac{1}{2}\,\varrho(z^2 + x^{*2}) = 0, \qquad (5.47)$$

where $\varrho = 1/r$ is its curvature. The normal vector $\vec{o}$, being proportional to (F_{x*}, F_{y*}, z), is here found to be given by

$$\vec{o} = (-\varrho x^*, \quad 0, \quad 1 - \varrho z)$$

since the proportionality constant is found, in this case, to be unity.

Proceeding much as in Chapter 4, we obtain the following calculation formulae for tracing a ray from its intersection with the plane $z = 0$ to the intersection point of the image ray with the same plane. We find

$$X = x\zeta, \quad Y = y\zeta$$
$$q^2 = (\varrho X\xi - \zeta^2)^2 - \varrho^2 X^2(\xi^2 + \zeta^2), \quad q = \zeta\,(\vec{o}\vec{s}) > 0$$
$$z = \frac{\zeta^2 - \varrho X\xi - q}{\varrho(\xi^2 + \zeta^2)} = \frac{\varrho X^2}{\zeta^2 - \varrho X\xi + q} \tag{5.48}$$
$$q'^2 = (n'^2 - n^2)\zeta^2 + q^2, \quad \psi = \Gamma/\zeta = (q' - q)/\zeta^2$$
$$\xi' = \xi - \psi\varrho(X + z\xi) \quad X' = (X + z\xi)\,[1 + \psi\,(1 - \varrho z)] - z\xi'$$
$$\eta' = \eta \qquad\qquad\qquad Y' = (Y + z\eta)\,[1 + \psi(1 - \varrho z)] - z\eta'$$
$$\zeta' = \zeta[1 + \psi\,(1 - \varrho z)] \quad x' = X'/\zeta', \quad y' = Y'/\zeta'.$$

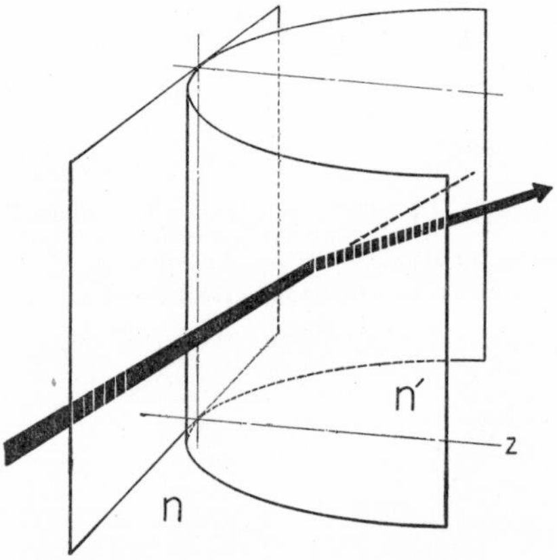

Fig. 5.13. Refraction at a cylindrical surface.

The formulae are valid for the case of a large radius ($\varrho \to 0$) provided the second form given is used to compute z.

We consider next an elliptic paraboloid with vertex at the origin, the equation being

$$2z = Ax^{*2} + By^{*2}. \tag{5.49}$$

Using the same general procedure as before, we find

$$\begin{aligned}
&D = \zeta^2 - AX\xi - BY\eta, \quad X = x\zeta, \quad Y = y\zeta \\
&q^2 = D^2 - (AX^2 + BY^2)(A\xi^2 + B\eta^2), \quad q > 0 \\
&\quad z = \frac{D - q}{A\xi^2 + B\eta^2} = \frac{AX^2 + BY^2}{D + q} \\
&X^* = X + z\xi \qquad R = \zeta^2 + A^2X^{*2} + B^2Y^{*2} \\
&Y^* = Y + z\eta \\
&q'^2 = q^2 + (n'^2 - n^2)R, \quad q' > 0, \quad \psi = (q' - q)/R \\
&(q' = -q \text{ for reflection}) \\
&\xi' = \xi - A\psi X^* \qquad X' = (1 + \psi)X^* - z\xi' \\
&\eta' = \eta - B\psi Y^* \qquad Y' = (1 + \psi)Y^* - z\eta' \\
&\zeta' = \zeta(1 + \psi) \qquad x' = X'/\zeta', \quad y' = Y'/\zeta'.
\end{aligned} \tag{5.50}$$

When A or B is zero in Equation (5.49), the equation is that of a parabolic cylinder. For instance, if $B = 0$, the cylinder lies along the y-axis and the tracing equations assume the form

$$\begin{aligned}
&D = \zeta^2 - AX\xi, \quad X = x\zeta, \quad Y = y\zeta \\
&q^2 = D^2 - A^2X^2\xi^2, \quad q > 0 \\
&\quad z = (D - q)/A\xi^2 = AX^2/(D + q) \\
&X^* = X + z\xi \qquad R = \zeta^2 + A^2X^{*2} \\
&Y^* = Y + z\eta \\
&q'^2 = q^2 + (n'^2 - n^2)R, \quad q' > 0, \quad \psi = (q' - q)/R \\
&\xi' = \xi - A\psi X^* \qquad X' = (1 + \psi)X^* - z\xi' \\
&\eta' = \eta \qquad Y' = (1 + \psi)Y^* - z\eta' \\
&\zeta' = \zeta(1 + \psi) \qquad x' = X'/\zeta', \quad y' = Y'/\zeta'.
\end{aligned} \tag{5.51}$$

When dealing with surfaces of order higher than the second, it is not feasible to write the tracing formulae in closed form as has been done above. In such cases (and also frequently in the second-order case, too) it is best to use an iterative procedure. We illustrate with an example of a rotation-symmetric surface, but the essential features of the method make it easily adaptable to unsymmetric surfaces such as a cylinder or elliptic paraboloid.

We assume the equation of a rotation-symmetric surface given in the form

$$z = f(u^*), \quad 2u^* = x^{*2} + y^{*2}. \tag{5.52}$$

As a concrete example, suppose this has the special form

$$F\,(u^*,z) = z - Bu^* - Cu^{*2}, \tag{5.53}$$

the origin being at the vertex. Introduction of the symmetric functions

$$\begin{aligned} 2u &= x^2 + y^2 = \vec{P}^2/(n^2 - \vec{S}^2) \\ v &= \frac{1}{\zeta}\,(x\xi + y\eta) = \vec{P}\vec{S}/(n^2 - \vec{S}^2) \\ 2w &= \frac{1}{\zeta^2}\,(\xi^2 + \eta^2) = \vec{S}^2/(n^2 - \vec{S}^2) \end{aligned} \tag{5.54}$$

leads by (4.10) to

$$u^* = u + vz + wz^2. \tag{5.55}$$

Substitution of this into (5.53) gives

$$z = B(u + vz + wz^2) + C(u + vz + wz^2)^2, \tag{5.56}$$

which is to be solved for the root z having the smallest numerical value. We calculate the successive approximate values of z indicated by

$$\begin{aligned} z_0 &= Bu + Cu^2 \\ z_1 &= B(u + vz_o + wz_o{}^2) + C(u + vz_o + wz_o{}^2)^2 \\ z_2 &= B(u + vz_1 + wz_1{}^2) + C(u + vz_1 + wz_1{}^2)^2 \end{aligned} \tag{5.57}$$

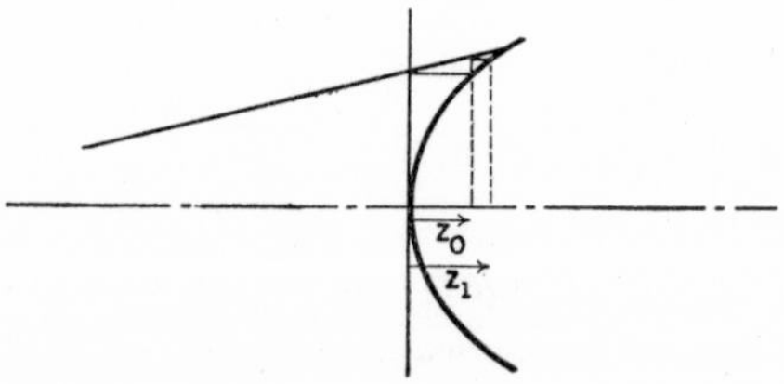

Fig. 5. 14. Iteration procedure for finding intersection point.

In general this sequence converges rapidly towards the solution of (5.56). Having found z, we obtain

$$F_{u*} = -(B + 2u^*), \quad F_z = 1, \tag{5.58}$$

after which the ray-trace can be carried out as in (4.21), (4.22), and (4.23). If, however, the vertex curvature B is small, it is advisable to use the modified quantities $\bar{t} = Bt$, $\bar{q} = Bq$, and $\bar{\psi} = (1/B)\psi$ as described above in this chapter.

CHAPTER SIX

Starting and Final Data

In Chapters 4 and 5 we have devised formulae for tracing a ray through a single surface. Let the intersection points of the rays with the vertex plane before and after refraction be given by vectors $\vec{A}$ and $\vec{A}'$ normal to the axis, and let the directions be given by the vectors $\vec{S}$ and $\vec{S}'$ normal to the axis. Then the coordinates of the four vectors are $\vec{A}(x, y, 0)$, $\vec{A}'(x', y', 0)$, $\vec{S}(\xi, \eta, 0)$, $\vec{S}'(\xi', \eta', 0)$. Instead of $\vec{A}$ and $\vec{A}'$, we may use the vectors $\vec{P}$ and $\vec{P}'$ defined by

$$\vec{P} = \vec{A}\zeta, \quad \vec{P}' = \vec{A}'\zeta'. \tag{6.1}$$

We had found the equations for refraction at a given surface—for instance, the νth surface—by Formulae (4.22):

$$\begin{aligned} \vec{P}_\nu' &= \varkappa_\nu \vec{P}_\nu + \lambda_\nu \vec{S}_\nu \\ \vec{S}_\nu' &= \mu_\nu \vec{P}_2 + \nu_\nu \vec{S}_\nu, \end{aligned} \tag{6.2}$$

with

$$\begin{aligned} \varkappa_\nu &= 1 + \psi_\nu t_\nu \quad & \lambda_\nu &= \psi_\nu t_\nu z_\nu \\ \mu_\nu &= -\psi_\nu & \nu_\nu &= 1 - \psi_\nu z_\nu. \end{aligned} \tag{6.3}$$

To transfer to the $(\nu + 1)$st surface, the equations

$$\begin{aligned} \vec{P}_{\nu+1} &= \vec{P}_\nu' + d_\nu \vec{S}_\nu' \\ \vec{S}_{\nu+1} &= \vec{S}_\nu' \end{aligned} \tag{6.4}$$

are used, where d_ν is the distance between the νth and the $(\nu + 1)$st vertices.

In this way one finally computes

$$\begin{aligned} \vec{P}_n' &= \varkappa \vec{P}_1 + \lambda \vec{S}_1 \\ \vec{S}_n' &= \mu \vec{P}_1 + \nu \vec{S}_1, \end{aligned} \tag{6.5}$$

where $\vec{P}_1$ has the coordinates $x_1\zeta, y_1\zeta$ (x_1, y_1 being the coordinates of the intersection at the first vertex plane) and $\vec{P}'$, the coordinates $x_n'\zeta'$, $y_n'\zeta'$, (x_n', y_n' being the coordinates at the last vertex plane). The coefficients $\varkappa, \lambda, \mu, \nu$ can be obtained by matrix multiplication. Setting

$$\begin{pmatrix} \varkappa & \lambda \\ \mu & \nu \end{pmatrix} = K, \quad \begin{pmatrix} \varkappa_\nu & \lambda_\nu \\ \mu_\nu & \nu_\nu \end{pmatrix} = K_\nu, \quad \begin{pmatrix} 1 & d_\nu \\ 0 & 1 \end{pmatrix} = \Delta_\nu, \tag{6.6}$$

we obtain in the language of matrix multiplication

$$K = K_n \Delta_{n-1} K_{n-1} \Delta_{n-2} \dots \Delta_1 K_1. \tag{6.7}$$

From (6.3) and (4.24) we derive

$$\varkappa_\nu \nu_\nu - \lambda_\nu \mu_\nu = 1 + \psi_\nu(t_\nu - z_\nu) = \frac{\zeta_\nu'}{\zeta_\nu} = \frac{\zeta_{\nu+1}}{\zeta_\nu}, \tag{6.8}$$

or the determinant $|K|$ of K becomes

$$|K| = \zeta'/\zeta = \varkappa\nu - \lambda\mu. \tag{6.9}$$

In this discussion, the initial ray is given by $\vec{P}_1$ and $\vec{S}_1$ and the final ray by $\vec{P}_n'$ and $\vec{S}_n'$. Two problems remain: (*a*) to find $\vec{P}_1$ and $\vec{S}_1$ if the entering ray is given by other data; (*b*) to calculate from $\vec{P}_n'$ and $\vec{S}_n'$ other data of the emerging ray, if so desired.

(*a*) As an example of the first problem, the entering ray may be given by the vector $\vec{a}$ (coordinates x, y, z) from the vertex to an arbitrary point on the ray and by the optical direction vector $\vec{s}$ (coordinates ξ, η, ζ) along the ray

$$\begin{aligned} X &= x_1\zeta = x\zeta + \xi z \\ Y &= y_1\zeta = y\zeta + \eta z \end{aligned} \tag{6.10}$$

and the coordinates of $\vec{S}$ as ($\xi, \eta, 0$).

(*b*) Analogously, we can compute the coordinates of an arbitrary point $\vec{a}'(x', y', z')$ on the image side from the coordinates of $\vec{P}'(X', Y', 0)$ and $\vec{S}'(\xi', \eta', 0)$, the result being

$$x' = (1/\zeta')(X' + \xi'z'), \quad y' = (1/\zeta')(Y' + \eta'z') \tag{6.11}$$

with

$$\zeta' = \sqrt{n'^2 - (\xi'^2 + \eta'^2)},$$

where the sign of ζ' is positive if the system contains no reflections or an even number of them.

In the theoretical and the practical evaluation of the ray-tracing formulae, it will be convenient, instead of giving the object and image rays by $\vec{P}$, $\vec{S}$ and $\vec{P}'$, $\vec{S}'$, respectively, to use a different set of vectors.

One such choice involves using the pairs of vectors $\vec{A}$, $\vec{T}$, $\vec{A}'$, $\vec{T}'$ [*cf.* (4.6)], where

$$\begin{aligned} \vec{P} &= \vec{A}\zeta & \zeta\vec{T} &= \vec{S} \\ \vec{P}' &= \vec{A}'\zeta' & \zeta'\vec{T}' &= \vec{S}'. \end{aligned} \tag{6.12}$$

If we use the vectors $\vec{A}$ and $\vec{T}$ to specify the rays, we can write

$$\begin{aligned} \vec{A}' &= a\vec{A} + b\vec{T} \\ \vec{T}' &= c\vec{A} + d\vec{T}. \end{aligned} \tag{6.13}$$

Using (6.12) and (6.9) and comparing (6.13) with (6.5), we find

$$\begin{aligned} a &= \frac{\varkappa}{\varkappa\nu - \lambda\mu} & b &= \frac{\lambda}{\varkappa\nu - \lambda\mu} \\ c &= \frac{\mu}{\varkappa\nu - \lambda\mu} & d &= \frac{\nu}{\varkappa\nu - \lambda\mu} \end{aligned} \tag{6.14}$$

and reciprocally

$$\begin{aligned} \varkappa &= \frac{a}{ad - bc} & \lambda &= \frac{b}{ad - bc} \\ \mu &= \frac{c}{ad - bc} & \nu &= \frac{d}{ad - bc}. \end{aligned} \tag{6.15}$$

The reader will notice that

$$ad - bc = \frac{1}{\varkappa\nu - \lambda\mu} = \frac{\zeta}{\zeta'}. \tag{6.16}$$

Let the object and image rays be given by $\vec{A}$, $\vec{S}$ and $\vec{A}'$, $\vec{S}'$. We find

$$\begin{aligned} \vec{A}' &= \alpha\vec{A} + \beta\vec{S} \\ \vec{S}' &= \gamma\vec{A} + \delta\vec{S} \end{aligned} \tag{6.17}$$

with

$$\begin{aligned}\alpha &= a = \frac{\varkappa}{\varkappa\nu - \lambda\mu}\\ \beta &= b/\zeta = \frac{\lambda/\zeta}{\varkappa\nu - \lambda\mu}\\ \gamma &= \frac{c\zeta}{ad - bc} = \mu\zeta\\ \delta &= \frac{d}{ad - bc} = \nu,\end{aligned} \tag{6.18}$$

which shows that

$$\alpha\delta - \beta\gamma = 1. \tag{6.19}$$

The formulae developed in this chapter can be used to transform a problem from one system of representative vectors to another. The reader should make himself well acquainted with these transformations, which will be used frequently throughout the book.

In the above treatment, a ray has been given by a point vector ($\vec{A}$) and a direction vector ($\vec{S}$). In theoretical investigations and even in practical applications, it is sometimes more convenient to give the ray by the coordinates of the intersections with two planes, for instance, by the coordinates of the object point and the coordinates of the intersection point with the plane of the entrance pupil (see Chapter 22).

Let $\vec{A}$ and $\vec{A}_P$ accordingly be the projected vectors of the object point and the intersection point, respectively, at the entrance pupil, and let k be the distance between the object plane and the plane of the entrance pupil. We then have

$$k\vec{T} = \vec{A} - \vec{A}_P \tag{6.20}$$

and therefore from (6.13)

$$\begin{aligned}\vec{A}' &= \left(a + \frac{b}{k}\right)\vec{A} - \frac{b}{k}\vec{A}_P\\ \vec{T}' &= \left(c + \frac{d}{k}\right)\vec{A} - \frac{d}{k}\vec{A}_P,\end{aligned} \tag{6.21}$$

giving the image data as functions of the object-plane and entrance-pupil intersections.

Formulae (6.21) reduce to (6.13) if we let the entrance pupil approach infinity, that is, if we make the transition

$$\frac{1}{k} \to 0, \quad -\frac{\vec{A}_P}{k} \to \vec{T}. \tag{6.22}$$

Finally, we shall prove once more that the calculation with the projected vectors is sufficient to give any desired information. Let us choose arbitrary origins in the object and image spaces, both origins being on the axis of rotation. Let the object ray be given by the vector $\vec{a}(x, y, z)$ to an arbitrary initial point and by the direction vector $\vec{s}$, of length n. Analogously, let the image ray be given by the vector $\vec{a}'(x', y', z')$ to an arbitrary terminal point on the image ray and the direction vector $\vec{s}'$ of length n'. We then have

$$\begin{aligned} \vec{a}' &= \alpha\vec{a} + \beta\vec{s} + C_1\vec{k} \\ \vec{s}' &= \gamma\vec{a} + \delta\vec{s} + C_2\vec{k} \\ \vec{k} &= \qquad\qquad\quad \vec{k} \end{aligned} \tag{6.23}$$

Projecting these equations onto a plane perpendicular to the z-axis, we obtain

$$\begin{aligned} \vec{A}' &= \alpha\vec{A} + \beta\vec{S} \\ \vec{S}' &= \gamma\vec{A} + \delta\vec{S}, \end{aligned} \tag{6.24}$$

which proves that the α, β, γ, δ in (6.24) are the same as those calculated before in (6.17) with

$$\alpha\delta - \beta\gamma = 1. \tag{6.25}$$

From this it follows, first, that

$$[\vec{a}'\vec{s}'\vec{k}] = (\alpha\delta - \beta\gamma)\,[\vec{a}\vec{s}\vec{k}] = [\vec{a}\vec{s}\vec{k}], \tag{6.26}$$

that is, $[\vec{a}\vec{s}\vec{k}]$ is a scalar invariant of the ray trace. Knowing α, β, γ, δ, we can compute C_1 and C_2 from (6.23), which give

$$\begin{aligned} z' &= \alpha z + \beta\zeta + C_1 \\ \zeta' &= \gamma z + \delta\zeta + C_2 \end{aligned} \tag{6.27}$$

since ζ and ζ' are known with $\vec{S}$ and $\vec{S}'$, and z' depends only on the arbitrary choice of the terminal point. Thus Equations (6.24) are sufficient to give all necessary data.

We draw to the reader's attention that the formulae considered in (6.1) to (6.10) may be rewritten with the $\vec{S}$ and $\vec{P}$ as determining vectors. We describe the calculation with $\vec{A}$ and $\vec{S}$ in somewhat more detail.

Abbreviating the refraction matrix at a single surface by (A_ν) so that

$$\begin{aligned}\vec{A}_\nu' &= \alpha_\nu \vec{A}_\nu + \beta_\nu \vec{S}_\nu \\ \vec{S}_\nu' &= \gamma_\nu \vec{A}_\nu + \delta_\nu \vec{S}_\nu\end{aligned} \quad \text{becomes} \quad \begin{pmatrix}\vec{A}_\nu' \\ \vec{S}_\nu'\end{pmatrix} = (A_\nu)\begin{pmatrix}\vec{A}_\nu \\ \vec{S}_\nu\end{pmatrix}, \tag{6.28}$$

and abbreviating the matrix giving the transition from one vertex to another by (D_ν), we can write

$$\begin{aligned}\vec{A}_{\nu+1} &= \vec{A}_\nu' + \frac{d_\nu}{\zeta_\nu'}\vec{S}_\nu' \\ \vec{S}_{\nu+1} &= \qquad\quad \vec{S}_\nu'\end{aligned} \quad \text{as} \quad \begin{pmatrix}\vec{A}_{\nu+1} \\ \vec{S}_{\nu+1}\end{pmatrix} = (D_\nu)\begin{pmatrix}\vec{A}_\nu' \\ \vec{S}_\nu'\end{pmatrix}, \tag{6.29}$$

with

$$(A_\nu) = \begin{pmatrix}\alpha_\nu & \beta_\nu \\ \gamma_\nu & \delta_\nu\end{pmatrix}, \quad (D_\nu) = \begin{pmatrix}1 & d_\nu \\ 0 & \zeta_\nu'\end{pmatrix}. \tag{6.30}$$

We then can write

$$\begin{pmatrix}\vec{A}' \\ \vec{S}'\end{pmatrix} = (A)\begin{pmatrix}\vec{A} \\ \vec{S}\end{pmatrix}, \tag{6.31}$$

where the matrix A is given by

$$A = A_n D_{n-1} A_{n-1} \dots D_1 A_1. \tag{6.32}$$

Formulae (6.31) and (6.32) are parallel to (6.5) and (6.7).

CHAPTER SEVEN

Point and Diapoint

In the preceding chapters the point-diapoint connection has been discussed in several places. Let a skew ray and its image ray be given in an optical system with symmetry of rotation around an axis. A one-to-one coordination of the points of the object and image rays may be given in the following way. Given an initial point on the object ray, there exists a well-defined plane through this point and the system axis. This plane is the meridional plane of the initial point, and we define the *diapoint* as the point in which the image ray intersects this plane.

Let the object and image rays be connected by the equations

$$\begin{aligned} \vec{A}' &= \alpha\vec{A} + \beta\vec{S} \\ \vec{S}' &= \gamma\vec{A} + \delta\vec{S}, \quad \alpha\delta - \beta\gamma = 1. \end{aligned} \tag{7.1}$$

An arbitrary point on the object ray is given by

$$\tilde{\vec{A}} = \vec{A} + l\vec{S}$$

and, analogously, an arbitrary point on the image ray by

$$\tilde{\vec{A}}' = \vec{A}' + l'\vec{S}'.$$

Replacing $\vec{A}$ and $\vec{A}'$ in (7.1) by $\tilde{\vec{A}}$ and $\tilde{\vec{A}}'$, we find for *arbitrary* initial and terminal points

$$\begin{aligned} \tilde{\vec{A}}' &= (\alpha + l'\gamma)\tilde{\vec{A}} + [(\beta + l'\delta) - l(\alpha + l'\gamma)]\vec{S} \\ \vec{S}' &= \gamma\tilde{\vec{A}} + (\delta - l\gamma)\vec{S}\,. \end{aligned} \tag{7.2}$$

If we choose l' such that the coefficient of $\vec{S}$ vanishes, that is,

$$l' = \frac{l\alpha - \beta}{\delta - l\gamma}, \tag{7.3}$$

we find that

$$\vec{\vec{A}}' = m\vec{\vec{A}}$$

$$\vec{S}' = \gamma\vec{\vec{A}} + (1/m)\,\vec{S}, \quad m = \frac{\alpha\delta - \beta\gamma}{\delta - l\gamma} = \frac{1}{\delta - l\gamma}, \tag{7.4}$$

or the coordination given by (7.3) between points on the object and image rays is the point-diapoint connection defined in earlier chapters for special types of systems. An initial point and its diapoint lie in a plane through the axis. The proportionality factor m may be called the *diamagnification*. Equation (7.4) gives the diamagnification as a function of the position of the initial point. Solving Equation (7.3) for l we find

$$l = \frac{l'\delta + \beta}{\alpha + l'\gamma}, \quad m = \alpha + l'\gamma, \tag{7.5}$$

which gives l and m as functions of l'. A more symmetrical way of writing the connection of l and l' can be obtained by comparing the equations for m in (7.4) and (7.5), the relation found being

$$(\alpha + l'\gamma)\,(\delta - l\gamma) = 1. \tag{7.6}$$

Equation (7.6) suggests the special investigation of the object-side point given by

$$l = \delta/\gamma \tag{7.7}$$

and the image-side point given by

$$l' = -\alpha/\gamma. \tag{7.8}$$

These points, to which, according to Equation (7.6), there correspond as diapoints the infinite point of the image ray and the infinite point of the object ray, respectively, are called the object- and image-side *diafocal points*, respectively [*cf.* (4.33) and (4.44)]. For the first case we have, from (7.2),

$$\vec{S}' = \gamma\vec{\vec{A}}_F, \tag{7.9}$$

and in the second case we obtain

$$\vec{\vec{A}}_{F'} = -(1/\gamma)\vec{S}, \tag{7.10}$$

which defines the object-side diafocal point as the intersection of the object ray with the plane through the axis parallel to the image ray, and the image-side focal point as the intersection of the image ray with the plane through the axis parallel to the object ray. The constant γ, which incidentally does not change if we shift the initial point along the object ray, is called the optical *diafocal length.* We have from (7.9) and (7.10)

$$\vec{S}' = \gamma \tilde{\vec{A}}_F, \; \vec{S} = -\gamma \tilde{\vec{A}}_{F'}. \tag{7.11}$$

A case to be investigated especially is the one in which γ is zero. A ray with $\gamma = 0$ is called an *afocal* ray because, in that case, (7.7) and (7.8) give no finite diafocal points. For an afocal ray, we have from (7.1), (7.3), and (7.4)

$$\begin{aligned} \alpha\delta &= 1 \\ l' &= l\alpha^2 - \beta\alpha \\ m &= 1/\delta = \alpha. \end{aligned} \tag{7.12}$$

Equations (7.4) show that, for the points of an afocal ray, the diamagnification is the same for all initial points:

$$\begin{aligned} \tilde{\vec{A}}' &= \alpha \tilde{\vec{A}} \\ \vec{S}' &= (1/\alpha)\vec{S}. \end{aligned} \tag{7.13}$$

Perspective Connection of Point and Diapoint

It may be of some geometrical interest that the coordination between point and diapoint can be interpreted for rays with $\gamma \neq 0$ as a perspective coordination.

Let us consider two arbitrary origins O and O' in the object and image spaces, respectively, and consider also the intersection points of the object ray and image ray with two fixed reference planes at distances z and z' from O and O', respectively. If $\vec{a}$ and $\vec{a}'$ are the vectors from O and O' to these points, we have

$$\begin{aligned} \vec{a} &= \vec{A} + z\vec{k} \qquad & \vec{s} &= \vec{S} + \zeta\vec{k} \\ \vec{a}' &= \vec{A}' + z'\vec{k} \qquad & \vec{s}' &= \vec{S}' + \zeta'\vec{k}, \end{aligned} \tag{7.14}$$

where $\vec{A}$, $\vec{A}'$, $\vec{S}$, and $\vec{S}'$ satisfy (7.1).

If now we wish to consider arbitrary points on the object and image rays, this may be done by an arbitrary choice of l and l' in the expressions

$$\begin{aligned}\tilde{\vec{a}} &= \vec{a} + l\vec{s} = \vec{A} + l\vec{S} + (z + l\zeta)\vec{k}\\ \tilde{\vec{a}}' &= \vec{a}' + l'\vec{s}' = \vec{A}' + l'\vec{S}' + (z' + l'\zeta')\vec{k}.\end{aligned} \tag{7.15}$$

In particular, the points given by $\tilde{\vec{a}}$ and $\tilde{\vec{a}}'$ will be point and diapoint if (7.3) is fulfilled, that is, if

$$l' = (l\alpha - \beta)/(\delta - l\gamma). \tag{7.16}$$

In this case the projected components

$$\tilde{\vec{A}} = \vec{A} + l\vec{S}, \quad \tilde{\vec{A}}' = \vec{A} + l'\vec{S}' \tag{7.17}$$

will satisfy the relation (7.4), that is,

$$\tilde{\vec{A}}' = m\tilde{\vec{A}}, \quad m = 1/(\delta + l\gamma). \tag{7.18}$$

We ask whether it is possible to choose the origins O and O' in such a way that the z-components in (7.15) will obey the same proportionality relation. That is, we suppose the reference planes to be held fixed and the origins (and with them, the distances z and z') adjusted so that for all values of l

$$z' + l'\zeta' = m\,(z + l\zeta), \quad l' = \frac{l\alpha - \beta}{\delta - l\gamma}, \quad m = \frac{1}{\delta - l\gamma}. \tag{7.19}$$

For $\gamma \neq 0$, these equations can be fulfilled if z and z' are chosen so that

$$z = (\zeta' - \delta\zeta)/\gamma, \quad z' = (\alpha\zeta' - \zeta)/\gamma. \tag{7.20}$$

The points thus determined on the axis are called the *central points* of the ray, and we see that the vectors from the central points to the object point and its diapoint, respectively, are proportional (parallel). For an afocal ray ($\gamma = 0$), the central points are at infinity. For a concentric system, the two central points fall together at the center of the system, this point, of course, being the same for all rays, whereas for non-centric systems the central points may vary from ray to ray.

Instead of using $\vec{A}$ and $\vec{S}$ to determine the ray, we might also have used $\vec{A}$ and $\vec{T}$, $\vec{P}$ and $\vec{S}$, or $\vec{A}$ and $\vec{A}_P$. The formulae giving the coordination of point and diapoint will not change, in principle, but a few facts may be of interest.

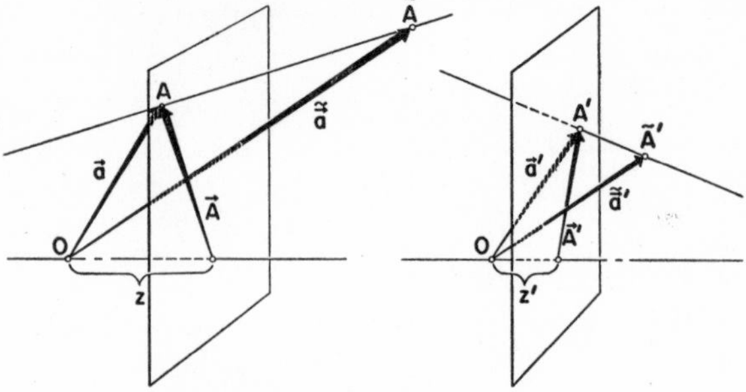

Fig. 7.1. Central points.

Using $\vec{A}$ and $\vec{P}$, we have

$$\vec{P}' = \varkappa\vec{P} + \lambda\vec{S}$$
$$\vec{S}' = \mu\vec{P} + \nu\vec{S}. \tag{7.21}$$

The diapoint is determined from (7.21) by setting

$$\vec{\tilde{P}}' = \vec{P}' + s'\vec{S}', \tag{7.22}$$

so that in the equation

$$\vec{\tilde{P}}' = (\varkappa + s'\mu)\,\vec{P} + (\lambda + s'\nu)\vec{S}, \tag{7.23}$$

the coefficient of $\vec{S}$ vanishes. This leads to

$$s' = -\,\lambda/\nu, \quad \vec{\tilde{P}}' = \frac{\varkappa\nu - \lambda\mu}{\nu}\,\vec{P}. \tag{7.24}$$

Recalling the formula

$$\varkappa\nu - \lambda\mu = \zeta'/\zeta \tag{7.25}$$

from the preceding chapter, it is seen that the diamagnification m is given by

$$m = 1/\nu. \tag{7.26}$$

Thus the geometrical meaning of the quantities ν and λ is seen to be connected with the diamagnification m and the z-coordinate s' of the diapoint. We have

$$\nu = 1/m, \quad \lambda = -\,s'/m, \tag{7.27}$$

relations which will be used in the image-error theory to be discussed in Chapter 21.

PART II
PRECALCULATION OF OPTICAL SYSTEMS

CHAPTER EIGHT

Gaussian Optics. General Laws

Let us assume arbitrary origins on the axis on object and image sides. Let the object ray be given by vector $\vec{A}$, coordinates $(x, y, 0)$, and vector $\vec{S}$, coordinates $(\xi, \eta, 0)$, and the image ray by vectors $\vec{A}'$ and $\vec{S}'$. We saw in Chapter 6 that we can calculate coefficients $\alpha, \beta, \gamma, \delta$ for each ray such that

$$\begin{aligned} \vec{A}' &= \alpha\vec{A} + \beta\vec{S} \\ \vec{S}' &= \gamma\vec{A} + \delta\vec{S} \qquad \alpha\delta - \beta\gamma = 1. \end{aligned} \tag{8.1}$$

The coefficients $\alpha, \beta, \gamma, \delta$ are functions of ξ, η, x, y, or, because of rotational symmetry, of their symmetric functions

$$\begin{aligned} \vec{A}^2 &= 2u = x^2 + y^2 \\ \vec{A}\vec{S} &= v = x\xi + y\eta \\ \vec{S}^2 &= 2w = \xi^2 + \eta^2, \end{aligned} \tag{8.2}$$

and each of the quantities $\alpha, \beta, \gamma, \delta$ can be developed into a power series according to u, v, w.

Replacing each function by its constant member, that is, by its value for $u = v = w = 0$, gives us *Gaussian optics*. This means that the laws of Gaussian optics hold strictly for those rays which are so near the axis in position and direction that $\vec{A}^2$, $\vec{A}\vec{S}$, and $\vec{S}^2$ can be neglected.

In spite of this restriction, the laws of Gaussian optics are used to give the approximate position and magnification for any optical image-formation, and Gaussian optics, with slight modifications, will be used as an approximate model throughout the book. The deviations from its laws will be considered as *aberrations* and studied in much the same way as the astronomer studies the deviations (perturbations) of the paths of planets from Kepler's ellipses. However, in trying to study the laws of Gaussian optics and in applying them to real optics, one must always keep in mind their limitations.

Under these assumptions, we assume (8.1) to have constant coefficients. The reader will notice that, within the limits of Gaussian optics, we have

$$\zeta = \sqrt{n^2 - \vec{S}^2} = n$$
$$\zeta' = \sqrt{n'^2 - \vec{S}'^2} = \varepsilon n', \tag{8.3}$$

where ε ordinarily equals $+1$, and is equal to -1 if and only if the system has an odd number of reflections.

Meridional Rays

The rays coming from an axis point at the distance $z = s$ satisfy the relation

$$\vec{A} + \frac{z}{\zeta}\vec{S} = \vec{A} + \frac{s}{n}\vec{S} = 0. \tag{8.4}$$

After traversing the system, they intersect the axis at a point at the distance $z' = s'$ from the reference plane. Introducing the symbol $s^{*\prime} = \varepsilon s'$, we have, by using (8.1) and (8.4),

$$0 = \vec{A}' + \frac{s'}{\zeta'}\vec{S}' = \vec{A}' + \frac{s^{*\prime}}{n'}\vec{S}' = \left[-\frac{\alpha s}{n} + \beta + \frac{s^{*\prime}}{n'}\left(-\frac{\gamma s}{n} + \delta\right)\right]\vec{S}. \tag{8.5}$$

The axis points satisfying (8.5) independently of $\vec{S}$, that is, connected by

$$\frac{s^{*\prime}}{n'} = \frac{\beta - \dfrac{\alpha s}{n}}{\gamma\dfrac{s}{n} - \delta} \quad \text{or} \quad \frac{s}{n} = \frac{\beta + \dfrac{s^{*\prime}}{n'}\delta}{\alpha + \dfrac{s^{*\prime}}{n'}\gamma} \tag{8.6}$$

are called *conjugate points*, meaning that all the rays from the object point unite (within the validity of Gaussian optics) at the image point. Equations (8.6) give a one-to-one coordination of the object and image points of the axis. Comparison of these formulae with those of Chapter 7 shows that Gaussian optics is a special case of the diapoint theory developed there.

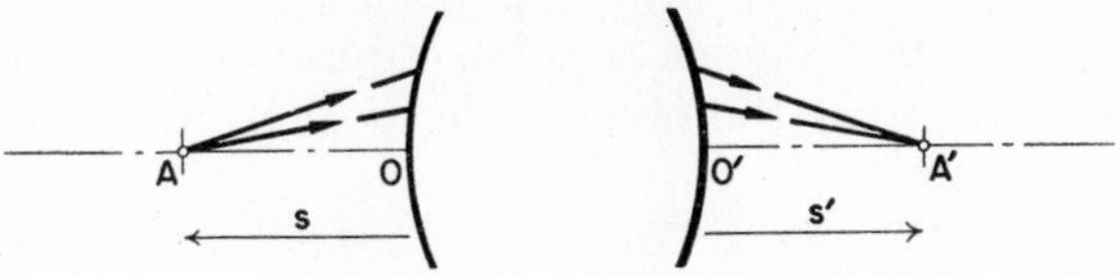

Fig. 8.1. Conjugate points.

The rays parallel to the axis in the object space are given by

$$\vec{S} = 0, \qquad \vec{A}' = \alpha\vec{A}$$
$$\vec{S}' = \gamma\vec{A}. \tag{8.7}$$

They meet at an axial point at the distance

$$\vec{s}_F{}^{*\prime}/n' = -\alpha/\gamma, \tag{8.8}$$

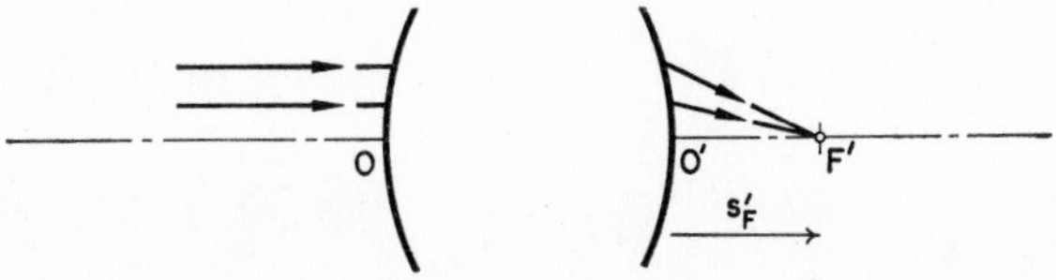

Fig. 8.2. Image-side focal point.

as is seen by comparison with the relation $\vec{A}' + (s_F{}^{*\prime}/n')\vec{S}' = 0$. This point is called the *image-side focal point* of the system.

Comparing (8.8) with (8.6) shows that $s_F{}^{*\prime}$ is the limiting value of the first equation of (8.6) as $s \to \infty$. This agrees with the terminology which will be used throughout the book in which a parallel bundle of rays is referred to as a bundle coming from an *infinite point*.

In the same way we find for $s' \to \infty$

$$s_F/n = \delta/\gamma \tag{8.9}$$

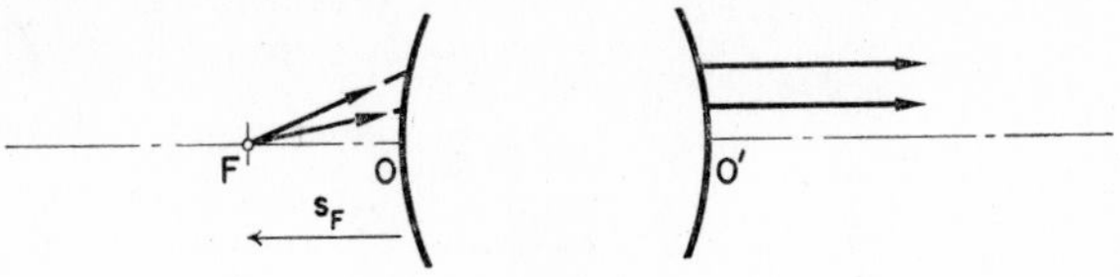

Fig. 8.3. Object-side focal point.

as defining the *object-side focal point*. Equation (8.1) shows that the rays coming from the object-side focal point, that is, satisfying the equation

$$0 = \vec{A} + \frac{s_F}{n}\vec{S} = \vec{A} + \frac{\delta}{\gamma}\vec{S} = \frac{1}{\gamma}(\gamma\vec{A} + \delta\vec{S}) = \frac{1}{\gamma}\vec{S}', \quad (8.10)$$

emerge from the system parallel to the axis.

Equations (8.8) and (8.9) have shown that for $\gamma \neq 0$, there exist on the object and image sides unique finite points conjugate to the infinite points and which we call the *focal points*. Moreover, for $\gamma = 0$, the infinite points of the axis are conjugate to each other.

Shifting Origins

Shifting the object and image origins by the distances z, z', respectively, along the axis gives

$$\begin{aligned} \tilde{\vec{A}}' &= \vec{A}' + \frac{z^{*\prime}}{n'}\vec{S}', \quad \vec{A}' = \alpha\vec{A} + \beta\vec{S}, \quad \vec{A} = \tilde{\vec{A}} - \frac{z}{n}\vec{S} \\ \tilde{\vec{S}}' &= \vec{S}', \quad \vec{S}' = \gamma\vec{A} + \delta\vec{S}, \quad \vec{S} = \tilde{\vec{S}}, \end{aligned} \quad (8.11)$$

or

$$\begin{aligned} \tilde{\vec{A}}' &= \tilde{\alpha}\tilde{\vec{A}} + \tilde{\beta}\tilde{\vec{S}} \\ \tilde{\vec{S}}' &= \tilde{\gamma}\tilde{\vec{A}} + \tilde{\delta}\tilde{\vec{S}} \end{aligned} \quad (8.12)$$

with

$$\begin{pmatrix} \tilde{\alpha} & \tilde{\beta} \\ \tilde{\gamma} & \tilde{\delta} \end{pmatrix} = \begin{pmatrix} 1 & \dfrac{z^{*\prime}}{n'} \\ 0 & 1 \end{pmatrix} \begin{pmatrix} \alpha & \beta \\ \gamma & \delta \end{pmatrix} \begin{pmatrix} 1 & -\dfrac{z}{n} \\ 0 & 1 \end{pmatrix} \quad (8.13)$$

or, written explicitly,

$$\begin{aligned} \tilde{\alpha} &= \alpha + \frac{z^{*\prime}}{n'}\gamma & \tilde{\beta} &= \beta + \frac{z^{*\prime}}{n'}\delta - \frac{z}{n}\left(\alpha + \frac{z^{*\prime}}{n'}\gamma\right) \\ \tilde{\gamma} &= \gamma & \tilde{\delta} &= \delta - \frac{z}{n}\gamma. \end{aligned} \quad (8.14)$$

Equations (8.6), (8.8), and (8.9) show that $\tilde{\alpha}$ vanishes if and only if the origin on the image side is shifted to the focal point, $\tilde{\beta}$ vanishes if and only if the object and image origins are conjugate, $\tilde{\delta}$ vanishes if and only if the object origin is at the focal point, $\tilde{\gamma}$ vanishes if and only if the system is without finite focal points, that is, if it is a system we call *afocal.*

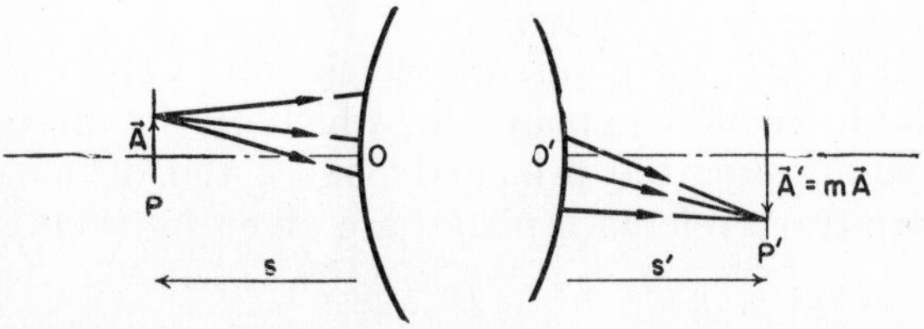

Fig. 8.4. Conjugate planes.

Conjugate Planes

If the two origins are placed at conjugate points, we have

$$\vec{\tilde{A}}' = \tilde{\alpha}\vec{\tilde{A}}$$
$$\vec{S}' = \tilde{\gamma}\vec{\tilde{A}} + \tilde{\delta}\vec{S}, \quad \tilde{\alpha}\tilde{\delta} = 1. \tag{8.15}$$

Equation (8.15) shows that the rays coming from the point $\vec{\tilde{A}}$ emerge from the system going through the point $m\vec{\tilde{A}} = \vec{\tilde{A}}'$, where

$$m = \tilde{\alpha} = \frac{1}{\tilde{\delta}} = \alpha + \frac{z^{*\prime}}{n'}\gamma = \frac{1}{\delta - (z/n)\,\gamma}\,. \tag{8.16}$$

This means that the points near the axis are sharply imaged, within the validity of Gaussian optics, with a *lateral magnification m,* which is given by (8.16) as a function of the object and image positions.

The second equation of (8.15):

$$\vec{S}' - (1/m)\,\vec{S} = \tilde{\gamma}\vec{\tilde{A}} \quad \text{or} \quad m\,\vec{S}' - \vec{S} = \tilde{\gamma}\vec{\tilde{A}}' \tag{8.17}$$

is the first form of an important law, the so-called *cosine law*, to be studied in Chapter 15. Here we note only that for the ray through the axis point ($\vec{\tilde{A}} = 0$) we have

$$m\vec{S}' = \vec{S}, \tag{8.18}$$

which is equivalent to saying that the *optical angular magnification* $\tilde{\delta}$ for the rays from an axial point is reciprocal to the *magnification*, $m = \tilde{a}$, with which the surface element is imaged.

Equation (8.16) shows that, if $\gamma \neq 0$, m can assume all possible values and that it assumes each value once and only once, but that, if $\gamma = 0$ (that is for afocal systems), m is constant for all positions.

In optical theory, the points for which $m = 1$ and $m = (n/n')\varepsilon$ have special interest. The points for which $m = 1$ are called the *principal points*. For the principal points, the distances s_P, s_P' from the arbitrary reference planes are given by (8.16) as

$$\frac{s_P}{n} = \frac{\delta - 1}{\gamma}, \quad \frac{s_P{}^{*\prime}}{n'} = \frac{1 - a}{\gamma}, \quad (s_P{}^{*\prime} = \varepsilon s_P') \tag{8.19}$$

and Equations (8.15) reduce to

$$\begin{aligned} \vec{\tilde{A}}' &= \vec{\tilde{A}} \\ \vec{S}' &= \gamma \vec{\tilde{A}} + \vec{S}. \end{aligned} \tag{8.20}$$

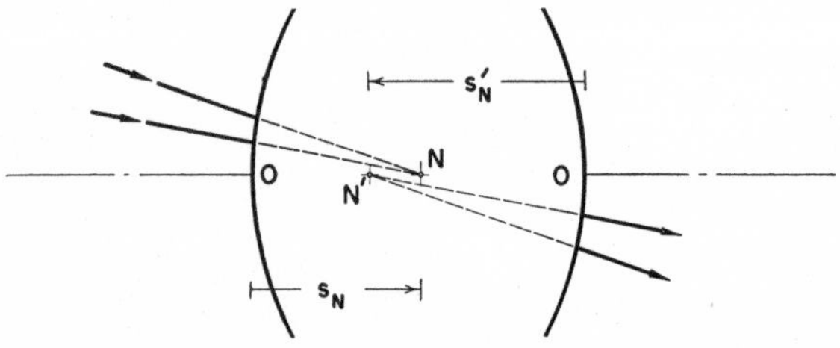

Fig. 8.5. Nodal points.

The points for which $m = (n/n')\varepsilon$ are called the *nodal points*. As (8.18) shows, every ray through the nodal points emerges from the sytem parallel to the entrance direction. Equation (8.16) gives for the distance of the nodal points from arbitrary origins

$$\frac{s_N}{n} = \frac{\delta - (n'/n)\,\varepsilon}{\gamma}, \quad \frac{s_N{}^{*\prime}}{n'} = \frac{(n/n')\,\varepsilon - a}{\gamma}. \tag{8.21}$$

We recall the fact that the positions of the focal points are given by (8.8) and 8.9) as

$$s_F/n = \delta/\gamma, \quad s_F{}^{*\prime}/n' = -\,a/\gamma. \tag{8.22}$$

The distance from the object or image principal point to its corresponding focal point is frequently called the object or image *focal length*, f or f', of the system, respectively. If the word *focal length* is used without qualification, f' is meant.

We find

$$\begin{aligned} f &= s_F - s_P = n/\gamma \\ f' &= s_F' - s_P' = -\varepsilon n'/\gamma, \end{aligned} \tag{8.23}$$

so that we have

$$\frac{\varepsilon f'}{n'} + \frac{f}{n} = 0. \tag{8.24}$$

The respective distances between *nodal points* and *focal points* on the object and image sides are given by

$$\begin{aligned} s_F - s_N &= \frac{n'}{\gamma}\varepsilon = -f' \\ s_F' - s_N' &= -\frac{n}{\gamma} = -f. \end{aligned} \tag{8.25}$$

The quantity γ [as is shown in (8.14)] does not change if the object and the image origins are shifted; it is a characteristic of the optical system. Its negative value (again the optical sign convention *versus* the mathematical sign convention)

$$\phi = -\gamma \tag{8.26}$$

is called the *power* of the optical system.

The points with magnification $m = -1$ and $m = -(n/n')\varepsilon$ also play a certain role in optical theory. They are called the *negative principal points* and the *negative nodal points*, respectively.

Focal Planes

Choosing, as reference points, the focal points on the object and image sides, we have

$$\alpha = \delta = 0, \quad \beta = -1/\gamma, \tag{8.27}$$

and Equations (8.1) become

$$\vec{A} = -(1/\gamma)\vec{S}$$
$$\vec{S}' = \gamma\vec{A}. \tag{8.28}$$

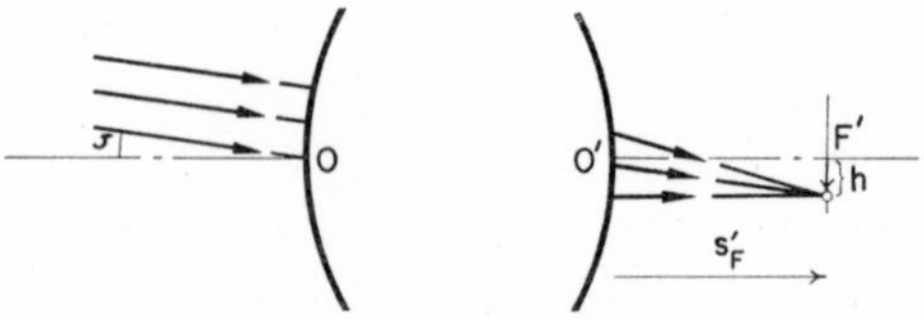

Fig. 8.6. Focal plane.

Equations (8.28) state that a bundle of parallel object rays $\vec{S} = \vec{S}_o$ unite in a point of the image focal plane

$$\vec{A}_o' = -(1/\gamma)\vec{S}_o \tag{8.29}$$

and that the rays from a point $\vec{A}_o$ in the object focal plane emerge as a parallel bundle such that

$$\vec{S}_o' = \gamma\vec{A}_o. \tag{8.30}$$

Special Reference Points

Let us choose the reference points at conjugate points of magnification m_o. Then

$$\alpha = m_o, \ \ \beta = 0, \ \ \gamma = -\phi, \ \ \delta = -1/m_o.$$

From (8.14) and (8.16) we find for the distances of conjugate points of magnification m that

$$m = m_o + \frac{z^{*\prime}}{n'}\gamma = \frac{1}{(1/m_o) - (z/n)\gamma}, \tag{8.31}$$

which leads to

$$\frac{n'm_o}{z^{*\prime}} - \frac{n}{m_o z} = -\gamma = \phi = \frac{n'}{f^{*\prime}} = -\frac{n}{f}, \tag{8.32}$$

where $f^{*\prime} = \varepsilon f'$. For $m_o = 1$, this gives the well-known equation for the distances of conjugate points from the principal points:

$$\frac{n'}{z^{*\prime}} - \frac{n}{z} = \frac{n'}{f^{*\prime}} = -\frac{n}{f} = \phi$$

$$m = 1 - \frac{z'}{f'} = \frac{1}{1 - (z/f)}, \tag{8.33}$$

and for the corresponding distances from the nodal points

$$\frac{\varepsilon}{nz} - \frac{1}{n'z^{*\prime}} = \frac{\gamma}{nn'}$$

$$\frac{\varepsilon m n'}{n} = 1 + \frac{z'}{f} = \frac{1}{1 + (z/f')}. \tag{8.34}$$

In all these equations, of course, we have $\varepsilon = -1$ only for systems with an odd number of reflections, $\varepsilon = +1$ in all other cases. Taking the focal points as reference points means [see (8.27)] that

$$\alpha = \delta = 0, \quad \beta = -1/\gamma. \tag{8.35}$$

The distances of conjugate points from the focal points are given by (8.16) as

$$m = -f/z = -z'/f' \tag{8.36}$$

or

$$z = -f/m, \quad z' = -f'm. \tag{8.37}$$

This gives

$$zz' = ff'. \tag{8.38}$$

Afocal System

A system for which $\gamma = 0$ has no finite focal point, and the laws governing these systems are therefore slightly different. We have

$$\begin{aligned} \vec{A}' &= \alpha\vec{A} + \beta\vec{S} \\ \vec{S}' &= (1/\alpha)\vec{S}, \end{aligned} \tag{8.39}$$

and we see from (8.14) with $\gamma = 0$, that α (and therefore also $\delta = 1/\alpha$) does not change if the origins are shifted.

That means, according to (8.16), that every object is imaged with the same *magnification*, $m_t = \alpha$. This is called *telescope magnification*. It is clear from (8.39), moreover, that a system of parallel rays emerges as a system of parallel rays. The corresponding angular magnification, $1/\alpha$, is the same for all rays and equal to $1/m_t$.

For the distances of conjugate points from the reference planes, Equations (8.6) give

$$m_t^2 \frac{s}{n} - \frac{s^{*\prime}}{n'} = m_t \beta, \tag{8.40}$$

which, if the reference planes are conjugate, reduces to

$$\frac{s^{*\prime}}{n'} = m_t^2 \frac{s}{n}. \tag{8.41}$$

These equations permit one to compute for every object position the position of the conjugate image. Either all points or none are principal points, and either all points or none are nodal points, depending on the value of the telescope magnification.

CHAPTER NINE

Gaussian Optics in Terms of the System Data

It is the object of this chapter to compute the coefficients $\alpha, \beta, \gamma, \delta$ as well as the object and image positions, focal points, focal lengths, etc. of a given optical system as functions of its data (radii, thicknesses, distances, and refractive indices).

With respect to nomenclature, we shall adopt the following conventions: (1) r_ν, ϱ_ν will signify the radius and curvature respectively at the νth vertex; (2) the indices of refraction will be numbered $n_0 = n, n_1, n_2, \ldots n_\varkappa = n'$, so that n_ν is the index between the νth and the $(\nu + 1)$st surfaces; (3) d_ν will represent the axial distance between the νth and the $(\nu + 1)$st vertices; (4) the projected position vectors $\vec{A}_\nu$, $\vec{A}_\nu'$ will indicate, respectively, the intersection of the ray with the νth vertex plane before and after refraction (or reflection) at the νth surface; and (5) the projected direction vectors $\vec{S}_\nu$, $\vec{S}_\nu'$, respectively, will give the direction of the ray before and after its intersection with the νth surface. It may be noted that

$$\vec{S}_\nu' = \vec{S}_{\nu+1}, \quad \vec{S}_0 = \vec{S}, \quad \vec{S}_\varkappa' = \vec{S}'.$$

With these designations, the equations of refraction (or reflection) at the νth surface can be written, within the validity of Gaussian optics,

$$\begin{aligned} \vec{A}_\nu' &= \vec{A}_\nu \\ \vec{S}_\nu' &= \gamma_\nu \vec{A}_\nu + \vec{S}_\nu, \quad \nu = 1, 2, \ldots \varkappa, \end{aligned} \tag{9.1}$$

where (4.40) gives

$$-\gamma_\nu = \phi_\nu = (n_\nu - n_{\nu-1})\,\varrho_\nu \tag{9.2}$$

and

$$-\gamma_\nu = \phi_\nu = -\,2n_{\nu-1}\,\varrho_\nu$$

for refraction and reflection, respectively.

The formulae for transferring the origin from one vertex to the next can be written

$$\vec{A}_{\nu+1} = \vec{A}_\nu' + \beta_\nu \vec{S}_\nu'$$
$$\vec{S}_{\nu+1} = \vec{S}_\nu', \quad \nu = 1, 2, \ldots \varkappa - 1 \tag{9.3}$$

where $\beta_\nu = d_\nu / n_\nu$.

Combining (9.1) to (9.3) for a set of $\varkappa$ surfaces, we obtain, with the first and last vertices as reference points,

$$\vec{A}' = \alpha \vec{A} + \beta \vec{S}$$
$$\vec{S}' = \gamma \vec{A} + \delta \vec{S} \tag{9.4}$$

with the α, β, γ, δ obtained by matrix multiplication from

$$\begin{pmatrix} \alpha & \beta \\ \gamma & \delta \end{pmatrix} = \begin{pmatrix} 1 & 0 \\ \gamma_\varkappa & 1 \end{pmatrix} \begin{pmatrix} 1 & \beta_{\varkappa-1} \\ 0 & 1 \end{pmatrix} \begin{pmatrix} 1 & 0 \\ \gamma_{\varkappa-1} & 1 \end{pmatrix} \cdots \begin{pmatrix} 1 & \beta_1 \\ 0 & 1 \end{pmatrix} \begin{pmatrix} 1 & 0 \\ \gamma_1 & 1 \end{pmatrix}. \tag{9.5}$$

As an illustration, let us calculate $\begin{pmatrix} \alpha & \beta \\ \gamma & \delta \end{pmatrix}$ for a "lens" consisting of two surfaces. We find

$$\begin{pmatrix} \alpha & \beta \\ \gamma & \delta \end{pmatrix} = \begin{pmatrix} 1 & 0 \\ \gamma_2 & 1 \end{pmatrix} \begin{pmatrix} 1 & \beta_1 \\ 0 & 1 \end{pmatrix} \begin{pmatrix} 1 & 0 \\ \gamma_1 & 1 \end{pmatrix} \tag{9.6}$$

or

$$\alpha = \beta_1 \gamma_1 + 1, \quad \beta = \beta_1$$
$$\gamma = \gamma_1 \beta_1 \gamma_2 + \gamma_1 + \gamma_2, \quad \delta = \beta_1 \gamma_2 + 1. \tag{9.7}$$

The coefficients in (9.7) are linear in each of the β_i and each of the γ_i. They are special cases of quantities known as *Gaussian brackets* and defined as follows.

If a_1, a_2, ... represent numbers, brackets containing *no* numbers, *one* number, and *two* numbers are defined by

$$[\,] = 1, \quad [a_1] = a_1, \quad [a, a_2] = a_1 a_2 + 1. \tag{9.8}$$

Higher brackets are then defined by means of a recursion formula:

$$[a_1 a_2 \ldots a_\varkappa] = [a_1 a_2 \ldots a_{\varkappa-2}] + [a_1 a_2 \ldots a_{\varkappa-1}] a_\varkappa. \tag{9.9}$$

Applying this to (9.8) we obtain

$$\begin{aligned}[a_1a_2a_3] &= [a_1] + [a_1a_2]a_3 \\ &= a_1 + (a_1a_2 + 1)a_3 \qquad (9.10) \\ &= a_1a_2a_3 + a_1 + a_3,\end{aligned}$$

and successive application of (9.9) can be used to obtain brackets of order four, five, and so on. For a discussion of some of the interesting and useful algebraic properties of Gaussian brackets, the reader is referred to the Appendix. It is proved there that the following properties (and others) hold for Gaussian brackets of any order.

(1) Every bracket is reversible:

$$[a_1a_2 \ldots a_{\varkappa-1}a_\varkappa] = [a_\varkappa a_{\varkappa-1} \ldots a_2a_1]. \qquad (9.11)$$

(2) As a result of (9.9) and (9.11) any bracket can be expanded according to its first element:

$$[a_1 \ldots a_\varkappa] = a_1 [a_2 \ldots a_\varkappa] + [a_3 \ldots a_\varkappa]. \qquad (9.12)$$

(3) A bracket can be expanded with respect to an interior element:

$$\begin{aligned}[a_1 \ldots a_\nu \ldots a_\varkappa] &= a_\nu [a_1 \ldots a_{\nu-1}] [a_{\nu+1} \ldots a_\varkappa] \\ &+ [a_1 \ldots a_{\nu-1} + a_{\nu+1} \ldots a_\varkappa]. \qquad (9.13)\end{aligned}$$

(4) A bracket can be expanded relative to its first ν elements:

$$\begin{aligned}[a_1 \ldots a_\nu \ldots a_\varkappa] &= [a_1 \ldots a_\nu] [a_{\nu+1} \ldots a_\varkappa] \\ &+ [a_1 \ldots a_{\nu-1}] [a_{\nu+2} \ldots a_\varkappa]. \qquad (9.14)\end{aligned}$$

(5) The following determinant rule holds:

$$\begin{vmatrix} [a_1 \; a_{\nu-1}] & [a_2 \; a_{\nu-1}] \\ [a_1 \quad a_\nu] & [a_2 \quad a_\nu] \end{vmatrix} = (-1)^{\nu-1}. \qquad (9.15)$$

With the help of Gaussian brackets Formulae (9.7) may be written

$$\begin{aligned}\alpha &= [\beta_1\gamma_1] & \beta &= [\beta_1] \\ \gamma &= [\gamma_2\beta_1\gamma_1] & \delta &= [\gamma_2\beta_1] \,. \qquad (9.16)\end{aligned}$$

We now wish to show that, for a system with $\varkappa$ surfaces,

α, β, γ, δ can be computed with the help of Gaussian brackets as

$$\begin{aligned}
\alpha &= [\beta_{\varkappa-1}, \gamma_{\varkappa-1}, \beta_{\varkappa-2}, \ldots \quad \beta_1, \gamma_1] \\
\beta &= [\beta_{\varkappa-1}, \gamma_{\varkappa-1}, \ldots \quad \beta_1] \\
\gamma &= [\gamma_{\varkappa}, \beta_{\varkappa-1}, \ldots \quad \beta_1, \gamma_1] \\
\delta &= [\gamma_{\varkappa}, \beta_{\varkappa-1}, \ldots \quad \beta_1].
\end{aligned} \tag{9.17}$$

The proof is given by induction. It is correct for $\varkappa = 2$ [see (9.16)]. We assume that it holds for $\varkappa - 1$ surfaces and show that it then follows for $\varkappa$ surfaces. Using α', β', γ', δ' to designate the brackets of the system with $(\varkappa - 1)$ elements, we have

$$\begin{pmatrix} \alpha & \beta \\ \gamma & \delta \end{pmatrix} = \begin{pmatrix} 1 & 0 \\ \gamma_\varkappa & 1 \end{pmatrix} \begin{pmatrix} 1 & \beta_{\varkappa-1} \\ 0 & 1 \end{pmatrix} \begin{pmatrix} \alpha' & \beta' \\ \gamma' & \delta' \end{pmatrix} \tag{9.18}$$

or

$$\begin{pmatrix} \alpha & \beta \\ \gamma & \delta \end{pmatrix} = \begin{pmatrix} 1 & 0 \\ \gamma_\varkappa & 1 \end{pmatrix} \begin{pmatrix} \alpha' + \beta_{\varkappa-1}\gamma' & \beta' + \beta_{\varkappa-1}\delta' \\ \gamma' & \delta' \end{pmatrix}. \tag{9.19}$$

Since

$$\begin{aligned}
\alpha' &= [\beta_{\varkappa-2}, \ldots \beta_1, \gamma_1], \; \beta' = [\beta_{\varkappa-2}, \ldots \beta_1] \\
\gamma' &= [\gamma_{\varkappa-1}, \ldots \quad \gamma_1], \; \delta' = [\gamma_{\varkappa-1}, \ldots \beta_1],
\end{aligned} \tag{9.20}$$

we find

$$\begin{aligned}
\alpha' + \beta_{\varkappa-1}\gamma' &= [\beta_{\varkappa-1}, \gamma_{\varkappa-1}, \ldots \gamma_1] = \alpha \\
\beta' + \beta_{\varkappa-1}\delta' &= [\beta_{\varkappa-1}, \gamma_{\varkappa-1}, \ldots \beta_1] = \beta,
\end{aligned} \tag{9.21}$$

and combining (9.19) with (9.21) leads to

$$\begin{aligned}
\gamma &= [\gamma_\varkappa, \beta_{\varkappa-1}, \ldots \gamma_1] \\
\delta &= [\gamma_\varkappa, \beta_{\varkappa-1}, \ldots \beta_1],
\end{aligned} \tag{9.22}$$

which proves the desired formulae. Into Formulae (9.17) we must insert

$$\begin{aligned}
\beta_\nu &= d_\nu / n_\nu \\
\gamma_\nu &= (n_{\nu-1} - n_\nu)\varrho_\nu
\end{aligned} \tag{9.23}$$

for a refracting surface, and

$$\gamma_\nu = 2n_{\nu-1}\,\varrho_\nu \tag{9.24}$$

for a reflecting surface.

The knowledge of $\alpha, \beta, \gamma, \delta$ now permits one to compute the optical data of a system with the help of Gaussian brackets. We find from (8.6) for the distances of conjugate points from the first and last vertices, respectively,

$$\frac{s^{*\prime}}{n'} = -\frac{\beta - \alpha(s/n)}{\delta - \gamma(s/n)} = -\frac{[\beta_{\varkappa-1}, \ldots \beta_1, \gamma_1, (-s/n)]}{[\gamma_\varkappa, \beta_{\varkappa-1}, \ldots \gamma_1, (-s/n)]}. \quad (9.25)$$

Object and image distances from the vertices as functions of the magnification m are given by (8.16) as

$$\frac{s}{n} = \frac{\delta - (1/m)}{\gamma} = \frac{[\gamma_\varkappa \ldots \beta_1] - (1/m)}{[\gamma_\varkappa \ldots \gamma_1]}$$

$$\frac{s^{*\prime}}{n'} = \frac{m - \alpha}{\gamma} = \frac{m - [\beta_{\varkappa-1} \ldots \gamma_1]}{[\gamma_\varkappa \ldots \gamma_1]}. \quad (9.26)$$

The power of the system is given by

$$-\phi = \gamma = [\gamma_\varkappa, \beta_{\varkappa-1} \ldots \beta_1, \gamma_1] \quad (9.27)$$

and the front focus and back focus by (8.22) as

$$s_F/n = \delta/\gamma, \quad s_F{}^{*\prime}/n' = -\alpha/\gamma, \quad (9.28)$$

respectively.

This completes the general theory. In the next chapter, we shall apply this theory to special types of optical systems.

CHAPTER TEN

The Gaussian Optics of Special Types of Systems

The Monoplet

(a) A Single Surface

The equations for refraction at a single surface (object and image origins at the vertex), having vertex curvature ϱ_1 and separating two media of index n_o and n_1, are

$$\vec{A}' = \vec{A}$$
$$\vec{S}' = \gamma\vec{A} + \vec{S} \tag{10.1}$$

that is,

$$\alpha = \delta = 1,\ \beta = 0,\ \gamma = (n_o - n_1)\,\varrho_1. \tag{10.2}$$

We see that the object and image side principal points of the system are both at the vertex. The nodal points are given by (9.26) as

$$s_N = s_N' = 1/\varrho_1 = r_1, \tag{10.3}$$

that is, the *nodal points* are at the center of curvature.

The object and image side *focal points* are given for the case of refraction by their vertex distances [see (9.28)]:

$$s_F = \frac{n_o r_1}{n_o - n_1},\quad s_F' = -\frac{n_1 r_1}{n_o - n_1}. \tag{10.4}$$

The power and focal length in the case of refraction are

$$\phi = -\gamma = (n_1 - n_o)\,\varrho_1$$
$$f' = -\frac{n_1}{\gamma} = \frac{n_1 r_1}{n_1 - n_o}. \tag{10.5}$$

In the case of reflection, we have

$$\phi = -\gamma = -2\,n_o\varrho_1, \tag{10.6}$$

and

$$s_N = s_N' = r_1$$
$$s_F = r_1/2 = s_F' \qquad (10.7)$$
$$f' = r_1/2 = f.$$

(*b*) *The Thin Lens*

A *lens* consists of a piece of glass bounded by two surfaces, usually surfaces having symmetry of rotation with respect to the axis. The distance between the vertices is called the *thickness* of the lens. Since air is cheap and glass is expensive, we will try in most cases to keep the thicknesses of the lenses as small as possible, especially since, as we shall see in a later chapter, a thick lens absorbs much light. Thus the lens thickness in many cases is negligible, and preliminary calculations can be made in which either d is neglected (the "*thin*" lens) or higher powers than the first of d are neglected (the "narrow" lens). The *thin* lens is obviously a fiction, but under some circumstances a useful one. In preliminary calculations, in which we replace the lenses by thin lenses, we usually do not neglect the air spaces between two "lenses," that is, we replace an optical system by a system of thin lenses separated by finite distances.

A system of thin lenses with no finite distances will be called a *monoplet*, a system of two monoplets with one finite distance, a *duplet*, and a system of three monoplets with two finite distances, a *triplet*.

We now discuss the Gaussian optics of a *thin lens* of index $n_1 = N$ in air ($n_0 = n_2 = 1$). We find

$$\vec{A}' = \vec{A}$$
$$\vec{S}' = \gamma\vec{A} + \vec{S}, \qquad (10.8)$$

where (9.17) gives

$$\gamma = [\gamma_1, 0, \gamma_2] = \gamma_1 + \gamma_2 = (1 - N)\varrho_1 + (N - 1)\varrho_2$$
$$= (N - 1)\,(\varrho_2 - \varrho_1). \qquad (10.9)$$

This leads to

$$\phi = (N - 1)\,(\varrho_1 - \varrho_2). \qquad (10.10)$$

Formula (10.10) shows that the power of a thin lens does not depend upon the radii, but only upon the difference of the curvatures. This means that the Gaussian optics of a thin lens is not changed if we change the radii so that $\varrho_1 - \varrho_2$ remains the same. Such a change is called a *bending* of the lens. While this statement is strictly correct only for thin lenses, it remains approximately correct for moderately thick lenses. Bending the lenses has, for this reason, become a valuable tool of the lens designer for the purpose of changing the system data without affecting the Gaussian optics.

Again, in the thin lens, the principal points coincide with the vertex, since $n_0 = n_2 = 1$, and the nodal points coincide with the principal points. The focal point distance therefore coincides with the focal length, and we have from (9.28)

$$s_F = \frac{1}{(N-1)(\varrho_2 - \varrho_1)} = f = -f'$$

$$s_F' = \frac{1}{(N-1)(\varrho_1 - \varrho_2)} = f'. \qquad (10.11)$$

The relation of the distances s, s' of two conjugate points from the vertices is given by (9.25) as

$$s' = s/(1 + \phi s) \qquad (10.12)$$

and

$$\frac{1}{s'} - \frac{1}{s} = \phi = \frac{1}{f'}, \quad m = \frac{1}{1 + \phi s} = \frac{s'}{s}. \qquad (10.13)$$

In an optical system, two or more lenses are frequently cemented together. Such a system can be approximated by a monoplet, a system of thin lenses without distances. For a monoplet the same equations hold as given in (10.1), with the exception that

$$\gamma = \Sigma \gamma_i = \Sigma (N_i - 1)(\varrho_{2i} - \varrho_{1i}), \qquad (10.14)$$

where $-\gamma_i$ is the power of the ith thin lens with radii ϱ_{1i} and ϱ_{2i}, respectively. All the formulae derived before hold, and we find

$$\phi = \Sigma \phi_i$$

$$s_F = f = -f' = -1/\phi$$

$$s_F' = f' = 1/\phi$$

$$\frac{1}{s'} - \frac{1}{s} = \phi, \quad m = \frac{s'}{s}. \qquad (10.15)$$

The nodal points and principal points coincide with the common vertex point assumed for the monoplet.

The Duplet

A duplet is defined as a system of two monoplets separated by a finite air space of distance d_1. We therefore have

$$\vec{A}' = \alpha\vec{A} + \beta\vec{S}$$
$$\vec{S}' = \gamma\vec{A} + \delta\vec{S}, \tag{10.16}$$

with

$$\begin{pmatrix}\alpha & \beta\\ \gamma & \delta\end{pmatrix} = \begin{pmatrix}1 & 0\\ -\phi_2 & 1\end{pmatrix}\begin{pmatrix}1 & d_1\\ 0 & 1\end{pmatrix}\begin{pmatrix}1 & 0\\ -\phi_1 & 1\end{pmatrix}, \tag{10.17}$$

which gives

$$\begin{aligned}\alpha &= 1 - d_1\phi_1 = [d_1\gamma_1]\\ \beta &= d_1 = [d_1]\\ \gamma &= -\phi = -(\phi_1 + \phi_2 - d_1\phi_1\phi_2) = [\gamma_2 d_1\gamma_1]\\ \delta &= 1 - d_1\phi_2 = [\gamma_2 d_1].\end{aligned} \tag{10.18}$$

We see that the formulae are the same as those derived in (9.16) for a system of two surfaces, the only difference being that the γ_i are now the powers of the thin lenses and d_1 is the distance between the thin lenses. The equivalent of (10.17) and (9.6) permits us immediately to apply Formulae (9.17) to find for the coefficients α, β, γ, δ of a system of thin lenses the corresponding expressions;

$$\begin{aligned}\alpha &= [\beta_{\varkappa-1} \ldots \beta_1, \gamma_1] \quad & \beta &= [\beta_{\varkappa-1} \ldots \beta_1]\\ \gamma &= [\gamma_\varkappa \ldots \gamma_1] & \delta &= [\gamma_\varkappa \ldots \beta_1],\end{aligned} \tag{10.19}$$

where we now have, however,

$$\gamma_i = -\phi_i, \quad \beta_i = d_i, \tag{10.20}$$

in which ϕ_i is the power of the ith lens:

$$\phi_i = (N_i - 1)(\varrho_i' - \varrho_i'') \tag{10.21}$$

and d_i is the distance between the ith and the $(i+1)$st lenses.

Applying this, in particular, to the duplet, we find the front focus and back focus (the distance of front and back focal points from the first and last vertices, respectively) to be

$$s_F = -\frac{[d_1\gamma_2]}{\phi}, \quad s_F\phi = d_1\phi_2 - 1$$

$$s_F' = \frac{[\gamma_1 d_1]}{\phi}, \quad s_F'\phi = 1 - d_1\phi_1, \tag{10.22}$$

and the respective distances of conjugate points from the vertices [*cf.* (9.26)]

$$m = s'\gamma + \alpha = \frac{1}{\delta - s\gamma}$$

$$= [s'\gamma_2 d_1\gamma_1] = \frac{1}{[\gamma_2 d_1 \gamma_1, (-s)]} \tag{10.23}$$

The nodal point (principal point) distances are given by

$$\phi s_N = d_1\phi_2, \quad \phi s_N' = -\, d_1\phi_1.$$

The Triplet

A triplet is a system of three monoplets with powers ϕ_1, ϕ_2, and ϕ_3 separated by distances d_1 and d_2. We find from (9.17)

$$\begin{aligned}
\alpha &= [d_2\gamma_2 d_1\gamma_1] = d_1 d_2\phi_1\phi_2 - d_2(\phi_1 + \phi_2) - d_1\phi_1 + 1 \\
\beta &= [d_2\gamma_2 d_1] = d_1 + d_2 - d_1 d_2\phi_2 \\
\gamma &= [\gamma_3 d_2\gamma_2 d_1\gamma_1] = -\,[d_1 d_2\phi_1\phi_2\phi_3 - d_2\phi_3(\phi_1 + \phi_2) \\
&\qquad - d_1\phi_1(\phi_2 + \phi_3) + \phi_1 + \phi_2 + \phi_3] \\
\delta &= [\gamma_3 d_2\gamma_2 d_1] = d_1 d_2\phi_2\phi_3 - d_2\phi_3 - d_1(\phi_2 + \phi_3) + 1.
\end{aligned} \tag{10.24}$$

The Thick Lens

A thick lens is a piece of glass of index $N = n_1$ bordered by a system of two rotation-symmetric surfaces a distance $d_1 = d$ apart and with air outside. We have from (9.17) and (9.2)

$$\begin{aligned}
\alpha &= [\beta_1\gamma_1] = 1 - (N - 1)\,\varrho\,(d/N) \\
\beta &= [\beta_1] = d/N \\
\gamma &= [\gamma_2\beta_1\gamma_1] = -\,\phi = -\,[N - 1)(\varrho_1 - \varrho_2] + \frac{(N-1)^2}{N} d\varrho_1\varrho_2] \\
\delta &= [\gamma_2\beta_1] = 1 + (N - 1)\varrho_2(d/N).
\end{aligned} \tag{10.25}$$

The respective distances of the nodal (principal) points from first and last vertices are

$$s_N\,\phi = -\frac{N-1}{N}\,\varrho_2 d, \quad s_N'\,\phi = -\frac{N-1}{N}\,\varrho_1 d. \quad (10.26)$$

Equations (10.26) show that, by bending a thick lens, we can influence the positions of the nodal points to a large extent. With respect to the signs of ϱ_1 and ϱ_2, a lens is called

Biconcave if $\varrho_1 < 0,\ \varrho_2 > 0$,

Biconvex if $\varrho_1 > 0,\ \varrho_2 < 0$,

Meniscus if ϱ_1 and ϱ_2 have the same sign,

Plano-convex / *Plano-concave* } if one of the curvatures is made zero in a {convex / concave} lens.

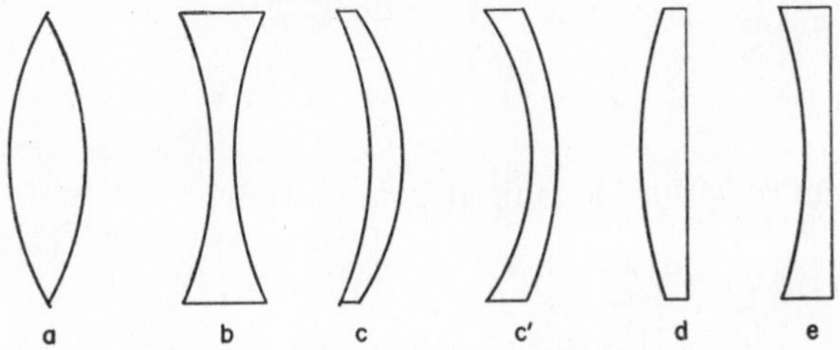

Fig. 10.1. Types of lenses: (a) biconvex, (b) biconcave, (c) positive meniscus, (c′) negative meniscus, (d) plano-convex, (e) plano-concave.

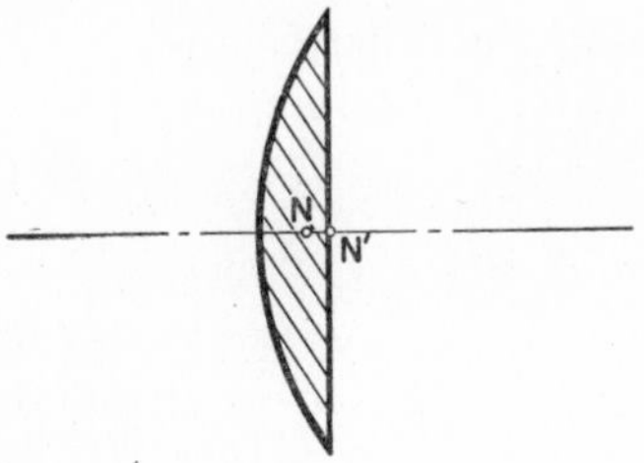

Fig. 10.2. Plano-convex lens with nodal points shown.

The Optical System with One Reflecting Surface

We shall now investigate a system of $\varkappa$ surfaces in which the last surface is reflecting so that the light traverses its way back through the same surfaces. Since the vector $\vec{s}$ after one reflection changes its direction and since the surfaces are traversed in the opposite direction, we have, within the realm of Gaussian optics,

$$\begin{aligned} \gamma_{\varkappa+1} &= \gamma_{\varkappa-1} & \beta_{\varkappa} &= \beta_{\varkappa-1} \\ \gamma_{\varkappa+2} &= \gamma_{\varkappa-2} & \beta_{\varkappa+1} &= \beta_{\varkappa-2} \\ \cdots & & \cdots & \\ \gamma_{2\varkappa-1} &= \gamma_1 & \beta_{2\varkappa-2} &= \beta_1, \end{aligned} \tag{10.27}$$

which give

$$\begin{aligned} \alpha &= [\beta_1, \gamma_2, \ldots \gamma_{\varkappa}, \beta_{\varkappa-1}, \gamma_{\varkappa-1}, \ldots \beta_1, \gamma_1] \\ \beta &= [\beta_1, \gamma_2, \ldots \beta_1] \\ \gamma &= [\gamma_1, \beta_2, \gamma_2, \ldots \gamma_{\varkappa}, \ldots \beta_1, \gamma_1] \\ \delta &= [\gamma_1, \beta_1, \gamma_2, \ldots \beta_1], \end{aligned} \tag{10.28}$$

that is, $\alpha = \delta$.

For the reflecting lens in air, for instance, we obtain

$$\begin{aligned} \alpha &= [\beta_1\gamma_2\beta_1\gamma_1] = [\beta_1\gamma_1]\,[\beta_1\gamma_2] + [\beta_1\gamma_1] - 1 \\ \beta &= [\beta_1\gamma_2\beta_1] = \beta_1{}^2\gamma_2 + 2\beta_1 \\ \gamma &= [\gamma_1\beta_1\gamma_2\beta_1\gamma_1] = \gamma_2\,[\gamma_1\beta_1]^2 + 2\gamma_1\,[\gamma_1\beta_1] \\ \delta &= [\gamma_1\beta_1\gamma_2\beta_1] = [\beta_1\gamma_1]\,[\beta_1\gamma_2] + [\beta_1\gamma_1] - 1. \end{aligned} \tag{10.29}$$

The nodal points (which here coincide with the negative principal points) are given by $m = \varepsilon n/n' = -1$. Thus Formulae (8.16) give

$$\begin{aligned} s_N &= \frac{\delta + 1}{\gamma} = \frac{[\beta_1\gamma_2] + 1}{\gamma_1[\beta_1\gamma_2] + \gamma_1 + \gamma_2} \\ s_N' &= \frac{\alpha + 1}{\gamma} = \frac{[\beta_1\gamma_2] + 1}{\gamma_1[\beta_1\gamma_2] + \gamma_1 + \gamma_2}. \end{aligned} \tag{10.30}$$

The nodal points fall together. This is equivalent to saying that the reflecting lens acts, with respect to Gaussian optics, like a single reflecting surface with its center at a distance s_N from the first surface, the lens having a power

$$\phi = -\gamma = -[\gamma_1\beta_1]\ (\gamma_1[\beta_1\gamma_2] + \gamma_1 + \gamma_2). \qquad (10.31)$$

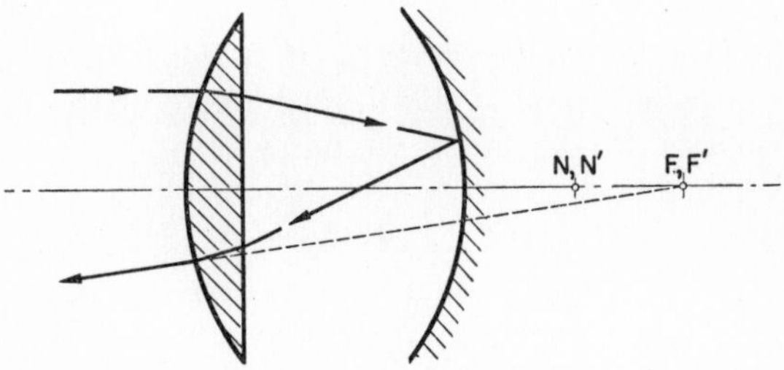

Fig. 10.3. Example of a system with one reflecting surface.

The above statement remains true for any such system having a single reflecting surface, the common index n in the first and last spaces being arbitrary. We obtain from (10.28)

$$\frac{s_N}{n} = \frac{s_N'}{n} = \frac{\delta + 1}{\gamma} = \frac{\alpha + 1}{\gamma} = \frac{[\beta_1\gamma_2 \ldots \gamma_\varkappa \ldots \beta_1\gamma_1] + 1}{[\gamma_1 \ldots \gamma_\varkappa \ldots \gamma_1]}. \qquad (10.32)$$

The coefficients α, β, γ, δ in (10.28) may be expressed in terms of the simpler brackets defined by

$$\begin{aligned} \theta_1 &= [\beta_{\varkappa-1} \ldots \gamma_1] \\ \theta_2 &= [\beta_{\varkappa-1} \ldots \beta_1] \\ \theta_3 &= [\gamma_{\varkappa-1} \ldots \gamma_1] \\ \theta_4 &= [\gamma_{\varkappa-1} \ldots \beta_1], \end{aligned} \qquad \begin{vmatrix} \theta_1 & \theta_2 \\ \theta_3 & \theta_4 \end{vmatrix} = 1, \qquad (10.33)$$

the result being

$$\begin{aligned} \alpha = \delta &= \theta_1\theta_4 + \theta_2\theta_3 + \theta_1\theta_2\gamma_\varkappa \\ &= \theta_1(2\theta_4 + \theta_2\gamma_\varkappa) - 1 \end{aligned}$$

$$\beta = \theta_2(2\theta_4 + \theta_2\gamma_\varkappa)$$
$$\gamma = \theta_1(2\theta_3 + \theta_1\gamma_\varkappa)$$
$$s_N = s_N' = \frac{2\theta_4 + \theta_2\gamma_\varkappa}{2\theta_3 + \theta_1\gamma_\varkappa}. \tag{10.34}$$

Holosymmetric Systems

A system is called *holosymmetric* if it consists of two parts such that the second part is the mirror image of the first. If the first part consists of $\varkappa$ surfaces, we have

$$\begin{aligned} \varrho_{\varkappa+\lambda+1} &= -\varrho_{\varkappa-\lambda} \\ n_{\varkappa+\lambda} &= n_{\varkappa-\lambda} \\ d_{\varkappa+\lambda} &= d_{\varkappa-\lambda} \end{aligned} \tag{10.35}$$

or

$$\begin{aligned} \gamma_{\varkappa+\lambda+1} &= \gamma_{\varkappa-\lambda} \\ \beta_{\varkappa+\lambda} &= \beta_{\varkappa-\lambda}. \end{aligned} \tag{10.36}$$

Let us use α', β', γ', δ' to denote the coefficients of the first part with the object and image origins at the first and last vertices of the first part, and α'', β'', γ'', δ'', the coefficients of the second part where the origins are at the first and last vertices of the second part. If $\Delta = d_\varkappa$ is the distance (in air) between the last vertex of the first part and the first vertex of the second part, we have

$$\begin{pmatrix} \alpha & \beta \\ \gamma & \delta \end{pmatrix} = \begin{pmatrix} \alpha'' & \beta'' \\ \gamma'' & \delta'' \end{pmatrix} \begin{pmatrix} 1 & \Delta \\ 0 & 1 \end{pmatrix} \begin{pmatrix} \alpha' & \beta' \\ \gamma' & \delta' \end{pmatrix}. \tag{10.37}$$

Because of (10.36), we find

$$\alpha'' = \delta', \ \beta'' = \beta', \ \gamma'' = \gamma', \ \delta'' = \alpha', \tag{10.38}$$

which leads to

$$\begin{aligned} \alpha &= \alpha'\delta' + \beta'\gamma' + \gamma'\delta'\,\Delta \\ \beta &= 2\beta'\delta' + \delta'^2\,\Delta \\ \gamma &= 2\alpha'\gamma' + \gamma'^2\,\Delta \\ \delta &= \alpha'\delta' + \beta'\gamma' + \gamma'\delta'\,\Delta, \end{aligned} \tag{10.39}$$

showing that α and δ are equal. The distances of the negative nodal points in the object and images spaces ($m = -1$) are found, because of the relation $\alpha'\delta' - \beta'\gamma' = 1$, to be

$$\bar{s}_N = \frac{\delta + 1}{\gamma} = \frac{\delta'}{\gamma'}$$

$$\bar{s}_N{}' = -\frac{\alpha + 1}{\gamma} = -\frac{\delta'}{\gamma'}. \tag{10.40}$$

Comparison with (9.28) shows that the negative nodal points (points of magnification -1) are the front focus of the first system and the back focus of the last system, that is, the rays through these points are parallel to the axis in the interspace.

We shall prove that the image of the nodal point in the interspace is the center of the interspace.

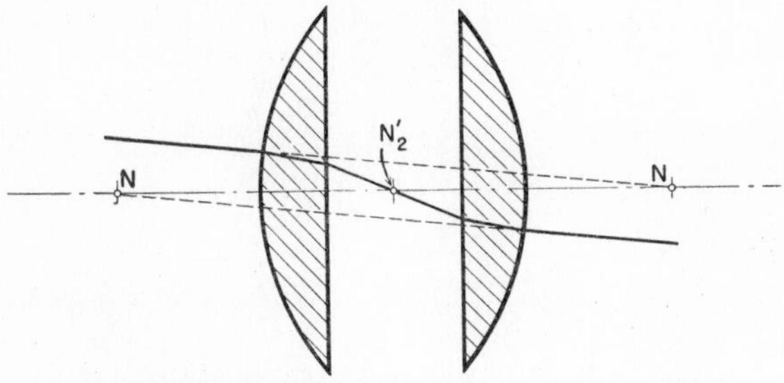

Fig. 10.4. Example of a holosymmetric system.

We have, for the object nodal point of the combined system,

$$s_N = \frac{\delta - 1}{\gamma} = \frac{2\beta' + \delta'\Delta}{2\alpha' + \gamma'\Delta}. \tag{10.41}$$

Its image s_i' in the interspace is given by

$$s_i' = \frac{\beta' - s_N\alpha'}{s_N\gamma' - \delta'} = \frac{\Delta}{2}. \tag{10.42}$$

With respect to the second system this point has the distance $s_i = -\Delta/2$, which leads, because of (10.38), to

$$s_N' = \frac{\beta' - s_i\delta'}{s_i\gamma' - \alpha'} = -\frac{2\beta' + \Delta\delta'}{\Delta\gamma' + 2\alpha'} = -\frac{\delta - 1}{\gamma} = \frac{1 - \alpha}{\gamma}, \tag{10.43}$$

showing that the image is at the image nodal point of the combined system.

Hemisymmetric Systems

A system is called *hemisymmetric* if it consists of two parts, the second part being the mirror image of the first part magnified by a factor k. We shall compute the coefficients of the whole system expressed by those of the first part. For this purpose, we shall first investigate how a system changes if all radii and distances are magnified. In the equations

$$\begin{aligned}\vec{A}' &= \alpha\vec{A} + \beta\vec{S}\\ \vec{S}' &= \gamma\vec{A} + \delta\vec{S},\end{aligned} \tag{10.44}$$

if we write

$$\vec{A} = \frac{1}{k}\vec{A}^*, \quad \vec{A}' = \frac{1}{k}\vec{A}^{*\prime}, \tag{10.45}$$

we find

$$\begin{aligned}\vec{A}^{*\prime} &= \alpha\vec{A}^* + \beta k\vec{S}\\ \vec{S}' &= \frac{\gamma}{k}\vec{A}^* + \delta\vec{S}.\end{aligned} \tag{10.46}$$

Thus we can write for a hemisymmetric system

$$\begin{pmatrix}\alpha & \beta\\ \gamma & \delta\end{pmatrix} = \begin{bmatrix}\delta' & \beta' k\\ \dfrac{\gamma'}{k} & \alpha'\end{bmatrix}\begin{pmatrix}1 & \Delta\\ 0 & 1\end{pmatrix}\begin{pmatrix}\alpha' & \beta'\\ \gamma' & \delta'\end{pmatrix} \tag{10.47}$$

or

$$\begin{aligned}\alpha &= \alpha'\delta' + \beta'\gamma' k + \delta'\gamma'\Delta\\ \beta &= \beta'\delta'(1 + k) + \delta'^2\Delta\\ \gamma &= \alpha'\gamma'\left(1 + \frac{1}{k}\right) + \frac{\gamma'^2}{k}\Delta\\ \delta &= \alpha'\delta' + \gamma'\beta'/k + \gamma'\delta'\Delta/k.\end{aligned} \tag{10.48}$$

Here the points of magnification $-k$, 1 are the points of symmetry. We have, from our general formulae, the object distance, the distance in the interspace, and the image distance for the point of magnification $-k$:

$$s = \frac{\delta + (1/k)}{\gamma} = \frac{\delta'}{\gamma'}, \quad s_i = \infty, \quad s' = -\frac{k + \alpha}{\gamma} = -\frac{k\alpha'}{\gamma'}, \tag{10.49}$$

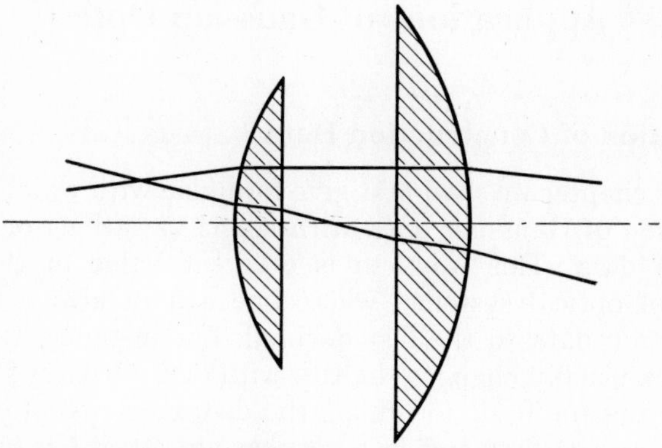

Fig. 10.5. Example of a hemisymmetric system.

and for the point of magnification $+1$

$$s = \frac{\beta' + \dfrac{\delta'}{k+1}\Delta}{\alpha' + \dfrac{\gamma'}{k+1}\Delta} \qquad s_i = -\frac{\Delta k}{k+1}$$

$$s_i' = \frac{\Delta}{k+1} \qquad s' = -\frac{\beta' + \dfrac{\delta'\Delta}{k+1}}{\alpha' + \dfrac{\gamma'\Delta}{k+1}}\,k. \tag{10.50}$$

That is, the internal image of the principal (nodal) points is the symmetry center of the system, the point dividing the inner space in the ratio of $1 : k$.

CHAPTER ELEVEN

Applications of Gaussian Optics

1. Variation of Construction Data

In this chapter we shall first give formulae with which to study the change of Gaussian data with slight variations of the construction data. This problem is of great value in the manufacture of optical systems, where one cannot always hold the construction data to the last decimal. For instance, the refractive index usually changes slightly with every batch of glass.

Repeating the basic formulae, the distances s, s' of conjugate points from the first and last vertices are given [*cf.* (9.25) and (9.26)] by

$$[(s'/n')^*,\ \gamma_\varkappa,\ \beta_{\varkappa-1}\ \gamma_1,\ (-\ s/n)] = 0 \tag{11.1}$$

$$m = [(s'/n')^*,\ \gamma_\varkappa\ \gamma_1] = \frac{1}{[\gamma_\varkappa\ \gamma_1,\ (-\ s/n)]}.$$

The asterisk denotes that, for an odd number of reflections, the minus sign has to be taken. The obvious signs of ellipsis (...) in the brackets are omitted in this chapter.

We introduce the abbreviations

$$\left(\frac{s'}{n'}\right)^* \cdot \frac{1}{m} = Z',\quad \frac{1}{m} = M, \tag{11.2}$$

quantities which will be used frequently throughout the book and which determine m and s' by

$$\left(\frac{s'}{n'}\right)^* = \frac{Z'}{M},\quad m = \frac{1}{M}. \tag{11.3}$$

This leads to

$$Z' = -[\beta_{\varkappa-1}\ \gamma_1, (-\ s/n)],\quad M = [\gamma_\varkappa\ \beta_{\varkappa-1}\ \gamma_1,\ (-\ s/n)]. \tag{11.4}$$

Differentiation of Z' and M with respect to β_ν and γ_ν gives

$$\begin{aligned}
\partial Z'/\partial\beta_\nu &= -[\beta_{\varkappa-1}\ \gamma_{\nu+1}]\,[\gamma_\nu\ \gamma_1, (-s/n)] \\
\partial Z'/\partial\gamma_\nu &= -[\beta_{\varkappa-1}\ \beta_\nu]\,[\beta_{\nu-1}\ \gamma_1, (-s/n)] \\
\partial M/\partial\beta_\nu &= \quad [\gamma_\varkappa\ \ \gamma_{\nu+1}]\,[\gamma_\nu\ \gamma_1, (-s/n)] \\
\partial M/\partial\gamma_\nu &= \quad [\gamma_\varkappa\ \ \beta_\nu]\,[\beta_{\nu-1}\ \gamma_1, (-s/n)]\,.
\end{aligned} \tag{11.5}$$

From (11.3) and (11.5) we can derive the interesting formulae

$$\frac{\partial\left(\dfrac{s'}{n'}\right)^*}{\partial\beta_\nu} = \frac{\dfrac{\partial Z'}{\partial\beta_\nu}M - \dfrac{\partial M}{\partial\beta_\nu}Z'}{M^2} =$$

$$= \frac{-\begin{vmatrix}[\beta_{\varkappa-1}\ \gamma_{\nu+1}] & [\beta_{\varkappa-1}\ \gamma_1, (-s/n)] \\ [\gamma_\varkappa\ \ \gamma_{\nu+1}] & [\gamma_\varkappa\ \ \gamma_1, (-s/n)]\end{vmatrix}[\gamma_\nu\ \gamma_1, (-s/n)]}{[\gamma_\varkappa\ \gamma_1, (-s/n)]^2} \tag{11.6}$$

$$\frac{\partial m}{\partial\beta_\nu} = -\frac{\partial M/\partial\beta_\nu}{M^2} = \frac{-[\gamma_\varkappa\ \gamma_{\nu+1}]\ [\gamma_\nu\ \gamma_1, (-s/n)]}{[\gamma_\varkappa\ \gamma_1, (-s/n)]^2}$$

with similar results for differentiation with respect to γ_ν. Using the determinant rule from the Appendix (B 78) leads to

$$\frac{\partial(s'/n')^*}{\partial\beta_\nu} = -\frac{[\gamma_\nu\ \gamma_1, (-s/n)]^2}{[\gamma_\varkappa\ \gamma_1, (-s/n)]^2}, \quad \frac{\partial m}{\partial\beta_\nu} = -\frac{[\gamma_\varkappa\ \gamma_{\nu+1}]\,[\gamma_\nu\ \gamma_1, (-s/n)]}{[\gamma_\varkappa\ \gamma_1, (-s/n)]^2}$$

$$\frac{\partial(s'/n')^*}{\partial\gamma_\nu} = \frac{[\beta_{\nu-1}\ \gamma_1, (-s/n)]^2}{[\gamma_\varkappa\ \ \gamma_1, (-s/n)]^2}, \quad \frac{\partial m}{\partial\gamma_\nu} = -\frac{[\gamma_\varkappa\ \beta_\nu]\,[\beta_{\nu-1}\ \gamma_1, (-s/n)]}{[\gamma_\varkappa\ \gamma_1, (-s/n)]^2}. \tag{11.7}$$

We can apply these formulae not only to the *surface-by-surface* analysis of ordinary systems, but also to preliminary calculations, in which we consider systems of *thin lenses with finite distances* (*cf.* Chapter 10).

In the surface-by-surface application we have

$$\gamma_\nu = (n_{\nu-1} - n_\nu)\varrho_\nu, \quad \beta_\nu = d_\nu/n_\nu, \tag{11.8}$$

where ϱ_ν is the curvature of the νth surface and d_ν the distance between the νth and the $(\nu+1)$st surfaces. However, for *thin lens precalculation* [*cf.* (10.19), (10.20), and (10.21)], we have

$$\gamma_\nu = (n_\nu - 1)\ (\varrho_\nu'' - \varrho_\nu'), \quad \beta_\nu = d_\nu, \tag{11.9}$$

where ϱ_ν' and ϱ_ν'' are the front and back curvatures of the νth lens, and d_ν the distance between the νth and $(\nu + 1)$st *lenses.*

In the *surface-by-surface* case we have, for a change of curvature,

$$\frac{\partial}{\partial \varrho_\nu} = (n_{\nu-1} - n_\nu) \frac{\partial}{\partial \gamma_\nu} = \frac{\gamma_\nu}{\varrho_\nu} \frac{\partial}{\partial \gamma_\nu}. \tag{11.10}$$

For a change of distance,

$$\frac{\partial}{\partial d_\nu} = \frac{1}{n_\nu} \frac{\partial}{\partial \beta_\nu} = \frac{\beta_\nu}{d_\nu} \frac{\partial}{\partial \beta_\nu}. \tag{11.11}$$

For a change of refractive index (n_ν), however, we have to consider that n_ν occurs in γ_ν, β_ν, and $\gamma_{\nu+1}$, so that we have

$$\frac{\partial}{\partial n_\nu} = - \varrho_\nu \frac{\partial}{\partial \gamma_\nu} - \frac{\mathrm{d}_\nu}{n_\nu^2} \frac{\partial}{\partial \beta_\nu} + \varrho_{\nu+1} \frac{\partial}{\partial \gamma_{\nu+1}}. \tag{11.12}$$

If we consider the precalculation, that is, systems of thin lenses with finite air separations, we have, for a change of the νth refractive index, the simple formula

$$\frac{\partial}{\partial n_\nu} = (\varrho_\nu'' - \varrho_\nu') \frac{\partial}{\partial \gamma_\nu} = \frac{\gamma_\nu}{n_{\nu-1}} \frac{\partial}{\partial \gamma_\nu}. \tag{11.13}$$

To investigate the image of the infinite object point, we write

$$(s_F'/n')^* \gamma = Z'_\infty = - [\beta_{\varkappa-1}\, \gamma_1] \tag{11.14}$$

$$\gamma = [\gamma_\varkappa, \beta_{\varkappa-1}\, \gamma_1],$$

which leads to

$$\begin{aligned}
\frac{\partial Z'_\infty}{\partial \gamma_\nu} &= - [\beta_{\varkappa-1}\, \beta_\nu]\, [\beta_{\nu-1}\, \gamma_1] \\
\frac{\partial Z'_\infty}{\partial \beta_\nu} &= - [\beta_{\varkappa-1}\, \gamma_{\nu+1}]\, [\gamma_\nu\, \gamma_1] \\
\frac{\partial \gamma}{\partial \gamma_\nu} &= [\gamma_\varkappa\, \beta_\nu]\, [\beta_{\nu-1}\, \gamma_1] \\
\frac{\partial \gamma}{\partial \beta_\nu} &= [\gamma_\varkappa\, \gamma_{\nu+1}]\, [\gamma_\nu\, \gamma_1].
\end{aligned} \tag{11.15}$$

Corresponding to (11.7), we find the formulae

$$\frac{\partial(s_F'/n')^*}{\partial\beta_\nu} = -\frac{[\gamma_\nu\ \gamma_1]^2}{[\gamma_\varkappa\ \gamma_1]^2}, \quad \frac{\partial[s_F'/n')^*}{\partial\gamma_\nu} = \frac{[\beta_{\nu-1}\ \gamma_1]^2}{[\gamma_\varkappa\ \gamma_1]^2}. \qquad (11.6)$$

2. The Problem of Vignetting and the Choice of Starting Data

In Part I we investigated the trace of a single ray through an optical system. In this part we shall study the practical question of how to select the rays to be traced. Moreover, we shall discuss here some of the other practical problems for which Gaussian optics gives a satisfactory approximation.

An optical system consists of a series of lenses, each of the lenses having two glass-air surfaces. Some of the lenses may be cemented together, whereas others may have finite distances between them. The lenses are, in general, mounted so as to have a common optical axis.

Owing to the mounting as well as to the fact that the pieces of glass of which each lens is made have finite diameters, not all the light rays coming from the object will actually go through the system. It is of importance to know, at least approximately, how much light coming from a given object point really traverses the system.

In most systems, especially in photographic systems, there is a special diaphragm, that is, a changeable opening which determines the "aperture" of the optical system. Since only the approximate aperture is needed for this purpose, it is sufficient to use Gaussian optics to compute in the object and image spaces the images of all the boundaries. For most optical systems, the first surface, the last surface, and the diaphragm form the boundaries. The Gaussian image of the diaphragm in object space (image space) is called the *entrance* (*exit*) pupil. Let us image the first and last surfaces into the object and image spaces and consider the entrance and exit pupils.

To find the light rays traversing the system from a given object point, we have only to compute the cone of rays with its apex at the object point and common to the three cones with the three object-side images (also called "apertures") as bases. A practical method of finding this cone consists in projecting the three apertures from the object point onto a plane perpendicular to the axis, for instance, the plane of the entrance pupil. We thus obtain, in general, three eccentric circles. Connecting the region common to these to the apex, we have approximately the cone of

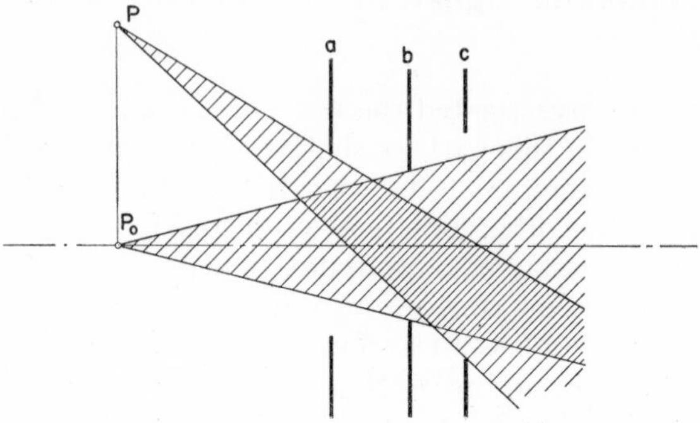

Fig. 11.1. Vignetting effect for finite points.

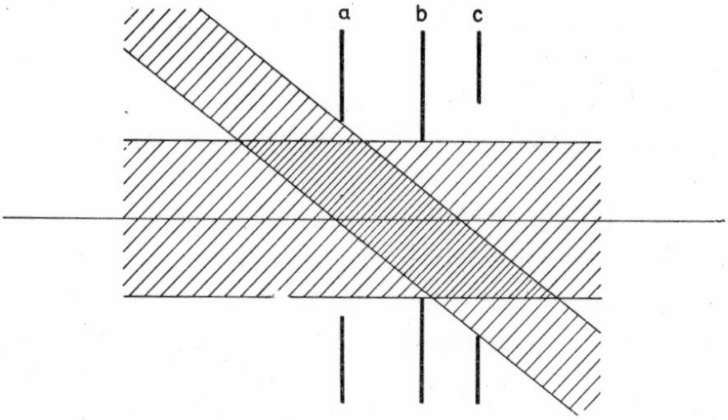

Fig. 11.2. Vignetting effect for infinite points.

light going through the system. The same construction can be made in the image space instead, where then the Gaussian image point is used.

Let us assume that the object, the first surface, and the Gaussian image of the last surface lie at the distances s, s_A, and s_B, respectively, from the entrance pupil and that the first surface, the entrance pupil, and the image of the last surface are circles

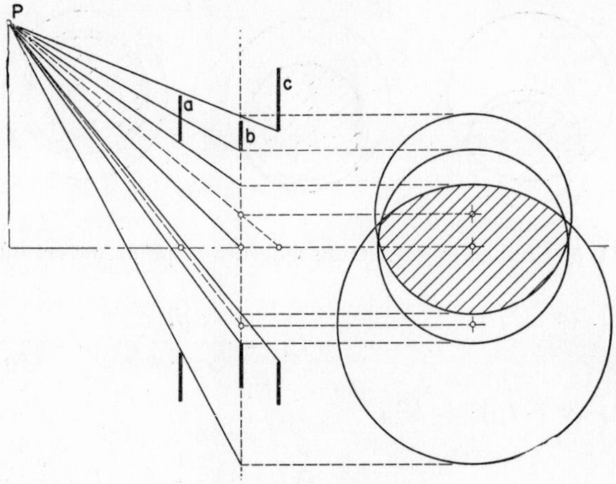

Fig. 11.3. Projection of apertures from finite point onto entrance pupil.

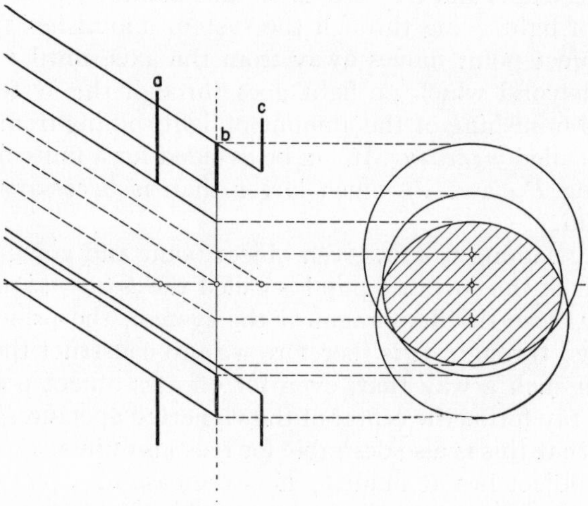

Fig. 11.4. Projection of apertures from infinite point onto entrance pupil.

with radii A, P, and B, respectively. The projection of the circles onto the entrance pupil from a point at the position $x = 0$, $y = h$ in the object plane is then given by

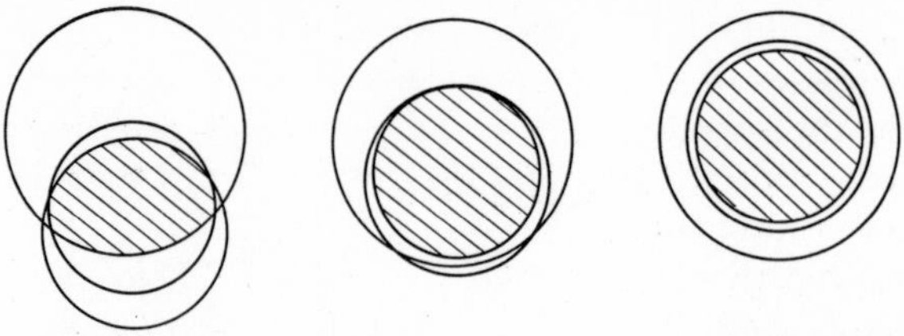

Fig. 11.5. Change in vignetting diagram as point moves off-axis.

$$x^2 + y^2 = P^2 \qquad t_A = \frac{s_A h}{s_A - s}, \quad t_B = \frac{s_B h}{s_B - s}$$

$$x^2 + (y - t_A)^2 = P^2{}_A \qquad (11.17)$$

$$x^2 + (y - t_B)^2 = P^2{}_B \qquad P_A = \frac{sA}{s_A - s}, \quad P_B = \frac{sB}{s_B - s}.$$

In Figure 11.5 we have shown the corresponding circles for a point on the axis and for various off-axis points. We see that the amount of light going through the system diminishes gradually as the object point moves away from the axis, until a point is reached beyond which no light goes through the system. This gradual diminishing of the amount of light coming from off-axis points is called *vignetting*. It can be avoided for a finite field only by making P_A and P_B much larger than is necessary for the axial beam.

The ray coming from a given object point and going through the center of the entrance pupil is called the *principal ray*. If we gradually close the diaphragm of the system, the principal ray will still go through. It is therefore wise to construct the optical system in such a way that, even for off-axis object points, the principal ray forms the center of the vignetted aperture. We shall see later that this is also desirable for reasons of image quality.

If the object lies at infinity, as is the case in a photographic objective, an axis point is equivalent to a manifold of rays parallel to the axis, an off-axis point to a manifold of rays all parallel to a meridional ray at an angle α with the axis. We then have, for the three circles of (11.17),

$$t_A = s_A \tan \alpha \qquad P_A = A$$
$$t_B = s_B \tan \alpha \qquad P_B = B. \qquad (11.18)$$

We have simplified the problem a little by investigating the Gaussian images of the first and last surfaces only. In practice, one should investigate whether or not one of the other surfaces or one of the mountings limits the rays. However, the investigation of more than three apertures makes no difference in the basic formulae given by (11.17) and (11.18), which can be applied as well to many apertures. Any limiting aperture has to be traced according to Gaussian optics into the object (or image) space with its Gaussian position and magnification by the partial intermediate system. After this is done, Formulae (11.17) or (11.18) may be used to draw what we call the *vignetting diagram*. The designer must keep in mind that any opening of limited size in the path of the rays must be considered in this respect, and that it may not always have a circular form. There is interesting literature on this subject.

In considering vignetting, one has always to be aware of the fact that the application of Gaussian optics to the problem gives only an approximate insight into the amount of light going through the system. However, this is usually sufficiently accurate for designing purposes. For a precise determination, ray-tracing alone can decide whether or not an individual ray goes through the system.

The remark may also be made at this place that artificial vignetting, that is, the introduction of vignetting boundaries in mount or system, can, and has been, used to cut out rays which, owing to image errors, do not contribute to the formation of a good image.

3. Starting Data in Optical Systems

The vignetting diagram gives us a reasonable method for selecting the rays to trace through an optical system. To obtain accurate information about the light distribution in the optical image, we should like to know the intersection point of a large number of rays evenly distributed over the vignetted entrance pupil.

This can be done in two ways: (*a*) By actual ray-tracing (this is not an impossible task if the designer has one of the electronic computing devices at his disposal); (*b*) by tracing only a few selected rays and then using an interpolation formula to approximate the results for a large number of rays, evenly distributed over the vignetted entrance pupil. It is of importance to distribute the rays *evenly* over the entrance pupil because only then can each ray be assumed to represent the same amount of energy as any other ray.

The simplest method of calculation is to trace rays through the points of a square grating, changing x and y by constant values. A more sophisticated way is to use points spaced in equilateral triangles.

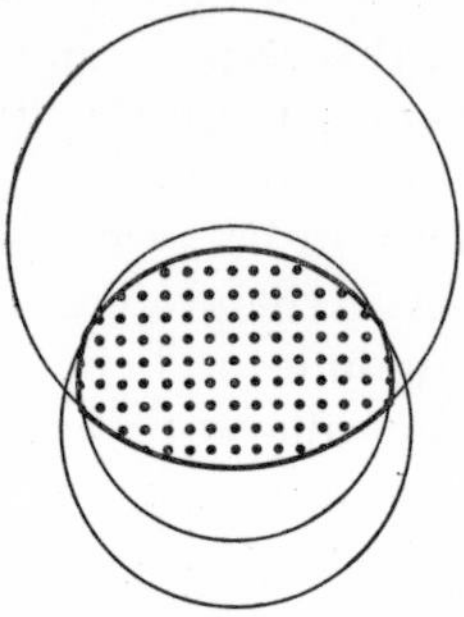

Fig. 11.6. Use of vignetting diagram for studying light distribution.

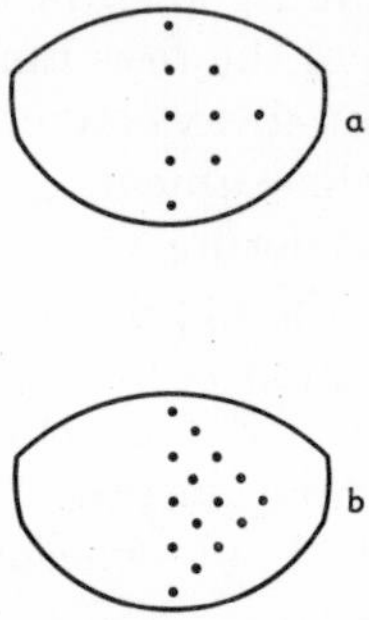

Fig. 11.7. Choice of rays for interpolation method.

Owing to the rotational symmetry, it is not necessary to trace all the rays. The rays going through points at the right of the center line (which represents meridional rays) are equivalent to rays going through the symmetrical points at the left of the center line. Thus it is sufficient to trace only the meridional rays and the rays on one side.

As to the interpolation procedure, the author has found it sufficient to choose rays as indicated in Figure 11.7a, that is, to trace five evenly spaced meridional rays, three rays of medium skewness, and one of large skewness. If more and finer insight into the light distribution is desirable, the 15 rays in Figure 11.7b will do the job. It is not advisable, in general, to fit the extreme rays since they have high aberrations, and, though they do not have much effect in the basic image formation, they can easily give misleading information.

It is the author's opinion, incidentally, that it is never a satisfactory procedure to trace *only* meridional rays. As we shall prove, the correction of the skew rays is independent of the correction of the meridional rays, and the correction of the meridional rays alone gives neither sufficient practical nor theoretical knowledge with respect to the image formation of the optical system. This statement is made in spite of the fact that most optical designers restrict their task to the investigation of meridional rays alone.

CHAPTER TWELVE

Dispersion

Dispersion of Optical Glass and Other Materials

The wavelength of light is in general measured in millimicrons, a millimicron (mμ) being the millionth part of a millimeter. The visible region of the spectrum goes from 400 mμ up to about 800 mμ.

Frequently the wavelength is expressed in angstroms, A:

$$1 \text{ m}\mu = 10 \text{ A}. \tag{12.1}$$

Optical glass is supposed to have been an invention of the Phoenicians, who first mixed sand and seaweed and burned the mixture to obtain a transparent substance. The application to spectacle glasses was known in early Rome; the German word *Brille* for spectacle glasses is supposed to be derived from the Latin *beryllium,* designating a transparent crystal. At the end of the nineteenth century glass was used to make telescopes and other optical instruments. *Newton* discovered that light of different colors has different refractive indices. His famous article in Philosophical Transactions, Volume I, page 128 (1672) tells of his experiments with a prism which once and for all made clear that color and refractive index are connected and that white light can be considered a mixture of light of different wavelengths. The problem arises as to whether we can correct an optical system for three or more colors. Let us consider first a monoplet consisting of a number of thin lenses in contact. The power of such a monoplet is given by (10.14) as

$$\phi = \Sigma\, \phi_i = \Sigma\, (n_i - 1)K_i \tag{12.2}$$

if $K_i = \varrho_i' - \varrho_i''$ is used as an abbreviation for the difference of the two successive curvatures of the lens.

Let us consider (12.2) for three colors. This leads to

$$\begin{aligned} \phi_\beta &= \Sigma\,(n_{i\beta} - 1)K_i \\ \phi_\beta - \phi_\alpha &= \Sigma(n_{i\beta} - n_{i\alpha})K_i \\ \phi_\lambda - \phi_\beta &= \Sigma(n_{i\lambda} - n_{i\beta})K_i, \end{aligned} \tag{12.3}$$

where λ denotes a variable wavelength.

Introducing the abbreviations

$$\nu_i = \frac{n_{i\beta} - 1}{n_{i\beta} - n_{i\alpha}}, \quad P_{i\lambda} = \frac{n_{i\lambda} - n_{i\beta}}{n_{i\beta} - n_{i\alpha}} \tag{12.4}$$

into Formulae (12.3), we can write them as

$$\begin{aligned} \phi_\beta &= \Sigma\phi_{i\beta} \\ \phi_\beta - \phi_\alpha &= \Sigma\phi_{i\beta}/\nu_i \\ \phi_\lambda - \phi_\beta &= \Sigma(\phi_{i\beta}/\nu_i)P_{i\lambda}. \end{aligned} \tag{12.5}$$

The values ν_i and $P_{i\lambda}$, or some reasonable facsimiles, are given in the glass catalogs of *Schott, Parra Mantois, Chance,* and *Bausch and Lomb.*

In the catalogs, ν-value is defined slightly differently. The ν-value is usually expressed as

$$\nu_{\mathrm{D}} = (n_{\mathrm{D}} - 1)/(n_{\mathrm{F}} - n_{\mathrm{C}}), \tag{12.4a}$$

where the wavelengths of C, D, F are those of the mean of two red hydrogen lines, C (6562.8 A), the mean of two yellow sodium lines, D (5892.9 A), and the blue hydrogen line, F (4861.327 A), respectively. The partial dispersion P_λ is usually defined as

$$P_\lambda = (n_\lambda - n_{\mathrm{F}})/(n_{\mathrm{F}} - n_{\mathrm{C}}) \tag{12.4b}$$

and can be found in the glass catalogs for the A′-line (mean of two potassium lines in the red part of the spectrum), $\lambda =$ 7681.9 A, the green mercury line, e, $\lambda = 5460.7$, the violet mercury g-line, $\lambda = 4358.3$, and the violet mercury h-line, $\lambda = 4046.6$. Bausch and Lomb uses, instead of the A′, the stronger potassium line (7664.9), whereas the Chance catalog and the Canadian Research Enterprises use, instead of A and A′, the red b-line (7065.188), which is a helium line.

TABLE I

Spectrum Lines for Refractometry

Name	*Color*	*Element*	*Wavelength (A)*	
A′	Red	K	7699.0 7664.9	7682.0
b	Red	He	7065.2	
C	Red	H	6562.8	
D	Yellow	Na	5895.9 5890.0	5892.9
d	Yellow	He	5875.7	
e	Green	Hg	5460.7	
F	Blue	H	4861.3	
g*	Violet	Hg	4358.3	
G′	Violet	H	4340.5	
h*	Violet	Hg	4046.6	
m	Ultraviolet	Hg	3650.1 †	

* The letters g and h were given by Fraunhofer to a calcium line at 4226.7 A and a hydrogen line at 4101.7 A, respectively. The mercury lines given in the table have supplanted Fraunhofer's because they are so much easier to produce.

† Plus two lines of comparable intensity and longer wavelength.

Other lines for which the glass catalogs give refractive indices are the helium d-line (yellow, $\lambda = 5875.7$), and a hydrogen line, G′ ($\lambda = 4340.5$).

Outside the visible spectrum the mercury m-line ($\lambda = 3650.1$) and the mercury line ($\lambda = 2536.5$) in the ultraviolet are used in optical design. For theoretical purposes. Formulae (12.4) are more convenient; however, the results hold for the catalog values (12.4a, b) with sufficient accuracy.

The quantity ν is called the *Abbe-number* or *ν-value* or the *reciprocal mean dispersion* of the glass, whereas the P_λ's are called the *partial dispersions*.

The investigation of Equations (12.5) together with the mathematical form of the dispersion formulae will give us all needed information about the color correction in optical systems.

To return to the historical survey, Newton measured crudely*

* In that he not only used a hole instead of a slit, but also failed to use a lens to image the spectrum on the screen.

TABLE II

Typical Data from Glass Catalogs

Type	$\nu = \frac{n_D - 1}{n_F - n_C}$	n_A'	n_C	n_D	n_F	n_h	$n_A' - n_F$ $\frac{n_A' - n_F}{n_F - n_C}$	$n_g - n_F$ $\frac{n_g - n_F}{n_F - n_C}$	$n_h - n_F$ $\frac{n_h - n_F}{n_F - n_C}$
BSC-2	64.5	1.51179	1.51461	1.51700	1.52262	1.53043	0.01083 1.352	0.00428 0.534	0.00781 0.975
LBC-1	59.9	1.53529	1.53842	1.54110	1.54746	1.55645	0.01217 1.346	0.00490 0.542	0.00899 0.994
DBC-1	58.8	1.60439	1.60793	1.61100	1.61832	1.62867	0.01393 1.341	0.00564 0.543	0.01035 0.996
CF-1	51.6	1.52217	1.52560	1.52860	1.53584	1.54633	0.01367 1.335	0.00569 0.556	0.01049 1.024
ELF-1	45.5	1.55086	1.55495	1.55850	1.56722	1.58010	0.01636 1.333	0.00695 0.566	0.01288 1.050
BF-1	46.0	1.57598	1.58013	1.58380	1.59282	1.60615	0.01684 1.327	0.00720 0.567	0.01333 1.050
DF-1	38.0	1.59536	1.60044	1.60500	1.61639	1.63361	0.02103 1.318	0.00924 0.579	0.01722 1.080
EDF-2	30.9	1.67584	1.68271	1.68900	1.70501	1.72996	0.02917 1.308	0.01326 0.595	0.02495 1.119

the dispersion of crown glass and of a prism containing water, which has nearly the same ν-value, and drew the conclusion that all optical substances have the same dispersion. If this were the case, Equations (12.5) would give

$$\phi_\beta - \phi_a = 1/\nu \, \Sigma \, \phi_{i\beta} = (1/\nu)\phi_\beta. \tag{12.6}$$

This would mean that such a system could not be corrected for color, and that was exactly Newton's conclusion. Therefore, he abandoned the study of refracting telescopes started so promisingly by Galileo and Kepler and suggested using reflecting systems for astronomical purposes, and several interesting types were developed by himself and his disciples.

However, before his time the Venetians (not the Phoenicians, proofreader) had already experimented with adding lead to the usual mixture of silica and potassium. This glass was called *flint* glass and was used mainly for beautiful vases, crystal glasses, and other objects of luxury. This flint glass (ν about 30) has a much higher dispersion or a much lower ν-value than the usual crown glass (ν about 60).

A justice of the peace, *Chester Moor Hall,* was the first (1733) to combine two lenses to design an achromat, that is, a lens corrected for two colors.

Equations (12.5) give for such an achromat, omitting the color indices,

$$\phi_1 + \phi_2 = \phi$$

$$\frac{\phi_1}{\nu_1} + \frac{\phi_2}{\nu_2} = 0 \tag{12.7}$$

or

$$\phi_1 = \frac{\nu_1}{\nu_1 - \nu_2}\phi, \quad \phi_2 = -\frac{\nu_2}{\nu_1 - \nu}\phi. \tag{12.8}$$

We see that the two parts of the achromat must have powers of the opposite sign. The crown lens must be positive and the flint lens negative, if the combination is to have a positive power. We see that it is advantageous to have a large difference in ν-value between the two materials to construct an achromat with relatively small powers ϕ_1 and ϕ_2 for the two elements.

The systematic manufacture of these lenses was undertaken

by *J. Dollond,* who acquired the first patent on achromats in 1758 (as now seems unjust, since Hall had anticipated the idea; see T. H. Court and M. von Rohr).

By varying the lead content, a series of optical glasses with varying index and ν-value were manufactured. It looked at the beginning of the nineteenth century as if the ν-value were a function of the index for a specific color, or, in the language of mathematics, as if optical glasses formed a one-dimensional manifold.

Further progress in our knowledge of optical glass had to await progress in the exact measurement of refractive index and chemical advances in glassmaking.

Joseph von Fraunhofer (1787–1826) investigated the fixed dark lines in the solar spectrum (see Table I) and the corresponding bright lines in the absorption spectra of other light sources. Kirchhoff and Bunsen related these lines to the chemical elements involved. This made possible the science of spectroscopy, the determination of wavelength of light, and the corresponding measurements in most other fields of physics. The reason that Newton did not see these lines is probably due to the fact that the prism he used was not optically perfect.

Fraunhofer devised instruments for the accurate measurement of the refractive indices of glasses and, in connection with *Utzschneider* and *Reichenbach,* founded the first glass factory in Benediktbeuern, near Munich. One of his collaborators was the Swiss, *P. Guinand,* whose sons emigrated to France to found the Parra Mantois factory near Paris.

In 1848 *Lucas Chance* founded a glass factory in England and obtained the right to use the Guinand patents. Investigation into the influence of chemical elements had been started by Fraunhofer and was continued on a small scale in France and England (Hopkinson was the first to investigate the influence of rare earths), but nearly all these glasses had one feature in common. The partial dispersions P_λ were linear functions of the ν-value; that is two functions $A_1(\lambda)$ and $A_2(\lambda)$ existed so that for all optical glasses

$$P(\lambda) = A_1(\lambda)\,\nu + A_2(\lambda). \tag{12.9}$$

If this were a universal law (and it nearly proved to be so), then two data, the index for one wavelength and the ν-value for another, would determine the dispersion of optical glass completely. For, if n_a and ν are known, n_β can be found from

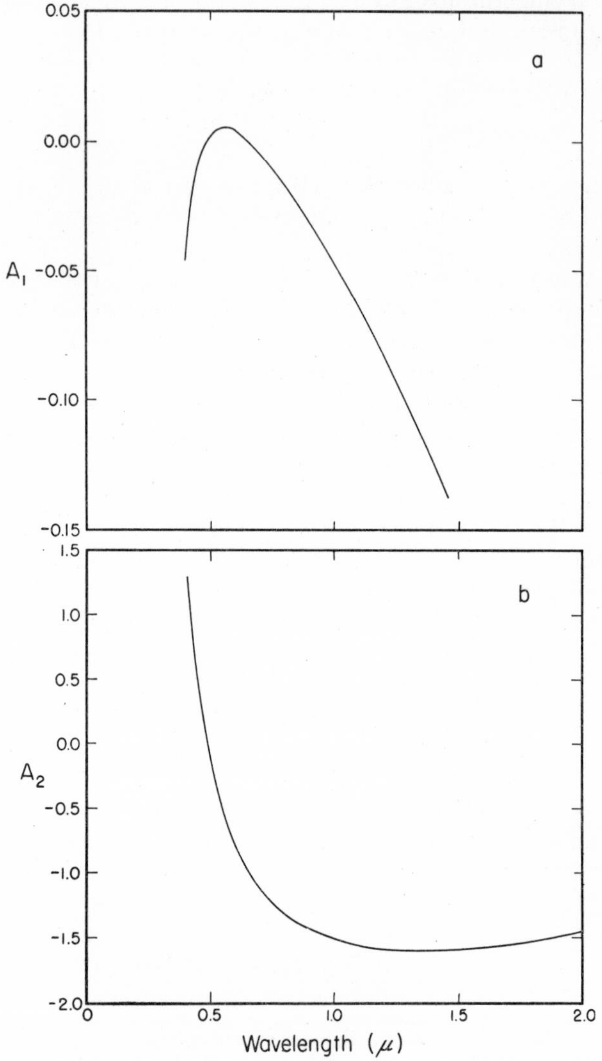

Fig. 12.1. Plot of universal functions A_1 and A_2 against wavelength. The functions are based on ν_D and on $P_\lambda = (n_\lambda - n_F)/(n_F - n_C)$.

$$\nu = (n_\beta - 1)/(n_\beta - n_\alpha),$$

P_λ can be found from (12.9), and consequently n_λ is determined by (12.4), which can be written as

$$P_\lambda = (n_\lambda - n_\beta)/(n_\beta - n_\alpha).$$

Moreover, we find from (12.5) and (12.9)

$$\phi_\lambda - \phi_\beta = A_2(\lambda)\,(\phi_\beta - \phi_\alpha) + A_1(\lambda)\,\phi_\beta. \qquad (12.10)$$

If ϕ is corrected for the two colors α and β, then

$$(\phi_\lambda - \phi_\beta)/\phi_\beta = A_1(\lambda). \qquad (12.11)$$

This means that correction for a third color, γ, would be possible only if the universal function $A_1(\lambda)$ could vanish for a value of λ different from α and β.

Figure 12.1 shows the values of the functions $A_i(\lambda)$ for different wavelengths. We see that the result would be that a lens system (a monoplet) could be corrected only for two colors. For instance, for an objective corrected for use with the eye, we can bring the blue (line F) image and the red (line C) image together. The other images will deviate slightly in size and position, so that we see

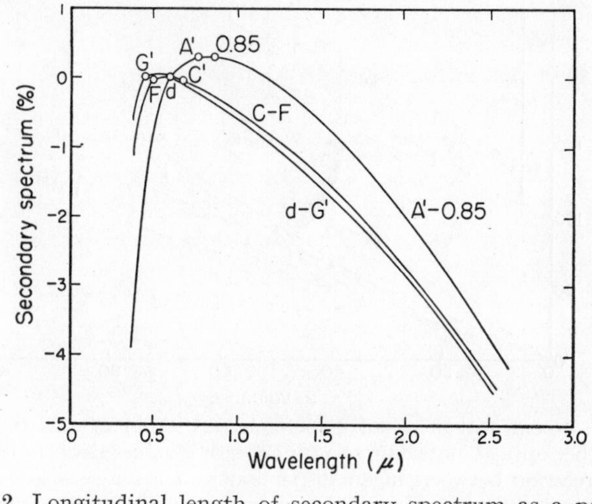

Fig. 12.2. Longitudinal length of secondary spectrum as a percentage of the focal length for various types of chromatic correction.

color fringes around the image. These fringes are called the *secondary spectrum.*

If we call glasses which fulfill Equations (12.9) *ordinary* glasses, we can say that the secondary spectrum cannot be corrected in a monoplet if ordinary glasses are used.

This secondary spectrum proved especially annoying in the design of high-power microscopes and telescopes.

Thus *Ernst Abbe,* the founder and scientific director of the Zeiss works, induced the chemist *Otto Schott* to investigate systematically the influence of different chemical elements on the optical qualities of glass.

It was found that the addition of barium oxide and other elements to the potassium-lime-silica combination gives a higher index for the same dispersion. This led to the barium crowns and barium flints, and later on to the very dense barium crown glasses (SK and SSK in the Schott system).

If we plot the "reciprocal dispersion" of glasses,

$$1/(n_\beta - n_\alpha) = N$$

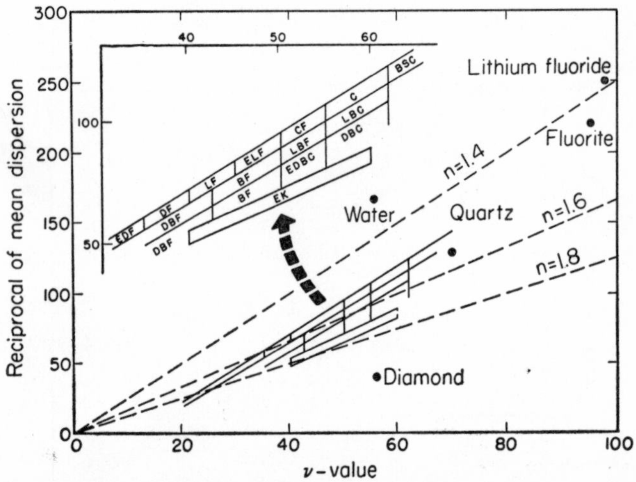

Fig. 12.3. Reciprocal of mean dispersion $(n_C - n_F)$ of glass types and certain other optical materials as a function of ν-value. Broken lines indicate the relation between mean dispersion and ν for selected values of refractive index n_D. EK, Kodak glasses; other symbols follow the Bausch and Lomb catalog, as in Table II.

against the ν-value, we find that the original series of glasses (the crowns, light flints, and heavy flints) lie practically on a straight line. The barium crowns, barium flints, and barium heavy flints are on a line parallel to it. The SK glasses and SSK glasses have a still higher index, and very significant further progress has been made by the introduction of the Kodak glasses, which do not contain silica at all. It is obvious from Figure 12.3 that there is a connection between chemical composition and dispersion, a connection which the glass chemists ought to study in detail.

The plot of $1/(n_\beta - n_\alpha) = N$ against ν has been recommended by the author since it permits at a glance estimation of the curvature differences K_1 and K_2 of a monoplet consisting of two lenses and corrected for color. The first two Equations (12.3) can be written

$$\phi_\beta = (n_{1\beta} - 1)K_1 + (n_{2\beta} - 1)K_2$$
$$0 = (n_{1\beta} - n_{1\alpha})K_1 + (n_{2\beta} - n_{2\alpha})K_2$$

or

$$\frac{\nu_1}{N_1}K_1 + \frac{\nu_2}{N_2}K_2 = \phi, \quad \frac{K_1}{N_1} + \frac{K_2}{N_2} = 0,$$

which leads to

$$K_1 = \frac{N_1}{\nu_1 - \nu_2}\phi, \quad K_2 = -\frac{N_2}{\nu_1 - \nu_2}\phi \qquad (12.12)$$

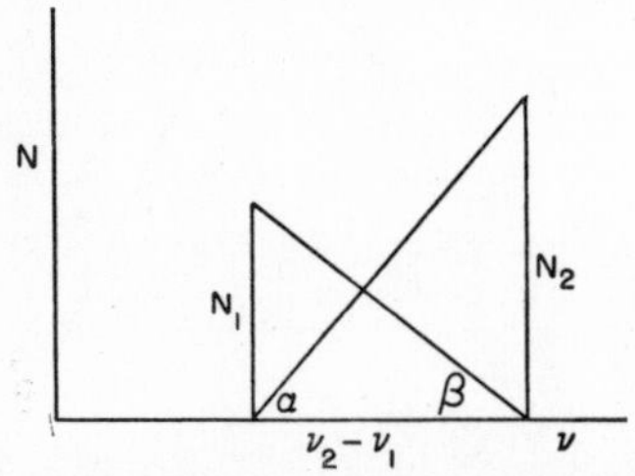

Fig. 12.4. Diagram for finding K_1 and K_2 from Figure 12.3 for a monoplet.

and this enables one to read the values of K_1 and K_2 if the two points in the N, ν diagram are given.

The new glasses introduced by Schott did not, however, vary sizeably in their dispersion from the formula given in (12.9), so that the new glasses with a few exceptions did not give any appreciable contribution to the correction of the secondary spectrum.

About the end of the 1880's, however, a new secret glass named "X" was inserted into microscope lenses designed by Abbe, and thereby the secondary spectrum was to a large degree reduced. In 1890 a paper by Abbe finally revealed the secret. He had used fluorite for optical purposes and by this means achieved what is called *apochromatic* correction, a term he gave to correction for three colors (when certain other corrections are also made).

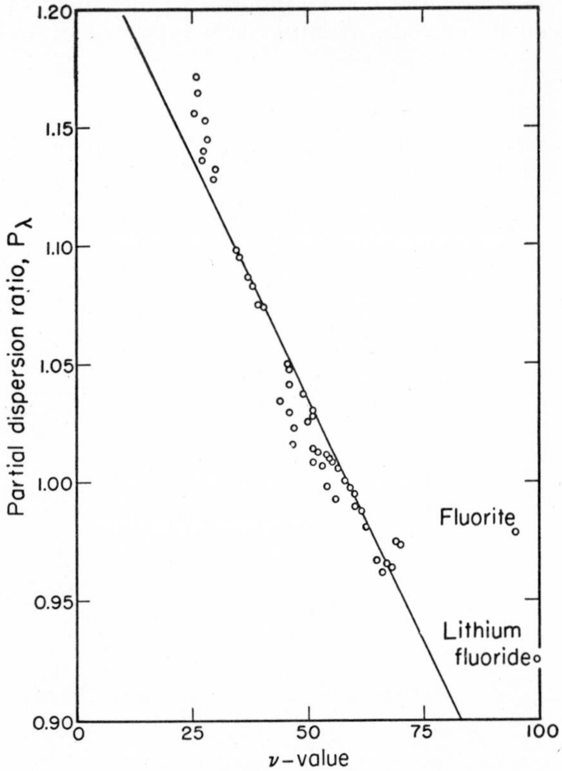

Fig. 12.5. Representative plot of partial dispersion ratio $P_\lambda = (n_\lambda - n_C)/(n_C - n_F)$ for ordinary and extraordinary glasses as a function of ν.

An optically corrected apochromat consisting of two lenses must simultaneously solve Equations (12.5):

$$\begin{aligned} &\phi_1 + \phi_2 = \phi \\ &\phi_1/\nu_1 + \phi_2/\nu_2 = 0 \\ &(\phi_1/\nu_1)P_1 + (\phi_2/\nu_2)P_2 = 0, \end{aligned} \qquad (12.13)$$

which can be fulfilled only if $P_1 = P_2$. This is impossible for ordinary glasses since, as Figure 12.5 shows, the lines in the P, ν diagram are inclined against the axis. But fluorite lies so far off the line that it is easily possible to fulfill (12.13).

The question now arises as to whether the deviations from Formula (12.9) are significant. Many more or less successful attempts have been made to construct glasses that deviate significantly; in fact there are sufficient deviations from Formula (12.9), for instance, for heavy flint, for the Kodak glasses, for the so-called *telescope flints,* and many other important transparent materials, such as sylvite, quartz, rocksalt, etc., to prove that the dispersion of optical glasses is not fully determined by two data.

During the 1930's the author made an extensive study of this manifold and concluded that for optical purposes the manifold of transparent substances can be given by four independent data. As such he proposed using the index of a medium wavelength, a ν-value, and the deviations π_λ* in the red and in the ultraviolet from Formula (12.9). It was found that the deviation from Formula (12.9) for any wavelength is again given by two universal functions $A_3(\lambda)$ and $A_4(\lambda)$ such that

$$\begin{aligned} P_\lambda &= A_1(\lambda)\nu + A_2(\lambda) + \pi_\lambda \\ \pi_\lambda &= A_3(\lambda)\,\pi_{A'} + A_4(\lambda)\pi_h. \end{aligned} \qquad (12.14)$$

The four functions $A_i(\lambda)$ were first found empirically but are consistent with the theoretical idea of a general dispersion formula, which will be discussed in the last part of this chapter.

Applying (12.14) to the general Formulae (12.5) for the

* π is the quantity called ϱ in M. Herzberger and H. Jenkins, "Color Correction in Optical Systems and Types of Glasses," J. Opt. Soc. Amer., *39,* 984 (Dec., 1949).

chromatic correction of a monoplet, we find (omitting some of the subscripts β)

$$\phi_\lambda - \phi_\beta = A_1\phi_\beta + A_2(\phi_\beta - \phi_\alpha) + A_3 \Sigma \frac{\phi_i \pi_{A'i}}{\nu_i} + A_4 \Sigma \frac{\phi_i \pi_{hi}}{\nu_i} \tag{12.15}$$

which leads to a system corrected for α, β, and λ only if

$$0 = A_1\phi_\beta + A_3 \Sigma \frac{\phi_i \pi_{A'i}}{\nu_i} + A_4 \Sigma \frac{\phi_i \pi_{hi}}{\nu_i}, \tag{12.16}$$

that is, $\pi_{A'i}$ and π_{hi} must balance the first member.

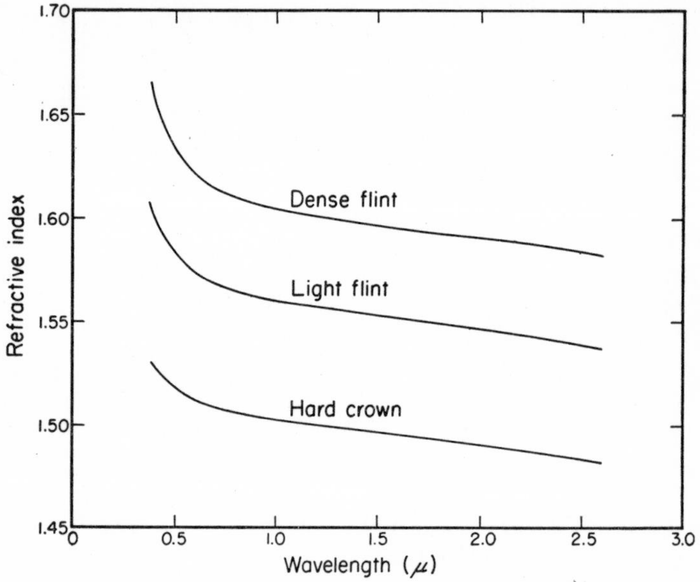

Fig. 12.6. Dispersion curves of certain glass types.

Dispersion Formulae

Figure 12.6 shows the refractive indices of a number of glasses plotted against λ.

It is obvious that each of the dispersion curves has an asymptote for small values of λ, indicating absorption in the ultraviolet region. Each also has another asymptote in the far infrared, but the latter one is so distant that it can be assumed to be at infinity. Theory requires the dispersion curve to be a function of λ^2. This accounts for the attempt by Cauchy to give the dispersion formula in the form

$$n = a + \frac{b}{\lambda^2} + \frac{c}{\lambda^4} + \frac{d}{\lambda^6} + \ldots, \tag{12.17}$$

which approximates the starting members of a *Laurent* series, and the *Neumann-Ketteler* formula, which assumes the form

$$n = a + b\lambda^2 + \ldots + \frac{c}{\lambda^2} + \frac{d}{\lambda^4} + \ldots, \tag{12.18}$$

and which takes account of the distant infrared absorption by introducing in the approximation formula the first members of a Taylor series.

In any case, it is desirable for our optical purposes to have a four-constant formula, preferably linear in these constants, so as to reproduce the refractive indices with the accuracy necessary for optical purposes and such that, for a given glass, the four coefficients can be found from the optical data n_D, ν, $\pi_{A'}$ and π_h of the glass and vice versa.

An examination of the graphs shows that the dispersion curves have different asymptotes, but that all these asymptotes are positive. Thus it is obviously wise to try to replace the asymptote at zero in (12.18) by an asymptote corresponding to an average position of the absorption band, and for this the author has found the optimum value $\lambda = 0.187$ or $\lambda^2 = 0.035$, thus suggesting

$$n = \mu_o + \mu_1\lambda^2 + \frac{\mu_2}{\lambda^2 - .035} + \frac{\mu_3}{(\lambda^2 - .035)^2} \tag{12.19}$$

as a dispersion formula. The reader should be warned that, in spite of its accuracy in the visible spectrum (which will be seen later), the formula is an approximation for a more precise but awkward formula

$$n = \frac{a}{\lambda^2 - \lambda_1^2} + \frac{b}{\lambda^2 - \lambda_2^2}, \tag{12.20}$$

where λ_1 is in the near ultraviolet and λ_2 is in the far infrared and is very large.* Application of the dispersion formula outside the visible spectrum therefore will become inaccurate if we approach the ultraviolet region, whereas its application in the infrared region up to 1μ will still give a satisfactory approximation.

The author has found that, although extrapolation of Formula (12.19) into the ultraviolet region gives inaccurate values of n owing to the rapid change of refractive index in the ultraviolet, the formula still determines the *slope* of the refractive index well enough so that the calculated indices still permit one to compute chromatic errors with sufficient accuracy.

We assume that an optical glass is given by four of its data. Thus, if n is known for four wavelengths, λ_i, substitution in (12.19) (assuming the formula to be correct) will give four linear equations for finding the four coefficients, $\mu_\varkappa$, for that type of glass.

While this method will produce the proper dispersion formula for any type of glass, a much more expedient method having additional theoretical importance has been found. We denote by $n_{A'}$, n_C, n_F, and n_h the indices of the given glass for wavelengths $\lambda_{A'}$, λ_C, λ_F, and λ_h, respectively. It was found empirically that n as a function of λ appeared to satisfy an equation of the form

$$n_\lambda = B_{A'}n_{A'} + B_C n_C + B_F n_F + B_h n_h, \tag{12.21}$$

in which the B_i are functions of λ which are *independent of the type of glass*. With tables of these four functions at hand, Equation (12.21) will then give n at once for any glass for an arbitrary wavelength if the values of $n_{A'}$, n_C, n_F, and n_h are known.

Since we assume that the refractive indices of all materials are given by a formula of the form (12.19), we might try to consider the universal functions B_i as functions of the same type; for instance

$$B_{A'} = \beta_{A'0} + \beta_{A'1}\lambda^2 + \frac{\beta_{A'2}}{\lambda^2 - .035} + \frac{\beta_{A'3}}{(\lambda^2 - .035)^2}. \tag{12.22}$$

* I want to thank R. and H. Kingslake and Ḣ. Brauckhoff for their measured data of refractive indices in the infrared. Without their work this investigation could never have been undertaken.

This formula has four constants, but it is obvious that $B_{A'}$ must fulfill four conditions since Equation (12.21) must produce the values $n_{A'}$ for $\lambda = \lambda_{A'}$, n_C for $\lambda = \lambda_C$, etc., i.e.,we must have $B_{A'} = 1$ for $\lambda = \lambda_{A'}$, and $B_{A'} = 0$ for $\lambda = \lambda_C$, λ_F, and λ_h. This determines the four constants completely and permits us to compute them as the solution of the four linear equations

$$\begin{aligned}
\beta_{A'0} + \beta_{A'1}\lambda_{A'}^2 + \frac{\beta_{A'2}}{\lambda_{A'}^2 - .035} + \frac{\beta_{A'3}}{(\lambda_{A'}^2 - .035)^2} &= 1 \\
\beta_{A'0} + \beta_{A'1}\lambda_C^2 + \frac{\beta_{A'2}}{\lambda_C^2 - .035} + \frac{\beta_{A'3}}{(\lambda_C^2 - .035)^2} &= 0 \\
\beta_{A'0} + \beta_{A'1}\lambda_F^2 + \frac{\beta_{A'2}}{\lambda_F^2 - .035} + \frac{\beta_{A'3}}{(\lambda_F^2 - .035)^2} &= 0 \\
\beta_{A'0} + \beta_{A'1}\lambda_h^2 + \frac{\beta_{A'2}}{\lambda_h^2 - .035} + \frac{\beta_{A'3}}{(\lambda_h^2 - .035)^2} &= 0.
\end{aligned} \tag{12.23}$$

Similarly, we can find the coefficients of B_C, B_F, B_h. That the use of these interpolation functions suffices to approximate the refractive indices of all materials shows that some undiscovered physical law must be responsible.

The actual computing proceeds as follows. Equations (12.23) and their analogous equations provide four systems of equations for finding the coefficients of the B_i. The matrix* of each system is

$$\Lambda = \begin{Vmatrix}
1 & \lambda_{A'}^2 & \dfrac{1}{\lambda_{A'}^2 - .035} & \dfrac{1}{(\lambda_{A'}^2 - .035)^2} \\
1 & \lambda_C^2 & \dfrac{1}{\lambda_C^2 - .035} & \dfrac{1}{(\lambda_C^2 - .035)^2} \\
1 & \lambda_F^2 & \dfrac{1}{\lambda_F^2 - .035} & \dfrac{1}{(\lambda_F^2 - .035)^2} \\
1 & \lambda_h^2 & \dfrac{1}{\lambda_h^2 - .035} & \dfrac{1}{(\lambda_h^2 - .035)^2}
\end{Vmatrix}. \tag{12.24}$$

* Readers unfamiliar with the theory of matrices may solve the four systems of equations indicated by (12.23) and thus find the sixteen quantities β_{ij}. Then the four equations indicated by (12.22) give the functions $B_{A'}$, B_C, B_F, and B_h, after which (12.21) gives the desired formula for $n(\lambda)$. However, a brief discussion of matrices is given in the Appendix.

If we form the matrix

$$B = \begin{bmatrix} \beta_{A'0} & \beta_{C0} & \beta_{F0} & \beta_{h0} \\ \beta_{A'1} & \beta_{C1} & \beta_{F1} & \beta_{h1} \\ \beta_{A'2} & \beta_{C2} & \beta_{F2} & \beta_{h2} \\ \beta_{A'3} & \beta_{C3} & \beta_{F3} & \beta_{h3} \end{bmatrix}, \qquad (12.25)$$

inspection of the product of these matrices in conjunction with (12.23) shows that

$$\Lambda B = E, \qquad (12.26)$$

E being the unit matrix

$$\begin{bmatrix} 1 & 0 & 0 & 0 \\ 0 & 1 & 0 & 0 \\ 0 & 0 & 1 & 0 \\ 0 & 0 & 0 & 1 \end{bmatrix}.$$

From this we have

$$B = \Lambda^{-1}, \qquad (12.27)$$

showing that the problem of finding the coefficients β_{ij} of the quantities B_i is simply that of finding the inverse of the given matrix Λ. Furthermore, the finding of the functions B_i themselves can be expressed in matrix form by the equation

$$\left[1 \;\; \lambda^2 \;\; \frac{1}{\lambda^2 - .035} \;\; \frac{1}{(\lambda^2 - .035)^2} \right] B = (B_{A'} \, B_C \, B_F \, B_h) \qquad (12.28)$$

as we see from Equation (12.22) and the rule for multiplying matrices.

We note further that the coefficients $\mu_\varkappa$ in (12.19) may be obtained by comparison with (12.21), for the right-hand sides of these equations must be identically equal as functions of λ, and we may replace the B_i by their formulae of type (12.22). We have

$$\mu_o + \mu_1\lambda^2 + \frac{\mu_2}{\lambda^2 - .035} + \frac{\mu_3}{(\lambda^2 - .035)^2}$$

$$\begin{aligned} &= n_{A'}\left(\beta_{A'0} + \beta_{A'1}\lambda^2 + \frac{\beta_{A'2}}{\lambda^2 - .035} + \frac{\beta_{A'3}}{(\lambda^2 - .035)^2}\right) \\ &+ n_C\,(\beta_{C0} + \beta_{C1}\lambda^2 + \dots\dots\dots\dots) \\ &+ n_F\,(\beta_{F0} + \beta_{F1}\lambda^2 + \dots\dots\dots\dots) \\ &+ n_h\,(\beta_{h0} + \beta_{h1}\lambda^2 + \dots\dots\dots\dots). \end{aligned} \tag{12.29}$$

We see that equating corresponding coefficients leads to the matrix equation

$$B \begin{bmatrix} n_{A'} \\ n_C \\ n_F \\ n_h \end{bmatrix} = \begin{bmatrix} \mu_0 \\ \mu_1 \\ \mu_2 \\ \mu_3 \end{bmatrix}, \tag{12.30}$$

which determines the coefficients $\mu_\varkappa$.

An important identity holds among the functions B_i, namely, that

$$B_{A'} + B_C + B_F + B_h = 1. \tag{12.31}$$

This can be established by summing Formulae (12.22) and their analogs, taking account of (12.23) and their analogs.

Equation (12.31) is of considerable significance in the fact that, as a result, a number of the formulae of this chapter hold if we replace the refractive indices n_i by $n_i - 1$. This can be true in particular for (12.21) only if (12.31) holds.

The fit of given refractive data with the help of the universal functions B_i can be improved since we have the data given only to five figures and must admit the possibility that the four given values $n_{A'}$, n_C, n_F, and n_h might be slightly inaccurate. If a sizeable number of indices are given, for instance, in the glass catalogs, we can compute from (12.21) improved values of $n_{A'}$, n_C, n_F, and n_h so that Equation (12.21) is fulfilled for the well-determined universal functions $B_{A'}$, B_C, B_F, and B_h. (This is done by least-square calculations.)

TABLE III. Differences in Fifth Decimal Place between Indices of Typical Glasses as Measured and Indices as Calculated by Equation (12.21)

		Ordinary glass											*Extraordinary glass*								
		A′	C	D	d	e	F	g	G′	h			A′	C	D	d	e	F	g	G′	h
BK	1	0	−1	0	0	0	+1	0	0	+1	FK	4	0	−1	+1	0	0	0	0	0	0
	3	0	−1	0	+1	0	0	0	0	0											
	10	0	0	0	0	0	+1	+1	−1	0	SF	1	+1	−2	0	0	+2	+1	−1	−1	−1
K	3	0	−1	0	+1	0	0	0	0	0		3	+1	−3	+1	+2	0	0	−2	−1	+1
	5	0	−1	0	+1	−1	0	0	0	0		4	+1	−2	0	+1	+1	+1	−1	0	+1
	11	0	0	−1	+1	+1	0	−1	−1	0		6	+1	−3	0	+2	+1	+1	−2	−1	+1
												10	+1	−2	0	+1	0	+2	−3	−1	+1
KF	1	0	−1	−1	0	+1	+1	−1	−1	0		11	+1	−2	0	0	+2	+2	−4	−1	+1
	3	0	−1	0	+1	0	0	0	0	0		13	+1	−2	0	0	+1	+1	−3	0	+1
	5	−2	0	0	0	0	0	0	0	0		14	+1	−2	−1	−1	+3	+1	−2	−1	+1
ZK	1	0	−1	0	0	0	0	0	0	0		15	+1	−1	0	0	+1	+2	−1	−1	+1
	5	0	−1	−1	+1	0	0	−1	0	0											
											KzF	1	0	0	−1	+1	+1	+1	−1	0	+1
LLF	6	0	0	0	0	0	0	0	0	0		2	0	−1	0	0	0	0	0	+1	0
	7	−1	0	0	0	+1	0	−1	0	0		3	0	0	0	0	0	+1	0	−1	0
F	3	0	−1	+1	0	−1	0	−1	0	0		5	0	0	0	0	0	+1	0	+1	+1
	6	+1	−2	+1	0	0	0	0	−1	+1		6	0	0	−1	0	+1	0	0	0	0
	8	0	−1	0	+1	0	0	0	0	0	PKS	1	0	−1	0	0	+1	0	0	0	0
											PSKS	1	0	0	0	0	0	0	0	0	0
BaK	2	0	−1	0	0	0	0	0	0	0											
	6	0	−1	0	−1	0	+1	0	−1	0	KzFS	1	0	−1	0	0	0	+1	0	+1	+2
BaLK	3	0	−1	0	0	0	0	−1	+1	−1		2	0	−1	0	0	+1	+1	−1	0	+1
BaLF	7	0	−1	+1	0	−1	0	0	0	0		3	0	−1	+1	0	−1	0	0	0	0
	8	+3	0	0	0	0	0	−1	+1	0											
											Quartz		+1	−2	0	−1	+2	0	+2	−3	+1
BaF	2	0	0	0	0	+1	0	−1	0	0											
	7	0	−1	0	0	+1	0	0	−1	0	LiF		0	0	0	0	0	0	−1	0	0
SK	8	0	−1	0	+1	0	0	0	0	0											
	11	0	0	0	0	+1	0	0	0	0	Fluorite		0	0	0	0	0	−1	−1	−2	0
	14	0	0	0	0	+1	+1	−1	0	0											
	16	0	0	−1	0	+1	0	−1	0	0											
	18	0	0	−1	+1	0	+1	−1	0	0											
SSK	1	0	−1	0	+1	0	−1	0	0	0	EK	110	0	0	0			+1	0	−1	0
	7	0	+1	0	0	+1	0	0	−1	0		210	0	0	0			+1	0	0	0
BaF	10	0	0	−1	0	+1	+1	−1	0	0		310	0	0	0			0	0	0	0
BaSF	3	0	0	0	0	0	0	0	0	0		320	0	0	0			+1	[illegible]	0	0

As Table III shows, the fit of the dispersion curves for glasses and other transparent substances becomes practically perfect throughout the visible spectrum.

It remains to combine the results in the first part of the chapter with the new dispersion formulae.

It should first be remarked that we obtain equally satisfactory results if we use data for four other wavelengths. This means only a linear transformation. Since

$$\begin{aligned} n_{\lambda 1} &= B_{A'\lambda 1}n_{A'} + B_{C\lambda 1}n_C + B_{F\lambda 1}n_F + B_{h\lambda 1}n_h \\ n_{\lambda 2} &= B_{A'\lambda 2}n_{A'} + B_{C\lambda 2}n_C + B_{F\lambda 2}n_F + B_{h\lambda 2}n_h \\ n_{\lambda 3} &= B_{A'\lambda 4}n_{A'} + B_{C\lambda 3}n_C + B_{F\lambda 3}n_F + B_{h\lambda 3}n_h \\ n_{\lambda 4} &= B_{A'\lambda 3}n_{A'} + B_{C\lambda 4}n_C + B_{F\lambda 4}n_F + B_{h\lambda 4}n_h, \end{aligned} \qquad (12.32)$$

we simply have to solve Equations (12.32) to find the $n_{A'}$, n_C, n_F, n_h as linear functions of the n_{λ_i}. Inserting these values into (12.21) gives the desired new interpolation formula.

It is somewhat difficult to find the functions described in the beginning of this chapter, especially if we make a concession to the glass catalog maker and consider as the ν-value of a glass a figure given by

$$\nu_D = (n_D - 1)/(n_F - n_C) \qquad (12.33)$$

and as the partial dispersion

$$P_\lambda = (n_\lambda - n_F)(n_F - n_C), \qquad (12.34)$$

the ν-value being slightly different from the one given by the present theory [*cf.* (12.4)]. However, it can be shown that the laws given by (12.9) and (12.14) hold for these values, too. For *most* glasses we have

$$P_\lambda = (n_\lambda - n_F)/(n_F - n_C) = A_1\nu + A_2, \qquad (12.35)$$

and for *all* glasses we have from (12.14)

$$P_\lambda = A_1\nu + A_2 + A_3\,\pi_{A'} + A_4\,\pi_h, \qquad (12.36)$$

where A_1, A_2, A_3, A_4 are universal functions and ν and P_λ are given by (12.33) and (12.34), respectively. Again, A_3 and A_4 can be taken as well-defined functions of λ.

If $\lambda = \lambda_{A'}$, by the definition of $\pi_{A'}$ we wish (12.36) to reduce to

$$P_{A'} = A_{1A'}\,\nu + A_{2A'} + \pi_{A'},$$

where $A_1(\lambda_{A'})$ is denoted by $A_{1A'}$, etc. This condition will be fulfilled if we choose

$$A_{3A'} = 1, \quad A_{4A'} = 0.$$

Similarly, we require that $A_{3h} = 0$, $A_{4h} = 1$. Now $P_F = 0$, as Equation (12.34) shows; hence in (12.36) we choose $A_{1F} = A_{2F} = A_{3F} = A_{4F} = 0$. Equation (12.36) may be written

$$n_\lambda - n_F = A_1(n_D - 1) + (A_2 + A_3\pi_{A'} + A_4\pi_h)\,(n_F - n_C), \tag{12.37}$$

and, setting $\lambda = \lambda_C$, we have

$$n_C - n_F = A_{1C}(n_D - 1) + (A_{2C} + A_{3C}\pi_{A'} + A_{4C}\pi_h)\,(n_F - n_C). \tag{12.38}$$

This will be fulfilled if we choose

$$A_{1C} = 0, \quad A_{2C} = -1, \quad A_{3C} = A_{4C} = 0. \tag{12.39}$$

We now have enough conditions to determine A_3 and A_4, assuming they are functions of the type (12.19).

However, the quantities A_1 and A_2 have to be computed empirically. Plotting, for a number of ordinary glasses and a given λ, the partials against the ν-values, we obtain values for $A_1(\lambda)$ and $A_2(\lambda)$. These values can be approximated with the help of a function of type (12.19):

$$A_1 = a_{10} + a_{11}\lambda^2 + \frac{a_{12}}{\lambda^2 - .035} + \frac{a_{13}}{(\lambda^2 - .035)^2}$$

$$A_2 = a_{20} + a_{21}\lambda^2 + \frac{a_{22}}{\lambda^2 - .035} + \frac{a_{23}}{(\lambda^2 - .035)^2}. \tag{12.40}$$

Table IV gives the functions A_i and B_i and Table V their values for the optically most important wavelengths throughout the spectrum.

Numerous advances in procuring optical materials have been made during the last decades. *Tillyer* of the American Optical Co. has published papers on the influence of phosphorus in optical glass. Many new optical materials have appeared during the past

TABLE IV

Formulae for Computing Universal Functions A_i and B_i

$$A_1 = +\ 0.002459 - 0.007841\lambda^2 + 0.000867/(\lambda^2-0.035) - 0.000199/(\lambda^2-0.035)^2$$

$$A_2 = -\ 2.052895 + 0.124839\lambda^2 + 0.382922/(\lambda^2-0.035) + 0.004920/(\lambda^2-0.035)^2$$

$$A_3 = B_{\mathrm{A}}' = -\ 9.748519 + 12.813951\lambda^2 + 2.005768/(\lambda^2-0.035) - 0.131427/(\lambda^2-0.035)^2$$

$$A_4 = B_{\mathrm{h}} = +\ 2.381957 - 2.006448\lambda^2 - 0.824828/(\lambda^2-0.035) + 0.088733/(\lambda^2-0.035)^2$$

$$B_{\mathrm{C}} = +\ 17.417526 - 18.928074\lambda^2 - 3.958817/(\lambda^2-0.035) + 0.272352/(\lambda^2-0.035)^2$$

$$B_{\mathrm{H}} = -\ 9.050963 + 8.120572\lambda^2 + 2.777877/(\lambda^2-0.035) - 0.229657/(\lambda^2-0.035)^2$$

TABLE V

Values of Universal Functions A_i and B_i for Certain Wavelengths

Wavelength	$A_1 + 1$	A_2	$A_3 = B_{A'}$	$A_4 = B_h$	B_C	B_F
h	+0.995901	+1.238601	0.0	+1.0	0.0	0.0
G′	+0.998173	+0.675998	+0.155895	+0.397817	−0.381788	+0.828076
g	+0.998274	+0.646975	+0.156141	+0.373359	−0.383371	+0.853718
0.45	+0.998951	+0.433848	+0.136624	+0.213978	−0.342799	+0.992197
F	+1.0	0.0	0.0	0.0	0.0	+1.0
0.5	+1.000223	−0.134217	−0.059083	−0.036481	+0.164271	+0.931293
e	+1.000539	−0.489750	−0.203894	−0.069320	+0.663536	+0.609678
0.55	+1.000544	−0.514890	−0.210798	−0.068421	+0.698585	+0.580634
d	+1.000476	−0.724356	−0.224918	−0.047524	+0.951915	+0.320527
D	+1.000469	−0.732829	−0.223231	−0.046255	+0.959810	+0.309676
0.6	+1.000417	−0.783152	−0.208184	−0.038224	+1.000920	+0.245488
0.65	+1.000055	−0.979199	−0.033719	−0.003420	+1.017900	+0.019239
C	+1.0	−1.0	0.0	0.0	+1.0	0.0
0.7	+0.999558	−1.126372	+0.303761	+0.014597	+0.757622	−0.075979
b	+0.999482	−1.142781	+0.359006	+0.015243	+0.704479	−0.078728
0.75	+0.998974	−1.239073	+0.789408	+0.008563	+0.244397	−0.042368
A 0.766491	+0.998770	−1.270373	+0.979546	+0.000948	+0.024134	−0.004622
A′0.768195	+0.998745	−1.273463	+1.0	0.0	0.0	0.0
A 0.769898	+0.998723	−1.276525	+1.020592	−1.000976	−0.024370	+0.004753
0.8	+0.998327	−1.326627	+1.408662	−0.023100	−0.495862	+0.110300

few decades — for example, Kodak glasses, the artifical fluorite and lithium glasses, and the innumerable plastics proposed for optical systems. Most of the data available on these new materials have not been published with sufficient accuracy; nevertheless, the suggested optical formula gives refractive indices throughout the visible spectrum with an accuracy of about one in the fifth place, if we have four or more indices measured with that accuracy.

Fraunhofer designated the lines in the solar spectrum by Latin letters, starting with A in the red end, up to h near the violet end. Some of these lines have been discovered to be double lines; others have been added since Fraunhofer because they are lines in the spectrum of light sources, such as the mercury arc, that are readily available nowadays. Table I gives the most important spectral lines, the corresponding colors, and the chemical elements that produce them.

Luminosity, Sensitivity, and Chromatic Aberration

We have discussed above the fact that, disregarding the use of a few very unusual optical materials, it is impossible to bring more than two wavelengths to a common focus; this means that there exists a residual chromatic aberration known as secondary spectrum. Chromatic correction is often accomplished by bringing the C and F foci together.

However, the C-to-F type of correction is not the only useful correction; another type may be required, depending on the particular use for which the optical system is designed.

Since the science of photography dates only from the latter half of the nineteenth century, and the use of photoelectric phenomena is even more recent, the only concern of the designers of the early optical instruments was the effect of the image on the eye. The sensitivity of the eye is not constant for all parts of the visual spectrum but varies with wavelength in the manner shown in Figure 12.7. The sensitivities shown are relative, with the maximum point arbitrarily set at unity. This curve is known as the *luminosity curve.*

It can be seen from this curve that the wavelengths C and F include between them all the colors to which the eye is most sen-

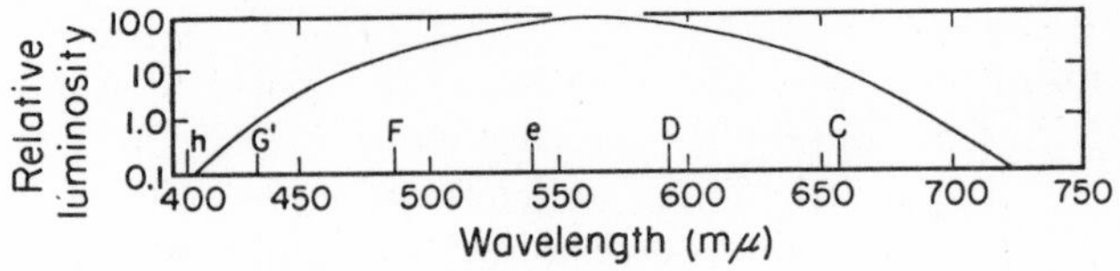

Fig. 12.7. Luminosity curve of the human eye (logarithmic scale).

sitive, and that the wavelengths outside have comparatively little effect. For this reason, the C-to-F type of chromatic correction is the best for optical instruments designed purely for visual use. That is why, in all the early optical instruments, chromatic correction was understood to be C-to-F correction.

With the development of the science of photography, cameras came into widespread use. The first photographers soon found that, after they focused a picture on the ground glass by eye, they had to introduce a slight shift of the lens away from the plate to obtain a sharp negative. This, of course, was because the first photographic emulsions were sensitive only to wavelengths below 500 mμ, the blue, violet, and near ultraviolet, often known as *actinic light*. Figure 12.8 shows the sensitivity curve for such a blue-sensitive emulsion.

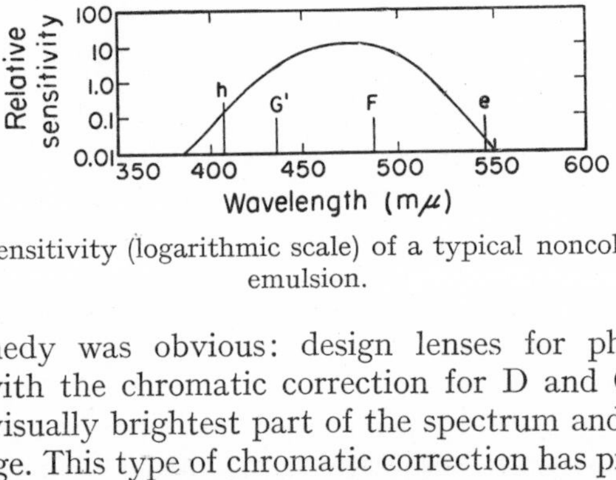

Fig. 12.8. Sensitivity (logarithmic scale) of a typical noncolor-sensitized emulsion.

The remedy was obvious: design lenses for photographic purposes with the chromatic correction for D and G′, that is, D for the visually brightest part of the spectrum and G′ for the actinic range. This type of chromatic correction has proved quite satisfactory for the original emulsions, and even for modern panchromatic films. A sensitivity curve for a representative panchromatic emulsion is shown in Figure 12.9, and it is apparent that the actinic light is still highly important.

However, the modification of the sensitivity of a film by adding

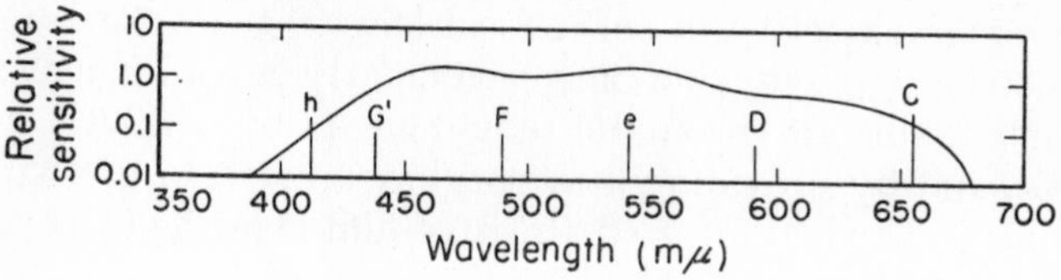

Fig. 12.9. Sensitivity (logarithmic scale) of representative panchromatic emulsion.

a filter might change the entire picture. The curve in Figure 12.10 shows how the addition of a deep yellow filter eliminates all wavelengths below 510 mμ, making unnecessary any consideration of G′ or F. It should be kept in mind that a photographic objective intended exclusively for use with filters will undoubtedly require a chromatic correction entirely different from the usual D-to-G′ type. For the filter illustrated in Figure 12.10, for instance, the chromatic correction should be for C and e.

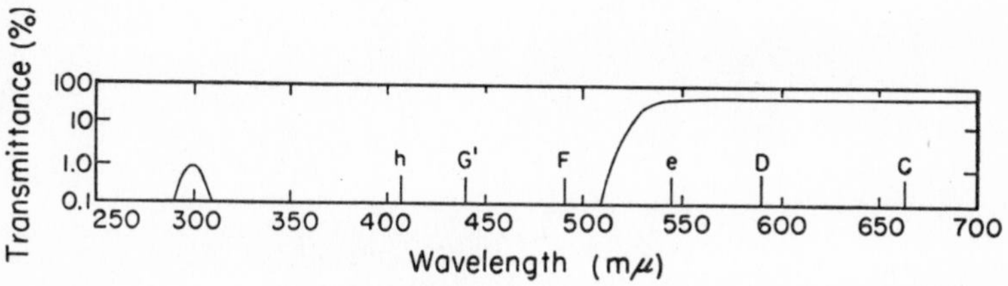

Fig. 12.10. Transmittance (logarithmic scale) of Kodak Wratten Filter No. 15 (G) as a function of wavelength.

In most cases, though, the lens will be used without a filter, or with any of several different kinds. To obtain better results, *W. Schade* suggested the use of compensating filters. The filter is cemented between glasses; not the usual plane-parallel plates, but very weak lenses of different ν-values calculated carefully to leave the focal length of the objective unchanged while changing the chromatic correction to secure the best conditions for the wavelengths which the filter transmits, at the expense of the wavelengths which the filter absorbs.

The use of such compensating filters is confined to lenses of long focal length, where the best definition must be attained; in the average objective of short focal length, their use is neither commercially practicable nor particularly advantageous. The designer fulfills all chromatic requirements by correcting for D and G′, and by providing a second index mark to use with the focusing scale when infrared-sensitive film is in the camera.

CHAPTER THIRTEEN

Color Correction in Optical Systems

In Chapter 11 we investigated the change of optical data if one of the two elements of the optical system varies. In Chapter 12 we derived the formulae showing the dependence of refractive index on wavelength. Combining this knowledge, we shall be able to investigate the problem of color correction in optical systems.

Formulae (11.2) through (11.4) introduced the abbreviations

$$M = 1/m = [\gamma_\varkappa\ \beta_{\varkappa-1}\quad \gamma_1, (-s/n)]$$
$$Z' = (s'^*/n')\,(1/m) = -[\beta_{\varkappa-1}\quad \gamma_1, (-s/n)]. \qquad (13.1)$$

Here $s(s')$ is the object (image) distance from the first (last) vertex, $s'^* = \pm s'$, and m is the magnification. We also have

$$\gamma_\nu = (n_{\nu-1} - n_\nu)\varrho_\nu$$
$$\beta_\nu = d_\nu/n_\nu, \qquad (13.2)$$

ϱ_ν being the curvature of the νth surface, d_ν the distance between the νth and $(\nu+1)$st vertices, and $n_{\nu-1}$, n_ν the indices of refraction before and after the νth surface.

Developing (13.1) with respect to s/n we obtain

$$M = \delta - \gamma s/n, \quad Z' = a s/n - \beta, \qquad (13.3)$$

where a, β, γ, δ are given, using (10.19), as

$$a = [\beta_{\varkappa-1}\ \gamma_1] \quad \beta = [\beta_{\varkappa-1}\ \beta_1]$$
$$\gamma = [\gamma_\varkappa\quad \gamma_1] \quad \delta = [\gamma_\varkappa\quad \beta_1]\,. \qquad (13.4)$$

Differentiation with respect to wavelength gives, for a fixed object point,

* As before, the asterisk (*) indicates that s' must be replaced by $-s'$ if the system has an odd number of reflections.

$$dM/d\lambda = d\delta/d\lambda - (s/n)\,(d\gamma/d\lambda)$$
$$dZ'/d\lambda = (s/n)\,(d\alpha/d\lambda) - (d\beta/d\lambda)\,. \qquad (13.5)$$

We shall first investigate the general problem of color correction and then consider the specific problem of how to achromatize a system for certain colors.

An object point is imaged free from color aberration in the realm of Gaussian optics if $dm/d\lambda = ds'^*/d\lambda = 0$, that is, if

$$dm/d\lambda = -(1/M^2)\,(dM/d\lambda) = 0$$
$$(1/n')\,(ds'^*/d\lambda) = (Z'dM/d\lambda - MdZ'/d\lambda)/M^2 = 0. \qquad (13.6)$$

This is fulfilled for *all* object points if and only if

$$\frac{d\alpha}{d\lambda} = \frac{d\beta}{d\lambda} = \frac{d\gamma}{d\lambda} = \frac{d\delta}{d\lambda} = 0. \qquad (13.7)$$

Such a system is called a *stable achromatic system*. If

$$\frac{d\alpha}{d\lambda}\,\frac{d\delta}{d\lambda} = \frac{d\beta}{d\lambda}\,\frac{d\gamma}{d\lambda}, \qquad (13.8)$$

we can find one and only one object point for which the system is free from chromatic error. Its distances from the first surface and the distance s' of the corresponding image point from the last surface are given by

$$\frac{s}{n} = \frac{d\beta/d\lambda}{d\alpha/d\lambda} = \frac{d\delta/d\lambda}{d\gamma/d\lambda}$$

$$\frac{s'^*}{n'} = -\,\frac{d\beta/d\lambda}{d\delta/d\lambda} = -\,\frac{d\beta/d\lambda}{d\gamma/d\lambda}\,. \qquad (13.9)$$

The last equation in (13.9) originates from the first, if one considers that reversal of object and image means the transformations $\alpha\to\delta$, $\delta\to\alpha$, $\beta\to-\beta$, $\gamma\to-\gamma$, as one sees immediately in solving (9.4) for $\vec{A}$ and $\vec{S}$.

The dependence of $\alpha, \beta, \gamma, \delta$ on λ can be computed from (13.4) since (13.2) gives the γ_ν and β_ν as functions of the n_ν. We find

$$\frac{d\gamma_\nu}{d\lambda} = \varrho_\nu \left(\frac{dn_{\nu-1}}{d\lambda} - \frac{dn_\nu}{d\lambda}\right) = \gamma_\nu \left(\frac{\dfrac{dn_{\nu-1}}{d\lambda} - \dfrac{dn_\nu}{d\lambda}}{n_{\nu-1} - n_\nu}\right)$$

$$\frac{d\beta_\nu}{d\lambda} = -\frac{d_\nu}{n_\nu^2}\frac{dn_\nu}{d\lambda}. \tag{13.10}$$

We shall now investigate the case in which the system consists of a series of thin lenses in air with finite distances. In this case, we can write

$$M = \delta - \gamma s, \quad Z' = \alpha s - \beta, \tag{13.11}$$

where [as in (10.19), (10.20), (10.21)]

$$\begin{aligned} \alpha &= [\beta_{\varkappa-1}\ \gamma_1] & \beta &= [\beta_{\varkappa-1}\ \beta_1] \\ \gamma &= [\gamma_\varkappa\ \ \gamma_1] & \delta &= [\gamma_\varkappa\ \ \beta_1]. \end{aligned} \tag{13.12}$$

Here, however, the quantities $(-\gamma_\nu)$ are the powers of the single lenses, or

$$\begin{aligned} \gamma_\nu &= (n_\nu - 1)\,(\varrho_\nu'' - \varrho_\nu') = -\phi_\nu \\ \beta_\nu &= e_\nu. \end{aligned} \tag{13.13}$$

In these equations, n_ν is the refractive index of the νth lens, ϱ_ν', ϱ_ν'' the first and last curvatures of the νth lens, and e_ν the distance in air from the νth to the $(\nu + 1)$st thin lens.

The Thin Lens

For a single thin lens in air, we have from (10.8)

$$\begin{aligned} \alpha &= 1 & \beta &= 0 \\ \gamma &= -\phi_1 & \delta &= 1 \end{aligned} \tag{13.14}$$

and

$$\frac{d\alpha}{d\lambda} = \frac{d\beta}{d\lambda} = \frac{d\delta}{d\lambda} = 0. \tag{13.15}$$

Equation (13.9) shows that, in any thin lens, the vertex, $s = 0$, is imaged free from color upon itself ($s' = 0$). The thin lens is achromatically stable if and only if $d\gamma/d\lambda = 0$.

The Monoplet

For a system of thin lenses without distances, we have [*cf.* (10.19)]

$$\alpha = 1 = \delta, \quad \beta = 0, \quad \gamma = -\sum_{1}^{\varkappa} \phi_\nu \tag{13.16}$$

and

$$\frac{d\alpha}{d\lambda} = \frac{d\beta}{d\lambda} = \frac{d\delta}{d\lambda} = 0, \quad \frac{d\gamma}{d\lambda} = -\sum_{1}^{\varkappa} \frac{\phi_\nu}{n_{\nu-1}} \frac{dn_\nu}{d\lambda}. \tag{13.17}$$

A monoplet can be made achromatically stable if the last power is chosen such that

$$\phi_\varkappa = -\frac{n_\varkappa - 1}{dn_\varkappa/d\lambda} \sum_{1}^{\varkappa-1} \frac{\phi_\nu}{n_\nu - 1} \frac{dn_\nu}{d\lambda}. \tag{13.18}$$

The Duplet

For two lenses with one finite distance, we have from (13.12)

$$\begin{aligned} \alpha &= [\beta_1\gamma_1] & \beta &= [\beta_1] \\ \gamma &= [\gamma_2\beta_1\gamma_1] & \delta &= [\gamma_2\beta_1]. \end{aligned} \tag{13.19}$$

Inserting (13.13) we obtain

$$\begin{aligned} \alpha &= 1 + \beta_1\gamma_1 = 1 - e_1\,\phi_1 \\ \beta &= \beta_1 = e_1 \\ \phi &= -\gamma = -(\gamma_1\gamma_2\,\beta_1 + \gamma_1 + \gamma_2) = \phi_1 + \phi_2 - e_1\phi_1\phi_2 \\ \delta &= 1 + \beta_1\gamma_2 = 1 - e_1\,\phi_2 \end{aligned} \tag{13.20}$$

and

$$\begin{aligned} \frac{d\alpha}{d\lambda} &= -e_1\frac{d\phi_1}{d\lambda} \qquad\qquad \frac{d\beta}{d\lambda} = 0 \\ -\frac{d\gamma}{d\lambda} &= \frac{d\phi_1}{d\lambda}(1 - e_1\phi_2) + \frac{d\phi_2}{d\lambda}(1 - e_1\,\phi_1) \\ \frac{d\delta}{d\lambda} &= -e_1\frac{d\phi_2}{d\lambda}. \end{aligned} \tag{13.21}$$

The system is achromatic if and only if

$$\frac{d\alpha}{d\lambda}\frac{d\delta}{d\lambda} - \frac{d\beta}{d\lambda}\frac{d\gamma}{d\lambda} = 0 = e_1{}^2 \frac{d\phi_1}{d\lambda}\frac{d\phi_2}{d\lambda}\,; \tag{13.22}$$

that is, (13.9) and (13.21) lead to the cases:

$$\begin{aligned} &(a)\ e_1 = 0,\ s = 0 = s' \\ &(b)\ d\phi_1/d\lambda = 0,\ s = e_1/(1 - e_1\phi_1), \\ &(c)\ d\phi_2/d\lambda = 0,\ s = 0,\ s' = e_1/(e_1\phi_1 - 1). \end{aligned} \tag{13.23}$$

Thus, for finite e_1, a duplet can be achromatic only if one of the monoplets is achromatic. It is achromatically stable only if both monoplets are achromatically stable:

$$\frac{d\phi_1}{d\lambda} = \frac{d\phi_2}{d\lambda} = 0, \tag{13.24}$$

as (13.21) shows.

The Triplet

For three thin lenses with two finite distances, we have

$$\begin{aligned} \alpha &= [\beta_2\gamma_2\beta_1\gamma_1] & \beta &= [\beta_2\gamma_2\beta_1] \\ \gamma &= [\gamma_3\beta_2\gamma_2\beta_1\gamma_1] & \delta &= [\gamma_3\beta_2\gamma_2\beta_1] \end{aligned} \tag{13.25}$$

or

$$\frac{d\alpha}{d\lambda} = \beta_2[\beta_1\gamma_1]\frac{d\gamma_2}{d\lambda} + [\beta_2\gamma_2\beta_1]\frac{d\gamma_1}{d\lambda}$$

$$\frac{d\beta}{d\lambda} = \beta_1\beta_2\frac{d\gamma_2}{d\lambda}$$

$$\frac{d\gamma}{d\lambda} = [\beta_2\gamma_2\beta_1\gamma_1]\frac{d\gamma_3}{d\lambda} + [\gamma_3\beta_2][\beta_1\gamma_1]\frac{d\gamma_2}{d\lambda} + [\gamma_3\beta_2\gamma_2\beta_1]\frac{d\gamma_1}{d\lambda}$$

$$\frac{d\delta}{d\lambda} = [\beta_2\gamma_2\beta_1]\frac{d\gamma_3}{d\lambda} + [\gamma_3\beta_2]\,\beta_1\frac{d\gamma_2}{d\lambda}\,.$$

The triplet is the simplest type of optical system which can be corrected for color for a finite object point without the single lenses being color-corrected.

We find as a necessary and sufficient condition, after a simple computation, that

$$\frac{d\alpha}{d\lambda}\frac{d\delta}{d\lambda} - \frac{d\beta}{d\lambda}\frac{d\gamma}{d\lambda} = 0,$$

which gives

$$\frac{d\gamma_1}{d\lambda}\frac{d\gamma_2}{d\lambda}\beta_1{}^2 + \frac{d\gamma_1}{d\lambda}\frac{d\gamma_3}{d\lambda}[\beta_1\gamma_2\beta_2]^2 + \frac{d\gamma_2}{d\lambda}\frac{d\gamma_3}{d\lambda}\beta_2{}^2 = 0. \quad (13.27)$$

If Equation (13.27) is satisfied, the object and image distances of a color-corrected object are found from (13.9), the result being

$$\frac{n}{s} = \frac{1}{\beta_1}[\beta_1\gamma_1] + \frac{1}{\beta_1\beta_2}[\beta_2\gamma_2\beta_1]\frac{d\gamma_1/d\lambda}{d\gamma_2/d\lambda}$$

$$-\frac{n'}{s'} = \frac{1}{\beta_2}[\gamma_3\beta_2] + \frac{1}{\beta_1\beta_2}[\beta_2\gamma_2\beta_1]\frac{d\gamma_3/d\lambda}{d\gamma_2/d\lambda}. \quad (13.28)$$

Equations (13.27) and (13.28) serve to determine the necessary relations between the system data in order to make a color-corrected triplet.

Equation (13.27) can be generalized for more than three thin lenses with finite distances. We find for $\varkappa$ lenses,

$$\frac{d\alpha}{d\lambda} = \sum_{\nu=1}^{\varkappa-1} [\beta_{\varkappa-1}\ \beta_\nu]\ [\beta_{\nu-1}\ \gamma_1]\frac{d\gamma_\nu}{d\lambda}$$

$$\frac{d\beta}{d\lambda} = \sum_{\nu=2}^{\varkappa-1} [\beta_{\varkappa-1}\ \beta_\nu]\ [\beta_{\nu-1}\ \beta_1]\frac{d\gamma_\nu}{d\lambda}$$

$$\frac{d\gamma}{d\lambda} = \sum_{\nu=1}^{\varkappa} [\gamma_\varkappa\beta_{\varkappa-1}\ \beta_\nu]\ [\beta_{\nu-1}\ \gamma_1]\frac{d\gamma_\nu}{d\lambda}$$

$$\frac{d\delta}{d\lambda} = \sum_{\nu=2}^{\varkappa} [\gamma_\varkappa\beta_{\varkappa-1}\ \beta_\nu]\ [\beta_{\nu-1}\ \beta_1]\frac{d\gamma_\nu}{d\lambda}. \quad (13.29)$$

The condition for achromatism is found to be

$$\frac{d\alpha}{d\lambda}\frac{d\delta}{d\lambda} - \frac{d\beta}{d\lambda}\frac{d\gamma}{d\lambda} = 0 = \sum_{\varrho<\nu} [\beta_{\nu-1}, \gamma_\nu\ \ldots\ \beta_\varrho]^2\frac{d\gamma_\nu}{d\lambda}\frac{d\gamma_\varrho}{d\lambda}. \quad (13.30)$$

Since all the coefficients in (13.30) are squares, it can be concluded that a system with finite distances corrected for color cannot have all positive values for the quantities $d\gamma_\nu/d\lambda$.

The Thick Lens in Air

We have for a thick lens in air, from (10.25),

$$\alpha = [\beta_1\gamma_1] \qquad \beta = [\beta_1]$$
$$\gamma = [\gamma_2\beta_1\gamma_1] \qquad \delta = [\gamma_2\beta_1]\,, \tag{13.31}$$

where

$$\beta_1 = d_1/n_1, \quad \gamma_1 = (1 - n_1)\varrho_1, \quad \gamma_2 = (n_1 - 1)\varrho_2,$$

which leads to

$$\frac{d\alpha}{d\lambda} = \beta_1\frac{d\gamma_1}{d\lambda} + \gamma_1\frac{d\beta_1}{d\lambda} = -\frac{d_1\varrho_1}{n_1^2}\frac{dn_1}{d\lambda}$$

$$\frac{d\beta}{d\lambda} = \frac{d\beta_1}{d\lambda} = -\frac{d_1}{n_1^2}\frac{dn_1}{d\lambda}$$

$$\frac{d\gamma}{d\lambda} = (\varrho_2 - \varrho_1 + \frac{1 - n_1^2}{n_1^2}\varrho_1\varrho_2 d_1)\frac{dn_1}{d\lambda}$$

$$\frac{d\delta}{d\lambda} = \frac{d_1\varrho_2}{n_1^2}\frac{dn_1}{d\lambda}\,. \tag{13.32}$$

The condition (13.8) for color correction in this case is that

$$d_1 = r_1 - r_2, \tag{13.33}$$

that is, the lens must be concentric. We find, in this case,

$$s = r_1, \; s' = r_2\,, \tag{13.34}$$

showing that the common center is imaged free of color. We draw to the attention of the reader that the suggestion of Bouwers and Maksutov for a color-free thick lens, namely,

$$r_1 - r_2 = \frac{n_1^2 - 1}{n_1^2}d_1, \tag{13.35}$$

gives an optical system in which only the *focal length* is corrected for color:

$$d\phi/d\lambda = 0. \tag{13.36}$$

Until now, we have spoken of color correction in an abstract way. Owing to the fact that the power of a *thin* lens is a linear function of the refractive index, we treated thin lenses with finite distances by replacing the differential quotient by a difference quotient. We warn out readers that this is only *approximately* correct for lenses with finite thicknesses.

A lens corrected for visible light is usually corrected for C and F [C lies in the red part of the spectrum, having a wavelength of 6563 A, whereas F lies in the blue part of the spectrum ($\lambda = 4861$ A); the D wavelength lies between these in the yellow part of the spectrum ($\lambda = 5893$ A)].

Because of the linear form of ϕ for a thin lens,

$$\phi = (n - 1)(\varrho' - \varrho''), \tag{13.37}$$

we can replace the differential quotient as follows:

$$\frac{1}{\phi}\,d\phi \sim \frac{\phi_F - \phi_C}{\phi_D} = \frac{n_F - n_C}{n_D - 1} = \frac{1}{\nu} \tag{13.38}$$

where ν is the Abbe ν-value for dispersion found in the glass catalogs. If we interpret $d\phi/d\lambda$ this way, $d\phi/d\lambda = 0$ means that the power of the system is corrected for C and F.

Applying this to a monoplet, we find

$$\Phi_F - \Phi_C = \sum_1^{\varkappa} \phi_i/\nu_i, \quad \Phi_D = \sum_1^{\varkappa} \phi_i, \tag{13.39}$$

where ν_i is the index of the ith surface. We see, in particular, that a monoplet of two or more lenses can be corrected for C and F by solving

$$\begin{aligned} \phi_1/\nu_1 + \phi_2/\nu_2 &= 0 \\ \phi_1 + \phi_2 &= \Phi_D, \end{aligned} \tag{13.40}$$

which leads to

$$\phi_1 = \frac{\nu_1}{\nu_1 - \nu_2}\,\Phi_D$$

$$\phi_2 = -\frac{\nu_2}{\nu_1 - \nu_2}\Phi_{\mathrm{D}}. \tag{13.41}$$

This shows that the two powers of an achromatic lens must have opposite signs, since the ν-values of glasses are positive numbers usually lying between 25 and 100. However, any ν-value can be artificially obtained for a monoplet by the equation

$$\frac{\Phi_{\mathrm{F}} - \Phi_{\mathrm{C}}}{\Phi_{\mathrm{D}}} = \frac{1}{N}, \tag{13.42}$$

corresponding to (13.38) for a single lens, where $N \to \infty$ corresponds to a corrected system. Using this artifice we can combine lenses to create a monoplet combination the value N of which can have an arbitrary value, even a negative one. This is a very important device when applied to the color correction of optical instruments.

Duplet. For a duplet we find from (13.21)

$$\begin{aligned} d\alpha &= -\frac{e_1\phi_1}{\nu_1}, \quad d\beta = 0 \\ d\gamma &= e_1\phi_1\phi_2\left(\frac{1}{\nu_1} + \frac{1}{\nu_2}\right) - \left(\frac{\phi_1}{\nu_1} + \frac{\phi_2}{\nu_2}\right) \\ d\delta &= -\frac{e_1\phi_2}{\nu_2}, \end{aligned} \tag{13.43}$$

and as the color correction equation (13.22),

$$e_1{}^2\frac{\phi_1}{\nu_1}\frac{\phi_2}{\nu_2} = 0, \tag{13.44}$$

which shows again that no color correction for C and F can be achieved for a duplet unless at least one of the two monoplets is corrected by itself.

Triplet. Equation (13.25) and the color-correcting equation (13.27) give

$$\frac{\phi_1}{\nu_1}\frac{\phi_2}{\nu_2}e_1{}^2 + \frac{\phi_1}{\nu_1}\frac{\phi_3}{\nu_3}(e_1 + e_2 - e_1e_2\phi_2)^2 + \frac{\phi_2}{\nu_2}\frac{\phi_3}{\nu_3}e_2{}^2 = 0$$

$$\phi_1 + \phi_2 + \phi_3 - e_1\phi_1(\phi_2 + \phi_3) - e_2\phi_3(\phi_1 + \phi_2) + e_1e_2\phi_1\phi_2\phi_3 = \Phi, \tag{13.45}$$

and (13.28) gives

$$\frac{n}{s} = \frac{1}{e_1}(1 - e_1\phi_1) + \frac{1}{e_1e_2}\frac{\phi_1\nu_2}{\phi_2\nu_1}(e_1 + e_2 - e_1e_2\phi_2)$$

$$-\frac{n'}{s'} = \frac{1}{e_2}(1 - e_2\phi_3) + \frac{1}{e_1e_2}\frac{\phi_3\nu_2}{\phi_2\nu_3}(e_1 + e_2 - e_1e_2\phi_2). \tag{13.46}$$

The analysis of these equations is very interesting and can be carried out in detail to give a graphical survey of all possible color-corrected triplets with given glasses.

The color correction for a *thick lens* can be calculated only approximately by replacing the differential quotients in (13.32) with difference quotients.

We consider now the problem of correcting monoplets for two *arbitrary* wavelengths. The glass catalogs give, besides the ν-value, the so-called partial dispersion (12.4b):

$$P_\lambda = (n_\lambda - n_\mathrm{F})/(n_\mathrm{F} - n_\mathrm{C}). \tag{13.47}$$

From (13.37) and (13.47) we derive for a thin lens

$$\phi_\lambda - \phi_\mathrm{F} = (P_\lambda/\nu)\phi_\mathrm{D}. \tag{13.48}$$

From this we derive, for a monoplet,

$$\Phi_\lambda - \Phi_\mathrm{F} = \Sigma\, \phi_{i\mathrm{D}}\,(P_{i\lambda}/\nu_i) \tag{13.49}$$

and the corresponding equations for a duplet or triplet. With the help of (13.49), we can write the condition in which two thin lenses without distance can be corrected for two arbitrary colors λ' and λ''. Setting $\lambda = \lambda'$ and $\lambda = \lambda''$ in (13.49) and subtracting, we obtain

$$\frac{P_{1\lambda'} - P_{1\lambda''}}{\nu_1}\phi_1 + \frac{P_{2\lambda'} - P_{2\lambda''}}{\nu_2}\phi_2 = 0, \tag{13.50}$$

which, by using the equation $\phi_1 + \phi_2 = \Phi$, gives for ϕ_1 and ϕ_2 the expressions

$$\phi_1 = \frac{(P_{2\lambda'} - P_{2\lambda''})\, \nu_1\, \Phi}{\begin{vmatrix} \nu_1 & \nu_2 \\ P_{1\lambda'} - P_{1\lambda''} & P_{2\lambda'} - P_{2\lambda''} \end{vmatrix}},$$

$$\phi_2 = - \frac{(P_{1\lambda'} - P_{1\lambda''})\, \nu_2\, \Phi}{\begin{vmatrix} \nu_1 & \nu_2 \\ P_{1\lambda'} - P_{1\lambda''} & P_{2\lambda'} - P_{2\lambda''} \end{vmatrix}}. \tag{13.51}$$

The corresponding relations for any monoplet can similarly be obtained from (13.49). It will be seen that, if we use only "ordinary glasses," a monoplet can be corrected for only two colors (*cf.* Chapter 12). For ordinary glasses we have (12.35):

$$P_\lambda = A_1\nu + A_2, \tag{13.52}$$

where A_1 and A_2 are the universal functions given in Chapter 12 (Table IV). From this and (13.49) and (13.39) we then calculate for any monoplet

$$\begin{aligned} \Phi_\lambda - \Phi_F &= \sum_i [A_1(\lambda)\nu_i + A_2(\lambda)]\phi_{iD}/\nu_i \\ &= A_1(\lambda)\Sigma\phi_{iD} + A_2(\lambda)\Sigma\phi_{iD}/\nu_i \\ &= A_1(\lambda)\Phi_D + A_2(\lambda)\,(\Phi_F - \Phi_C), \end{aligned} \tag{13.53}$$

giving

$$\Phi_{\lambda'} - \Phi_{\lambda''} = [A_1(\lambda') - A_2(\lambda'')]\Phi_D + [A_2(\lambda') - A_2(\lambda'')](\Phi_F - \Phi_C). \tag{13.54}$$

If the system is corrected for C and F ($\Phi_F = \Phi_C$), it cannot be corrected with ordinary glasses for a third color λ, as is obvious from (13.53) and the form of A as a function of λ (see Chapter 12, Table IV). Likewise, two other colors cannot be brought together, as (13.54) shows. The curve given by $A_1(\lambda)$ is called the *curve of secondary spectrum.* It is easy to calculate the secondary spectrum if the system is corrected for two *other* wavelengths, for instance λ' and λ''. Formula (13.54) leads to

$$\Phi_F - \Phi_C = - \frac{A_1(\lambda') - A_1(\lambda'')}{A_2(\lambda') - A_2(\lambda'')}\Phi_D + \frac{(\Phi_{\lambda'} - \Phi_{\lambda''})}{A_2(\lambda') - A_2(\lambda'')} \tag{13.55}$$

whence we obtain, for $\Phi_{\lambda'} - \Phi_{\lambda''} = 0$,

$$\Phi_\lambda - \Phi_F = \Phi_D \left[A_1(\lambda) - A_2(\lambda) \frac{A_1(\lambda') - A_1(\lambda'')}{A_2(\lambda') - A_2(\lambda'')} \right], \quad (13.56)$$

the coefficient of Φ_D giving us the *secondary spectrum* when the system is corrected for λ' and λ'' instead of C and F.

We see then that when using ordinary glasses we cannot correct the secondary spectrum of a monoplet, and, for the same reason, the same thing is true for a system of monoplets with finite distances.

However, if extraordinary glasses, in particular, fluorite, are used, the results are different.

We have for a monoplet the equations

$$\begin{aligned} \Phi_D &= \Sigma\phi_i \\ \Phi_F - \Phi_C &= \Sigma\, \phi_i/\nu_i \\ \Phi_\lambda - \Phi_F &= \Sigma\, \phi_i P_{i\lambda}/\nu_i, \end{aligned} \quad (13.57)$$

which permit us to correct Φ for three wavelengths C, F, λ by choosing the ν-values and partials $P_{i\lambda}$ so that these equations are consistent, which is possible if and only if the three glasses are extraordinary glasses, since otherwise, because of (13.52), the determinant of Equation (13.57) vanishes.

PART III. GENERAL LAWS

CHAPTER FOURTEEN

The Basic Formulae of Hamilton and Lagrange

In the first part of the book we followed a single ray through an optical system. We now wish to investigate what happens to a manifold of rays.

A single ray may be given by its initial point (vector $\vec{a}$ from an arbitrary origin) and the direction vector $\vec{s}$ of length n (n being the refractive index). Its intersection points with the consecutive surfaces may be given by $\vec{b}_1 \ldots \vec{b}_\varkappa$, the incidence normals by $\vec{o}_1 \ldots \vec{o}_\varkappa$. We then have the vector equations

$$\begin{aligned} \vec{b}_1 &= \vec{a} + l\vec{s} & \vec{s}_1 - \vec{s} &= \Gamma_1\vec{o}_1 \\ \vec{b}_2 &= \vec{b}_1 + l_1\vec{s}_1 & \vec{s}_2 - \vec{s}_1 &= \Gamma_2\vec{o}_2 \\ \vec{b}_3 &= \vec{b}_2 + l_2\vec{s}_2 & \ldots\ldots & \\ \ldots\ldots & & & \\ \vec{a}' &= \vec{b}_\varkappa + l'\vec{s}' & & \end{aligned} \tag{14.1}$$

where l_ν is the distance between the intersection points with the νth and $(\nu + 1)$st surfaces divided by the refractive index n_ν.

We now consider a one-dimensional manifold, that is, we assume $\vec{a}$ and $\vec{s}$ and likewise all the $\vec{b}_\nu$, $\vec{o}_\nu$ and l_ν to be functions of a single parameter u (with continuous second derivatives). This involves assuming the refracting surfaces to be regular, that is, having continuous tangential planes.

We have, writing $\vec{s}_u$, $\vec{b}_u$ as abbreviations for $d\vec{s}/du$, $d\vec{b}/du$,

$$\vec{s}\vec{s}_u = 0, \quad \vec{o}\vec{b}_u = 0. \tag{14.2}$$

The first of these equations is obtained by differentiating $\vec{s}^2 = n^2$; the second holds since $\vec{o}$ is the surface normal at the intersection point. Differentiating the left-hand equations of (14.1), multiplying by the respective $\vec{s}_\nu$, and multiplying the right-hand side of (14.1) by the respective $\vec{b}_u$, we find therefore

$$\vec{b}_{1u}\vec{s} = \vec{a}_u\vec{s} + n^2 l_u \qquad \vec{b}_{1u}\vec{s}_1 - \vec{b}_{1u}\vec{s} = 0.$$
$$\vec{b}_{2u}\vec{s}_1 = \vec{b}_{1u}\vec{s}_1 + n_1{}^2 l_{1u} \qquad \vec{b}_{2u}\vec{s}_2 - \vec{b}_{2u}\vec{s}_1 = 0 \tag{14.3}$$
$$\cdots \qquad \cdots\cdot$$
$$\vec{a}_u{}'\vec{s}' = \vec{b}_{\varkappa u}\vec{s}' + n'^2 l'_u$$

Addition leads to the important formula

$$\vec{a}_u{}'\vec{s}' - \vec{a}_u\vec{s} = E_u \tag{14.4}$$

with

$$E = \Sigma\, n_\nu{}^2 l_\nu. \tag{14.5}$$

The quantity E is the sum of the lengths of paths between consecutive surfaces multiplied in each case by the corresponding refractive index and is called the *optical path* from initial to terminal point.

Equation (14.4) was discovered by *W. R. Hamilton.* It is the most important discovery in geometrical optics (and probably in the whole field of mathematical physics) since the discovery of the Law of Refraction. It contains implicitly all the laws of optical image formation. The manifolds $\vec{a}(u)$ and $\vec{a}'(u)$ and the function $E(u)$ are not restricted, a fact which enables one to adapt (14.4) to any special problem.

The manifold of rays in space is four-dimensional, that is, four parameters are sufficient to identify the rays. We can, for instance, choose as parameters the coordinates of the intersection points of the rays with two parallel planes.

We can immediately generalize Formula (14.4) by considering a manifold of two, three, or four parameters, that is, assuming that the starting point (vector $\vec{a}$) and the starting direction (vector $\vec{s}$) depend on two or more independent parameters. In this way we find two, three, or, in the most general case, four equations of the form (14.4). Let u, v, w, and t be the parameters; we find (using partial derivatives)

$$\begin{aligned} \vec{a}_u{}'\vec{s}' - \vec{a}_u\vec{s} &= E_u \\ \vec{a}_v{}'\vec{s}' - \vec{a}_v\vec{s} &= E_v \\ \vec{a}_w{}'\vec{s}' - \vec{a}_w\vec{s} &= E_w \\ \vec{a}_t{}'\vec{s}' - \vec{a}_t\vec{s} &= E_t, \end{aligned} \tag{14.6}$$

where E always designates the light path from the initial point $\vec{a}$

to the terminal point $\vec{a}'$. The reader may take notice of the fact that Formulae (14.6) contain only the *derivatives* of $\vec{a}$ and $\vec{a}'$. This permits us to choose different coordinate origins in the object and image spaces, enabling us to derive the general laws of optical image formation from (14.6) merely by considering the image formation in the object and image spaces without considering what happens in between.

Hamilton also made use of the fact that Equation (14.4) can be transformed by replacing E, the light path from initial to final point, by one of the functions

$$\begin{aligned} V &= E + \vec{a}\vec{s} \\ V' &= E - \vec{a}'\vec{s}' \\ W &= E + \vec{a}\vec{s} - \vec{a}'\vec{s}'. \end{aligned} \tag{14.7}$$

Since $\vec{a}\vec{s}$ is the light path to the initial point from the footpoint of the perpendicular dropped from the origin to the object ray, and $\vec{a}'\vec{s}'$ is the analogous light path in the image space, the three functions V, V', and W have well-defined geometrical meanings.*

The quantity V is the light path from the object footpoint to the terminal point, V' from the initial point to the image footpoint, and W from the object footpoint to the image footpoint. Comparison of (14.4) with (14.7) now leads to

$$\begin{aligned} V_u &= \vec{a}_u{}'\vec{s}' + \vec{s}_u\vec{a} \\ V_u{}' &= -\vec{s}_u{}'\vec{a}' - \vec{a}_u\vec{s} \\ W_u &= -\vec{s}_u{}'\vec{a}' + \vec{s}_u\vec{a}, \end{aligned} \tag{14.8}$$

where, of course, for a higher dimensional manifold, equivalent equations for the other variables have to be added.

Following the suggestion of J. L. Synge we call E the *point characteristic*, and V and V' the *mixed characteristics*, whereas W will be called the *angle characteristic*.

These functions expressed for suitable parameters will be used later to determine completely the image formation in optical systems.

* It should be noted that essentially only the derivatives of V, V', W will be used. Hence any one of these functions needs only to be known within an arbitrary additive constant.

The Bilinear Invariant

If we investigate at least a two-dimensional manifold of rays, then the four expressions (14.4) and (14.8) for the general law of optical image formation can be combined into one by eliminating the characteristic functions. Differentiating the two equations

$$\vec{a}_u'\vec{s}' - \vec{a}_u\vec{s} = E_u$$
$$\vec{a}_v'\vec{s}' - \vec{a}_v\vec{s} = E_v, \tag{14.9}$$

the first with respect to v, the second with respect to u, and subtracting we obtain

$$\vec{a}_u'\vec{s}_v' - \vec{a}_v'\vec{s}_u' = \vec{a}_u\vec{s}_v - \vec{a}_v\vec{s}_u. \tag{14.10}$$

The quantity appearing in this equation is called the *optical differential invariant*. It is equivalent to the "Lagrange bracket" studied in the calculus of variations.

If we study a higher dimensional manifold of rays, we have, of course, an equation of the form (14.10) for any two variables. Thus, if we consider the image formation for all the rays, we will have $\binom{4}{2} = 6$ equations of the form (14.10).

If we integrate (14.2) over a simple connected region in the uv-plane bounded by a regular curve, we obtain an integral invariant

$$\iint (\vec{a}_u'\vec{s}_v' - \vec{a}_v'\vec{s}_u')du\, dv = \iint (\vec{a}_u\vec{s}_v - \vec{a}_v\vec{s}_u)\, du\, dv. \tag{14.11}$$

The integral invariant is called in optics the *geometrical energy flux* through the part of the surface $\vec{a}(u, v)$ given by the simply connected region.

The Laws of Fermat and Malus-Dupin

Let us apply the basic formula of Hamilton to the study of the rays originating at a point in the object space. The manifold of rays coming from an object point is two-dimensional, that is, it can be given by two parameters u and v, which we can choose arbitrarily. The assumption that the object point $\vec{a}$ is fixed gives

$$\vec{a}_u = \vec{a}_v = 0. \tag{14.12}$$

Inserting this into (14.4) we find

$$\vec{s}'\vec{a}_u' = E_u, \quad \vec{s}'\vec{a}_v' = E_v , \tag{14.13}$$

and inserting (14.12) into (14.10) we see that

$$\vec{a}_u'\vec{s}_v' - \vec{a}_v'\vec{s}_u' = 0, \tag{14.14}$$

that is, for the rays from a point, the differential invariant vanishes.

Let us now construct a surface of points optically equidistant from the object point. This leads to

$$E_u = E_v = 0, \tag{14.15}$$

and therefore

$$\vec{s}'\vec{a}_u' = \vec{s}'\vec{a}_v' = 0. \tag{14.16}$$

Equation (14.16) asserts that the manifold $\vec{a}'\ (u, v)$ thus constructed is normal to the rays in the image space, or in other words that the rays are normals of the surface $\vec{a}'$, which we call a *wave-surface*. To each value of E (E = constant) belongs a wave-surface, and two wave-surfaces have a constant optical distance between them on all rays and a constant optical distance from the object point. These facts were clearly enunciated and simply proved by Hamilton (1828). However, *Malus* (in 1808) gave a geometrical proof which he erroneously assumed to be valid for only a single refraction or reflection. *Dupin* (in 1813) corrected an error in the Malus proof and gave the first correct proof of the general theorem.

The law of Malus-Dupin is more general than announced by them and states that a manifold of rays normal to a surface, a so-called *normal system*, remains a normal system after refraction and reflection.

We shall prove it in the general form. A two-dimensional manifold of rays given by an arbitrary initial surface $\vec{a}\ (u, v)$ (which is not necessarily a wave-surface) with direction vector $\vec{s}\ (u, v)$, one ray going through each of the points $\vec{a}\ (u, v)$ of the surface, is a normal system if and only if there exists a surface

$$\vec{b}\ (u,v) = \vec{a} + l\vec{s} \tag{14.17}$$

which is normal to all these rays so that

$$\vec{b}_u\vec{s} = \vec{b}_v\vec{s} = 0. \tag{14.18}$$

Inserting (14.17) into (14.18), we find as a necessary condition (which is also sufficient) that

$$\begin{aligned} \vec{a}_u\vec{s} + l_u n^2 &= 0 \\ \vec{a}_v\vec{s} + l_v n^2 &= 0. \end{aligned} \tag{14.19}$$

Elimination of l from (14.19) by differentiating with respect to u and v leads to

$$\vec{a}_u\vec{s}_v - \vec{a}_v\vec{s}_u = 0, \tag{14.20}$$

that is, a normal system is characterized by the fact that the optical differential invariant vanishes for the manifold in question. That the converse holds true is now immediately evident, since (14.20) is the integrability condition necessary and sufficient for the existence of a function l such that

$$dl = -(1/n^2)\vec{s}d\vec{a}, \tag{14.21}$$

which makes it possible for (14.19) and therefore (14.18) to be fulfilled. Any integral of (14.21) leads to a surface $\vec{b} = \vec{a} + l\vec{s}$ normal to all rays.

The law of Malus-Dupin stating that normal systems are imaged as normal systems is now simply an application of the law of Lagrange (14.10) applied to the case in which the Lagrange bracket vanishes for all values of u and v.

The fact that all the rays emerging from a point form a normal system, since for them $\vec{a} = \vec{a}_o$, or $\vec{a}_u = \vec{a}_v = 0$, shows the importance of normal systems for optical image formation. We shall therefore investigate especially the geometrical properties of these systems.

If all the rays from an object point come to a point, we say we have a *sharp* image of the object point. Since in Equation (14.9)

$$\vec{a}_u = \vec{a}_v = \vec{a}_u{}' = \vec{a}_v{}' = 0,$$

we find in this case

$$E_u = E_v = 0 \tag{14.22}$$

or the *theorem of Fermat*: If an object point has a sharp image, the light path must be the same along all the rays connecting the object and image points.

The theorem of Fermat can also be considered as a special case of a more general theorem. Let us assume a continuous one-dimensional manifold of rays coming from an object point $\vec{a}_o$ and uniting in the image space in a point $\vec{a}_o'$. Then Equation (14.4) gives $E_u = 0$ or $E =$ constant. The result may be stated as follows:

Generalized Law of Fermat: The light path on a *continuous* manifold connecting two points $\vec{a}_o$, $\vec{a}_o'$, one in the object space and one in the image space, is the same for all the rays of the continuous manifold.

The word *continuous* in this connection is of great importance. For instance, if we consider a cone of rays around the axis of a rotation-symmetric optical system and coming from a point A, this cone is imaged (because of rotation symmetry) into a cone of rays symmetrical to the optical axis and meeting in a point A' such that the light path is the same for all the rays of the cone. This path is, however, not equal to the light path along the axis, in spite of the fact that this isolated ray also goes through A and A'.

A one-dimensional continuous manifold of rays connecting two points will be described in this book as giving a *half-sharp* image of the point. As an illustration of half-sharp image formation, we study the case in which *all* the rays from an object point intersect a curve $\vec{a}'(v)$. Let us in this case take as the parameter v the arc length of the image curve. According to the generalized law of Fermat $E(u,v)$, the light path from the object point to the image curve, must be independent of u, that is, it must be a function of v alone.

We have, moreover, since $\vec{a}_u = 0$,

$$\vec{s}'\vec{a}'_v = E_v; \tag{14.23}$$

and, since E is independent of u, E_v likewise is independent of u, that is, it has a constant value for all the rays meeting at a point of the curve. But v was taken as the arc length of the curve. So $\vec{a}_v'$ is the same as the unit tangent vector $\vec{t}'$ to the curve. Hence, if v is held constant, we find

$$\vec{s}'\vec{t}' = C, \tag{14.24}$$

which gives the following *theorem*: If all the rays from an object point intersect a curve in the image space, then all the rays going through a point of the curve ($v =$ const.) form a constant angle

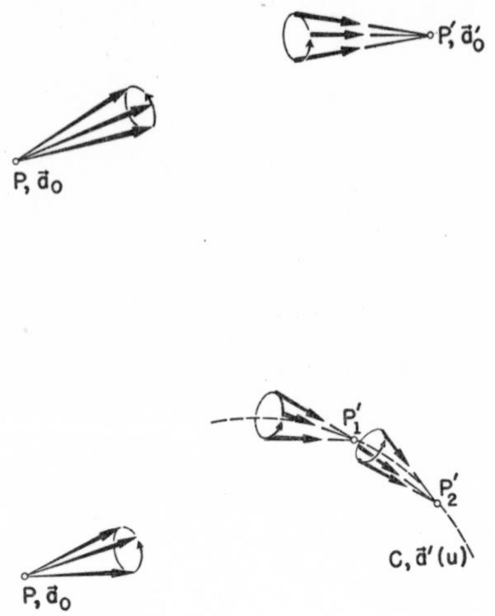

Fig. 14.1. Sharp image of a point, half-symmetrical image of a point.

with the tangent line, that is, they lie on a cone around the tangent line. Such a point is said to be imaged *half-symmetrically*. The point is said to have a *symmetrical* image if the intersected curve is a straight line.

One of the earliest discoveries in optics (F. Maurolycus, 1575) was that the rays of a normal system are tangential to a surface, the so-called *caustic surface*, and that the general ray is tangential to the caustic surface in two points.

This can be shown as follows. Let $\vec{a}\,(u, v)$ be an arbitrary surface and the system a normal system, that is, (14.20) is fulfilled. Then a second surface $\vec{c}\,(u, v)$ such that $\vec{s}\,(u, v)$ lies in its tangent plane can be given in the form

$$\vec{c} = \vec{a} + \varkappa\vec{s}, \qquad (14.25)$$

where the fact that the ray lies in the tangential plane of $\vec{c}$ leads to the equation

$$[\vec{c}_u\, \vec{c}_v\, \vec{s}] = 0. \tag{14.26}$$

Eliminating $\vec{c}$ with the help of (14.25) gives

$$[\vec{d}_u + \varkappa\vec{s}_u,\ \vec{d}_v + \varkappa\vec{s}_v,\ \vec{s}] = 0 \tag{14.27}$$

or developed with respect to powers of $\varkappa$,

$$\varkappa^2[\vec{s}_u\vec{s}_v\vec{s}] + \varkappa\,([\vec{d}_u\vec{s}_v\vec{s}] + [\vec{s}_u\vec{d}_v\vec{s}]) + [\vec{d}_u\vec{d}_v\vec{s}] = 0. \tag{14.28}$$

It remains to be shown that Equation (14.28) has two real solutions, that is, that

$$([\vec{d}_u\vec{s}_v\vec{s}] + [\vec{s}_u\vec{d}_v\vec{s}])^2 - 4[\vec{s}_u\vec{s}_v\vec{s}]\,[\vec{d}_u\vec{d}_v\vec{s}] \geq 0. \tag{14.29}$$

To prove this inequality, we express $\vec{d}_u$ and $\vec{d}_v$ in the coordinate system given by the (in general independent) vectors $\vec{s}_u$, $\vec{s}_v$, and $\vec{s}$, or

$$\begin{aligned} \vec{d}_u &= \alpha\vec{s}_u + \beta\vec{s}_v + C_1\vec{s} \\ \vec{d}_v &= \gamma\vec{s}_u + \delta\vec{s}_v + C_2\vec{s}\,. \end{aligned} \tag{14.30}$$

This leads to

$$\begin{aligned} [\vec{d}_u\vec{d}_v\vec{s}] &= (\alpha\delta - \beta\gamma)\,[\vec{s}_u\vec{s}_v\vec{s}] \\ [\vec{d}_u\vec{s}_v\vec{s}] + [\vec{s}_u\vec{d}_v\vec{s}] &= (\alpha + \delta)\,[\vec{s}_u\vec{s}_v\vec{s}]\,, \end{aligned} \tag{14.31}$$

which means that Equation (14.28) and the quantity in (14.29) are equivalent to

$$\begin{aligned} \varkappa^2 + \varkappa\,(\alpha + \delta) + \alpha\delta - \beta\gamma = 0 \\ D = (\alpha + \delta)^2 - 4(\alpha\delta - \beta\gamma) = (\alpha - \delta)^2 + 4\beta\gamma \end{aligned} \tag{14.32}$$

respectively.

To establish D as positive, we must use (14.20):

$$\vec{s}_u\vec{d}_v = \vec{s}_v\vec{d}_u, \tag{14.33}$$

which, combined with (14.30), gives

$$\gamma\vec{s}_u{}^2 + (\delta - \alpha)\vec{s}_u\vec{s}_v - \beta\vec{s}_v{}^2 = 0. \tag{14.34}$$

Multiplication of (14.32) by $\vec{s}_u{}^2$ and $\vec{s}_v{}^2$ in turn gives

$$\begin{aligned} D\vec{s}_u{}^2 &= (\alpha-\delta)^2\vec{s}_u{}^2 + 4\beta\gamma\vec{s}_u{}^2 = (\alpha-\delta)^2\vec{s}_u{}^2 + 4\beta^2\vec{s}_v{}^2 - 4\beta(\delta-\alpha)\vec{s}_u\vec{s}_v \\ &= ((\alpha-\delta)\vec{s}_u + 2\beta\vec{s}_v)^2 \end{aligned}$$

$$D\vec{s}_v{}^2 = (\alpha-\delta)^2\vec{s}_v{}^2 + 4\beta\gamma\vec{s}_v{}^2 = (\alpha-\delta)^2\vec{s}_v{}^2 + 4\gamma^2\vec{s}_u{}^2 + 4\gamma(\delta-\alpha)\vec{s}_u\vec{s}_v$$
$$= ((\alpha-\delta)\vec{s}_v - 2\gamma\vec{s}_u)^2.$$

Equations (14.35) prove that the discriminant of (14.28) is positive, that is, that (14.28) has two real solutions. The case that $\vec{s}_u$, $\vec{s}_v$, $\vec{s}$ are dependent is trivial, since in that case (14.28) degenerates to a linear equation.

CHAPTER FIFTEEN

The General Laws of Image Formation

Hamilton's basic law gives a method for studying image formation.

In the last chapter we distinguished four cases for the image of a point. It is either

(*a*) imaged *sharply*—all the rays from the object point come to a common focus, or

(*b*) imaged *symmetrically*—all the rays go through a straight line, forming cones each with the straight line as a bisectrix, or

(*c*) imaged *half-symmetrically*—all the rays go through a curved line, forming cones each with the tangent to the curved line as a bisectrix, or

(*d*) imaged with rays tangent to a general caustic.

In this section we shall first investigate the conditions under which the points of a curve are sharply, half-symmetrically, or symmetrically imaged.

Sharp Image of a Curve

Let us assume that each point of a curve $\vec{a}(t)$ is sharply imaged at a corresponding point of a curve $\vec{a}'(t)$. Let $\vec{s}(u, v)$ and $\vec{s}'(u, v)$

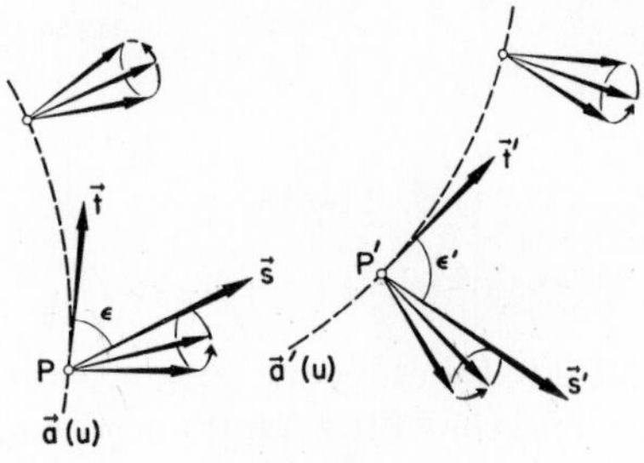

Fig. 15.1. Sharp image of a curve.

designate the directions of the corresponding rays in the object and image spaces for a fixed value of t.

The law of Fermat says that the light path between $\vec{a}(t)$ and $\vec{a}'(t)$ is a function of t alone, independent of u and v. We then have

$$\vec{s}'\vec{a}_t' - \vec{s}\vec{a}_t = E_t. \tag{15.1}$$

Let us introduce the arc lengths τ,τ' along the object and image curves and the "magnification" $m = d\tau'/d\tau$. Let $\vec{t},\vec{t}'$ be the unit vectors tangential to $\vec{a}$ and $\vec{a}'$; then we obtain

$$m\vec{s}'\vec{t}' - \vec{s}\vec{t} = E_\tau. \tag{15.2}$$

Inserting the angles ε and ε' between the rays and the respective tangent vectors, we obtain the famous *cosine law*

$$mn' \cos \varepsilon' - n \cos \varepsilon = C \tag{15.3}$$

since E_τ is constant for the rays joining a pair of corresponding points of the object and image curves. The value of the constant C is determined if we know the angles ε, ε' for one special ray connecting $\vec{a}$ and $\vec{a}'$. We obtain

$$mn' \cos \varepsilon' - n \cos \varepsilon = mn' \cos \varepsilon_0' - n \cos \varepsilon_0$$

or

$$mn' (\cos \varepsilon' - \cos \varepsilon_0') = n (\cos \varepsilon - \cos \varepsilon_0) \tag{15.4}$$

or

$$mn' \sin \frac{\varepsilon' + \varepsilon_0'}{2} \sin \frac{\varepsilon' - \varepsilon_0'}{2} = n \sin \frac{\varepsilon + \varepsilon_0}{2} \sin \frac{\varepsilon - \varepsilon_0}{2}.$$

Two cases are of special interest.

(1) There exists a ray perpendicular to both the object and the image curves: $\varepsilon_0 = \varepsilon_0' = \pi/2$. We then have

$$mn' \cos \varepsilon' = n \cos \varepsilon. \tag{15.5}$$

(2) There exists a ray tangential to both the object and the image curves: $\varepsilon_0 = \varepsilon_0' = 0$. Then

$$mn' \sin^2 (\varepsilon'/2) = n \sin^2 (\varepsilon/2). \tag{15.6}$$

The results obtained here can be generalized to *half-sharp* images. Let us assume that for each point of a given curve a one-dimensional manifold of rays comes to a focus at a corresponding point on a second curve. Then all equations from (15.1) to (15.6) remain valid with the exception that $\vec{s}$ and $\vec{s}'$ are functions of *one* parameter instead of two and that Equations (15.4) hold only for the cone of imaging rays.

Let us now reverse the viewpoint. Let us assume that every one-dimensional (or two-dimensional) manifold of rays fulfills the condition (15.2). In this case we say that a line element in the direction of $\vec{t}$ is *sharply* (or *half-sharply*) imaged upon a line element in the direction of $\vec{t}'$. It should be clearly understood, however, that this condition can hold at a point without necessarily having any of the neighboring points sharply or half-sharply imaged.

Half-Symmetrical Image of a Line Element

As an example of the half-sharp image we consider the half-symmetrical image of a line element.

We assume that all the rays through a given point of the curve $\vec{a}(t)$ intersect in the image space a corresponding curve $\vec{a}'(t, u)$; that is, we consider a three-dimensional manifold of rays given by $\vec{a}(t)$, $\vec{s}(t, u, v)$ and their image rays, given by $\vec{a}'(t, u)$ and $\vec{s}'(t, u, v)$.

We found in Chapter 14 that the rays from an object point can be arranged in cones with the corresponding curve $\vec{a}'(t, u)$ as bisectrix. We also have the three equations

$$\begin{aligned} E_t &= \vec{s}'\vec{a}_t' - \vec{s}\vec{a}_t \\ E_u &= \vec{s}'\vec{a}_u' \\ E_v &= 0. \end{aligned} \tag{15.7}$$

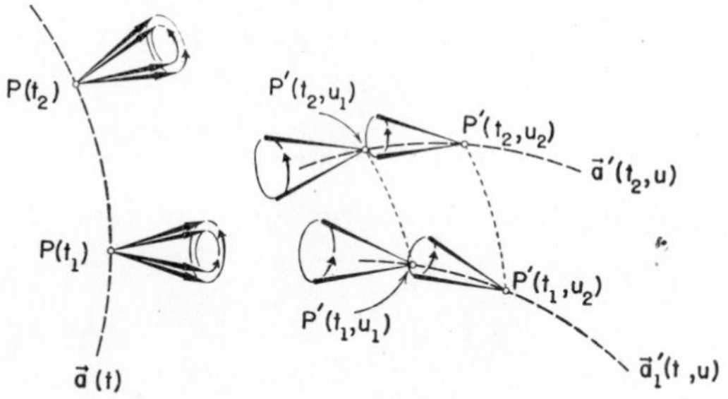

Fig. 15.2. Half-symmetrical image of a curve.

It is geometrically obvious, since the image curves $\vec{a}'(t, u)$ form a surface element, that any line element lying on this surface and connecting two points, one on the image curve $\vec{a}'(t_o, u)$ and the other on a neighboring image curve, is a half-sharp image of the object line element.

We shall now prove that we can choose new variables $\bar{u}$ and $\bar{t}$ such that Equations (15.7) hold with respect to the new variables and also

$$\vec{a}_{\bar{t}}'\vec{a}_{\bar{u}}' = 0. \tag{15.8}$$

Suppose we choose the new variables so that

$$\bar{u} = \bar{u}(u, t), \quad \bar{t} = t \tag{15.9}$$

with

$$\begin{aligned} d\bar{u} &= \frac{\partial \bar{u}}{\partial u} du + \frac{\partial \bar{u}}{\partial t} dt \\ d\bar{t} &= \qquad\qquad\quad dt. \end{aligned}$$

This leads to

$$\begin{aligned} E_t &= E_{\bar{u}}\bar{u}_t + E_{\bar{t}} \qquad & \vec{a}_t' &= \vec{a}_{\bar{u}}'\bar{u}_t + \vec{a}_{\bar{t}}' \\ E_u &= E_{\bar{u}}\bar{u}_u & \vec{a}_u' &= \vec{a}_{\bar{u}}'\bar{u}_u, \end{aligned} \tag{15.10}$$

and therefore Equations (15.7) lead to

$$\begin{aligned} E_{\bar{t}} &= \vec{s}\,'\vec{a}_{\bar{t}}' - \vec{s}\vec{a}_{\bar{t}} \\ E_{\bar{u}} &= \vec{s}\,'\vec{a}_{\bar{u}}'. \end{aligned} \tag{15.11}$$

Thus a transformation of the form (15.9) leaves the form of Equations (15.7) unchanged. Equations (15.10) now show that $\bar{u}$ can be chosen so that Equation (15.8) is fulfilled.

As an example, we shall consider the symmetrical image of a line element; that is, we shall assume the curves $\vec{a}'(t, u)$ to be straight lines through the origin:

$$\vec{a}'(t, u) = u\vec{l}'(t) \tag{15.12}$$

where $\vec{l}'(t)$ are unit vectors giving the directions of the straight lines. Equations (15.7) give

$$\begin{aligned} E_u &= \vec{s}\,'\vec{l}' \\ E_t &= u\left(\vec{s}\,'\frac{d\vec{l}'}{dt}\right) - \vec{s}\frac{d\vec{a}}{dt} \end{aligned} \tag{15.13}$$

with

$$\vec{l}'\frac{d\vec{l}'}{dt} = \tfrac{1}{2}\frac{d}{dt}\vec{l}'^2 = 0,$$

so that in this example (15.8) is fulfilled.

Sharp Image of a Surface Element

Let us assume that every point of a surface $\vec{a}(t, w)$ is imaged sharply upon a corresponding point of a surface $\vec{a}'(t, w)$ (owing to the one-to-one correspondence, t and w can also be regarded as surface parameters for the second surface). The manifold of

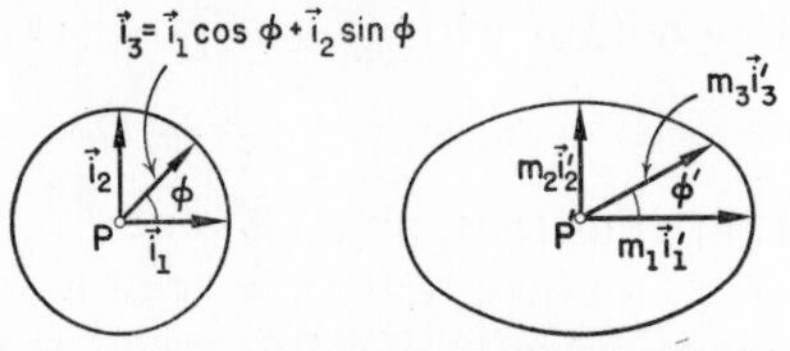

Fig. 15.3. Sharp image of a surface element.

rays thus considered has four parameters (u, v, t, w), and we obtain two equations in cosine form, the light path E being a function of t and w alone (independent of u and v):

$$\begin{aligned} E_t &= \vec{s}'\vec{a}_t' - \vec{s}\vec{a}_t \\ E_w &= \vec{s}'\vec{a}_w' - \vec{s}\vec{a}_w. \end{aligned} \tag{15.14}$$

Let us consider the rays through a fixed point (t_o, w_o). Then E_t and E_w are constants (that is, they are independent of u and v).

Since $\vec{a}(t, w)$ and $\vec{a}'(t, w)$ designate two surfaces, we may assume

$$\vec{a}_t \times \vec{a}_w \neq 0, \quad \vec{a}_t' \times \vec{a}_w' \neq 0, \tag{15.15}$$

or $\vec{a}_t$, $\vec{a}_w$, $\vec{a}_t \times \vec{a}_w$, and $\vec{a}_t'$, $\vec{a}_w'$, $\vec{a}_t' \times \vec{a}_w'$ are two sets of independent vectors or bases of the vector space.

It will be convenient, however, to replace these by two new bases as follows. Let $\vec{a}_t^*$ and $\vec{a}_w^*$ be two vectors in the plane of $\vec{a}_t$ and $\vec{a}_w$ such that

$$\begin{aligned} &\vec{a}_t\,\vec{a}_t^* = 1 \qquad && \vec{a}_t\,\vec{a}_w^* = 0 \\ &\vec{a}_w\vec{a}_t^* = 0 && \vec{a}_w\vec{a}_w^* = 1. \end{aligned} \tag{15.16}$$

To show that $\vec{a}_t{}^*$ and $\vec{a}_w{}^*$ can be uniquely determined, we write

$$\begin{aligned} \vec{a}_t{}^* &= \alpha_{11}\vec{a}_t + \alpha_{12}\vec{a}_w \\ \vec{a}_w{}^* &= \alpha_{21}\vec{a}_t + \alpha_{22}\vec{a}_w. \end{aligned} \qquad (15.17)$$

Multiplication of each of these scalarly by $\vec{a}_t$ and $\vec{a}_w$ and the use of (15.17) yield linear equations with a non-zero determinant for finding the coefficients α_{ij}. In similar fashion we can define $\vec{a}_t{}'^*$ and $\vec{a}_w{}'^*$.

Finally we can express $\vec{s}$ and $\vec{s}\,'$ in terms of the new bases

$$\begin{aligned} \vec{s} &= \alpha\vec{a}_t{}^* + \beta\vec{a}_w{}^* + \gamma\,(\vec{a}_t \times \vec{a}_w) \\ \vec{s}\,' &= \alpha'\vec{a}_t{}'^* + \beta'\vec{a}_w{}'^* + \gamma'\,(\vec{a}_t{}' \times \vec{a}_w{}'). \end{aligned} \qquad (15.18)$$

From this we now obtain with the help of (15.14) and (15.16)

$$\alpha' - \alpha = E_t, \; \beta' - \beta = E_w. \qquad (15.19)$$

Equations (15.19) tell us that, given E_t and E_w, we can calculate α', β', γ' if α, β, γ are known, that is, we can uniquely coordinate object and image rays. The important result is that in this case one function of two coordinates, $E(t, w)$, determines the image formation completely, so that no arbitrary additional condition can be imposed.

We can now obtain a more distinct picture of the laws of image formation if we introduce the unit vectors $\vec{j}_1$ and $\vec{j}_1{}'$ in the direction of $\vec{a}_t$ and $\vec{a}_t{}'$ and $\vec{j}_2$ and $\vec{j}_2{}'$ in the direction of $\vec{a}_w$ and $\vec{a}_w{}'$, respectively. Let m_1 and m_2 be the differential magnifications with which the curves in these directions are imaged. Equations (15.14) are then equivalent to

$$\begin{aligned} m_1\vec{s}\,'\vec{j}_1{}' - \vec{s}\vec{j}_1 &= C_1 \\ m_2\vec{s}\,'\vec{j}_2{}' - \vec{s}\vec{j}_2 &= C_2, \end{aligned} \qquad (15.20)$$

which say that an element in the direction of $\vec{j}_1$ is sharply imaged into an element in the direction of $\vec{j}_1{}'$ and correspondingly for $\vec{j}_2$ and $\vec{j}_2{}'$, the magnifications being m_1 and m_2.

Multiplying Equations (15.20) by any scalars α and β, respectively, and adding, we find

$$(m_1\alpha\vec{j}_1{}' + m_2\beta\vec{j}_2{}')\vec{s}\,' - (\alpha\vec{j}_1 + \beta\vec{j}_2)\vec{s} = \alpha C_1 + \beta C_2. \qquad (15.21)$$

Therefore, if α and β are chosen so that $(\alpha\vec{j}_1 + \beta\vec{j}_2)^2 = 1$, an object element in the direction of $\vec{j}_3 = \alpha\vec{j}_1 + \beta\vec{j}_2$ is imaged sharply with the magnification m_3 upon an element in the direction of the unit vector $\vec{j}_3'$, m_3 and $\vec{j}_3'$ being given by

$$m_3\vec{j}_3' = m_1\alpha\vec{j}_1' + m_2\beta\vec{j}_2', \ \vec{j}_3^2 = 1. \qquad (15.22)$$

This is a linear affine transformation. We can therefore find two line elements $\vec{j}_1, \vec{j}_2$ such that they, as well as their image elements, are perpendicular to each other. To show this we proceed as follows.

Let $\vec{j}_1$ be perpendicular to $\vec{j}_2$ and let $\vec{j}_3$ and $\vec{j}_4$ be two other mutually perpendicular unit vectors in the plane of $\vec{j}_1$ and $\vec{j}_2$. Then we may write

$$\begin{aligned} \vec{j}_3 &= \cos\phi\,\vec{j}_1 + \sin\phi\,\vec{j}_2 \\ \vec{j}_4 &= -\sin\phi\,\vec{j}_1 + \cos\phi\,\vec{j}_2. \end{aligned} \qquad (15.23)$$

We wish to show that the parameter ϕ may be chosen so that the image line elements $\vec{j}_3'$ and $\vec{j}_4'$ are mutually perpendicular.

Now by (15.22)

$$\begin{aligned} m_3\vec{j}_3' &= m_1\cos\phi\,\vec{j}_1' + m_2\sin\phi\,\vec{j}_2' \\ m_4\vec{j}_4' &= -m_1\sin\phi\,\vec{j}_1' + m_2\cos\phi\,\vec{j}_2' \end{aligned} \qquad (15.24)$$

and

$$\begin{aligned} m_3m_4\vec{j}_3'\vec{j}_4' &= -m_1^2\cos\phi\sin\phi + m_2^2\sin\phi\cos\phi \\ &\quad + m_1m_2(\cos^2\phi - \sin^2\phi)\,\vec{j}_1'\vec{j}_2' \qquad (15.25) \\ &= \tfrac{1}{2}(m_2^2 - m_1^2)\sin 2\phi + m_1m_2\cos 2\phi\vec{j}_1'\vec{j}_2'. \end{aligned}$$

Therefore the scalar product $\vec{j}_3'\,\vec{j}_4'$ will vanish in general if

$$\tan 2\phi = \frac{2m_1m_2\vec{j}_1'\vec{j}_2'}{m_1^2 - m_2^2}. \qquad (15.26)$$

In case $m_1^2 - m_2^2 = 0$, it is sufficient to choose $\cos 2\phi = 0$, that is, $\phi = \pi/4$.

Let us assume the $\vec{j}_i$ in (15.20) to be so chosen; that is, $\vec{j}_1\,\vec{j}_2 = \vec{j}_1'\,\vec{j}_2' = 0$. We have then

$$\begin{aligned} m_1\vec{s}'\vec{j}_1' - \vec{s}\vec{j}_1 &= C_1 \\ m_2\vec{s}'\vec{j}_2' - \vec{s}\vec{j}_2 &= C_2 \end{aligned} \qquad (15.27)$$

and for any third direction

$$\vec{\jmath}_3 = \cos\phi\,\vec{\jmath}_1 + \sin\phi\,\vec{\jmath}_2$$
$$\vec{\jmath}_3{}' = \cos\phi'\vec{\jmath}_1{}' + \sin\phi'\vec{\jmath}_2{}' \tag{15.28}$$

and

$$m_3\vec{s}'\vec{\jmath}_3{}' - \vec{s}\vec{\jmath}_3 = C_3. \tag{15.29}$$

With the help of (15.22) and (15.21) we find, therefore,

$$m_3{}^2 = m_1{}^2\cos^2\phi + m_2{}^2\sin^2\phi$$
$$\cos\phi' = \frac{m_1}{m_3}\cos\phi,\ \sin\phi' = \frac{m_2}{m_3}\sin\phi \tag{15.30}$$
$$C_3 = C_1\cos\phi + C_2\sin\phi.$$

Equations (15.30) tell us that the surface element is imaged so that a small circle corresponds to a small ellipse with axes proportional to m_1 and m_2. The quantities m_1 and m_2 are maximum and minimum magnifications, as we see by differentiating the first of Equations (15.30). If $m_1 = m_2$, every line element is imaged with the same magnification.

We can, moreover, verify a statement of Bruns which says that at least one pair of directions exists for which C_3 vanishes. It is given by

$$\tan\phi = -C_1/C_2, \tag{15.31}$$

and we thus see that C_3 vanishes either for a *single* well-determined direction or for *all* directions, namely, when $C_1 = C_2 = 0$.

Two special cases are worth examining. The first is the case in which there exists a ray which is perpendicular to the surface elements in both the object and the image spaces. Let its directions be $\vec{s}_o$ and $\vec{s}_o{}'$ in the object and image spaces, respectively. We have

$$\vec{\jmath}_1\vec{s}_o = \vec{\jmath}_2\vec{s}_o = \vec{\jmath}_1{}'\vec{s}_o{}' = \vec{\jmath}_2{}'\vec{s}_o{}' = 0 \tag{15.32}$$

and therefore $C_1 = C_2 = 0$,

or

$$m_1\vec{s}'\vec{\jmath}_1{}' = \vec{s}\vec{\jmath}_1$$
$$m_2\vec{s}'\vec{\jmath}_2{}' = \vec{s}\vec{\jmath}_2 \tag{15.33}$$

for all the rays through the given point.

The other case is that in which the surface element, as Carathéodory says, *lies in the field of the instrument,* that is, a manifold of rays exists which are tangential to the surface elements in both the object and the image spaces. Let us represent $\vec{s}$ and $\vec{s}'$ by their coordinates with respect to the orthogonal bases $\vec{j}_1, \vec{j}_2, \vec{j}_1 \times \vec{j}_2$ and $\vec{j}_1', \vec{j}_2', \vec{j}_1' \times \vec{j}_2'$:

$$\vec{s} = \xi\vec{j}_1 + \eta\vec{j}_2 + \zeta(\vec{j}_1 \times \vec{j}_2), \quad \vec{s}' = \xi'\vec{j}_1' + \eta'\vec{j}_2' + \zeta'(\vec{j}_1' \times \vec{j}_2'). \tag{15.34}$$

We then have

$$\begin{aligned} m_1\xi' &= \xi + C_1 \\ m_2\eta' &= \eta + C_2. \end{aligned} \tag{15.35}$$

Rays tangential to the surface elements are given by

$$\zeta = \zeta' = 0,$$

or

$$\xi^2 + \eta^2 = n^2$$

$$\xi'^2 + \eta'^2 = \frac{1}{m_1^2}(\xi + C_1)^2 + \frac{1}{m_2^2}(\eta + C_2)^2 = n'^2. \tag{15.36}$$

The two equations (15.36) represent a circle and an ellipse in the $\xi\eta$-plane. Two such curves can have a continuous manifold of points in common only if they are identical, that is, only if

$$\frac{1}{m_1^2} = \frac{1}{m_2^2} = \frac{n'^2}{n^2}, \quad C_1 = C_2 = 0, \tag{15.37}$$

which proves *Carathéodory's Theorem*: Two surface elements can be imaged by a continuous manifold lying in the field of the instrument only if the optical lengths of the object and image elements are equal ($n'd\tau' = \pm\, nd\tau$).

Sharp Image of a Spatial Element

The case in which the points of a spatial element are imaged sharply could be reduced to the last theorem since in this case every ray lies in the field of the instrument.

However, the direct proof may be given as follows. Let $\vec{i}_1$, $\vec{i}_2$, $\vec{i}_3$ and $\vec{i}_1{}'$, $\vec{i}_2{}'$, $\vec{i}_3{}'$ be sets of mutually perpendicular unit vectors imaged upon each other with magnifications m_1, m_2, m_3 respectively. We than have

$$\begin{aligned} m_1\vec{s}'\vec{i}_1{}' - \vec{s}\vec{i}_1 &= C_1 \\ m_2\vec{s}'\vec{i}_2{}' - \vec{s}\vec{i}_2 &= C_2 \\ m_3\vec{s}'\vec{i}_3{}' - \vec{s}\vec{i}_3 &= C_3. \end{aligned} \tag{15.38}$$

Writing

$$\begin{aligned} \vec{s} &= \xi\vec{i}_1 + \eta\vec{i}_2 + \zeta\vec{i}_3 \\ \vec{s}' &= \xi'\vec{i}_1{}' + \eta'\vec{i}_2{}' + \zeta'\vec{i}_3{}' \end{aligned} \tag{15.39}$$

gives

$$\begin{aligned} m_1\xi' &= \xi + C_1 \\ m_2\eta' &= \eta + C_2 \\ m_3\zeta' &= \zeta + C_3. \end{aligned} \tag{15.40}$$

Thus at the same time ξ, η, ζ must identically fulfill

$$\frac{\xi^2 + \eta^2 + \zeta^2}{n^2} = 1$$

$$\frac{\xi'^2 + \eta'^2 + \zeta'^2}{n'^2} = \left(\frac{\xi + C_1}{m_1 n'}\right)^2 + \left(\frac{\eta + C_2}{m_2 n'}\right)^2 + \left(\frac{\zeta + C_3}{m_3 n'}\right)^2 = 1. \tag{15.41}$$

These equations are compatible for arbitrary ξ, η, ζ only if

$$\begin{aligned} C_1 = C_2 = C_3 &= 0 \\ m_1{}^2 = m_2{}^2 = m_3{}^2 &= n^2/n'^2. \end{aligned} \tag{15.42}$$

That is, a spatial element can be imaged sharply only if the object and image elements have the same optical length.

The Tetrality Principle and the Image of Infinite Points

The Lagrange differential invariant (14.10) tells us that, for any two-dimensional manifold of rays,

$$\vec{s}_u{}'\vec{a}_v{}' - \vec{s}_v{}'\vec{a}_u{}' = \vec{s}_u\vec{a}_v - \vec{s}_v\vec{a}_u. \tag{15.43}$$

Formula (15.43), instead of the refraction formula, could be taken as the starting point for developing geometrical optics, since all the other laws can be derived from it.

Since Equation (15.43) remains unchanged if we make one of the following transformations

$$\begin{aligned}&(1)\ \vec{a} \to -\vec{s},\ \vec{s} \to \vec{a}\\ &(2)\ \vec{a}' \to -\vec{s}',\ \vec{s}' \to \vec{a}'\\ &(3)\ \vec{a} \to -\vec{s},\ \vec{s} \to \vec{a},\ \vec{a}' \to -\vec{s}',\ \vec{s}' \to \vec{a}',\end{aligned} \tag{15.44}$$

we can expect that any equation between $\vec{a}$, $\vec{s}$, $\vec{a}'$, and $\vec{s}'$ remains valid if any of the above transformations is performed. This fact was announced by the author in 1932 as the *Tetrality Principle.*

The points of a ray in the object and image spaces are given by $\vec{a} + l\vec{s}$ and $\vec{a}' + l'\vec{s}'$, respectively. As a matter of terminology in this book, we shall speak of infinite points on object and image rays. These will be designated by the direction vectors $\vec{s}$ and $\vec{s}'$ in the object and image spaces, respectively.

If $\vec{s}$ is a function of one parameter, we suppose that to each value of the parameter there corresponds an infinite point so that we may say in this case that the totality of rays covers an *infinite curve* or *line.* Similarly, a plane at infinity is characterized by the vector $\vec{s}$ given as a function of two parameters.

The Tetrality Principle thus can and will be used to obtain the laws of image formation for an infinite object point (or line or plane).

We have seen in the last paragraph that the image of a single surface determines the characteristic function in general. In this way we shall be able to divide optical systems into four classes:

(1) Systems which image a finite object more or less sharply upon a finite object (reproduction objectives, for instance, these being designed for a finite magnification).

(2) Systems which image an infinite (or distant) object upon a finite image surface. (The most familiar examples are the photographic objective and the human eye.)

(3) Systems which image a finite object into infinity. (Microscopes and eyepieces or oculars are examples of this type.)

(4) Systems which image an infinite object into infinity. (Telescopes are the most important examples.)

The Tetrality Principle gives a method of transforming the laws obtained in one of the fields to each of the others. By way of illustration, we shall carry out this transformation in one or two cases.

We can, for example, apply the Tetrality Principle to Hamilton's law asserting the existence of a characteristic function E. This law, (14.4), may be written in the form

$$\vec{s}'d\vec{a}' - \vec{s}d\vec{a} = dE, \tag{15.45}$$

and this leads to the other characteristic functions introduced in (14.7). For, if the expression (15.45) is a total differential, the expressions

$$\begin{aligned} \vec{s}'d\vec{a}' + \vec{a}d\vec{s} &= dV \\ -\vec{a}'d\vec{s}' - \vec{s}d\vec{a} &= dV' \\ -\vec{a}'d\vec{s}' + \vec{a}d\vec{s} &= dW \end{aligned} \tag{15.46}$$

must be total differentials too.

In this chapter, as another application of the Tetrality Principle, we shall find the laws for imaging the points of the infinite plane. The rays from an infinite point are given by $\vec{s} =$ const. or $d\vec{s} = 0$. In general, this leads to a two-dimensional manifold of image rays with

$$\vec{s}'d\vec{a}' = dV. \tag{15.47}$$

If therefore a two-dimensional manifold of parallel rays, given by $\vec{a}(u, v)$, $\vec{s} = \vec{s}_o$, is imaged sharply into a point, then $d\vec{a}' = 0$, giving

$$V_u = V_v = 0. \tag{15.48}$$

From the geometrical meaning of V (see Chapter 14), we see that V, the light path from a plane through the origin perpendicular to the rays (a wave surface) to the image point, is constant.

Again we can speak of a *half-sharp* image of the infinite point if (15.48) is valid only for a one-dimensional manifold of rays.

An infinite point is half-symmetrically imaged if there exists an image curve $\vec{a}'(u)$ such that all the rays go through the image curve. We then have $\vec{a}(u, v)$, $\vec{s} = \vec{s}_o$ on the object side, and $\vec{a}'(u)$, $\vec{s}'(u, v)$ on the image side; thus from (15.47)

$$V_u = \vec{s}'\vec{a}_u, \quad V_v = 0. \tag{15.49}$$

We can take the parameter u as the arc length of the image curve, which gives

$$\vec{s}'\vec{t}' = \phi(u), \tag{15.50}$$

where $\vec{t}'$ is the unit vector tangential to the image curve. Thus we see again that the rays form a series of cones with the curve as bisectrix.

We now discuss the image of the points of an infinite curve. Let us assume a sharp image of the points of the curve. That means that to a manifold of rays $\vec{s}(t)$ a curve $\vec{a}'(t)$ corresponds such that each parallel bundle is united there. In this case (15.46) shows that, if $\vec{a}$ and $\vec{s}$ are regarded as functions of (u, v, t),

$$\begin{aligned} \vec{s}'\vec{a}_t{}' + \vec{a}\vec{s}_t &= V_t \\ V_u = V_v &= 0. \end{aligned} \tag{15.51}$$

The choice of the manifold $\vec{a}(u, v, t)$ in this formula is arbitrary; we can, for instance, choose $\vec{a}$ to be the point where the ray intersects the plane perpendicular to $\vec{s}_o$ through the origin, which gives

$$\vec{a}\vec{s}_o = 0. \tag{15.52}$$

In the same way we can treat the half-symmetrical image of an infinite line as well as the sharp and half-symmetrical images of the infinite plane.

CHAPTER SIXTEEN

The Characteristic Functions and the Direct Method

The fundamental importance of Hamilton's theorem was shown in the preceding chapters, and it was also shown how the optical laws might all be derived from a single function. As a fair appraisal of Hamilton's contributions, it may be said that he solved the problem "in the small," that is, he found characteristic functions for the rays "in the neighborhood of" a single object point and its image,* while later attacks on the problem have been made with the idea of finding a single function which might be given in closed form for all the rays of an optical system.

Most of Hamilton's early work was in the field of optics. His basic papers on that subject were published originally in Transactions of the Royal Irish Academy (Dublin), which did not have a very large circulation, especially on the Continent. These papers appeared between 1827 and 1837, the first when he was only twenty-two years old. Hamilton soon found that the techniques he had developed for handling optical problems were also important tools for use in other fields of physics and mathematics, particularly in mechanics and the calculus of variations. The later papers on these subjects were printed in Philosophical Transactions of the Royal Academy of Sciences (London) in 1834 and 1835. They had a great influence on the developments in these fields, thanks especially to Jacobi, who realized immediately the importance of some of Hamilton's ideas.

The Hamilton-Jacobi theory of partial differential equations has become an integral part of the working knowledge of every mathematician, while Hamilton's original papers on optics were mostly unknown or forgotten. Only a few of the great English

* This limitation does not, however, apply to the *angle characteristic* which is discussed in detail below.

physicists, such as Maxwell and Lord Rayleigh, knew of Hamilton's work in optics and used his methods.

In recent years, Hamilton's work has become more widely known. A German edition of his papers on optics, translated and annotated by Georg Prange, was published in 1933.* The volume was completely prepared and ready for printing in 1915, but publication was prevented by the inflation in Germany, and it was not until 1933 that the necessary financial support was found.

A comprehensive volume, in English, of Hamilton's optical papers was published in 1931, edited for the Royal Irish Academy by A. W. Conway and J. L. Synge of Dublin.† This volume contains papers reprinted from Transactions of the Royal Irish Academy, Philosophical Magazine, and other journals and is also augmented by a number of previously unpublished manuscripts.

Hamilton's methods of applying the characteristic functions are described immediately below, followed by some of the modifications introduced by Bruns and the present author.

In Chapter 14 it was shown [see (14.4)] that, for any manifold of rays, for any manifold of initial points $\vec{a}$, and for any manifold of terminal points $\vec{a}'$,

$$\vec{s}'d\vec{a}' - \vec{s}d\vec{a} = dE; \tag{16.1}$$

that is, that the expression $\vec{s}'d\vec{a}' - \vec{s}d\vec{a}$ is a total differential of a function E, which may be interpreted as the optical path, or the total optical distance, between $\vec{a}$ and $\vec{a}'$ measured along the ray or rays.

Applying the Tetrality Principle to (16.1), three more total differentials were found. They are:

$$\begin{aligned} dV &= \vec{s}'d\vec{a}' + \vec{a}d\vec{s} \\ dV' &= -\vec{a}'d\vec{s}' - \vec{s}d\vec{a} \\ dW &= \vec{a}d\vec{s} - \vec{a}'d\vec{s}', \end{aligned} \tag{16.2}$$

where E is called the *point characteristic*, W, the *angle characteris-*

* "Abhandlung zur Strahlenoptik," Akademische Verlagsgesellschaft, Leipzig, 1933.

† "The Mathematical Papers of Sir William Rowan Hamilton," Vol. I, "Geometrical Optics," Cambridge University Press, 1931.

tic, and V and V', *mixed characteristics*. All four functions were introduced by Hamilton in his "Essays on the Theory of System of Rays."

In comparing Equations (16.1) and (16.2), it was seen that the new characteristics are related to E by the expressions

$$
\begin{aligned}
V &= E + \vec{a}\vec{s} \\
V' &= E - \vec{a}'\vec{s}' \qquad (16.3) \\
W &= E + \vec{a}\vec{s} - \vec{a}'\vec{s}'.
\end{aligned}
$$

From these relations it was deduced that the geometrical interpretation of V is the optical path to the terminal point $\vec{a}'$ from the footpoint of the perpendicular dropped on the object ray from the origin, V' is the optical path from the initial point $\vec{a}$ to the footpoint of the perpendicular dropped on the image ray from the second origin, and W is the optical path between the two footpoints.

It should always be kept in mind that Equations (16.1) and (16.2) are correct under any circumstances, regardless of the optical system involved or the choice of initial and terminal manifolds.

If a Cartesian coordinate system is assumed, the scalar equivalents of these equations are

$$
\begin{aligned}
dE &= \xi' dx' + \eta' dy' + \zeta' dz' - \xi dx - \eta dy - \zeta dz \\
dV &= \xi' dx' + \eta' dy' + \zeta' dz' + x d\xi + y d\eta + z d\zeta \\
dV' &= -x' d\xi' - y' d\eta' - z' d\zeta' - \xi dx - \eta dy - \zeta dz \qquad (16.4) \\
dW &= x d\xi + y d\eta + z d\zeta - x' d\xi' - y' d\eta' - z' d\zeta'.
\end{aligned}
$$

In applying Hamilton's characteristic to an optical system, certain difficulties are encountered. These difficulties and limitations will be explained first in connection with the point characteristic E.

Hamilton's Point Characteristic

The purpose of the point characteristic, as shown in (16.4), is to give the directions of the object and image rays, if the coordinates x, y, z of a point on the object ray and the coordinates

x', y', z' of a point on the image ray are known. If one and only one ray goes through the two given points, there will be one and only one ray passing through any selected pair of points in the neighborhood. The "neighborhood" may be infinitesimal or of considerable finite extent.

For such a neighborhood, Equation (16.4) may ordinarily* be split into the six relations:

$$\begin{array}{lll} \partial E/\partial x' = \xi' & \partial E/\partial y' = \eta' & \partial E/\partial z' = \zeta' \\ \partial E/\partial x = -\xi & \partial E/\partial y = -\eta & \partial E/\partial z = -\zeta. \end{array} \quad (16.5)$$

Thus a function of six variables is obtained which gives the directions of the object and image rays for the points of a particular neighborhood. However, it is obvious that the relations (16.5) become indeterminate if there is more than one ray which passes through the two points x, y, z and x', y', z', that is, at the caustic. Moreover, because

$$\begin{aligned} \xi^2 + \eta^2 + \zeta^2 &= n^2 \\ \xi'^2 + \eta'^2 + \zeta'^2 &= n'^2, \end{aligned} \quad (16.6)$$

the function E cannot be purely arbitrary but must be a solution of the two partial differential equations

$$\begin{aligned} (\partial E/\partial x)^2 + (\partial E/\partial y)^2 + (\partial E/\partial z)^2 &= n^2 \\ (\partial E/\partial x')^2 + (\partial E/\partial y')^2 + (\partial E/\partial z')^2 &= n'^2. \end{aligned} \quad (16.7)$$

As examples of the application of the point characteristic, the characteristic functions will be derived to describe refraction and reflection at a single plane surface.

The Point Characteristic for a Plane Surface

For refraction at a plane surface, $z = 0$, the law of refraction gives

$$\xi' = \xi, \quad \eta' = \eta. \quad (16.8)$$

We wish to find the light path E from an object point $\vec{a}$ to an

* If $x, y, z; x', y', z'$ are independent, for example, this can be done.

image point $\vec{a}'$ in terms of the coordinates $x, y, z; x', y', z'$ of the two points. We have [*cf.* (14.5)]:

$$\begin{aligned} E &= ln^2 + l'n'^2 \\ \vec{a} + l\vec{s} &= \vec{b} \\ \vec{b} + l'\vec{s}' &= \vec{a}' \\ \vec{s}^2 &= \xi^2 + \eta^2 + \zeta^2 = n^2 \\ \vec{s}'^2 &= \xi'^2 + \eta'^2 + \zeta'^2 = n'^2. \end{aligned} \tag{16.9}$$

Furthermore, since $\vec{b}$, the vector giving the intersection point of the ray with the surface, is perpendicular to $\vec{k}$, the unit vector in the z direction, we have

$$\begin{aligned} \vec{a}\vec{k} + l\vec{s}\vec{k} &= \vec{b}\vec{k} = 0 \\ \vec{b}\vec{k} + l'\vec{s}'\vec{k} &= \vec{a}'\vec{k} \end{aligned} \tag{16.10}$$

or

$$z + l\zeta = 0, \quad l'\zeta' = z'.$$

From (16.9) we obtain

$$\vec{a}' = \vec{a} + l\vec{s} + l'\vec{s}' \tag{16.11}$$

or with the help of (16.8) and (16.10)

$$\begin{aligned} x' &= x + (l + l')\xi \\ y' &= y + (l + l')\eta \\ z &= -l\sqrt{n^2 - (\xi^2 + \eta^2)} \\ z' &= l'\sqrt{n'^2 - (\xi^2 + \eta^2)}. \end{aligned} \tag{16.12}$$

Writing

$$(x' - x)^2 + (y' - y)^2 = \varkappa, \quad \xi^2 + \eta^2 = \tau, \tag{16.13}$$

we then find

$$\varkappa = (l + l')^2\tau, \quad l = \frac{-z}{\sqrt{n^2 - \tau}}, \quad l' = \frac{z'}{\sqrt{n'^2 - \tau}} \tag{16.14}$$

or

$$E = \frac{n'^2 z'}{\sqrt{n'^2 - \tau}} - \frac{n^2 z}{\sqrt{n^2 - \tau}}, \tag{16.15}$$

with the equation

$$\varkappa = \left(\frac{z'}{\sqrt{n'^2 - \tau}} - \frac{z}{\sqrt{n^2 - \tau}} \right) \tau \tag{16.16}$$

to determine τ. We note that we cannot give E explicitly since finding τ from (16.16) involves an equation of the sixth degree. For the case of *reflection* the situation is simpler since we have

$$n = n'$$

with

$$\xi' = \xi, \quad \eta' = \eta. \tag{16.17}$$

This leads to

$$\begin{aligned} x' &= x + (l + l')\,\xi \\ y' &= y + (l + l')\,\eta \\ z &= -l\sqrt{n^2 - (\xi^2 + \eta^2)} \\ z' &= -l'\sqrt{n^2 - (\xi^2 + \eta^2)}. \end{aligned} \tag{16.18}$$

We note here that ζ' is negative since the reflected ray goes from right to left. Hence the optical distance is given by

$$E = n^2(l + l'). \tag{16.19}$$

But from (16.18)

$$\begin{aligned} (x' - x)^2 + (y' - y)^2 &= (l + l')^2\tau \\ (z + z')^2 &= (l + l')^2\,(n^2 - \tau). \end{aligned} \tag{16.20}$$

Hence

$$(x' - x)^2 + (y' - y)^2 + (z' + z)^2 = (l + l')^2 n^2,$$

and

$$E = n\sqrt{(x' - x)^2 + (y' - y)^2 + (z' + z)^2}. \tag{16.21}$$

Differentiation of E gives

$$E_x = \frac{-n(x' - x)}{\sqrt{(x' - x)^2 + (y' - y)^2 + (z' + z)^2}} \tag{16.22}$$

with similar formulae for the other derivatives. We can show that, if $x = x'$, $y = y'$, $z = -z'$, then the point $\vec{a}$ is imaged sharply on the point $\vec{a}'$. We note, as expected, that (16.22) is indeterminate in this case since numerator and denominator are zero.

Hamilton's Angle Characteristic

The angle characteristic W requires a somewhat different development because its parameters $\xi, \eta, \zeta, \xi', \eta', \zeta'$ are never independent, but instead

$$\begin{aligned} \xi^2 + \eta^2 + \zeta^2 &= n^2 \\ \xi'^2 + \eta'^2 + \zeta'^2 &= n'^2. \end{aligned} \tag{16.23}$$

This means that W must fulfill simultaneously the three conditions

$$\begin{aligned} &dW = xd\xi + yd\eta + zd\zeta - x'd\xi' - y'd\eta' - z'd\zeta' \\ &\xi d\xi + \eta d\eta + \zeta d\zeta = 0 \\ &\xi' d\xi' + \eta' d\eta' + \zeta' d\zeta' = 0. \end{aligned} \tag{16.24}$$

There are various methods of handling these differential expressions, some suggested by Lagrange, others by Hamilton himself. Of course, the case must be excluded in which specifying the directions of a ray in the object and image spaces does not determine the ray, that is, where parallel entering rays emerge parallel, as in refraction by a plane surface.

If the second and third equations of (16.24) are multiplied, respectively, by the arbitrary quantities l and $-l'$ and added to the first, we find

$$\begin{aligned} dW = &(x + l\xi)d\xi + (y + l\eta)d\eta + (z + l\zeta)d\zeta \\ &- (x' + l'\xi')d\xi' - (y' + l'\eta')d\eta' - (z' + l'\zeta')d\zeta', \end{aligned} \tag{16.25}$$

which can be split into

$$\begin{aligned} W_\xi &= x + l\xi & W_{\xi'} &= -(x' + l'\xi') \\ W_\eta &= y + l\eta & W_{\eta'} &= -(y' + l'\eta') \\ W_\zeta &= z + l\zeta & W_{\zeta'} &= -(z' + l'\zeta'). \end{aligned} \tag{16.26}$$

For any given form of W (as a function of $\xi, \eta, \zeta, \xi', \eta', \zeta'$), the Lagrange multipliers l, l' can be found.

That the form of W as a function of the six variables is not uniquely determined can be seen from the fact that, anywhere, unity can be replaced by a power of $(\xi^2 + \eta^2 + \zeta^2)/n^2$ or $(\xi'^2 + \eta'^2 + \zeta'^2)/n'^2$. If we want to make the form of W unique, we must add other conditions. The simplest condition to require is that W be homogeneous (for instance, of zero order) in ξ, η, ζ, ξ', η', ζ', respectively. (Hamilton, in some problems, investigates the case in which W is homogeneous of higher order.) By doing this, l and l' can be computed easily. Euler's equations demand that

$$W_\xi \, \xi + W_\eta \, \eta + W_\zeta \zeta = 0, \quad W_{\xi'} \xi' + W_{\eta'} \eta' + W_{\zeta'} \zeta' = 0, \tag{16.27}$$

which lead to

$$\begin{aligned} x\xi + y\eta + z\zeta + l(\xi^2 + \eta^2 + \zeta^2) &= 0 \\ x'\xi' + y'\eta' + z'\zeta' + l'(\xi'^2 + \eta'^2 + \zeta'^2) &= 0 \end{aligned} \tag{16.28}$$

or

$$\vec{a}\vec{s} + l\vec{s}^2 = 0, \quad \vec{a}'\vec{s}' + l'\vec{s}'^2 = 0.$$

Equation (16.26) therefore gives

$$\begin{aligned} W_\xi &= x_p = x + l\xi & W_{\xi'} &= -x_p' \\ W_\eta &= y_p = y + l\eta & W_{\eta'} &= -y_p' \\ W_\zeta &= z_p = z + l\zeta & W_{\zeta'} &= -z_p', \end{aligned} \tag{16.29}$$

where $x_p, y_p, z_p; x_p', y_p' z_p'$, respectively, are the coordinates of the footpoints of the perpendiculars dropped from the origins to the object and the image rays, and W is the optical path between these two footpoints.

As an example of the angle characteristic, we shall find the function W for a spherical refracting surface. We place both origins at the center and denote the footpoints of the perpendiculars to the object and image rays by $\vec{a}_p$ and $\vec{a}_p'$. We then have

$$\begin{aligned} &\vec{a}_p + l\vec{s} = \vec{b}, \quad \vec{b} + l'\vec{s}' = \vec{a}_p' \\ &\vec{a}_p\vec{s} = \vec{a}_p'\vec{s}' = 0. \end{aligned} \tag{16.30}$$

Hence

$$ln^2 = \vec{b}\vec{s}, \quad l'n'^2 = -\vec{b}\vec{s}' \tag{16.31}$$

and

$$W = ln^2 + l'n'^2 = \vec{b}(\vec{s} - \vec{s}').$$

The law of refraction gives

$$\vec{s}' - \vec{s} = \Gamma\vec{\sigma} = -(\Gamma/r)\vec{b}, \tag{16.32}$$

from which

$$W = (\Gamma/r)\vec{b}^2 = r\Gamma. \tag{16.33}$$

From (16.32) we also have

$$\Gamma^2 = (\vec{s}' - \vec{s})^2, \tag{16.34}$$

with

$$\Gamma = \vec{s}'\vec{\sigma} - \vec{s}\vec{\sigma}, \quad \vec{s}' \times \vec{\sigma} = \vec{s} \times \vec{\sigma}, \tag{16.35}$$

the latter equation giving

$$\vec{s}'^2\vec{\sigma}^2 - (\vec{s}'\vec{\sigma})^2 = \vec{s}^2\vec{\sigma}^2 - (\vec{s}\vec{\sigma})^2$$

or

$$(\vec{s}'\vec{\sigma})^2 - (\vec{s}\vec{\sigma})^2 = n'^2 - n^2 \tag{16.35a}$$

to determine the sign of Γ according as n' is greater or less than n. Thus

$$W = r\Gamma = \pm r\sqrt{(\xi' - \xi)^2 + (\eta' - \eta)^2 + (\zeta' - \zeta)^2}. \tag{16.36}$$

We now write this in a homogeneous form of zero order in the six variables

$$W = \pm r\sqrt{n^2 + n'^2 - \frac{2nn'(\xi\xi' + \eta\eta' + \zeta\zeta')}{\sqrt{\xi^2 + \eta^2 + \zeta^2}\sqrt{\xi'^2 + \eta'^2 + \zeta'^2}}}. \tag{16.37}$$

The Mixed Characteristics

In general the development of the mixed characteristic functions follows a pattern similar to that already shown. The function V may be required to be homogeneous in ξ, η, and ζ of zero order.

The characteristics V and V' are the solutions of the differential equations

$$(\partial V/\partial x')^2 + (\partial V/\partial y')^2 + (\partial V/\partial z')^2 = n'^2$$
$$(\partial V'/\partial x)^2 + (\partial V'/\partial y)^2 + (\partial V'/\partial z)^2 = n^2. \tag{16.38}$$

Imposing the condition for homogeneity leads to the relations

$$\begin{aligned} \partial V/\partial x' &= \xi' & \partial V/\partial \xi &= x_p \\ \partial V/\partial y' &= \eta' & \partial V/\partial \eta &= y_p \\ \partial V/\partial z' &= \zeta' & \partial V/\partial \zeta &= z_p \end{aligned} \tag{16.39}$$

and analogously

$$\begin{aligned} -\partial V'/\partial x &= \xi & -\partial V'/\partial \xi' &= x'_p \\ -\partial V'/\partial y &= \eta & -\partial V'/\partial \eta' &= y'_p \\ -\partial V'/\partial z &= \zeta & -\partial V'/\partial \zeta' &= z'_p. \end{aligned} \tag{16.40}$$

Equations (16.39) become indeterminate if the terminal point (x', y', z') lies on the caustic of the rays coming from an infinite object point, and Equations (16.40) become indeterminate if two rays from the same initial point (x, y, z) emerge from the system parallel to each other.

So much for the Hamiltonian characteristic. Next will be an explanation of the modified characteristic developed by Bruns* in 1895. Bruns called it the "eikonal," from the Greek word *ikon* meaning *image*.

Heinrich Bruns

Although Hamilton's characteristic function has had widespread application in other fields of mathematical physics, the use of Bruns' method has so far been confined to geometrical optics.

Oddly enough, Bruns, not knowing of Hamilton's papers on optics, believed that he was making an original step in applying to optics the methods Hamilton had developed for classical mechanics. Bruns was a pupil of Sophus Lie, a mathematician who had tried to gain a greater understanding of the problems of partial differential equations by treating them geometrically. While Bruns' methods may properly be considered only as modifications of Hamilton's ideas, they contain nevertheless a significant and valuable contribution.

* Bruns, H., "Das Eikonal," Sächs. Ber. d. Wiss. *21*, 1895.

The Eikonals of Bruns

Bruns argued that, since the manifold of all the rays in space is four-dimensional, that is, a ray may be defined in space by four parameters, it should be suitable to give the characteristic of an optical system as a function of four variables. His procedure may be described as follows.

Let us assume that $\vec{a}(u, v)$ and $\vec{a}'(u', v')$ are two surfaces such that one and only one ray goes from one point of $\vec{a}$ to a point of $\vec{a}'$.

We then have

$$dE = \vec{s}'\vec{a}'_{u'}du' + \vec{s}'\vec{a}'_{v'}dv' - \vec{s}\vec{a}_u du - \vec{s}\vec{a}_v dv, \tag{16.41}$$

which leads to

$$\begin{aligned} E_{u'} &= \vec{s}'\vec{a}'_{u'} \qquad & E_u &= -\vec{s}\vec{a}_u \\ E_{v'} &= \vec{s}'\vec{a}'_{v'} \qquad & E_v &= -\vec{s}\vec{a}_v \end{aligned} \tag{16.42}$$

since u, v, u', v' are independent. We see that, if $\vec{a}$, $\vec{a}'$, and E are given as functions of u, v, u', v', we can compute $\vec{s}$ and $\vec{s}'$ from (16.42) combined with

$$\vec{s}^2 = n^2, \quad \vec{s}'^2 = n'^2. \tag{16.43}$$

We have thus coordinated an image ray to each object ray and *vice versa* in such a way that this one-to-one correspondence fulfills all the laws of optics.

This reduces the somewhat hazy problem of discussing the general laws of optical systems to the simple problem of investigating the qualities of a single general function of four variables, a problem which subsequently will be simplified for concentric and rotation-symmetrical systems.

In the same way, the other characteristic functions of Hamilton can be replaced by functions of four variables, and these likewise we call *eikonals*. If $\vec{s}(u, v)$ designates the direction of the object rays and $\vec{a}'(u', v')$ a surface in the image space such that no two rays that are parallel in the object space go to the same point of $\vec{a}'$, we can use the eikonal $V(u, v, u', v')$ and split the equation

$$dV = \vec{s}'d\vec{a}' + \vec{a}d\vec{s} = \vec{s}'\vec{a}'_{u'}du' + \vec{s}'\vec{a}'_{v'}dv' + \vec{a}\vec{s}_u du + \vec{a}\vec{s}_v dv \tag{16.44}$$

into

$$V_u = \vec{a}\vec{s}_u \qquad V_{u'} = \vec{s}'\vec{a}'_{u'}$$
$$V_v = \vec{a}\vec{s}_v \qquad V_{v'} = \vec{s}'\vec{a}'_{v'}. \tag{16.45}$$

Again an arbitrary function $V(u, v, u', v')$ describes the general optical system.

The angle eikonal W with

$$dW = \vec{a}d\vec{s} - \vec{a}'d\vec{s}' = \vec{a}\vec{s}_u du + \vec{a}\vec{s}_v dv - \vec{a}'\vec{s}'_{u'}du' - \vec{a}'\vec{s}'_{v'}dv' \tag{16.46}$$

leads to

$$W_u = \vec{a}\vec{s}_u \qquad W_{u'} = -\vec{a}'\vec{s}'_{u'}$$
$$W_v = \vec{a}\vec{s}_v \qquad W_{v'} = -\vec{a}'\vec{s}'_{v'} \tag{16.47}$$

Here we could take as suitable variables, for instance, the direction cosines ξ, η, ξ', η'.

The reader will see that, in the treatment of Hamilton and Bruns, two of the four data of the ray belong to the object space, and two to the image space. The problem of finding, for a given object ray (four data in the object space), the corresponding image ray (through four of its data in the image space) cannot be solved directly with Hamilton's and Bruns' methods. We need to eliminate either the object data or the image data from the basic Bruns-Hamilton equations.

Although an elimination process does not frighten a mathematician, it is not analytically possible in the case of practical optical problems to carry out such a process. For this reason the author of this book suggested* employing a so-called Direct Method—trying to express the data in the image space as a function of the data in the object space. The computation formulae developed in Part 1 enable one to express the image data analytically as functions of the object data. The problem of elimination is reduced to a problem of substitution, since the calculation formulae give for a single surface the coordination between the object and the image rays.

The Direct Method serves also to obtain the data for a combined system if the formula for each part is given. One cannot use the characteristic functions, or eikonals, for this purpose since the

* "Direct Methods in Geometrical Optics," Trans. Am. Math. Soc., *53*, No. 2, 218-229, 1943.

differential form does not split up into the contribution of the object and the image sides when the coordinates are the four data on the object side. However, we can introduce the Lagrangian invariant into the Direct Method to solve the problem.

In the general case we have four variables (u, v, t, w). Let us assume $\vec{a}$ as a surface in the object space (depending on two parameters u, v) and let $\vec{s}$ be the direction vector (depending on two parameters t, w). Let $\vec{a}'$ be the intersection of the rays with a surface in the image space, and let $\vec{s}'$ be the image-side direction vector. We obtain the following six equations for optical image formation [*cf.* (14.10)]:

$$\begin{aligned} &\vec{s}_u'\vec{a}_v' - \vec{s}_v'\vec{a}_u' = 0 && \vec{s}_v'\vec{a}_w' - \vec{s}_w'\vec{a}_v' = -\vec{s}_w\vec{a}_v \\ &\vec{s}_u'\vec{a}_t' - \vec{s}_t'\vec{a}_u' = -\vec{s}_t\vec{a}_u && \vec{s}_v'\vec{a}_t' - \vec{s}_t'\vec{a}_v' = -\vec{s}_t\vec{a}_v \\ &\vec{s}_u'\vec{a}_w' - \vec{s}_w'\vec{a}_u' = -\vec{s}_w\vec{a}_u && \vec{s}_w'\vec{a}_t' - \vec{s}_t'\vec{a}_w' = 0. \end{aligned} \tag{16.48}$$

These equations form the bases for the so-called Direct Method in optics.

We shall later use the eikonal method and the characteristic function to derive further general laws of image formation. We shall use the Direct Method to discuss the numerical treatment of various given systems.

In Part IV we shall specialize our results and consider the case of concentric systems, and then in Part V we shall investigate image formation in systems with symmetry of rotation.

CHAPTER SEVENTEEN

The Surfaces of Descartes

In the last chapter, the problem of image formation in an optical system was discussed. In this chapter, we shall give some important examples of this image formation. First we investigate the Cartesian surfaces, that is, surfaces which have the property of refracting the rays coming from a point in such a way that the refracted rays again go through a point.

The problem leads by its nature to a surface that is rotationally symmetric about the line joining the two points, this being the optical axis. Let us choose the origin at the vertex of the refracting (reflecting) surface and the z-axis as usual along the optical axis. Let $\vec{b}$ (with components x, y, z) be the vector to the refracting surface and let $\vec{a}$ represent the (axis) object point and $\vec{a}'$ its (axis) image point. We then have

$$\begin{aligned} \vec{b} &= \vec{a} + l\vec{s} \\ \vec{a}' &= \vec{b} + l'\vec{s}'. \end{aligned} \tag{17.1}$$

By virtue of Fermat's theorem, the optical path from $\vec{a}$ to $\vec{a}'$ is equal to

$$n^2l + n'^2l' = L + L', \tag{17.2}$$

where L and L' are the axis *optical* paths from the object point to the vertex and from the vertex to the image point, respectively.

On the other hand we can write

$$\begin{aligned} \vec{a} &= -(L/n)\,\vec{k} = -(nl_o)\vec{k} \\ \vec{a}' &= (L'/n')\vec{k} = (n'l_o')\vec{k}. \end{aligned} \tag{17.3}$$

It may be noted that with this notation a positive value of $L(L')$ designates a real object (image) and a negative value, a virtual object (image).

The condition that the refractive surface be Cartesian is then given by

$$n^2l + n'^2l' = n^2l_o + n'^2l_o' = L + L'. \tag{17.4}$$

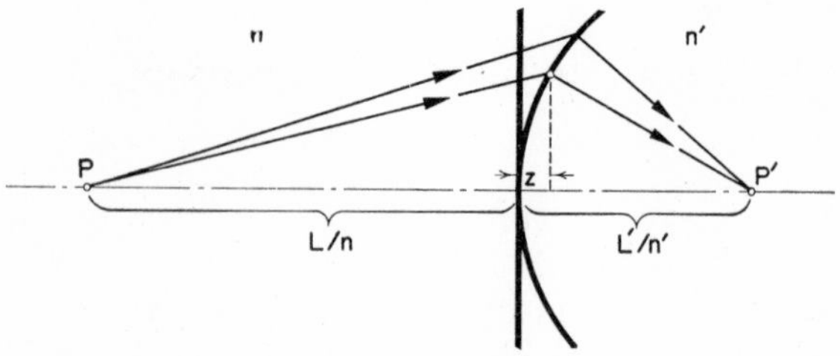

Fig. 17.1. Figure for deriving Cartesian surfaces for refraction.

We find from Figure 17.1

$$n^2l = n\sqrt{x^2 + y^2 + (z + L/n)^2}$$
$$n'^2l' = n'\sqrt{x^2 + y^2 + (z - L'/n')^2}, \tag{17.5}$$

which also apply for a virtual object or image if the respective roots have the same signs as L and L'. We thus obtain the equation

$$\sqrt{n'^2(x^2 + y^2) + (n'z - L')^2} + \sqrt{n^2(x^2 + y^2) + (nz + L)^2} = L + L', \tag{17.6}$$

which leads to the fourth-order equation

$$[(x^2 + y^2 + z^2)(n'^2 - n^2) - 2z(n'L' + nL)]^2 = 4(L + L')[(x^2 + y^2 + z^2)(n^2L' + n'^2L) + 2zLL'(n - n')]. \tag{17.7}$$

These are the so-called *Cartesian surfaces* of fourth order with rotation symmetry about the axis. Of special interest is the Cartesian surface for which $L + L' = 0$. In this case Equation (17.7) reduces to

$$(x^2 + y^2 + z^2)(n'^2 - n^2) = 2z(nL + n'L'), \tag{17.8}$$

which represents a sphere. Since $L' = -L$, we find the radius to be

$$r = -L/(n + n')$$

or

$$-L = L' = (n + n')r. \tag{17.9}$$

Because of the central symmetry for the image formation of the sphere, not only the axis point with the center distance

$$-\left(\frac{L}{n} + r\right) = \frac{n'}{n} r \tag{17.10}$$

but also the points of an entire sphere through this point are imaged sharply, the vertex of the image sphere being at the distance

$$\frac{L'}{n'} - r = \frac{n}{n'} r \tag{17.11}$$

from the center of the refracting sphere. (These are the aplanatic surfaces of Chapter 2.)

For negative r, the object is real and the image is virtual; for positive r, the object is virtual and the image is real.

We have here an example of the sharp imaging of one surface on another. However, either the object or the image surface is virtual, that is, inaccessible. Unfortunately all the theoretical sharp image formations which have been realizable are of the same type.

The case of reflection will be obtained from Figure 17.2, where we set $n = n' = 1$. After reflection the light changes its direction. Instead of (17.6) we therefore must write

$$\sqrt{x^2 + y^2 + (z + L)^2} + \sqrt{x^2 + y^2 + (z - L')^2} = L - L'$$

or

$$\frac{\left(z - \dfrac{L' - L}{2}\right)^2}{\left(\dfrac{L' - L}{2}\right)^2} - \frac{x^2 + y^2}{LL'} = 1, \tag{17.12}$$

which is the vertex equation of a hyperboloid or ellipsoid depending on whether L and L' have the same or opposite signs. These

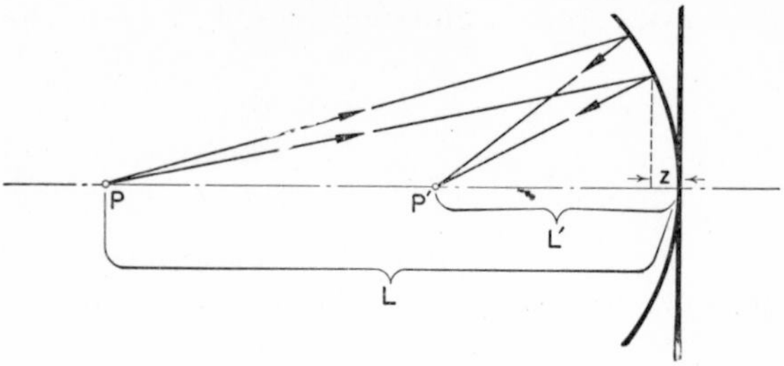

Fig. 17.2. Figure for deriving Cartesian surfaces for reflection (finite object point).

focal qualities of the conic sections, which were considered also in Chapter 5, were known by the Greeks and are described in detail in Euclid's "Catoptrics" and in Hero of Alexandria's book on optics.

In this chapter we have solved the problem of refracting or reflecting a spherical wave, that is, a wave originating at a finite object point in such a way that it converges to a point. For completeness we shall ask for the surface imaging a parallel bundle of rays (the rays from an infinite object point) at a point. We can consider as wave-surface the plane tangential to the refracting (reflecting) surface. Figure 17.1 with P at infinity shows the condition for sharp image formation to be

$$nz + \sqrt{n'^2(x^2 + y^2) + (L' - n'z)^2} = L'$$

or

$$\frac{\left(z - \dfrac{L'}{n + n'}\right)^2}{\dfrac{L'^2}{(n + n')^2}} - \frac{x^2 + y^2}{\dfrac{L'^2}{n'^2}\,\dfrac{n - n'}{n + n'}} = 1, \tag{17.13}$$

which for $n > n'$ is the equation of a hyperbola and for $n < n'$ an ellipse. This result is in agreement with those of Chapter 5. Since a plane surface does not change the direction of the rays of a parallel bundle normal to it, we can thus, with Descartes, construct a plano-convex lens whose second surface is the above hyperbola and which refracts a parallel entering bundle into a point. These are the famous hyperbolic lenses Descartes asked a Swiss optician to grind long before Snell discovered the refraction law and which explain why Dr. Boegehold assumed that one must ascribe the discovery of the refraction law to Descartes.

In the case of reflection, we find the well-known focal characteristic of the parabola (see Chapter 5) of reflecting all rays parallel to its axis into its focal point or, conversely, of reflecting the rays from the focal point into a bundle parallel to its axis. If we set $n = n' = 1$ and examine Figure 17.3, we obtain

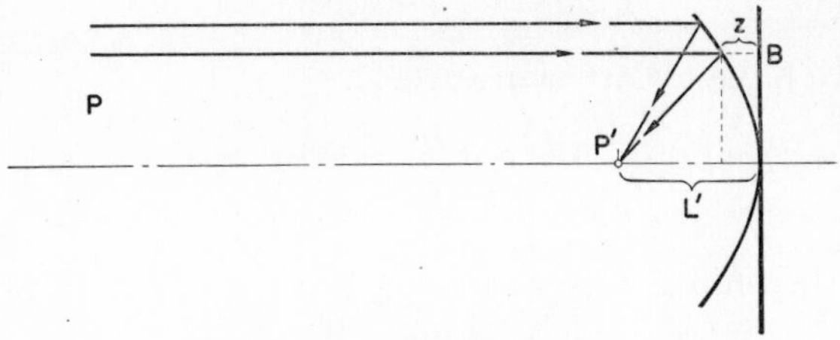

Fig. 17.3. Figure for deriving Cartesian surfaces for reflection (infinite object point).

$$z + \sqrt{x^2 + y^2 + (z - L')^2} = -L'$$

or

$$x^2 + y^2 = 4L'z, \tag{17.14}$$

which is the equation of a parabola. The point at the optical path distance L' is the focal point.

Until now, we have shown that the paths from the object point to the Cartesian surface and thence to the image point multiplied by their respective refractive indices is constant. It remains to prove that the object and the image rays are connected by the refraction law.

Let $\vec{a}$ be the vector to the initial point, $\vec{a}'$ the vector to the terminal point and $\vec{b}$ the vector to the Cartesian surface. We then have, as in (17.1),

$$\vec{b} = \vec{a} + l\vec{s}$$
$$\vec{a}' = \vec{b} + l'\vec{s}'. \tag{17.15}$$

Differentiating according to any parameter, we have (since $d\vec{a} = d\vec{a}' = 0$)

$$d\vec{b} = l d\vec{s} + \vec{s} dl$$

$$0 = d\vec{b} + l' d\vec{s}' + \vec{s}' dl', \tag{17.16}$$

and because of $\vec{s}^2 = n^2, \quad \vec{s}'^2 = n'^2,$
which give

$$\vec{s} d\vec{s} = \vec{s}' d\vec{s}' = 0, \tag{17.17}$$

we find, after multiplying (17.16) scalarly by $\vec{s}$ and $\vec{s}'$,

$$\vec{s} d\vec{b} = n^2 dl$$

$$\vec{s}' d\vec{b} = -n'^2 dl'. \tag{17.18}$$

Since we have a Cartesian surface,

$$n^2 l + n'^2 l' = \text{const.}$$

$$n^2 dl + n'^2 dl' = 0. \tag{17.19}$$

We find, therefore,

$$(\vec{s}' - \vec{s}) d\vec{b} = 0, \tag{17.20}$$

which tells us that $(\vec{s}' - \vec{s})$ is normal to the surface, that is, the rays fulfill the law of refraction.

It is interesting to inquire whether the image-forming rays fulfill the sine condition. It is obvious that

$$\sin u = h/nl, \quad \sin u' = -h/n'l', \tag{17.21}$$

which leads to

$$\frac{n \sin u}{n' \sin u'} = -\frac{l'}{l}. \tag{17.22}$$

If this ratio is to be constant and l, l' are not constants, then

$$n^2 l + n'^2 l' = \text{const.} \tag{17.23}$$

can obviously be fulfilled only if the constant in (17.23) vanishes. This leads to the aplanatic surfaces of a sphere and the magnification

$$m = \frac{n \sin u}{n' \sin u'} = \frac{n^2}{n'^2} \tag{17.24}$$

with which the aplanatic surfaces are imaged upon each other.

PART IV. CONCENTRIC SYSTEMS

CHAPTER EIGHTEEN

General Laws

A knowledge of the laws of concentric systems is of great value to the optical designer, being, in spite of their variety, sufficiently simple so that all the problems can be solved explicitly, an aim not yet approached for the case of rotational symmetry. The method of ray-tracing through such a system was discussed in Chapter 3.

A concentric system consists of a number of spherical surfaces with a common center. We shall choose this center as origin for both the object and the image spaces.

Given an initial point, vector $\vec{a}$, and the direction vector $\vec{s}$ (of length n) along the ray, we then know that, for an arbitrary terminal point (vector $\vec{a}'$) and the direction vector $\vec{s}'$ (of length n') in the direction of the image ray, we have as follows from (2.9) for the case of a single sphere with center at the origin:

$$\vec{a} \times \vec{s} = \vec{a}' \times \vec{s}' = \vec{J}. \tag{18.1}$$

The vector $\vec{J}$ is perpendicular to the plane through the initial point, the center, and the ray, and we have seen and proved previously that this plane of incidence contains the terminal ray. The intersection point $\vec{a}'$ of the terminal ray with the pseudoaxis (line through the object point and the center) was called the *diapoint* of the initial point, and Equation (3.22) shows that for the connection of point and diapoint we have the equations

$$\begin{aligned} \vec{a}' &= m\vec{a} \\ \vec{s}' &= -\phi\,\vec{a} + (1/m)\,\vec{s}, \end{aligned} \tag{18.2}$$

where m is the diamagnification and ϕ the power of the system. For the rays through a given initial point $\vec{a}$, m and ϕ are then general functions of one variable which we could take, for instance, as $\vec{J}^2 = (\vec{a} \times \vec{s})^2$.

Equations (18.2) are the basic formulae of the theory of concentric systems. To these we can add the equation obtained by squaring the second equation in (18.2), giving

$$n'^2 = \phi^2\vec{a}^2 - 2\frac{\phi}{m}\vec{a}\vec{s} + \frac{n^2}{m^2}, \tag{18.3}$$

which connects ϕ and m or $1/m$.

Equation (18.2) shows that all the diapoints of a given object point lie on the pseudoaxis, and this means (see Chapter 14) that every object point has at least a symmetrical image. If for a given initial point $m = m_o$, that is, m is constant, we find that this point is sharply imaged. It is clear that in this case the whole sphere containing the object point is sharply imaged, but it is not obvious that in this case, as we shall prove later, all the points of a second sphere are imaged sharply at the same time.

It is evident from (18.2) that the center $\vec{a} = 0$ is imaged sharply upon itself since $\vec{a}' = 0$, the magnification being

$$m = n/n' \tag{18.4}$$

(or $m = -n/n'$ if the system has an odd number of reflections).

To treat the concentric systems parallel to the treatment that will be followed for the rotation-symmetric system, we shall introduce first some of the characteristic functions and then discuss the Direct Method introduced in Chapter 16.

The introduction of the mixed characteristic V' suggests the use of $\vec{a}$ and $\vec{s}'$ as data since we have [see (16.2)]

$$d(-V') = \vec{s}d\vec{a} + \vec{a}'d\vec{s}'. \tag{18.5}$$

Equations (18.2) transform to

$$\begin{aligned} \vec{a}' &= m\vec{a} \\ \vec{s} &= m\phi\vec{a} + m\vec{s}'. \end{aligned} \tag{18.6}$$

Inserting (18.6) into (18.5), we obtain

$$d(-V') = m\phi\vec{a}\,d\vec{a} + m\,d(\vec{a}\vec{s}'). \tag{18.7}$$

This formula suggests introducing as variables

$$\begin{aligned} A &= \tfrac{1}{2}\,\vec{a}^2 \\ B &= \vec{a}\vec{s}', \end{aligned} \tag{18.8}$$

leading to

$$- dV' = (m\phi)\, dA + mdB, \tag{18.9}$$

which means that V' can be considered as a function of two variables A and B such that

$$\begin{aligned} \partial V'/\partial A &= V_A' = - m\phi \\ \partial V'/\partial B &= V_B' = - m. \end{aligned} \tag{18.10}$$

Inserting (18.10) into the second equation of (18.6) squared shows that V' is not an arbitrary function of A and B, but one which fulfills the quadratic differential equation

$$2V_A'^2 A + 2V_A'V_B' B + V_B'^2 n'^2 = n^2. \tag{18.11}$$

Equations (18.6) now can be written

$$\begin{aligned} \vec{a}' &= - V_B'\vec{a} \\ \vec{s} &= - V_A'\vec{a} - V_B'\vec{s}'. \end{aligned} \tag{18.12}$$

We shall first discuss the special case in which $V_A' = 0$. We find

$$\begin{aligned} \vec{a}' &= - V_B'\vec{a} \\ \vec{s} &= - V_B'\vec{s}'. \end{aligned} \tag{18.13}$$

Since the vectors $\vec{s}$, $\vec{s}'$ have the lengths n, n' and the same direction if the system has no reflections, or an even number of them, and opposite directions if the system has an odd number of reflections, we find that $V_B' = \pm\, n/n'$. Thus for systems with no reflections or an even number of them

$$\begin{aligned} V' &= - (n/n')\, B \\ \vec{a}' &= (n/n')\, \vec{a} \\ \vec{s} &= (n/n')\, \vec{s}', \end{aligned} \tag{18.14}$$

which shows that in this case every point in space is sharply imaged with a magnification n/n', and each object ray and its image ray are parallel.

For systems with one or an odd number of reflections, we find

$$\begin{aligned} V' &= (n/n')\, B \\ \vec{a}' &= - (n/n')\, \vec{a} \\ \vec{s} &= - (n/n')\, \vec{s}', \end{aligned} \tag{18.15}$$

giving again a sharp image formation for all points in space, object and image rays being again parallel to each other. These systems are examples of *spatial* systems, which by definition image every point of space sharply.

In other systems, the knowledge of a characteristic function $V'(A, B)$ obeying the differential equation (18.11) suffices to compute for every object point $A = A_o$, its corresponding diapoint. It also permits one to determine the points of the caustic for any object point, the procedure being as follows.

There is obviously no loss of generality in assuming the initial point to be on the z-axis with coordinates $(0, 0, z)$. Let $\vec{s}$ have the coordinates (ξ, η, ζ) with $\xi^2 + \eta^2 + \zeta^2 = n^2$, and analogously $\vec{a}'$ have the coordinates $(0, 0, z')$ and $\vec{s}'$ the coordinates ξ', η', ζ'.

Making use of (18.12) and the fact that

$$A = \tfrac{1}{2}\vec{a}^2 = \tfrac{1}{2}z^2$$
$$B = \vec{a}\vec{s}' = z\zeta' , \qquad (18.16)$$

we can express the four vectors $\vec{a}, \vec{a}', \vec{s}, \vec{s}'$, with the help of ξ' as parameter, where $\sqrt{2A}$ is, of course, given the sign of z:

$$\vec{a} : (0, 0, z)$$
$$\vec{s} : (-V_B'\xi', -V_B'\sqrt{n'^2-\xi'^2-B^2/(2A)}, -V_A'\sqrt{2A}-V_B'B/\sqrt{2A})$$
$$\vec{a}' : (0, 0, -V_B'\sqrt{2A})$$
$$\vec{s}' : (\xi', \sqrt{n'^2-\xi'^2-B^2/(2A)}, B/\sqrt{2A}). \qquad (18.17)$$

In considering the rays from a point, we must assume A to be constant, so that, ξ' and B are then the parameters of the problem. According to Chapter 14 [Formula (14.28)], the distance $\varkappa$ of the points of the caustic from the diapoint is given by the equation:

$$\varkappa^2[\vec{s}'\vec{s}_1'\vec{s}_2'] + \varkappa\{[\vec{s}'\vec{a}_1'\vec{s}_2'] + [\vec{s}'\vec{s}_1'\vec{a}_2']\} + [\vec{s}'\vec{a}_1'\vec{a}_2'] = 0. \qquad (18.18)$$

Differentiating (18.17) we obtain

$$\vec{s}'_{\xi'} : (1, -\xi'/\sqrt{n'^2-\xi'^2-B^2/(2A)}, 0)$$
$$\vec{s}'_B : (0, -B/(2A\sqrt{n'^2-\xi'^2-B^2/(2A)}), 1/\sqrt{2A} \qquad (18.19)$$
$$\vec{a}'_{\xi'} : (0, 0, 0)$$
$$\vec{a}'_B : (0, 0, -V_{BB}'\sqrt{2A}),$$

which leads to

$$\varkappa_1 = 0, \qquad \varkappa_2 = \frac{2An^2 - B^2}{n'^2} V_{BB}' \tag{18.20}$$

This permits one to compute the caustic for any object point.

The Angle Characteristic

Having investigated the "telescopic" systems ($\phi = 0$), we can make use of the angle characteristic W. Equation (16.2) gives

$$dW = \vec{a}d\vec{s} - \vec{a}'d\vec{s}', \tag{18.21}$$

which suggests solving Equations (18.2) with respect to $\vec{a}$ and $\vec{a}'$ by writing

$$\begin{aligned} \vec{a} &= (1/\phi m)\,(\vec{s} - m\vec{s}') \\ \vec{a}' &= (1/\phi)\,(\vec{s} - m\vec{s}'). \end{aligned} \tag{18.22}$$

Inserting (18.22) into (18.21) we obtain

$$dW = -\,(1/\phi)\,d(\vec{s}\vec{s}'), \tag{18.23}$$

which suggests that the angle characteristic W for a concentric system can be considered as a function of a single variable

$$b = \vec{s}\vec{s}' \tag{18.24}$$

with

$$W_b = -\,1/\phi.$$

This leads to

$$\begin{aligned} \vec{a} &= -\,(1/m)\,W_b\,(\vec{s} - m\vec{s}') \\ \vec{a}' &= -\,W_b\,(\vec{s} - m\vec{s}'). \end{aligned} \tag{18.25}$$

Squaring Equations (18.25) we find

$$m^2\vec{a}^2 = \vec{a}'^2 = W_b{}^2(n^2 + m^2n'^2 - 2mb), \tag{18.26}$$

which permits one, if W (and therefore W_b) is given, to compute, for a given object position, $\vec{a}^2 = L^2$, the magnification m, and therefore the image distance $L' = mL$ as a function of b.

This leads one to ask what form W must assume so that, for a given object distance L_o, the diamagnification will have a given constant value $m = m_o$. That leads to

$$W_b = -m_0 L_o / \sqrt{n^2 + n'^2 m_0^2 - 2bm_o} \tag{18.27}$$

or

$$W = L_o \sqrt{n^2 + n'^2 m_0^2 - 2bm_o},$$

which is a characteristic function of the form

$$W = \sqrt{C_1 - 2bC_2}, \tag{18.28}$$

where

$$C_2 = L_o^2 m_0$$

$$C_1 = L_o^2 m_0 \left(\frac{n^2}{m_0} + n'^2 m_0 \right).$$

Inserting $m = m_0$ and (18.27) into (18.26), we see that the system images the sphere of radius $-L_o$ upon the sphere of radius $-m_0 L_o$.

However, in computing L_o and m_0 from C_1 and C_2, we find two solutions. That is, for any solutions m_0 and L_o, the values m_1 and L_1 are also solutions where

$$m_1 = \frac{n^2}{n'^2} \frac{1}{m_0}$$

$$L_1 = -\frac{n'}{n} L_o m_0 \tag{18.29}$$

$$L_1' = -\frac{n}{n'} L_o = -\frac{n}{n' m_0} L_o'.$$

We see, in general, that if one object point is imaged sharply, *two* object spheres are imaged sharply. Such systems are called *two-sphere* systems, and we shall investigate in the next chapter all such two-sphere systems that can be realized.

The Direct Method

The same problems can be solved with the Direct Method of approach. Equations (18.2) give

$$\vec{a}' = m\vec{a}$$

$$\vec{s}' = -\phi\, \vec{a} + (1/m)\, \vec{s}. \tag{18.30}$$

The two functions ϕ and m are connected by Equation (18.3):

$$n'^2 = \phi^2\vec{a}^2 - 2\,(\phi/m)\,\vec{a}\vec{s} + (1/m^2)\,n^2. \tag{18.31}$$

There is also another connection derived from the fact that, for two arbitrary parameters, the Lagrangian formulae hold:

$$\vec{a}_1'\vec{s}_2' - \vec{a}_2'\vec{s}_1' = \vec{a}_1\vec{s}_2 - \vec{a}_2\vec{s}_1, \tag{18.32}$$

in which 1 and 2 indicate differentiation according to two arbitrary parameters. Inserting for $\vec{a}'$ and $\vec{s}'$ the values from Equation (18.30), we find for ϕ and m the following differential equation (expressed with $\vec{a}^2 = 2\,u$; $\vec{a}\vec{s} = v$):

$$\begin{vmatrix} m_1, & 2u\phi_1 + \phi u_1 - (1/m)v_1 \\ m_2, & 2u\phi_2 + \phi u_2 - (1/m)v_2 \end{vmatrix} = m \begin{vmatrix} \phi_1 & u_1 \\ \phi_2 & u_2 \end{vmatrix} \tag{18.33}$$

Differentiating (18.31) we find

$$u_\nu\phi^2 + 2\phi u\phi_\nu - v_\nu\frac{\phi}{m} - v\frac{\phi_\nu}{m} = (n^2 - v\phi m)\frac{m_\nu}{m^3}\,. \tag{18.34}$$

Eliminating m_1 and m_2 from (18.33) and (18.34) leads to

$$\begin{vmatrix} \phi_1, & u_1 n^2 - v_1 v \\ \phi_2, & u_2 n^2 - v_2 v \end{vmatrix} = 0, \tag{18.35}$$

which shows that ϕ is a function of

$$\tau^2 = 2un^2 - v^2 = (\vec{a} \times \vec{s})^2 = \vec{J}^2 \tag{18.36}$$

alone. Choosing τ and $u = \frac{1}{2}\vec{a}^2$ as variables, Equation (18.31) leads to the following equation connecting ϕ and m:

$$\frac{n^2}{m^2} - \frac{2\phi}{m}\sqrt{2un^2 - \tau^2} + 2u\,\phi^2 - n'^2 = 0. \tag{18.37}$$

If ϕ is given as a function of τ, Equation (18.37) determines $1/m$ and consequently m as a function of τ and u. Of interest again are the special cases in which the optical system is either a *spatial* system or a *two-sphere* system.

The spatial system is given by $\phi = 0$, which leads to

$$\begin{aligned} m &= \pm (n/n') \\ \vec{a}' &= \pm (n/n')\, \vec{a} \\ \vec{s}' &= \pm (n'/n)\, \vec{s}\,, \end{aligned} \tag{18.38}$$

where the negative sign is used if the system has an odd number of reflections. In a spatial system, each object ray is parallel to its image ray and the diamagnification of every object point in space is the same.

The two-sphere systems (as we have seen) are systems in which at least one object point is sharply imaged. Let vector $\vec{a}$, of length L, represent a point imaged sharply with a magnification m_0. Multiplication of (18.30) by $\vec{a}$ gives

$$\vec{a}^2\phi = -\,\vec{a}\vec{s}' + (1/m)\,\vec{a}\vec{s}. \tag{18.39}$$

We have from (18.36)

$$\begin{aligned} \vec{a}\vec{s} &= \sqrt{n^2L^2 - \tau^2} = nL\sqrt{1 - \frac{\tau^2}{(nL)^2}} \\ \vec{a}\vec{s}' &= \sqrt{n'^2L^2 - \frac{\tau^2}{m^2}} = \pm\, n'L\sqrt{1 - \frac{\tau^2}{m^2L^2n'^2}}\,, \end{aligned} \tag{18.40}$$

where the sign of $\vec{a}\vec{s}$ is by definition equal to the sign of L and the sign of $\vec{a}\vec{s}'$ is the same except for an odd number of reflections, where it reverses. We then have

$$\frac{\phi}{nn'} = \frac{1}{n'm_0L_o}\sqrt{1 - \frac{\tau^2}{L_o{}^2n^2}} \mp \frac{1}{nL_o}\sqrt{1 - \frac{\tau^2}{m_0{}^2L_o{}^2n'^2}} \tag{18.41}$$

as the form of ϕ for which the sphere of distance L_o is imaged sharply upon the sphere of distance $L_o' = m_0L_o$. (The plus sign holds only for an odd number of reflections.) Written with two arbitrary constants, ϕ assumes the form

$$\frac{\phi}{nn'} = \frac{1}{a}\sqrt{1 - \frac{\tau^2}{b^2}} - \frac{1}{b}\sqrt{1 - \frac{\tau^2}{a^2}}\,, \tag{18.42}$$

which shows that, instead of

$$a = m_0 L_o n'$$
$$b = L_o n \tag{18.43}$$

($b = -n\,L_o$ for an odd number of reflections), we could have

$$a = -\,nL_o = n'm_1L_1$$
$$b = -\,n'm_0L_o = nL_1, \tag{18.44}$$

so that the same system images sharply the sphere of radius

$$L_1 = -\,m_0L_on'/n \tag{18.45}$$

with the magnification

$$m_1 = n^2/n'^2m_0, \tag{18.46}$$

in agreement with the results previously obtained.

It will be the aim of the next chapter to investigate all possible realizations of spatial and two-sphere concentric systems.

CHAPTER NINETEEN

Specific Concentric Systems

The equations for refraction at a single spherical surface of radius r are given by (2.8) and (2.19) as

$$\vec{a}' = m\vec{a}$$
$$\vec{s}' = -\phi\vec{a} + (1/m)\,\vec{s}, \qquad (19.1)$$

where

$$\phi = (1/r)\left(\sqrt{n'^2 - \tau^2/r^2} - \sqrt{n^2 - \tau^2/r^2}\right),\ \tau^2 = \vec{J}^2 = (\vec{a} \times \vec{s})^2$$
$$= (\vec{a}' \times \vec{s}')^2. \qquad (19.2)$$

Comparison with Formula (18.41) shows that a single refracting spherical surface is a two-sphere surface, giving a sharp image of the center ($r = 0$), of itself,

$$L_1 = -r = L_1', \quad m_1 = 1 \qquad (19.3)$$

(the minus sign comes from the optical sign convention), and of the aplanatic surface given by

$$L_2 = (n'/n)\,r \qquad m_2 = n^2/n'^2, \qquad (19.4)$$
$$L_2' = (n/n')\,r$$

which is in agreement with the results of Chapter 2 [*cf.* (2.29)].

In the case of reflection, we have [*cf.* (2.19) with $Q' = -Q$]

$$\phi = -(2/r)\sqrt{n^2 - (\tau^2/r^2)}, \qquad (19.5)$$

which gives a double image of the surface

$$L_1 = L_2 = -r = L_1' = L_2', \quad m_1 = m_2 = 1. \qquad (19.6)$$

It is the purpose of this chapter to discuss the image in a general concentric system with radii $r_1, r_2 \ldots r_\varkappa$ and refractive indices $n = n_0, n_1, n_2 \ldots n_{\varkappa-1}, n_\varkappa = n'$.

We follow a ray from the initial point (vector $\vec{a}$) to the intersection points (vectors b_ν) with the consecutive surfaces and obtain the following formulae, which are derived from (14.1) by setting

$$\vec{o}_\nu = -\vec{b}_\nu/r_\nu, \quad \phi_\nu = \Gamma_\nu/r_\nu = \Gamma_\nu \varrho_\nu:$$

$$\begin{aligned}
&\vec{b}_1 = \vec{a} + l_o\vec{s} && \vec{s}_1 - \vec{s} = -\phi_1\vec{b} \\
&\vec{b}_2 = \vec{b}_1 + l_1\vec{s}_1 && \vec{s}_2 - \vec{s}_1 = -\phi_2\vec{b}_2 \\
&\cdots\cdot && \cdots\cdot \\
&\vec{b}_\varkappa = \vec{b}_{\varkappa-1} + l_{\varkappa-1}\vec{s}_{\varkappa-1} && \vec{s}' - \vec{s}_{\varkappa-1} = -\phi_\varkappa\vec{b}_\varkappa. \\
&\vec{a}' = \vec{b}_\varkappa + l'\vec{s}'
\end{aligned} \tag{19.7}$$

Considering that $\vec{s}_\nu^2 = n_\nu^2$, $\vec{b}_\nu^2 = r_\nu^2$, we obtain from (19.7) by scalar multiplication with $\vec{s}_\nu$ and $\vec{b}_\nu$, respectively,

$$\begin{aligned}
&\vec{b}_1\vec{s} = \vec{a}\vec{s} + l_o n^2 && \vec{b}_1\vec{s}_1 - \vec{b}_1\vec{s} = -\phi_1 r_1^2 \\
&\vec{b}_2\vec{s}_1 = \vec{b}_1\vec{s}_1 + l_1 n_1^2 && b_2\vec{s}_2 - \vec{b}_2\vec{s}_1 = -\phi_2 r_2^2 \\
&\cdots\cdot && \cdots\cdot \\
&\vec{b}_\varkappa\vec{s}_{\varkappa-1} = \vec{b}_{\varkappa-1}\vec{s}_{\varkappa-1} + l_{\varkappa-1}n^2_{\varkappa-1} && \vec{b}_\varkappa\vec{s}' - \vec{b}_\varkappa\vec{s}_{\varkappa-1} = -\phi_\varkappa r_\varkappa^2. \\
&\vec{a}'\vec{s}' = \vec{b}_\varkappa\vec{s}' + l'n'^2
\end{aligned} \tag{19.8}$$

Summing these formulae and considering that $l_\nu n_\nu^2$ is the optical path in the νth medium, so that

$$\Sigma l_\nu n_\nu^2 = E \tag{19.9}$$

is the light path from $\vec{a}$ to $\vec{a}'$, we find

$$\vec{a}'\vec{s}' - \vec{a}\vec{s} = E - \Sigma\phi_\nu r_\nu^2. \tag{19.10}$$

Since $\tau^2 = \vec{J}^2 = (\vec{a} \times \vec{s})^2$ is an invariant of the optical system, we find the light path E from an arbitrary initial point to an arbitrary terminal point (neglecting reflection for the moment) by deriving from (19.2) and (18.40) the equations

$$\begin{aligned}
&\phi_\nu = \frac{1}{r_\nu}\left(n_\nu\sqrt{1 - \frac{\tau^2}{n_\nu^2 r_\nu^2}} - n_{\nu-1}\sqrt{1 - \frac{\tau^2}{n_{\nu-1}^2 r_\nu^2}}\right) \\
&\vec{a}'\vec{s}' = n'L'\sqrt{1 - \frac{\tau^2}{n'^2L'^2}}, \quad \vec{a}\vec{s} = nL\sqrt{1 - \frac{\tau^2}{n^2L^2}}
\end{aligned} \tag{19.11}$$

and entering (19.11) into (19.10). Then

$$E = n'L' \sqrt{1 - \frac{\tau^2}{n'^2L'^2}} - nL \sqrt{1 - \frac{\tau^2}{n^2L^2}}$$

$$+ \Sigma\, n_\nu r_\nu \sqrt{1 - \frac{\tau^2}{n_\nu^2 r_\nu^2}} - \Sigma n_{\nu-1} r_\nu \sqrt{1 - \frac{\tau^2}{n_{\nu-1}^2 r_\nu^2}}. \qquad (19.12)$$

If and only if, for a given value of L, a value L' can be found so that, for all values of τ, E is constant, then and only then do we have a sharp image of a sphere of radius $(-L)$ onto a sphere of radius $(-L')$.

It may interest the reader that, if $\vec{a}'$ is chosen as the diapoint of $\vec{a}$, we find from

$$\vec{a}' = m\vec{a}$$

$$\vec{s}' = -\phi\vec{a} + \frac{1}{m}\vec{s}, \qquad (19.13)$$

the equations

$$\phi\, \vec{a}\vec{a}' = \vec{a}\vec{s} - \vec{a}'\vec{s}'$$

$$\frac{\phi}{nn'} = \frac{1}{n'L'} \sqrt{1 - \frac{\tau^2}{n^2L^2}} - \frac{1}{nL} \sqrt{1 - \frac{\tau^2}{n'^2L'^2}}, \qquad (19.14)$$

giving the function ϕ for any concentric refracting system.

We shall now prove the basic theorem of concentric systems, which states that a function of the form (19.12) can be constant only if it is zero and if the terms in (19.12) cancel each other in pairs.

The proof is as follows. According to the binomial theorem,

$$a \sqrt{1 - \frac{\tau^2}{a^2}} = a\left(1 - \frac{\tau^2}{a^2}\right)^{1/2} = \sum_{i=o}^{\infty} (-1)^i \frac{\tau^{2i}}{a^{2i-1}} \binom{\frac{1}{2}}{i}. \qquad (19.15)$$

Let us assume we have an equation holding for all values of τ and having the form

$$\sum_{\nu=1}^{\varkappa} a_\nu \sqrt{1 - \frac{\tau^2}{a_\nu^2}} \equiv C, \qquad (19.16)$$

with $a_1^2 \geqq a_2^2 \geqq \ldots a_\varkappa^2 > 0$. We then conclude, by inserting (19.15) and comparing the coefficients of powers of τ^2, that for all $i > 0$

$$\sum_\nu \frac{1}{a^{2i-1}} = 0 . \tag{19.17}$$

The first $\varkappa$ of these equations can be considered as linear equations for $a_1, \ldots, a_\varkappa$. The functional determinant is the well-known Vandermonde determinant, the value of which is given by a product

$$D = \begin{vmatrix} 1/a_1^2 & 1/a_\varkappa^2 \\ 1/a_1^4 & 1/a_\varkappa^4 \\ & \\ 1/a_1^{2\varkappa} & 1/a_\varkappa^{2\varkappa} \end{vmatrix} = \prod_{i<\varkappa} (1/a_i^2 - 1/a_\varkappa^2), \tag{19.18}$$

which can vanish only if there exist two indices i and $i + 1$ for which

$$a_i + a_{i+1} = 0 . \tag{19.19}$$

Eliminating these two functions from (19.16), we can apply the same argument to the remainder, so that we finally obtain the identities

$$a_1 + a_2 = a_3 + a_4 = a_5 + a_6 = \ldots = 0, \quad C = 0, \tag{19.20}$$

which prove our basic theorem and permit us to construct all concentric optical systems for which $E = 0$.

Equation (19.12) now teaches us that this aim can be obtained in two different ways. If in (19.12) the members containing the r's cancel each other in pairs, it suffices to choose

$$L' = (n/n')L \tag{19.21}$$

to make E vanish; that is, the system under consideration images every point in space sharply with the magnification n/n'. This characterizes the refractive *spatial systems*.

If on the other hand the members on the right-hand side containing the r's do not cancel completely, but only $n - 2$ of them cancel, then we have two equations, one in which nL is equal to one of the $n_\nu r_\nu$ or equal to one of the $-n_{\nu-1} r_\nu$, whereas the $n'L'$

is negatively equal to the second remaining quantity, $n_\lambda r_\lambda$ or $-n_{\tau-1}r_\tau$.

It is obvious immediately that in this case there are two solutions. If

$$\begin{aligned} nL_1 &= n_\lambda r_\lambda \\ n'L_1' &= n_{\tau-1}r_\tau \end{aligned} \qquad (19.22)$$

is a solution, then

$$\begin{aligned} nL_2 &= -\, n_{\tau-1}r_\tau \\ n'L_2' &= -\, n_\lambda r_\lambda \end{aligned} \qquad (19.23)$$

solves our problem at the same time, the magnification being in the two cases

$$m_1 = \frac{n}{n'}\,\frac{n_{\tau-1}r_\tau}{n_\lambda r_\lambda}$$

$$m_2 = \frac{n}{n'}\,\frac{n_\lambda r_\lambda}{n_{\tau-1}r_\tau}, \qquad m_1 m_2 = \frac{n^2}{n'^2} \qquad (19.24)$$

as demanded by the general theory. We have proved again that, in a system imaging *one* point sharply, *two* spheres are imaged sharply at the same time.

It is our aim now to show how to give explicitly the radii and the refractive indices for all possible spatial and two-sphere systems.

Spatial Systems

Let us first consider a spatial concentric refracting system in which the radii have the same sign, that is, where they are both positive. Then for obvious geometrical reasons we have

$$r_1 > r_2 > \ldots > r_\varkappa > 0. \qquad (19.25)$$

Let us write

$$\begin{aligned} nr_1 &= \alpha_1 & n_1r_1 &= \beta_1 \\ n_1r_2 &= \alpha_2 & n_2r_2 &+ \beta_2 \\ &\ldots & &\ldots \\ n_{\varkappa-1}r_\varkappa &= \alpha_\varkappa & n_\varkappa r_\varkappa &= \beta_\varkappa. \end{aligned} \qquad (19.26)$$

All the α's and all the β's are positive and therefore our basic equations must be obtained by equating each α to one of the β's. The inequality (19.25) gives

$$\beta_\nu > \alpha_{\nu+1}, \tag{19.27}$$

which means that to every α_ν (except α_1) we can find a $\beta_{\nu-1}$ which is larger, and to every β_ν (except $\beta_\varkappa$) we can find an $\alpha_{\nu+1}$ which is smaller. We conclude from this (and the fact that each of the α's is equal to one of the β's and *vice versa*) that α_1 is the largest and $\beta_\varkappa$ is the smallest of the set in (19.26).

Ordering the equations in size, we write them as follows:

$$\begin{aligned} \alpha_1 &= \beta_{\nu_1} \\ \alpha_{\nu_1+1} &= \beta_{\nu_2} \\ \alpha_{\nu_2+1} &= \beta_{\nu_3} \\ \alpha_{\nu_{\varkappa-1}+1} &= \beta_\varkappa. \end{aligned} \tag{19.28}$$

The set of equations thus chosen must exhaust all the relationships between the α_i and β_ν. Let us, for the sake of argument, assume this is not so. Then the remaining equations could again be ordered according to size. Let α_i be the largest of these; now α_i cannot be α_1, since α_1 was contained in the first set; it cannot be another of the α's, because that would demand the existence of a larger β_ν which could neither be contained in the new set, because α_i was supposed to be the largest, nor be contained in the set of (19.28) because then this set according to construction would contain α_1.

Thus we can describe any spatial system with the help of a permutation symbol, writing the indices of the α's in the first row and the indices of the β's in the second row:

$$\begin{pmatrix} 1 & \nu_1+1 & \nu_2+1 & \nu_3+1 & \dots & \nu_{\varkappa-1}+1 \\ \nu_1 & \nu_2 & \nu_3 & \nu_4 & \dots & \varkappa \end{pmatrix}. \tag{19.29}$$

We exclude the case in which

$$\nu_i + 1 = \nu_{i+1}, \tag{19.30}$$

which would lead to

$$\alpha_{\nu_i+1} = n_{\nu_i} r_{\nu_i+1} = \beta_{\nu_i+1} = n_{\nu_i+1} r_{\nu_i+1} \tag{19.31}$$

or

$$n_{\nu_i} = n_{\nu_i+1}$$

as uninteresting, since it contains an ineffective surface.

Thus, for every possible permutation starting with unity and ending with $\varkappa$, provided no cycle of *one* exists, that is, no number corresponds to itself, we obtain an actual spatial system.

Since the product of all the α's must equal the product of all the β's, Equation (19.26) gives the interesting condition

$$n = n_\varkappa = n', \tag{19.32}$$

showing that, in a spatial system with positive elements, the object and image spaces must have the same refractive index.

We shall write all possible spatial systems with positive radii and fewer than six surfaces. In permutation form, these systems can be expressed as:

One Surface: None.

Two Surfaces: None.

Three Surfaces: $\begin{pmatrix} 1 & 3 & 2 \\ 2 & 1 & 3 \end{pmatrix}.$

Four Surfaces: $\begin{pmatrix} 1 & 4 & 3 & 2 \\ 3 & 2 & 1 & 4 \end{pmatrix}.$

Five Surfaces:

$$\begin{pmatrix} 1 & 3 & 2 & 5 & 4 \\ 2 & 1 & 4 & 3 & 5 \end{pmatrix}, \begin{pmatrix} 1 & 3 & 5 & 2 & 4 \\ 2 & 4 & 1 & 3 & 5 \end{pmatrix}, \begin{pmatrix} 1 & 3 & 5 & 4 & 2 \\ 2 & 4 & 3 & 1 & 5 \end{pmatrix}, \begin{pmatrix} 1 & 4 & 2 & 5 & 3 \\ 3 & 1 & 4 & 2 & 5 \end{pmatrix},$$

$$\begin{pmatrix} 1 & 4 & 3 & 5 & 2 \\ 3 & 2 & 4 & 1 & 5 \end{pmatrix}, \begin{pmatrix} 1 & 5 & 3 & 2 & 4 \\ 4 & 2 & 1 & 3 & 5 \end{pmatrix}, \begin{pmatrix} 1 & 5 & 4 & 3 & 2 \\ 4 & 3 & 2 & 1 & 5 \end{pmatrix}, \begin{pmatrix} 1 & 5 & 2 & 4 & 3 \\ 4 & 1 & 3 & 2 & 5 \end{pmatrix}.$$

In explicit form, these expressions become:

Three Surfaces:

$$\begin{aligned} nr_1 &= n_2 r_2 \\ n_2 r_3 &= n_1 r_1 \\ n_1 r_2 &= n_3 r_3. \end{aligned}$$

Four Surfaces:

$$\begin{aligned} nr_1 &= n_3r_3 \\ n_3r_4 &= n_2r_2 \\ n_2r_3 &= n_1r_1 \\ n_1r_2 &= n_4r_4. \end{aligned}$$

etc.

Spatial Systems with Radii of Different Sign

Let us assume r_1 to $r_\varkappa$ to be positive and $r_{\varkappa+1}$ to r_n, negative. Again equating to zero the sum of the r_i terms in (19.12), we can rewrite this equation so as to have only positive values on each side. This shows that each of the positive expressions in the first column of

$$\begin{array}{ll} -n_\varkappa r_{\varkappa+1} = \alpha_1 & -n_{\varkappa-1}r_{\varkappa+1} = \beta_1 \\ -n_{\varkappa+1}r_{\varkappa+2} = \alpha_2 & \quad \cdots\cdot \\ \quad \cdots\cdot & \\ -n_{n-1}r_n = \alpha_{n-\varkappa} & -n_nr_n = \beta_{n-\varkappa} \\ \quad n_\varkappa r_\varkappa = \alpha_1' & \quad n_{\varkappa-1}r_\varkappa = \beta_1' \\ \quad \cdots\cdot & \quad \cdots\cdot \\ \quad n_1r_1 = \alpha_\varkappa' & \quad n_or_1 = \beta_\varkappa' \end{array} \tag{19.33}$$

is equal to one of the expressions in the second column. The subscripts of the α's and β's are counted from the center outward in both directions. This makes the formulae more symmetrical. Multiplication of the α's and of the β's in (19.33) and cancellation of the common factors leads in this case to the remarkable result that

$$n_\varkappa^2 = n_0n_n. \tag{19.34}$$

Again, each $\alpha(\alpha')$ must be equal to a β or β'.

Again we can conclude from

$$r_1 > r_2 > \ldots > r_\varkappa > r_{\varkappa+1} > \ldots > r_n$$

that

$$\alpha_{\nu+1} > \beta_\nu, \quad \alpha'_{\nu+1} > \beta_\nu'. \tag{19.35}$$

However, we have here two values, α_1 and α_1', to which we cannot coordinate a smaller β and two values, β_1' and $\beta_{n-\varkappa}$, to which we cannot coordinate a larger α.

We proceed to find a set of possible equalities between the α_i and β_i. We start with α_i, which may be equal either to one of the β_λ or to one of the β_λ'; accordingly we choose either $\alpha_{\lambda+1}$ or $\alpha_{\lambda+1}'$ and continue until we come to an α which is equal to one of the terminal β's, that is, $\beta_\varkappa'$ or $\beta_{n-\varkappa}$. Then we begin with α_1', look for the corresponding β or β', and continue until we end at the remaining terminal element. Again we see that all equations are thus exhausted.

As an example we take systems with two to five surfaces.

Two Surfaces: one negative, one positive

$$\left(\begin{array}{c|c} 1 & 1' \\ 1' & 1 \end{array}\right).$$

two negative surfaces; none.

Three Surfaces: one negative

$$\left(\begin{array}{c|cc} 1 & 1' & 2 \\ 2 & 1 & 1' \end{array}\right).$$

Four Surfaces: one negative

$$\left(\begin{array}{ccc|c} 1 & 3 & 2 & 1' \\ 2 & 1 & 1' & 3 \end{array}\right), \left(\begin{array}{cc|cc} 1 & 3 & 1' & 2 \\ 2 & 1' & 1 & 3 \end{array}\right), \left(\begin{array}{c|ccc} 1 & 1' & 3 & 2 \\ 1' & 2 & 1 & 3 \end{array}\right), \left(\begin{array}{c|ccc} 1 & 1' & 3 & 2 \\ 3 & 2 & 1 & 1' \end{array}\right).$$

two negative

$$\left(\begin{array}{cc|cc} 1 & 2' & 1' & 2 \\ 1' & 2 & 1 & 2' \end{array}\right), \left(\begin{array}{ccc|c} 1 & 2' & 2 & 1' \\ 1' & 1 & 2' & 2 \end{array}\right), \left(\begin{array}{c|ccc} 1 & 1' & 2 & 2' \\ 2' & 1 & 1' & 2 \end{array}\right).$$

In forming these substitutions the following rule is helpful. The bottom row of indices in each symbol is divided into two groups. The first must not begin with 1 and must end in $\varkappa$ or $(n - \varkappa)'$. The second must not begin with 1' and must end in $\varkappa$ or $(n - \varkappa)'$. It is forbidden for $\nu + 1$ to follow ν or $(\nu + 1)'$ to follow ν'. The top row is of course completely determined if the bottom row is known.

Systems with three surfaces, two being negative, or with four surfaces, three being negative, are, of course, the same as the above but in reverse order.

Two-Sphere Systems

In this case we have [aside from Equations (19.33)] to find an α equal to nL (or $-nL$, if L is negative) and a β equal to $n'L'$ (or $-n'L'$), $-L = R$ and $-L' = R'$ being the radii of object and image spheres in (19.12). It is obvious that we obtain a second solution here by equating

$$\begin{aligned} nL_1 &= \alpha_\tau & \qquad nL_2 &= \beta_\lambda \\ n'L_1' &= \beta_\lambda & \qquad n'L_2' &= \alpha_\tau \end{aligned} \tag{19.36}$$

in agreement with (19.22) and (19.23), since *two* surfaces are imaged sharply with reciprocal optical magnifications.

To find all such systems, there is therefore no loss of generality if we add $nL_1 = \beta_o''$ and $n'L_1' = \alpha_o''$ to Equations (19.33) and consider α_o'' and β_o'' as exceptional starting and final elements. We proceed as follows. We start with α_1, which is equal to one of the β's, say β_ν or β_ν'. Either $\alpha_{\nu+1}$ or $\alpha_{\nu+1}'$ is then equal to another β, and we continue until we find an α which is equal to one of the three terminal elements $\beta_\varkappa$, $\beta_{n-\varkappa}$, or β_o''. Then we equate α_1' to a β and continue until we come to another terminal element. The last stage starts with α_o''. Again we exhaust all possible equations in this way, and we can characterize the equation by writing the substitutions of the subscripts of the α's and β's.

As an example we shall investigate systems with one, two, and three radii.

One Radius:

$$\left(\begin{array}{c|c} 1 & 0 \\ 0 & 1 \end{array}\right).$$

Two Radii: two positive

$$\left(\begin{array}{cc|c} 1 & 0 & 0 \\ 2 & 1 & 2 \end{array}\right);$$

one positive

$$\begin{pmatrix} 1 & 1' & 0 \\ 1' & 0 & 1 \end{pmatrix}_{\!\!\text{(}|\text{)}}$$

$$\left(\begin{array}{c|c|c} 1 & 1' & 0 \\ 1' & 0 & 1 \end{array}\right), \quad \left(\begin{array}{c|c|c} 1 & 1' & 0 \\ 0 & 1 & 1' \end{array}\right).$$

Three Radii: three positive

$$\left(\begin{array}{ccc|c|c} 1 & 3 & 2 & 0 & \\ 2 & 1 & 0 & 3 & \end{array}\right), \quad \left(\begin{array}{cc|cc} 1 & 3 & 0 & 2 \\ 2 & 0 & 1 & 3 \end{array}\right), \quad \left(\begin{array}{c|ccc} 1 & 0 & 3 & 2 \\ 3 & 2 & 1 & 0 \end{array}\right), \quad \left(\begin{array}{c|ccc} 1 & 0 & 3 & 2 \\ 0 & 2 & 1 & 3 \end{array}\right);$$

two positive

$$\left(\begin{array}{c|cc|c} 1 & 1' & 2 & 0 \\ 0 & 1 & 1' & 2 \end{array}\right), \quad \left(\begin{array}{c|c|cc} 1 & 1' & 0 & 2 \\ 0 & 2 & 1 & 1' \end{array}\right), \quad \left(\begin{array}{c|c|cc} 1 & 1' & 0 & 2 \\ 2 & 0 & 1 & 1' \end{array}\right),$$

$$\left(\begin{array}{c|cc|c} 1 & 1' & 2 & 0 \\ 2 & 1 & 0 & 1' \end{array}\right), \quad \left(\begin{array}{c|cc|c} 1 & 1' & 2 & 0 \\ 1' & 1 & 0 & 2 \end{array}\right), \quad \left(\begin{array}{c|c|cc} 1 & 1' & 0 & 2 \\ 1' & 2 & 1 & 0 \end{array}\right).$$

PART V
ROTATION-SYMMETRIC SYSTEMS

CHAPTER TWENTY

The Characteristic Functions and the Direct Method

The problem most frequently encountered in optical design is the investigation of the image rays coming from all the points of a plane (which may be the infinite plane, in which case we investigate the image rays of all bundles of parallel rays entering the system).

We shall compute the points of intersection of the image rays with one or more planes perpendicular to the axis and thus investigate the light distribution in any such plane, which may, for instance, be the plane of the film of a photographic system.

The object surfaces, as well as the image surfaces, are, of course, not necessarily planes, and we shall derive the laws in such a manner as to enable us to investigate the images of all points in space. The problem is a complicated one because the ordering of the image rays into bundles coming from various object points is not easy to visualize. It is therefore very fortunate that, in systems that are rotationally symmetric, a study of the diapoints gives complete information about the image formation. The main part of the remainder of this book will be devoted to a study of the interrelation between the diapoint configuration and the optical imagery.

Some of the rigorous laws of image formation will be considered in Part V, and in Parts VI and VII *approximation* methods for studying the image will be derived. In Part VIII we shall describe a mathematical model of an optical system and show how to obtain this by tracing a few rays through the system and interpolating a large number of other rays.

The rays coming from an object point in a rotation-symmetric system, as we saw in Chapter 14, form a normal bundle which has the plane through the object point and the axis as a plane of symmetry. The points in which the image rays intersect this plane were called *diapoints*.

Let us consider coordinate systems on the object and image sides with the origins on the system axis and such that the y and y' and the x and x' axes are, respectively, parallel to each other, while the z and z' axes coincide with the axis of rotation. Let $\vec{a}$ and $\vec{a}'$ be the vectors from the respective origins to a starting point A and a terminal point A', respectively. Let $\vec{s}$ and $\vec{s}'$ be the vectors, of length n and n', respectively, along the rays, and let us split each of these vectors into its component along the axis (unit vector $\vec{k}$) and the component perpendicular to it:

$$\begin{aligned} \vec{a} &= \vec{A} + z\vec{k} & \vec{s} &= \vec{S} + \zeta\vec{k} \\ \vec{a}' &= \vec{A}' + z'\vec{k} & \vec{s}' &= \vec{S}' + \zeta'\vec{k}. \end{aligned} \tag{20.1}$$

(*a*) *Initial and terminal points lie on planes perpendicular to the axis.*

Let us, first, assume that the initial and terminal points A and A' are restricted to planes perpendicular to the axis. A suitable choice of the coordinate origins then permits us to assume $z = z' = 0$ in Equation (20.1). The vectors $\vec{A}$ and $\vec{S}$ ($\vec{A}'$ and $\vec{S}'$) then suffice to determine the object (image) ray, since ζ (ζ') can be determined from

$$\zeta^2 = n^2 - \vec{S}^2, \qquad \zeta'^2 = n'^2 - \vec{S}'^2. \tag{20.2}$$

Equations (6.17) and (6.19) tell us that the four vectors $\vec{A}$, $\vec{S}$, $\vec{A}'$, $\vec{S}'$ are connected by the equations

$$\begin{aligned} \vec{A}' &= \alpha\vec{A} + \beta\vec{S} \\ \vec{S}' &= \gamma\vec{A} + \delta\vec{S}, \end{aligned} \tag{20.3}$$

with

$$\alpha\delta - \beta\gamma = 1,$$

where α, β, γ, δ are functions of x, y, ξ, η, that is, the coordinates of $\vec{A}$ and $\vec{S}$.

The last equation of (20.3), connecting α, β, γ, δ, can, for instance, be derived from the existence of the scalar invariant, since in general

$$[\vec{a}\vec{s}\vec{k}] = [\vec{A}\vec{S}\vec{k}] = [\vec{a}'\vec{s}'\vec{k}] = [\vec{A}'\vec{S}'\vec{k}] \tag{20.4}$$

and the first equations of (20.3) give

$$[\vec{A}'\vec{S}'\vec{k}] = (\alpha\delta - \beta\gamma)\,[\vec{A}\vec{S}\vec{k}].$$

Assuming $\vec{A}$ and $\vec{A}'$ as known, we can calculate $\vec{S}$ and $\vec{S}'$ from (20.3) (if $\beta \neq 0$) as

$$\begin{aligned} -\vec{S} &= E_1\vec{A} + E_2\vec{A}' \\ \vec{S}' &= E_2\vec{A} + E_3\vec{A}', \end{aligned} \qquad (20.5)$$

where E_1, E_2, E_3 are abbreviations for

$$E_1 = \alpha/\beta, \quad E_2 = -1/\beta, \quad E_3 = \delta/\beta. \qquad (20.6)$$

Assuming $\vec{A}$ and $\vec{S}'$ to be known, we can compute $\vec{A}'$ and $\vec{S}$ (if $\delta \neq 0$) by

$$\begin{aligned} -\vec{S} &= V_1\vec{A} + V_2\vec{S}' \\ -\vec{A}' &= V_2\vec{A} + V_3\vec{S}', \end{aligned} \qquad (20.7)$$

with

$$V_1 = \gamma/\delta, \quad V_2 = -1/\delta, \quad V_3 = -\beta/\delta.$$

Finally, assuming $\vec{S}$ and $\vec{S}'$ to be known, we can compute $\vec{A}$ and $\vec{A}'$ (in case $\gamma \neq 0$) from

$$\begin{aligned} \vec{A} &= W_1\vec{S} + W_2\vec{S}' \\ -\vec{A}' &= W_2\vec{S} + W_3\vec{S}', \end{aligned} \qquad (20.8)$$

with

$$W_1 = -\delta/\gamma, \quad W_2 = 1/\gamma, \quad W_3 = -\alpha/\gamma.$$

Let us now remember the existence of characteristic functions. Equation (16.1) shows that there exists in an optical system a characteristic function E such that, for all rays,

$$dE = \vec{s}'d\vec{a}' - \vec{s}d\vec{a}, \qquad (20.9)$$

where E is the light path between the initial and terminal points $\vec{a}$ and $\vec{a}'$.

Taking as initial and terminal points the intersection points with the planes $z = 0$, $z' = 0$, we find

$$dE = \vec{S}'d\vec{A}' - \vec{S}d\vec{A}. \qquad (20.10)$$

Inserting for $\vec{S}$ and $\vec{S}'$ their expressions from (20.5), we obtain

$$dE = E_3\vec{A}'d\vec{A}' + E_2(\vec{A}d\vec{A}' + \vec{A}'d\vec{A}) + E_1\vec{A}d\vec{A}. \quad (20.11)$$

Abbreviating the symmetric functions of $\vec{A}$ and $\vec{A}'$ by

$$\begin{aligned} \vec{A}^2 &= 2e_1 = x^2 + y^2 \\ \vec{A}\vec{A}' &= e_2 = xx' + yy' \\ \vec{A}'^2 &= 2e_3 = x'^2 + y'^2, \end{aligned} \quad (20.12)$$

we see that Equation (20.10) transforms to

$$dE = E_1de_1 + E_2de_2 + E_3de_3 \quad (20.13)$$

or, in other words, E can be considered as a function of e_1, e_2, e_3 with

$$E_1 = \frac{\partial E}{\partial e_1}, \quad E_2 = \frac{\partial E}{\partial e_2}, \quad E_3 = \frac{\partial E}{\partial e_3}. \quad (20.14)$$

Thus, if E is given as a function of e_1, e_2, e_3, one can compute $\vec{S}$ and $\vec{S}'$, and therefore $\vec{s}$ and $\vec{s}'$, as functions of e_1, e_2, e_3, that is, as a function of the coordinates of $\vec{A}$ and $\vec{A}'$, the projected vectors of the initial and terminal points.

Equations (20.5) are therefore closely connected with the existence of the point characteristic E. In the same way Equations (20.7) are connected with the mixed characteristic V' and (20.8) with the angle characteristic W [see (16.2)]. We find from

$$dV' = -\vec{a}'d\vec{s}' - \vec{s}d\vec{a} = -(\vec{A}'d\vec{S}' + \vec{S}d\vec{A}), \quad (20.15)$$

by inserting (20.7), that

$$dV' = V_1\vec{A}d\vec{A} + V_2(\vec{A}d\vec{S}' + \vec{S}'d\vec{A}) + V_3\vec{S}'d\vec{S}', \quad (20.16)$$

so that, if we consider V' as function of

$$v_1 = \tfrac{1}{2}\vec{A}^2, \quad v_2 = \vec{A}\vec{S}', \quad v_3 = \tfrac{1}{2}\vec{S}'^2, \quad (20.17)$$

then

$$dV' = V_1dv_1 + V_2dv_2 + V_3dv_3$$

or

$$V_1 = \frac{\partial V'}{\partial v_1}, \quad V_2 = \frac{\partial V'}{\partial v_2}, \quad V_3 = \frac{\partial V'}{\partial v_3}. \quad (20.18)$$

This means that a knowledge of the characteristic function V' permits us to compute $\vec{S}$ and $\vec{A}'$ for a ray given by $\vec{A}$, its initial point, and $\vec{s}'$, the vector of length n' in the direction of the image ray. The formulae are

$$-\vec{S} = V_1\vec{A} + V_2\vec{S}'$$
$$-\vec{A}' = V_2\vec{A} + V_3\vec{S}', \qquad (20.19)$$

with

$$\vec{S}' = \vec{s}' - \zeta'\vec{k}.$$

Analogously, if the object and image rays are determined by their direction vectors $\vec{s}$, $\vec{s}'$, the angle characteristic leads to

$$dW = W_1dw_1 + W_2dw_2 + W_3dw_3 = -\vec{a}'d\vec{s}' + \vec{a}d\vec{s}$$
$$= -\vec{A}'d\vec{S}' + \vec{A}d\vec{S}, \qquad (20.20)$$

with

$$2w_1 = \vec{S}^2 = \xi^2 + \eta^2$$
$$w_2 = \vec{S}\vec{S}' = \xi\xi' + \eta\eta' \qquad (20.21)$$
$$2w_3 = \vec{S}'^2 = \xi'^2 + \eta'^2$$

and

$$W_1 = \frac{\partial W}{\partial w_1}, \quad W_2 = \frac{\partial W}{\partial w_2}, \quad W_3 = \frac{\partial W}{\partial w_3}. \qquad (20.22)$$

We can find the points of intersection with the planes $z = 0$, $z' = 0$ by

$$\vec{A} = W_1\vec{S} + W_2\vec{S}'$$
$$-\vec{A}' = W_2\vec{S} + W_3\vec{S}'. \qquad (20.23)$$

We have thus shown that, in (20.5), (20.7), and (20.8), the coefficients E_i, V_i, W_i are not independent but each of the three sets can be derived from a characteristic function of three variables. The three functions E, V', W, in the case of a rotation-symmetric system, are each functions of symmetric functions of their respective coordinates. Any one of the three functions can be used to determine the connection between all object and image rays, provided only that the coordinates chosen determine the rays unequivocally. This means that the point characteristic E can be chosen if $\vec{A}$ and $\vec{A}'$ determine the ray, that is, if no two rays from the same object point (vector $\vec{A}$) intersect the plane $z' = 0$ in the same point (vector $\vec{A}'$). In an actual optical system, this condition is fulfilled if the image origin is far away from the

Gaussian image of the object origin, which is the case, for instance, if the image origin is at the exit pupil.

The mixed characteristic V' can be chosen if $\vec{A}$ and $\vec{S}'$ determine the ray uniquely. This is the case in practical systems if the object origin is chosen far away from the object focal point.

The angle characteristic W can be chosen if $\vec{S}$ and $\vec{S}'$ determine the ray uniquely, that is, if rays entering the system parallel to each other do not leave the system parallel to each other. This forbids the use of the angle characteristic for telescopic systems.

While each of these characteristic functions fails in certain cases, Equations (20.3) can always be used. By means of (20.3) the optical image formation is described as giving a one-to-one correspondence, coordinating to each object ray one and only one image ray and *vice versa*. In (20.3) α, β, γ, δ can be regarded as functions of

$$\begin{aligned} u &= \tfrac{1}{2}\vec{A}^2 = \tfrac{1}{2}(x^2 + y^2) \\ v &= \vec{A}\vec{S} = x\xi + y\eta \\ w &= \tfrac{1}{2}\vec{S}^2 = \tfrac{1}{2}(\xi^2 + \eta^2), \end{aligned} \tag{20.24}$$

that is, of the symmetric functions of $\vec{A}$ and $\vec{S}$. These functions are, however, not only connected by the finite equation $\alpha\delta - \beta\gamma = 1$, but, moreover, by three differential relations, which we shall now derive. In (14.10) we proved, in the case of a manifold of rays with two parameters, the existence of a differential invariant

$$\vec{s}_\nu{}'\vec{a}_\mu{}' - \vec{s}_\mu{}'\vec{a}_\nu{}' = \vec{s}_\nu\vec{a}_\mu - \vec{s}_\mu\vec{a}_\nu, \tag{20.25}$$

where the indices μ and ν designate differentiation with respect to the two parameters.

With the initial and terminal points on the planes $z = 0$, $z' = 0$, respectively, Equation (20.25) is equivalent to

$$\vec{S}_\nu{}'\vec{A}_\mu{}' - \vec{S}_\mu{}'\vec{A}_\nu{}' = \vec{S}_\nu\vec{A}_\mu - \vec{S}_\mu\vec{A}_\nu. \tag{20.26}$$

From (20.3) we obtain

$$\begin{aligned} \vec{A}_\nu{}' &= \alpha\vec{A}_\nu + \beta\vec{S}_\nu + \alpha_\nu\vec{A} + \beta_\nu\vec{S} \\ \vec{S}_\nu{}' &= \gamma\vec{A}_\nu + \delta\vec{S}_\nu + \gamma_\nu\vec{A} + \delta_\nu\vec{S} \end{aligned} \tag{20.27}$$

and from (20.24),

$$\begin{aligned} u_\nu &= \vec{A}\vec{A}_\nu \\ v_\nu &= \vec{A}\vec{S}_\nu + \vec{S}\vec{A}_\nu \\ w_\nu &= \vec{S}\vec{S}_\nu. \end{aligned} \tag{20.28}$$

Inserting (20.27) into (20.26) we obtain the equation

$$\begin{aligned} &(\gamma\vec{A}_\nu + \delta\vec{S}_\nu + \gamma_\nu\vec{A} + \delta_\nu\vec{S})\,(\alpha\vec{A}_\mu + \beta\vec{S}_\mu + \alpha_\mu\vec{A} + \beta_\mu\vec{S}) \\ &- (\gamma\vec{A}_\mu + \delta\vec{S}_\mu + \gamma_\mu\vec{A} + \delta_\mu\vec{S})\,(\alpha\vec{A}_\nu + \beta\vec{S}_\nu + \alpha_\nu\vec{A} + \beta_\nu\vec{S}) = \vec{S}_\nu\vec{A}_\mu - \vec{S}_\mu\vec{A}_\nu, \end{aligned} \tag{20.29}$$

and using (20.28) we arrive at the following equation, which can be written in determinant form as

$$\begin{vmatrix} \alpha_\mu & 2\gamma_\mu u + \delta_\mu v + \gamma u_\mu + \frac{1}{2}\delta v_\mu \\ \alpha_\nu & 2\gamma_\nu u + \delta_\nu v + \gamma u_\nu + \frac{1}{2}\delta v_\nu \end{vmatrix} + \begin{vmatrix} \beta_\mu & \gamma_\mu v + \delta_\mu 2w + \frac{1}{2}\gamma v_\mu + \delta w_\mu \\ \beta_\nu & \gamma_\nu v + \delta_\nu 2w + \frac{1}{2}\gamma v_\nu + \delta w_\nu \end{vmatrix}$$

$$= \begin{vmatrix} \gamma_\mu & \alpha u_\mu + \frac{1}{2}\beta v_\mu \\ \gamma_\nu & \alpha u_\nu + \frac{1}{2}\beta v_\nu \end{vmatrix} + \begin{vmatrix} \delta_\mu & \frac{1}{2}\alpha v_\mu + \beta w_\mu \\ \delta_\nu & \frac{1}{2}\alpha v_\nu + \beta w_\nu \end{vmatrix}. \tag{20.30}$$

The reader may notice that, in deriving this equation, we left free the choice of parameters. If we choose these to be the variables u, v, w, (20.30) leads to the three equations

$$\begin{vmatrix} \alpha_u & 2\gamma_u u + \delta_u v + \gamma \\ \alpha_v & 2\gamma_v v + \delta_v v + \frac{1}{2}\delta \end{vmatrix} + \begin{vmatrix} \beta_u & \gamma_u v + 2\delta_u w \\ \beta_v & \beta_v v + 2\delta_v w + \frac{1}{2}\gamma \end{vmatrix} = \begin{vmatrix} \gamma_u & \alpha \\ \gamma_v & \frac{1}{2}\beta \end{vmatrix} + \begin{vmatrix} \delta_u & 0 \\ \delta_v & \frac{1}{2}\alpha \end{vmatrix}$$

$$\begin{vmatrix} \alpha_v & 2\gamma_v u + \delta_v v + \frac{1}{2}\delta \\ \alpha_w & 2\gamma_w u + \delta_w v \end{vmatrix} + \begin{vmatrix} \beta_v & \gamma_v v + 2\delta_v w + \frac{1}{2}\gamma \\ \beta_w & \gamma_w v + 2\delta_w w + \delta \end{vmatrix} = \begin{vmatrix} \gamma_v & \frac{1}{2}\beta \\ \gamma_w & 0 \end{vmatrix} + \begin{vmatrix} \delta_v & \frac{1}{2}\alpha \\ \delta_w & \beta \end{vmatrix}$$

$$\begin{vmatrix} \alpha_w & 2\gamma_w u + \delta_w v \\ \alpha_u & 2\gamma_u u + \delta_u v + \gamma \end{vmatrix} + \begin{vmatrix} \beta_w & \gamma_w v + 2\delta_w w + \delta \\ \beta_u & \gamma_u v + 2\delta_u w \end{vmatrix} = \begin{vmatrix} \gamma_w & 0 \\ \gamma_u & \alpha \end{vmatrix} + \begin{vmatrix} \delta_w & \beta \\ \delta_u & 0 \end{vmatrix} \tag{20.31}$$

Equations (20.31) are three differential equations for four nonindependent functions. We can eliminate the derivatives of one of them, for instance α, by remembering that

$$\begin{aligned} \alpha\delta - \beta\gamma &= 1 \\ \alpha_\nu\delta &= \beta_\nu\gamma + \beta\gamma_\nu - \alpha\delta_\nu. \end{aligned} \tag{20.32}$$

Inserting this into (20.31) gives the three equations indicated by

$$\begin{vmatrix} \beta_\nu & \gamma_\nu \\ \beta_\mu & \gamma_\mu \end{vmatrix} (2u\gamma + v\delta) + \begin{vmatrix} \beta_\nu & \delta_\nu \\ \beta_\mu & \delta_\mu \end{vmatrix} (v\gamma + 2w\delta) + \begin{vmatrix} \gamma_\nu & \delta_\nu \\ \gamma_\mu & \delta_u \end{vmatrix} (2u\alpha + v\beta)$$

$$+\begin{vmatrix} \beta_\nu & \gamma^2 u_\nu + \gamma\delta v_\nu + \delta^2 w_\nu \\ \beta_\mu & \gamma^2 u_\mu + \gamma\delta v_\mu + \delta^2 w_\mu \end{vmatrix} - \begin{vmatrix} \gamma_\nu & u_\nu \\ \gamma_\mu & u_\mu \end{vmatrix} - \begin{vmatrix} \delta_\nu & \alpha\gamma u_\nu + \alpha\delta v_\nu + \beta\delta w_\nu \\ \delta_\mu & \alpha\gamma u_\mu + \alpha\delta v_\mu + \beta\delta w_\mu \end{vmatrix} = 0. \tag{20.33}$$

When desired, α itself can, of course, be eliminated since $\alpha = (\beta\gamma + 1)/\delta$.

From these equations, we can eliminate the β_ν's or the δ_ν's by the following procedure. The coefficient of β_ν in (20.33) is

$$B_\mu = \gamma_\mu(2u\gamma + v\delta) + \delta_\mu(v\gamma + 2w\delta) + \gamma^2 u_\mu + \gamma\delta v_\mu + \delta^2 w_\mu.$$

The coefficient of δ_μ in (20.33) is

$$D_\nu = \beta_\nu(v\gamma + 2w\delta) + \gamma_\nu(2u\alpha + v\beta) + \alpha\gamma u_\nu + \alpha\delta v_\nu + \beta\delta w_\nu.$$

Multiplying by the $B_\varkappa$'s and $D_\varkappa$'s, respectively, and summing over $\varkappa$ gives, if we again identify the indices ν, μ, $\varkappa$ as differentiation with respect to u, v, w, the two equations

$$\begin{vmatrix} \gamma_u & \delta_u & 2w \\ \gamma_v & \delta_v & -v \\ \gamma_w & \delta_w & 2u \end{vmatrix} + \begin{vmatrix} \gamma_u & 0 & 1 \\ \gamma_v & \gamma & 0 \\ \gamma_w & \delta & 0 \end{vmatrix} + \begin{vmatrix} \delta_u & 0 & \gamma \\ \delta_v & 0 & \delta \\ \delta_w & 1 & 0 \end{vmatrix} = 0$$

and (20.34)

$$\begin{vmatrix} \gamma_u & \beta_u & 2w \\ \gamma_v & \beta_v & -v \\ \gamma_w & \beta_w & 2u \end{vmatrix} + \begin{vmatrix} \gamma_u & 0 & 1 \\ \gamma_v & \alpha & 0 \\ \gamma_w & \beta & 0 \end{vmatrix} + \begin{vmatrix} \beta_u & 0 & \gamma \\ \beta_v & 0 & \delta \\ \beta_w & 1 & 0 \end{vmatrix} = 0.$$

From (20.34) we can compute β_u and δ_u as functions of the other quantities involved. Thus

$$\delta_u(2u\gamma_v + v\gamma_w + \delta) = (2u\delta_v + v\delta_w)\gamma_u + 2w(\gamma_v\delta_w - \gamma_w\delta_v) + \\ + \gamma_v\delta - \gamma_w\gamma + \gamma\delta_v$$

$$\beta_u(2u\gamma_v + v\gamma_w + \delta) = (2u\beta_v + v\beta_w)\gamma_u + 2w(\gamma_v\beta_w - \gamma_w\beta_v) + \\ + \gamma_v\beta - \gamma_w\alpha + \gamma\beta_v\,. \tag{20.35}$$

Adding to these equations the one obtained by setting $\nu = v$, $\mu = w$ in (20.33), that is,

$$\begin{vmatrix} \beta_v & \gamma_v \\ \beta_w & \gamma_w \end{vmatrix} (2u\gamma+v\delta) + \begin{vmatrix} \beta_v & \delta_v \\ \beta_w & \delta_w \end{vmatrix} (v\gamma+2w\delta)+ \begin{vmatrix} \gamma_v & \delta_v \\ \gamma_w & \delta_w \end{vmatrix} (2u\alpha+v\beta) +$$
$$+ \begin{vmatrix} \beta_v & \gamma\delta \\ \beta_w & \delta^2 \end{vmatrix} - \begin{vmatrix} \delta_v & \alpha\delta \\ \delta_w & \beta\delta \end{vmatrix} = 0, \tag{20.36}$$

we have three relations between the nine first-order derivatives

$$\beta_\nu,\ \gamma_\nu,\ \delta_\nu.$$

(*b*) *Initial point lies on plane through axis; terminal point is taken at diapoint.*

Assuming the terminal point to be the diapoint of the initial point, we have (7.4):

$$\vec{A}' = m\vec{A}$$
$$\vec{S}' = \gamma\vec{A} + (1/m)\vec{S}, \tag{20.37}$$

where, setting $l = 0$ in (7.4),

$$1/m = \delta,$$

and the distance z' of the diapoint is given by

$$z' = -\,(\beta/\delta)\zeta'. \tag{20.38}$$

It will be useful to introduce, instead of m and z', the quantities M and Z' given by

$$M = 1/m = \delta,\ Z' = z'/m = -\,\beta\zeta'. \tag{20.39}$$

The mixed characteristic V', applied to the point and diapoint representation, gives

$$dV' = -\,(\vec{s}d\vec{a} + \vec{a}'d\vec{s}') = -\,(\vec{S}d\vec{A} + \vec{A}'d\vec{S}' + z'd\zeta'). \tag{20.40}$$

Equations (20.37) may be written

$$\vec{S} = -\,m\gamma\vec{A} + m\vec{S}'$$
$$\vec{A}' = m\vec{A}, \tag{20.41}$$

and inserting these into (20.40) gives

$$dV' = -\,m\gamma\, d(\tfrac{1}{2}\vec{A}^2) + m\, d(\vec{A}\vec{S}') - z'd\zeta'. \tag{20.42}$$

Abbreviating again with

$$\vec{A}^2 = 2v_1, \quad \vec{A}\vec{S}' = v_2 \tag{20.43}$$

and considering V' as a function of v_1, v_2, and ζ', we obtain

$$\begin{aligned} \vec{S} &= V_1\vec{A} + V_2\vec{S}' \\ \vec{A}' &= V_2\vec{A} \\ -z' &= V_{\zeta}', \end{aligned} \tag{20.44}$$

where

$$V_1 = \partial V'/\partial v_1, \quad V_2 = \partial V'/\partial v_2, \quad V_{\zeta}' = \partial V'/\partial \zeta'.$$

This proves that a knowledge of V' as a function of v_1, v_2, and ζ' permits one to compute, for any given point in the object plane, the coordinates of the corresponding diapoints.

In using the angle characteristic, the coordinates of $\vec{S}$ and $\vec{S}'$ are used as variables. From (20.37) we obtain

$$\begin{aligned} \gamma\vec{A} &= \vec{S}' - (1/m)\vec{S} \\ \gamma\vec{A}' &= m[\vec{S}' - (1/m)\vec{S}] = m\vec{S}' - \vec{S}. \end{aligned} \tag{20.45}$$

Substituting these into the equation for the angle characteristic,

$$dW = \vec{a}\,d\vec{s} - \vec{a}'d\vec{s}' = \vec{A}\,d\vec{S} - \vec{A}'d\vec{S}' - z'd\zeta'. \tag{20.46}$$

Writing

$$2w_1 = \vec{S}^2, \quad w_2 = \vec{S}\vec{S}' \tag{20.47}$$

and remembering that

$$\begin{aligned} &\vec{S}'^2 + \zeta'^2 = n'^2 \\ &\vec{S}'d\vec{S}' + \zeta'd\zeta' = 0, \end{aligned} \tag{20.48}$$

we obtain

$$dW = -\frac{1}{\gamma m}\,dw_1 + \frac{1}{\gamma}\,dw_2 + \left(\frac{m\zeta'}{\gamma} - z'\right)d\zeta'. \tag{20.49}$$

Thus, if W is given as a function of w_1, w_2, and ζ', the intersection point with the object plane and its diapoint are connected by the equations

$$\vec{A} = W_1\vec{S} + W_2\vec{S}'$$

$$\vec{A}' = -\left(W_2\vec{S} + \frac{W_2^2}{W_1}\vec{S}'\right)$$

$$z' = -\left(W_\zeta' + \frac{W_2^2}{W_1}\zeta'\right), \quad m = -\frac{W_2}{W_1}. \qquad (20.50)$$

For the case of the Direct Method, we found differential equations (20.34) and (20.36) for the plane-to-plane analysis of a system. We now find the corresponding differential equations for the diapoint analysis. The four functions M, Z', γ, and ζ' are connected by the equations

$$\zeta'^2 = n'^2 - \vec{S}'^2 = n'^2 - (2u\gamma^2 + 2\gamma Mv + 2M^2w), \qquad (20.51)$$

with

$$2u = \vec{A}^2, \quad v = \vec{A}\vec{S}, \quad 2w = \vec{S}^2.$$

We find from

$$\vec{A}_\nu'\vec{S}_\mu' - \vec{A}_\mu'\vec{S}_\nu' + z_\nu'\zeta_\mu' - z_\mu'\zeta_\nu' = \vec{A}_\nu\vec{S}_\mu - \vec{A}_\mu\vec{S}_\nu \qquad (20.52)$$

and

$$\vec{A}_\nu' = m_\nu\vec{A} + m\vec{A}_\nu$$
$$\vec{S}_\mu' = \gamma_\mu\vec{A} + \gamma\vec{A}_\mu + M_\mu\vec{S} + M\vec{S}_\mu \qquad (20.53)$$

the differential equations (with ν, μ indicating any two parameters):

$$\begin{vmatrix} \gamma_\nu & M_\nu \\ \gamma_\mu & M_\mu \end{vmatrix} 2u - \gamma \begin{vmatrix} M_\nu & u_\nu \\ M_\mu & u_\mu \end{vmatrix} - M \begin{vmatrix} M_\nu & v_\nu \\ M_\mu & v_\mu \end{vmatrix}$$
$$- M \begin{vmatrix} \gamma_\nu & u_\nu \\ \gamma_\mu & u_\mu \end{vmatrix} + M^2 \begin{vmatrix} z_\nu' & \zeta_\nu' \\ z_\mu' & \zeta_\mu' \end{vmatrix} = 0. \qquad (20.54)$$

Inserting

$$-\zeta'\zeta'_\nu = (2\gamma u + Mv)\gamma_\nu + (\gamma v + 2Mw)M_\nu + \gamma^2 u_\nu + \gamma M v_\nu + M^2 w_\nu \qquad (20.55)$$

[obtained by differentiating (20.51)] and

$$M^2 z_\nu' = Z_\nu' M - M_\nu Z' \qquad (20.56)$$

[obtained by differentiating (20.39)] into (20.54), we obtain the three equations indicated by

$$| M_\nu \, \gamma_\mu \,|\, 2u\zeta' + |\, M_\nu, \ \gamma u_\mu + M v_\mu \,|\, \zeta' + |\, \gamma_\nu \, u_\mu \,|\, M\zeta'$$
$$+ \,|\, Z_\nu' M - M_\nu Z', \ (2u\gamma + vM)\gamma_\mu + (\gamma v + 2Mw)M_\mu + \gamma^2 u_\mu$$
$$+ \gamma M v_\mu + M^2 w_\mu \,| = 0, \qquad (20.57)$$

in which $| M_\nu \ \gamma_\mu |$ means the determinant

$$\begin{vmatrix} M_\nu & \gamma_\nu \\ M_\mu & \gamma_\mu \end{vmatrix},$$

etc. These formulae can be transformed by the method used to obtain (20.34). Replacing ν and μ in (20.57) by $u, v; v, w; w, u,$ respectively, and eliminating the Z's gives

$$\begin{vmatrix} M_u & \gamma_u & 2w \\ M_v & \gamma_v & -v \\ M_w & \gamma_w & 2u \end{vmatrix} = \begin{vmatrix} M_u & 0 & \gamma \\ M_v & 0 & M \\ M_w & 1 & 0 \end{vmatrix} + \begin{vmatrix} \gamma_u & 0 & 1 \\ \gamma_v & \gamma & 0 \\ \gamma_w & M & 0 \end{vmatrix}, \qquad (20.58)$$

which is, of course, identical with the first of (20.34), since $\delta = M$. Eliminating the M_ν's gives

$$\begin{vmatrix} MZ_u' & \gamma_u & 2w \\ MZ_v' & \gamma_v & -v \\ MZ_w' & \gamma_w & 2u \end{vmatrix} = \begin{vmatrix} MZ_u' & 0 & \gamma \\ MZ_v' & 0 & M \\ MZ_w' & 1 & 0 \end{vmatrix} + \begin{vmatrix} \gamma_u & 0 & 1 \\ \gamma_v & Z'\gamma - \zeta' & 0 \\ \gamma_w & MZ' & 0 \end{vmatrix}. \qquad (20.59)$$

Reordering Equations (20.58) and (20.59), we obtain

$$M_u(2u\gamma_v + v\gamma_w + M) = M_v(2u\gamma_u - 2w\gamma_w + \gamma)$$
$$+ M_w(v\gamma_u + 2w\gamma_v) + \gamma_v M - \gamma\gamma_w \qquad (20.60)$$

$$MZ_u'(2u\gamma_v + v\gamma_w + M) = MZ_v'(2u\gamma_u - 2w\gamma_w + \gamma)$$
$$+ MZ_w'(v\gamma_u + 2w\gamma_v) + \gamma_v MZ' - \gamma_w(Z'\gamma - \zeta') \, .$$

These two equations, together with the one obtained by replacing μ and ν in (20.57) by v and w, that is,

$$\begin{vmatrix} M_v & (2u\gamma_v + M)\zeta' - Z'[(2u\gamma + vM)\gamma_v + \gamma M] \\ M_w & 2u\gamma_w\zeta' - Z'[(2u\gamma + vM)\gamma_w + M^2] \end{vmatrix.$$

$$\left. \begin{matrix} - Z_v'M(\gamma_v + 2wM) \\ - Z_w'M(\gamma_v + 2wM) \end{matrix} \right| + \begin{vmatrix} MZ_v' & (2u\gamma + vM)\gamma_v + \gamma M \\ MZ_w' & (2u\gamma + vM)\gamma_w + M^2 \end{vmatrix} = 0, \tag{20.61}$$

are the differential equations which hold when the Direct Method and the diapoint analysis of a system are used.

CHAPTER TWENTY-ONE

Finite Image-Error Theory

In Chapter 20 we saw that the coordination of object and image rays can be described either by means of one of the characteristic functions or with the help of the so-called Direct Method. We there specialized the problem by assuming, with *Bruns*, that the initial point $\vec{a}$ and the terminal point $\vec{a}'$ for all rays lie on two fixed planes perpendicular to the system axis, one in the object space, the other in the image space. In this case, the projections $\vec{A}$, $\vec{A}'$, $\vec{S}$, $\vec{S}'$ of the above vectors normal to the system axis are sufficient to give the connections between the object and the image rays.

Having found these connections, we shall be able, in principle, to compute the image of every point in space. Some problems can be treated most easily with the help of one of the characteristic functions; for others the Direct Method will be more satisfactory. Frequently we shall also have to vary the choice of coordinates to investigate special aspects of practical problems. For instance, instead of giving the object ray by an object point (vector $\vec{a}$) and the direction vector $\vec{s}$, it might be desirable to give it by two of its points, for instance, the object point $\vec{A}$ and its intersection point with the entrance pupil (vector $\vec{A}_P$). That is easily done, for if k is the horizontal distance from the object point to the entrance pupil, we have

$$\begin{aligned} \vec{A}_P &= \vec{A} + (k/\zeta)\vec{S} \\ \vec{S} &= (\zeta/k)\,(\vec{A}_P - \vec{A}). \end{aligned} \tag{21.1}$$

In order to leave such possibilities open, it is best to keep the solution of the problem in the most general form.

Let us therefore suppose we know, for a ray given by $\vec{A}$ and $\vec{S}$ (object point and direction vectors), the vectors $\vec{A}'$ and $\vec{S}'$ (the vector of intersection with a fixed plane perpendicular to the

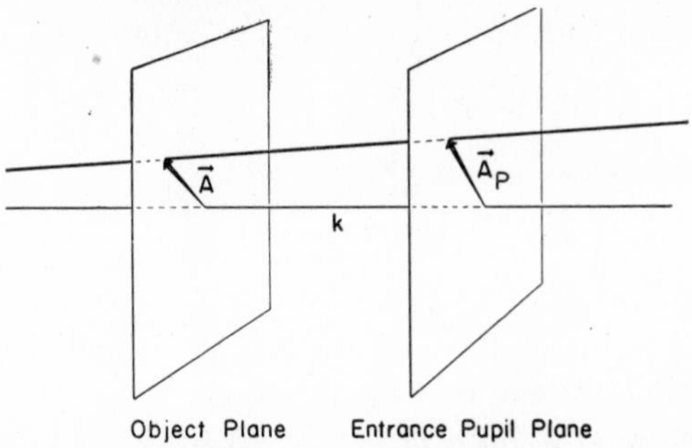

Fig. 21.1. Figure to illustrate Equations (21.1).

axis in the image space and the direction vector $\vec{S}'$). For a given fixed object point $\vec{A}$, the vectors $\vec{A}'$ and $\vec{S}'$ are functions of two parameters, which at the moment we shall assume to be arbitrary, and we indicate the differentiation with respect to these parameters by the indices 2 and 3. If we investigate the images of all the points of the object plane, we shall have $\vec{A}'$ and $\vec{S}'$ as functions of three parameters.

The problems we want to solve are the following:

First. We want to find the intersection of the image ray with an arbitrary plane perpendicular to the axis at the distance k' from the terminal plane chosen. This problem is solved by computing the vector

$$\vec{A}'_{k'} = \vec{A}' + (k'/\zeta')\vec{S}'. \tag{21.2}$$

Second. We want to compute the diapoint, that is, the point where the image ray intersects the plane through the object point and the axis. Letting z_D' be the z-coordinate of the diapoint, we have

$$\vec{A}_D' = m\vec{A} = \vec{A}' + (z_D'/\zeta')\vec{S}', \tag{21.3}$$

where m is the diamagnification.

Third. For a given object point, we find (for each ray) according to (14.25) the distance $\varkappa$ of the points of the caustic from the diapoint:

$$\begin{aligned} \vec{A}_\varkappa' &= \vec{A}_D' + \varkappa\vec{S}' \\ z_\varkappa' - z_D' &= \varkappa\zeta', \end{aligned} \tag{21.4}$$

the quantity $\varkappa$ being the solution of the equation

$$\varkappa^2[\vec{s}_2'\vec{s}_3'\vec{s}'] + \varkappa([\vec{a}_2'\vec{s}_3'\vec{s}'] + [\vec{s}_2'\vec{a}_3'\vec{s}']) + [\vec{a}_2'\vec{a}_3'\vec{s}'] = 0, \quad (21.5)$$

where

$$\vec{a}' = \vec{A}_D' + z_D'\vec{k} = m\vec{A} + z_D'\vec{k}$$
$$\vec{s}' = \vec{S}' + \zeta'\vec{k}. \quad (21.6)$$

With respect to image formation we can distinguish, in a system that is rotationally symmetric, the following possibilities.

(*a*) *The image of a point is sharp*. All the rays from the object point meet at the image point. Because of symmetry, this point must lie in the meridional plane, that is, the diapoints of the object point fall together or

$$z_{D2}' = z_{D3}' = 0$$
$$m_2 = m_3 = 0. \quad (21.7)$$

(*b*) *The image of a point is half-symmetrical*. In this case all the rays from the object point go through a curve, which must lie in the plane of symmetry, that is, the diapoints must form a curve. The condition for this is that

$$\begin{vmatrix} m_2 & z_{D2}' \\ m_3 & z_{D3}' \end{vmatrix} = 0. \quad (21.8)$$

The image is symmetrical if the diapoints form a straight line. In this case two constants C_1, C_2 exist such that

$$m = C_1 z_D' + C_2. \quad (21.9)$$

From (21.6) can be derived

$$\vec{a}_2' = m_2\vec{A} + z_2'\vec{k}$$
$$\vec{a}_3' = m_3\vec{A} + z_3'\vec{k} \quad (21.10)$$

(we write z_D' simply as z') or

$$[\vec{a}_2'\vec{a}_3'\vec{s}'] = (m_2z_3' - m_3z_2')[\vec{A}\vec{k}\vec{s}']. \quad (21.11)$$

This shows that $\varkappa = 0$ is a solution of (21.5) in the case of half-symmetry, that is, the diapoints in this case form part of the caustic. Equation (21.11) shows, moreover, that $\varkappa = 0$ is a solution of (21.5) for the meridional rays, since for them

$$[\vec{A}'\vec{k}\vec{s}'] = [\vec{A}\vec{k}\vec{s}'] = 0.$$

(*c*) In the general case, where (21.8) is not fulfilled, the dia-points form a two-dimensional manifold. In this case we can consider the value of the determinant

$$\begin{vmatrix} m_2 & z_2' \\ m_3 & z_3' \end{vmatrix} = \Delta \tag{21.12}$$

as a measure of the asymmetry of the image.

Let us now consider the actual computation of some of the above quantities with the help of the characteristic functions and/or by using the Direct Method.

The Mixed Characteristic V'

Using the mixed characteristic V', with coordinates

$$\begin{aligned} 2v_1 &= \vec{A}^2 = x^2 + y^2 \\ v_2 &= \vec{A}\vec{S}' = x\xi' + y\eta' \\ 2v_3 &= \vec{S}'^2 = \xi'^2 + \eta'^2, \end{aligned} \tag{21.13}$$

we have (20.7):

$$\begin{aligned} -\vec{S} &= V_1\vec{A} + V_2\vec{S}' \\ -\vec{A}' &= V_2\vec{A} + V_3\vec{S}', \end{aligned} \tag{21.14}$$

V_i designating the differentiation of V' with respect to v_i.

We have

$$\zeta' = \sqrt{n'^2 - 2v_3} \tag{21.15}$$

and compute the diapoint from (21.3) as

$$\vec{A}' + \frac{z'}{\sqrt{n'^2 - 2v_3}}\vec{S}' = -V_2\vec{A} + \left(\frac{z'}{\sqrt{n'^2 - 2v_3}} - V_3\right)\vec{S}' = m\vec{A}, \tag{21.16}$$

which leads to

$$m = -V_2, \quad z' = V_3\sqrt{n'^2 - 2v_3}. \tag{21.17}$$

The condition for *half-symmetry* is then

$$\begin{vmatrix} m_2 & z_2' \\ m_3 & z_3' \end{vmatrix} = 0 \quad \text{or} \quad (V_{22}V_{33} - V_{23}^2)\,(n'^2 - 2v_3) - V_3V_{22} = 0 \tag{21.18}$$

and for *sharpness* is

$$V_{22} = V_{23} = 0, \quad V_{33}(n'^2 - 2v_3) = V_3, \tag{21.19}$$

which means, when integrated, that

$$V_3 = C/\sqrt{n'^2 - 2v_3.} \tag{21.20}$$

For the intersection of the rays with the plane at the distance k', we find from (21.2)

$$\vec{A}'_{k'} = \vec{A}' + \frac{k'}{\zeta'}\vec{S}' = -V_2\vec{A} + \left(\frac{k'}{\sqrt{n'^2 - 2v_3}} - V_3\right)\vec{S}', \tag{21.21}$$

and for the diapoint

$$\vec{A}_D' = m\vec{A} = -V_2\vec{A}$$
$$z_D' = V_3\sqrt{n'^2 - 2v_3}\,. \tag{21.22}$$

For the distance $\varkappa$ of the points of the caustic from the diapoints, we obtain from (21.5) the equation

$$n'^2\varkappa^2 - \varkappa\{V_{22}(2n'^2v_1 - v_2^2) + 2V_{23}v_2(n'^2 - 2v_3) + 2v_3[(n'^2 - 2v_3)V_{33} - V_3]\} + (4v_1v_3 - v_2^2)[(V_{22}V_{33} - V_{23}^2)(n'^2 - 2v_3) - V_3V_{22}] = 0. \tag{21.23}$$

The Angle (Diapoint) Characteristic

The angle characteristic W can be used to investigate in full the diapoints of all the points in space simultaneously. If W is given as a function of

$$w_1 = \tfrac{1}{2}\vec{S}^2 \quad w_2 = \vec{S}\vec{S}' \quad w_3 = \tfrac{1}{2}\vec{S}'^2, \tag{21.24}$$

the vectors to the intersection points with the planes $z = 0$, $z' = 0$ are given by

$$\begin{aligned} \vec{A} &= W_1\vec{S} + W_2\vec{S}' \\ -\vec{A}' &= W_2\vec{S} + W_3\vec{S}'. \end{aligned} \tag{21.25}$$

The intersection points with the planes $z = z_o$, $z' = z_o'$ are given by

$$\vec{A}_z = \vec{A} + \frac{z}{\sqrt{n^2 - 2w_1}}\,\vec{S} = \left(W_1 + \frac{z}{\sqrt{n^2 - 2w_1}}\right)\vec{S} + W_2\vec{S}'$$

$$\vec{A}'_{z'} = \vec{A}' + \frac{z'}{\sqrt{n'^2 - 2w_3}}\,\vec{S}' = -W_2\vec{S} - \left(W_3 - \frac{z'}{\sqrt{n'^2 - 2w_3}}\right)\vec{S}'. \tag{21.26}$$

Now $\vec{A}'_{z'}$ is the diapoint of $\vec{A}_z$ only if $\vec{A}'_{z'} = m\vec{A}_z$, where m is the diamagnification. This leads to

$$\begin{aligned} W_2 &= -m\left(W_1 + \frac{z}{\sqrt{n^2 - 2w_1}}\right) \\ W_3 &= \frac{z'}{\sqrt{n'^2 - 2w_3}} - W_2 m. \end{aligned} \tag{21.27}$$

Equations (21.27) give for a fixed ray (fixed w_1, w_2, w_3) the z values of object point and diapoint for a given magnification m as:

$$\begin{aligned} z &= -\left(W_1 + \frac{1}{m}\,W_2\right)\sqrt{n^2 - 2w_1} \\ z' &= (m\,W_2 + W_3)\,\sqrt{n'^2 - 2w_3}, \end{aligned} \tag{21.28}$$

which, inserted into (21.26), gives

$$\begin{aligned} \vec{A}_m &= W_2\left(\vec{S}' - \frac{1}{m}\,\vec{S}\right) \\ \vec{A}_m' &= m\,W_2\left(\vec{S}' - \frac{1}{m}\,\vec{S}\right), \end{aligned} \tag{21.29}$$

from which we derive

$$m\,\vec{A}_m^2 = \frac{1}{m}\,\vec{A}_m'^2 = 2W_2^2\left(mw_3 - w_2 + \frac{1}{m}\,w_1\right). \tag{21.30}$$

We now introduce into W new variables, writing

$$W\,(w_1, w_2, w_3) = G\,(g_1, g_2, g_3), \tag{21.31}$$

where

$$\begin{aligned} g_1 &= \sqrt{n^2 - 2w_1} \\ g_2 &= \sqrt{2\left(mw_3 - w_2 + \frac{1}{m}\,w_1\right)} \\ g_3 &= \sqrt{n'^2 - 2w_3}, \end{aligned} \tag{21.32}$$

or, reversed,

$$\begin{aligned} 2w_1 &= n^2 - g_1{}^2 \\ 2w_2 &= mn'^2 + \frac{1}{m}\,n^2 - mg_3{}^2 - g_2{}^2 - \frac{1}{m}\,g_1{}^2 \\ 2w_3 &= n'^2 - g_3 \end{aligned} \tag{21.33}$$

and m is considered as a parameter. The reader may notice that g_1 and g_3 are the respective optical direction cosines ζ, ζ' of the object and image rays with respect to the z-axis, and g_2 appears in Formula (21.30).

Differentiation leads to

$$\begin{aligned} dg_1 &= -\frac{1}{g_1}\,dw_1 \\ dg_2 &= \frac{1}{g_2}\left(\frac{1}{m}\,dw_1 - dw_2 + mdw_3\right) \\ dg_3 &= -\frac{1}{g_3}\,dw_3, \end{aligned} \tag{21.34}$$

that is,

$$\begin{aligned} W_1 &= -\frac{1}{g_1}\,G_1 + \frac{1}{mg_2}\,G_2 & \qquad & G_1 = -\,g_1\left(W_1 + \frac{1}{m}\,W_2\right) \\ W_2 &= -\frac{1}{g_2}\,G_2 & \text{or} \qquad & G_2 = -\,g_2 W_2 \\ W_3 &= \frac{m}{g_2}\,G_2 - \frac{1}{g_3}\,G_3 & \qquad & G_3 = -\,g_3\,(W_3 + mW_2). \end{aligned} \tag{21.35}$$

Inserting (21.35) into (21.29) and (21.28) leads to

$$\vec{A}_m = -\frac{1}{g_2} G_2 \left(\vec{S}' - \frac{1}{m} \vec{S} \right) \qquad z_m = G_1$$

$$\vec{A}_m{}' = -\frac{m}{g_2} G_2 \left(\vec{S}' - \frac{1}{m} \vec{S} \right) \qquad z_m{}' = -G_3, \quad (21.36)$$

which determines immediately the points of diamagnification m on every ray. These very interesting equations will be analyzed in the next chapter, where we study the limitations of optical systems. The function G may be called the *diapoint characteristic.*

The Direct Method

The Direct Method applied to initial and final points lying in the coordinate planes $z = 0$, $z' = 0$ leads to the equations

$$\begin{aligned} \vec{A}' &= \alpha \vec{A} + \beta \vec{S} \\ \vec{S}' &= \gamma \vec{A} + \delta \vec{S}, \end{aligned} \qquad (21.37)$$

where α, β, γ, δ are related by one finite equation

$$\alpha\delta - \beta\gamma = 1 \qquad (21.38)$$

and three differential equations, such as, for instance, (20.34) and (20.36), where

$$2u = \vec{A}^2, \quad v = \vec{A}\vec{S}, \quad 2w = \vec{S}^2 \qquad (21.39)$$

are taken as variables.

The direction cosines ζ, ζ' of the object and image rays with the axis are given by

$$\begin{aligned} \zeta^2 &= n^2 - 2w \\ \zeta'^2 &= n'^2 - \vec{S}'^2 = n'^2 - (2u\gamma^2 + 2v\gamma\delta + 2w\delta^2), \end{aligned} \qquad (21.40)$$

where ζ and ζ' are positive, exept that ζ' is negative after an odd number of reflections.

The diapoint of $\vec{A}$ is given by [*cf.* (20.37) and (20.38)]

$$\begin{aligned} \vec{A}_D{}' &= m\vec{A} = (1/\delta)\, \vec{A} \\ z_D{}' &= -(\beta/\delta)\zeta'. \end{aligned} \qquad (21.41)$$

The intersection points with the plane at the distance z' is given by

$$\vec{A}'_{z'} = \vec{A}' + \frac{z'}{\zeta'}\vec{S}' = \left(a + \frac{z'}{\zeta'}\gamma\right)\vec{A} + \left(\beta + \frac{z'}{\zeta'}\delta\right)\vec{S}. \quad (21.42)$$

The reader may recall that in Chapter 4 we introduced, instead of $\vec{A}$ and $\vec{A}'$, the vectors $\vec{P} = \vec{A}\zeta$ and $\vec{P}' = \vec{A}'\zeta'$ as determining the ray in conjunction with $\vec{S}$ and $\vec{S}'$. We had (4.26)

$$\begin{aligned} \vec{P}' &= \varkappa\vec{P} + \lambda\vec{S} \\ \vec{S}' &= \mu\vec{P} + \nu\vec{S}, \end{aligned} \quad (21.43)$$

with (4.24) giving

$$\varkappa\nu - \lambda\mu = \zeta'/\zeta. \quad (21.44)$$

Also, from (6.18) we have

$$\varkappa = a\zeta'/\zeta, \quad \lambda = \beta\zeta', \quad \mu = \gamma/\zeta, \quad \nu = \delta. \quad (21.45)$$

Comparison of (21.45) with (21.41) allows the introduction of the following names. The quantity $\nu = \delta$ is the *reciprocal diamagnification*, and its variation for the rays coming from an object point, we shall call *lateral aberrations*.

The quantity $\lambda = -z_D'/m$ we shall call the *reduced diapoint distance* and its variations for the rays from an object point, *longitudinal aberrations*.

If λ and ν are constant for all rays from a given object point, z_D' and m are also constant, that is, the object has a *sharp* image. The object point has a *half-symmetrical* image if z_D' is a function of m, or, what is equivalent, if λ is a function of ν, that is,

$$\lambda_2\nu_3 - \lambda_3\nu_2 = 0, \quad (21.46)$$

and the image *symmetrical* if λ is a *linear* function of ν.

Shifting the image plane by the distance z' gives

$$\begin{aligned} \vec{P}'_{z'} &= (\varkappa + z'\mu)\,\vec{P} + (\lambda + z'\nu)\,\vec{S} \\ \vec{S}' &= \mu\vec{P} + \nu\vec{S} \end{aligned} \quad (21.47)$$

or

$$\begin{aligned} \tilde{\varkappa} &= \varkappa + z'\mu \qquad & \tilde{\lambda} &= \lambda + z'\nu \\ \tilde{\mu} &= \mu & \tilde{\nu} &= \nu\,. \end{aligned} \quad (21.48)$$

Instead of specifying a ray by $\vec{P}$ and $\vec{S}$, we may specify it by $\vec{P}$ and $\vec{P}_P$, where $\vec{P}_P = \vec{A}_P\zeta$, $\vec{A}_P$ being the projected vector at the entrance pupil. Let k be the distance between object plane and the entrance pupil, that is,

$$\vec{P}_P = \vec{P} + k\vec{S}. \tag{21.49}$$

Inserting this into (21.43), we find

$$\begin{aligned} \vec{P}' &= \left(\varkappa - \frac{\lambda}{k}\right)\vec{P} + \frac{\lambda}{k}\vec{P}_P \\ \vec{S}' &= \left(\mu - \frac{\nu}{k}\right)\vec{P} + \frac{\nu}{k}\vec{P}_P\,. \end{aligned} \tag{21.50}$$

Equation (21.50) can serve for investigating the image errors as functions of the position of the stop. In later chapters we shall use these formulae to investigate not only the dependence of the errors on the *stop* position, but also the change of errors when the object is moved.

In considering (21.43) to (21.50) it will be understandable if we say that (21.43) gives the image formation under the assumption of an *infinite pupil* (pupil at infinity), whereas (21.50) assumes a finite pupil. Of course, it will be found convenient in the latter case to introduce as variables

$$\begin{aligned} U &= u \\ V &= 2u + kv \\ W &= u + kv + k^2 w \end{aligned} \tag{21.51}$$

and insert into $\varkappa, \lambda, \mu, \nu$ for u, v, w their values as functions of U, V, W, namely,

$$\begin{aligned} u &= U \\ v &= (1/k)(V - 2U) \\ w &= (1/k^2)(W - V + U). \end{aligned} \tag{21.52}$$

CHAPTER TWENTY-TWO

Limitations of Optical Image Formation

The simplest approach to the problems treated in this chapter is by means of the following interesting lemma.

LEMMA. Let $\vec{a}$ and $\vec{a}^*$ be two points on a ray in an optical system with symmetry of rotation and l the reduced distance between them. Let $\vec{a}'$ and $\vec{a}^{*\prime}$ be their diapoints, with m and m^* the corresponding diamagnifications and l' the distance between the diapoints.

If

$$\vec{a}^* = \vec{a} + l\vec{s} \qquad \vec{A}' = m\vec{A}$$
$$\vec{a}^{*\prime} = \vec{a}' + l'\vec{s}' \qquad \vec{A}^{*\prime} = m^*\vec{A}^*, \tag{22.1}$$

we shall prove that

$$mm^*l = l'. \tag{22.2}$$

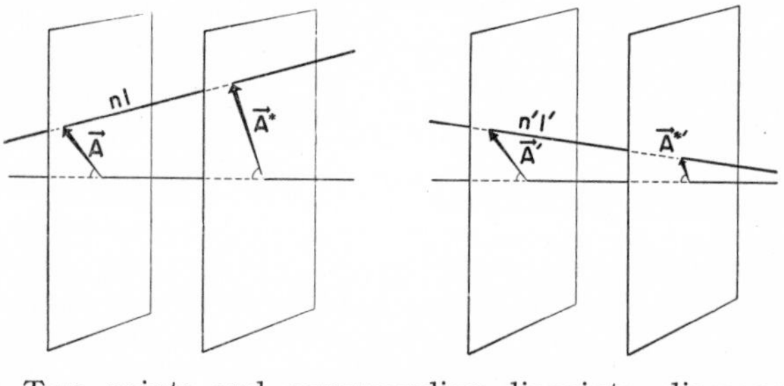

Fig. 22.1. Two points and corresponding diapoints, diamagnifications satisfy (22.2): $mm^*l = l'$.

The proof is as follows. We have [Equations (7.4) with $\phi = -\gamma$]

$$\vec{A}' = m\vec{A}$$
$$\vec{S}' = -\phi\vec{A} + (1/m)S, \tag{22.3}$$

and from (22.1) and (22.3) we derive

$$\vec{A}^{*\prime} = m^*\vec{A}^* = m^*(\vec{A} + l\vec{S}) = \vec{A}' + l'\vec{S}'$$
$$= m\vec{A} + l'(-\phi\vec{A} + (1/m)\vec{S}). \qquad (22.4)$$

Comparison of the coefficients of the independent vectors $\vec{A}$ and $\vec{S}$ gives the desired equation

$$mm^*l = l'$$

and also the relation

$$m - m^* = l'\phi = l\, mm^*\phi. \qquad (22.5)$$

It is obvious that, in the case of a system with symmetry of rotation, the sharp image of a point requires the sharp image of all the points of a circle around the axis.

Let us now investigate the case in which two off-axis object points, and therefore two circles around the axis, are sharply imaged with diamagnifications m and m^*, respectively. Let x, y, z and x^*, y^*, z^* be the coordinates of the points and mx, my, z', m^*x^*, m^*y^*, $z^{*\prime}$, the coordinates of their image points, and let us abbreviate with

$$\begin{aligned} 2a &= h^2 = x^2 + y^2 = \vec{A}^2 & x'^2 + y'^2 &= 2m^2a \\ b &= xx^* + yy^* = \vec{A}\vec{A}^* & x'x^{*\prime} + y'y^{*\prime} &= mm^*b \quad (22.6) \\ 2c &= h^{*2} = x^{*2} + y^{*2} = \vec{A}^{*2} & x^{*\prime 2} + y^{*\prime 2} &= 2m^{*2}c. \end{aligned}$$

We then find from (22.1) that

$$l^2\vec{s}^2 = l^2n^2 = (\vec{a}^* - \vec{a})^2 = 2(a - b + c) + (z - z^*)^2$$
$$l'^2\vec{s}'^2 = l'^2n'^2 = (\vec{a}^{*\prime} - \vec{a}')^2$$
$$= 2(m^2a - mm^*b + m^{*2}c) + (z' - z^{*\prime})^2. \qquad (22.7)$$

Equation (22.2) then leads to

$$2m^2(m^{*2}n'^2 - n^2)a - 2mm^*(mm^*n'^2 - n^2)b + 2m^{*2}(m^2n'^2 - n^2)c$$
$$+ n'^2m^2m^{*2}(z - z^*)^2 - n^2(z' - z^{*\prime})^2 = 0. \qquad (22.8)$$

If we let x, y, z and x^*, y^*, z^* traverse the circles around the axis, z, z^*, a, c, m, m^* remain constant while $b = \vec{A}\vec{A}^*$ varies. This is possible if and only if the coefficients of b in (22.8) vanish, that is, if

$$n'^2mm^* = n^2. \qquad (22.9)$$

We thus have the theorem:

THEOREM. If, on a ray traversing an optical system, two points are sharply imaged, the two diamagnifications must be optically reciprocal—Equation (22.9) must be fulfilled.

Finally let us investigate the conditions in which two surfaces $z(a)$ and $z^*(c)$ are sharply imaged. Let $z'(a)$ and $z^{*\prime}(c)$ be the equations of the image surfaces.

In this case m and m^*, the diamagnifications, must be the same for all points of the first and the second object surfaces, respectively. For, if we connect one of the points of the first surface with all the points of the second surface, we find from (22.9) that all the points of the second surface have the same magnification, which is given by (22.9) as $m^* = n^2/n'^2m$. This argument can be reversed for the points of the first surface.

Moreover, we point out that in (22.8) z and z' can now be considered as functions of a alone whereas z^* and $z^{*\prime}$ are functions of c alone. Differentiation of (22.8) under these conditions with respect to a and c leads to

$$\begin{aligned} m^2(m^{*2}n'^2 - n^2) + n'^2m^2m^{*2}(z - z^*)z_a - n^2(z' - z^{*\prime})z_a' &= 0 \\ m^{*2}(m^2n'^2 - n^2) - n'^2m^2m^{*2}(z - z^*)z^*_c + n^2(z' - z^{*\prime})z_c^{*\prime} &= 0. \end{aligned} \tag{22.10}$$

Differentiation of these equations with respect to c and a, respectively, gives

$$n^2z_c^*z_a = n'^2z_c^{*\prime}z_a' \tag{22.11}$$

or

$$n'^2z_a'/z_a = n^2z_c^*/z_c^{*\prime}. \tag{22.12}$$

The right-hand side of (22.12) is a function of c alone, the function on the left-hand side, of a alone. This is possible only if each is constant. This leads to

$$\begin{aligned} z' &= \tau z + C \\ z^{*\prime} &= \tau^*z^* + C^*, \end{aligned} \tag{22.13}$$

where τ, τ^*, C, C^* are constants, τ and τ^* being connected by

$$n'^2\,\tau\tau^* = n^2. \tag{22.14}$$

The values of the constants C and C^* depend upon the choice of the coordinate origins. Let us shift the origins by the distances k and k', respectively. We then have

$$z' - k' = \tau(z - k) + C$$
$$z^{*\prime} - k' = \tau^* (z^* - k) + C^* \qquad (22.15)$$

or

$$z' = \tau z + C + k' - \tau k$$
$$z^{*\prime} = \tau^* z^* + C^* + k' - \tau^* k.$$

Choosing k and k' according to

$$k = (C - C^*)/(\tau - \tau^*)$$
$$k' = (\tau^* C - \tau C^*)/(\tau - \tau^*), \qquad (22.16)$$

we obtain

$$z' = \tau z$$
$$z^{*\prime} = \tau^* z^*.$$

We assume the respective origins to be chosen according to (22.16). Equation (22.8) can then be reordered and written as

$$2a(m^{*2}n'^2 - n^2)m^2n'^2/n^2 + n^2z^2 - n'^2\tau^2z^2$$
$$+ 2c(m^2n'^2 - n^2)m^{*2}n'^2/n^2 + n^2z^{*2} - n'^2\tau^{*2}z^{*2} = 0, \qquad (22.17)$$

which again splits into the two equations, by virtue of (22.9) and (22.19),

$$2an^2\left(1 - \frac{n^2}{n'^2m^{*2}}\right) + n^2z^2\left(1 - \frac{n^2}{n'^2\tau^{*2}}\right) = \varkappa$$

$$2cn^2\left(1 - \frac{n^2}{n'^2m^2}\right) + n^2z^{*2}\left(1 - \frac{n^2}{n'^2\tau^2}\right) = -\varkappa. \qquad (22.18)$$

Equations (22.18) can now be used to compute the equations of the two object and the two image surfaces. Introducing

$$2a = h^2 = h'^2/m^2$$
$$2c = h^{*2} = h^{*\prime 2}/m^{*2} \qquad (22.19)$$

and considering the identities

$$\frac{n'^2}{n^2} m^2 = \frac{n^2}{n'^2} \frac{1}{m^{*2}}$$

$$\frac{n'^2}{n^2} \tau^2 = \frac{n^2}{n'^2} \frac{1}{\tau^{*2}}, \tag{22.20}$$

we find for the two object surfaces

$$n^2h^2\left(1 - \frac{n'^2}{n^2} m^2\right) + n^2z^2\left(1 - \frac{n'^2}{n^2}\tau^2\right) = \varkappa$$

$$n^2h^{*2}\left(1 - \frac{n'^2}{n^2} m^{*2}\right) + n^2z^{*2}\left(1 - \frac{n'^2}{n^2}\tau^{*2}\right) = -\varkappa \tag{22.21}$$

and for the two image surfaces

$$n'^2h'^2\left(1 - \frac{n'^2}{n^2} m^{*2}\right) + n'^2z'^2\left(1 - \frac{n'^2}{n^2}\tau^{*2}\right) = -\varkappa$$

$$n'^2h^{*2}\left(1 - \frac{n'^2}{n^2} m^2\right) + n'^2z^{*\prime 2}\left(1 - \frac{n'^2}{n^2}\tau^2\right) = \varkappa. \tag{22.22}$$

Hence we have the following theorem:

THEOREM. The only possibility that an optical system images two surfaces is when the following conditions hold. Both object surfaces (and both image surfaces) are second-order surfaces with the same center. Each object surface is imaged with a constant lateral magnification m (m^*) and a constant longitudinal magnification τ (τ^*) such that

$$h' = mh \qquad z' = \tau z$$

$$h^{*\prime} = m^*h \qquad z^{*\prime} = \tau^*z^*, \tag{22.23}$$

with

$$mm^* = \tau\tau^* = n^2/n'^2.$$

The first object and the second image surface, and analogously the second object surface and the first image surface, are similar with a similarity coefficient of n'/n.

In the case of $m = \tau$, the four surfaces become spheres and the solution of the problem becomes identical with the discussion of the two-sphere imaging systems discussed in Chapter 19.

The reader may notice that the four surfaces are ellipsoids if

$[(n'/n)m]^2$ and $[(n'/n)\tau]^2$ are both smaller (or larger) than unity; the other case leads to four hyperboloids.

Let us now try to find the characteristic function W for the two-surface imaging systems. We shall put the problem in a more general form. In Chapter 21 we found a characteristic function G [see (21.31)] of three variables g_1, g_2, g_3 such that the coordinates of point and diapoint of diamagnification m are given by (21.36) as

$$
\begin{aligned}
2U_m = G_2{}^2/m &= h_m{}^2 \qquad & z &= G_1 \qquad & h_m &= G_2\sqrt{1/m} \\
G_2{}^2 m &= h_m'^2 & z' &= -G_3 & h_m' &= G_2\sqrt{m}.
\end{aligned}
\tag{22.24}
$$

A study of the function G will help us in the investigation of image formation. Let us assume, for instance, that all object points in space are half-symmetrically imaged, that is, for any given m, the rays through a point z, h_m go through a fixed point $z', h_m' = mh_m$. In this case, $z' = -G_3$ must (for all m) be a function of G_1 and G_2, which is equivalent to saying that for all m the functional determinant

$$
g_{123} = \begin{vmatrix} G_{11} & G_{12} & G_{13} \\ G_{21} & G_{22} & G_{23} \\ G_{31} & G_{32} & G_{33} \end{vmatrix} \tag{22.25}
$$

must vanish.

Let us assume that the points of diamagnification m form a surface which is sharply imaged, the diamagnification m being constant.

Then we must have in (22.24)

$$
\begin{aligned}
h_m &= f(z) \quad \text{or} \quad & G_2 &= \sqrt{m}\, f(G_1) \\
h_m' &= f'(z') & G_2 &= (1/\sqrt{m})\, f'(-G_3),
\end{aligned}
\tag{22.26}
$$

which is equivalent to the statement that all the subdeterminants of g_{123} vanish:

$$
g_{11} = g_{12} = g_{13} = g_{22} = g_{23} = g_{33} = 0. \tag{22.27}
$$

The problem of finding G for systems with two surfaces that are sharply imaged is therefore reduced to the investigation of whether all the g_{ik} can vanish for two values of m, and we shall also see what conclusion can be drawn in this case.

All such types of problems suggest the investigation of how the function G, its first- and second-order derivatives, the determinant g_{123}, and its subdeterminants g_{ik} change with a change in m.

The All-Symmetric Systems

In Chapter 18 we have seen that in concentric systems every object point has a symmetrical image. All the rays from the object point intersect the line from the object point to the system center, that is, the pseudoaxis, in the image space. It is the purpose of this paragraph to investigate whether or not there are any different systems which give a (half) symmetrical image of every point in space.

This, as previously indicated, is equivalent to asking whether or not a diacharacteristic G exists so that for *all* m the determinant g_{123} given by (22.25) vanishes.

To investigate this problem we examine the connection of G with the angle characteristic W, taking as variables of W

$$a = \zeta \qquad b = \vec{S}\vec{S}' = \xi\xi' + \eta\eta' \qquad c = \zeta'. \tag{22.28}$$

From

$$G\,(g_1, g_2, g_3) = W\,(a, b, c) \tag{22.29}$$

with [*cf.* (21.32)]

$$\begin{aligned} g_1 &= a \\ g_2{}^2 &= (1/m)\,(n^2 - a^2) - 2b + m\,(n'^2 - c^2) \\ g_3 &= c, \end{aligned} \tag{22.30}$$

we find

$$\begin{aligned} dg_1 &= da \\ g_2 dg_2 &= -\left(\frac{1}{m}\, ada + db + mcdc\right) \\ dg_3 &= dc \end{aligned} \tag{22.31}$$

or

$$\begin{aligned} da &= dg_1 \\ db &= -\left(\frac{1}{m} g_1 dg_1 + g_2 dg_2 + m g_3 dg_3\right) \qquad (22.32) \\ dc &= dg_3. \end{aligned}$$

This leads to

$$\begin{aligned} G_1 &= W_1 - (a/m)\, W_2 \\ G_2 &= -\, g_2 W_2 \qquad (22.33) \\ G_3 &= W_3 - mcW_2 \end{aligned}$$

and

$$\begin{aligned} G_{11} &= W_{11} - \frac{2a}{m} W_{12} + \frac{a^2}{m^2} W_{22} - \frac{1}{m} W_2 \\ G_{12} &= -\, g_2 \left(W_{12} - \frac{a}{m} W_{22}\right) \\ G_{13} &= W_{13} - \frac{a}{m} W_{23} - mc\, W_{21} + acW_{22} \\ G_{22} &= g_2{}^2 \left(W_{22} - \frac{W_2}{g_2{}^2}\right) \\ G_{23} &= -\, g_2 \,(W_{23} - mcW_{22}) \\ G_{33} &= W_{33} - 2cW_{23} + m^2c^2W_{22} - mW_2, \qquad (22.34) \end{aligned}$$

which finally gives for g_{123}

$$\begin{aligned} g_{123} = {} & g_2{}^2 \left(w_{123} - \frac{1}{m} W_2 w_{11} - mW_2 w_{33} + W_2{}^2 w_{22}\right) \\ & - W_2 \left[w_{22} + 2mcw_{23} + m^2c^2w_{33} + \frac{2a}{m} w_{12} + \frac{a^2}{m^2} w_{11} + 2acw_{13}\right] \\ & + W_2{}^2 \left[\frac{1}{m} (W_{33} + a^2W_{22}) - 2cW_{23} - 2aW_{12} + m(W_{11} + c^2W_{22})\right] - W_2{}^3. \end{aligned} \qquad (22.35)$$

Inserting the value of $g_2{}^2$ from (22.30) and ordering the terms with respect to powers of m, we obtain

$$(1/m^2)\, n^2 W_2 w_{11} - (1/m)\,[(n^2 - a^2) w_{123} - 2W_2\,(a w_{12} - b w_{11}) + W_2{}^2\,(W_{33} + n^2 W_{22})] \tag{22.36}$$
$$+ \{2b w_{123} + W_2\,[(n^2 - a^2)\, w_{33} + 2ac w_{13} + w_{22} + (n'^2 - c^2) w_{11}] + W_2{}^2 (2aW_{12} + 2bW_{22} + 2cW_{23}) + W_2{}^3\}$$
$$- m\,[(n'^2 - c^2) w_{123} - 2W_2\,(c w_{23} - b w_{33}) + W_2{}^2\,(W_{11} + n'^2 W_{22})] + m^2 n'^2 W_2 w_{33} = 0,$$

where

$$w_{11} = \begin{vmatrix} W_{22} & W_{23} \\ W_{23} & W_{33} \end{vmatrix}$$

etc. This is equivalent to asking for the solution W of the five simultaneous differential equations:

$$w_{11} = 0, \qquad w_{33} = 0$$
$$(n^2 - a^2)\, w_{123} - 2W_2 a w_{12} + W_2{}^2\,(W_{33} + n^2 W_{22}) = 0$$
$$(n'^2 - c^2)\, w_{123} - 2W_2 c w_{23} + W_2{}^2\,(W_{11} + n'^2 W_{22}) = 0$$
$$2b w_{123} + W_2\,(2ac w_{13} + w_{22}) + W_2{}^2\,(2aW_{12} + 2bW_{22} + 2cW_{23}) + W_2{}^3 = 0. \tag{22.37}$$

The first two equations lead us to conclude that W_1 can be considered as a function of W_2 and c, while W_3 can be considered as a function of W_2 and a:

$$W_1 = f\,(W_2, c)$$
$$W_3 = g\,(W_2, a). \tag{22.38}$$

Designating by a prime the differentiation with respect to W_2, we find

$$W_{13} = f'\,W_{23} + f_c = f'g'W_{22} + f_c = g'W_{12} + g_a = g'f'W_{22} + g_a, \tag{22.39}$$

that is,

$$g_a = f_c. \tag{22.40}$$

Since g_a is not dependent on c nor f_c on a, each must be independent of a and c, that is, g and f must be linear functions of c and a, respectively. We can write

$$W_1 = \phi + hc$$
$$W_3 = \psi + ha, \tag{22.41}$$

where ϕ, ψ, and h are functions of W_2 alone. From (22.41) we derive

$$W_{11} = (\phi' + h'c)^2 W_{22} \qquad W_{23} = (\psi' + h'a) W_{22}$$
$$W_{12} = (\phi' + h'c) W_{22} \qquad W_{33} = (\psi' + h'a)^2 W_{22}$$
$$W_{13} = h + (\phi' + h'c)(\psi' + h'a) W_{22}. \qquad (22.42)$$

This leads to

$$w_{11} = 0 \qquad w_{22} = -h^2 - 2hW_{22}(\phi' + h'c)(\psi' + h'a)$$
$$w_{12} = h(\psi' + h'a) W_{22} \quad w_{23} = h(\phi' + h'c) W_{22} \qquad (22.43)$$
$$w_{13} = -hW_{22} \qquad w_{33} = 0$$
$$w_{123} = -h^2 W_{22}.$$

Inserting these results into the third and fourth equations of (22.37) and dividing by W_{22} leads to

$$(W_2(\psi' + h'a) - ah)^2 = n^2(h^2 - W_2^2)$$
$$(W_2(\phi' + h'c) - ch)^2 = n'^2(h^2 - W_2^2). \qquad (22.44)$$

In Equations (22.44), h, ϕ, ψ are function of W_2 alone. Therefore we can conclude that

$$h'W_2 = h, \qquad (22.45)$$

that is,

$$h = CW_2, \qquad (22.46)$$

where C is a constant. Inserting this into (22.44), we find

$$\psi' = \varepsilon n \sqrt{C^2 - 1}$$
$$\phi' = \varepsilon' n' \sqrt{C^2 - 1}, \qquad (22.47)$$

where $\varepsilon = \pm 1$, $\varepsilon' = \pm 1$, or, integrated,

$$\phi = \varepsilon' n' \sqrt{C^2 - 1}\, W_2 + k_1$$
$$\psi = \varepsilon n \sqrt{C^2 - 1}\, W_2 + k_2, \qquad (22.48)$$

where k_1 and k_2 are constant. Inserting (22.46) and (22.48) into (22.41), we find

$$W_1 = (\varepsilon' n' \sqrt{C^2 - 1} + Cc) W_2 + k_1$$
$$W_3 = (\varepsilon n \sqrt{C^2 - 1} + Ca) W_2 + k_2. \qquad (22.49)$$

Differentiating these quantities and inserting them into the last differential equation in (22.37) leads to the differential equation for W_2:

$$(C^2 - 1)\{W_2 + 2W_{22}[b + (a\varepsilon' n' + c\varepsilon n)\sqrt{C^2 - 1}$$
$$C(ac + \varepsilon\varepsilon' nn')]\} = 0. \qquad (22.50)$$

Equation (22.50) has three solutions:

(*a*) $C = 1$, that is, W is essentially an arbitrary function of $(b + ac)$. More precisely, the solution of (22.49) is

$$W = F(b + ac) + k_1 a + k_2 c. \qquad (22.51)$$

(*b*) $C = -1$, in which case integration of (22.49) leads to

$$W = F(b - ac) + k_1 a + k_2 c. \qquad (22.52)$$

(*c*) $W_2 + 2W_{22}[b + C(ac + \varepsilon\varepsilon' nn')$
$$+ (a\varepsilon' n' + c\varepsilon n)\sqrt{C^2 - 1}] = 0,$$

which gives, when integrated and compared with (22.49),

$$W = r\sqrt{b + C(ac + \varepsilon\varepsilon' nn') + (a\varepsilon' n' + c\varepsilon n)\sqrt{C^2 - 1}}$$
$$+ k_1 a + k_2 c. \qquad (22.53)$$

We shall investigate these three cases in order.

(*a*) $C = 1$, *the pseudoconcentric systems*. Inserting the diapoint characteristic, we find

$$G = F(t) + k_1 g_1 + k_3 g_3$$
$$t = b + ac = \tfrac{1}{2}\left[\frac{n^2}{m^2} + mn'^2 - g_2^2 - \frac{1}{m}(g_1 - mg_3)^2\right]. \qquad (22.54)$$

Differentiation leads to

$$G_1 = -F'(1/m)(g_1 - mg_3) + k_1$$
$$G_2 = -F' g_2 \qquad (22.55)$$
$$G_3 = F'(g_1 - mg_3) + k_2$$

and hence from (22.24) for the coordinates of the diapoint of magnification m,

$$h = -(1/\sqrt{m})\,F'g_2 \qquad h' = -\sqrt{m}\,F'g_2$$
$$z = -F'(1/m)\,(g_1 - mg_3) + k_1 \qquad z' = -F'\,(g_1 - mg_3) - k_2. \tag{22.56}$$

Equations (22.56) show that, for a suitable choice of origins, we can make $k_1 = k_2 = 0$. We will do so in the following. Moreover, we see that

$$h/z = h'/z', \tag{22.57}$$

that is, the diapoints of an object point lie on a line through the image origin parallel to the line connecting the object point with the object origin.

Comparison with the results of Chapter 18 shows that concentric systems are a special case of the pseudoconcentric type, the concentric case being characterized by the property that, when the origins are chosen so that $k_1 = k_2 = 0$, the two origins fall together.

In concentric systems it was seen that a system is completely determined by a single function $\phi\,(\tau)$, where $\tau = (\vec{a} \times \vec{s})^2$. This is equivalent to specifying the system by a single function of $b + ac$, for Equations (18.2) give

$$\vec{s}' = -\phi\vec{a} + (1/m)\vec{s} \tag{22.58}$$

and therefore

$$(\vec{s} \times \vec{s}')^2 = \phi^2(\vec{s} \times \vec{a})^2$$

or

$$n^2n'^2 - (\vec{s}\vec{s}')^2 = \phi^2\tau^2. \tag{22.59}$$

Hence

$$(b + ac)^2 = (\vec{S}\vec{S}' + \zeta\zeta')^2 = (\vec{s}\vec{s}')^2 = n^2n'^2 - \phi^2\tau^2. \tag{22.60}$$

A pseudoconcentric system can be shown to be equivalent to a concentric system with two plane mirrors added.

(*b*) $C = -1$, *second type of pseudoconcentric system.* After the proper choice of origins, W is an arbitrary function of $b - ac$. In the special case in which the origins fall together, this is a concentric system with an odd number of reflections. This case is very similar to case (*a*). Here the diapoints of a given object point are found to lie on a straight line through the image origin not parallel to the line from the object point to the object origin but parallel to its mirror image.

(c) $C^2 > 1$. As in cases (a) and (b) the origins may be chosen so that k_1 and k_2 are zero. Equations (22.53) may then be written in the form

$$G = r\{\tfrac{1}{2}[(1/m)(n^2 - g_1^2) - g_2^2 + m(n'^2 - g_3^2)] + C(g_1g_3 + \varepsilon\varepsilon' nn') + (g_1\varepsilon' n' + g_3\varepsilon n)\sqrt{C^2 - 1}\}^{1/2} \quad (22.61)$$

and therefore

$$z = G_1 = \frac{r^2}{2G}\left[-\frac{1}{m}g_1 + Cg_3 + \varepsilon' n'\sqrt{C^2 - 1}\right]$$

$$h = \frac{1}{\sqrt{m}}G_2 = -\frac{r^2}{2G}\frac{g_2}{\sqrt{m}} \quad (22.62)$$

$$z' = -G_3 = -\frac{r^2}{2G}\left[-mg_3 + Cg_1 + \varepsilon n\sqrt{C^2 - 1}\right].$$

Elimination of g_1, g_2, and g_3 from (22.61) and (22.62) leads to

$$mz^2 - 2Czz' + \frac{z'^2}{m} = (C^2 - 1)\left(\frac{r^2}{2} + mh^2\right), \quad (22.63)$$

from which z' can be calculated if m, z, and r are given. Furthermore, multiplication by mh^2 and introduction of the relation $h' = mh$ gives the equation

$$h^2z'^2 - 2Chh'zz' + h'^2[z^2 - h^2(C^2 - 1)] = hh'(r^2/2)(C^2 - 1), \quad (22.64)$$

showing that, for a given object point (values h, z), the diapoints lie along a second-degree curve lying in the meridional plane and passing through the image origin. Likewise, a fixed point (z', h') in the image space corresponds to a second-degree curve in the object space. Analysis of the discriminant shows that the curves are hyperbolas.

PART VI. APPROXIMATION THEORY FOR NORMAL SYSTEMS

CHAPTER TWENTY-THREE

The Geometry of a Normal System Having a Plane of Symmetry

The rays coming from a point in the object space form in the image space the normals of a set of wave surfaces [*cf.* Chapter 14]. If the optical system has symmetry of rotation about a system axis, the rays from an off-axis object point have a symmetry plane, namely, the plane through the object point and the axis. This plane we have called the *meridional* plane. The rays from an axis point form a normal system that is rotationally symmetric with the system axis as symmetry line. The intersection points of the image rays with the meridional plane are called the *diapoints* of the object point, and it will be one of our aims to show that a knowledge of the diapoints of an object point is sufficient to describe the image qualities of the normal system. This, as we shall show, will make it possible to transform the analysis of the optical image to the study of a set of curves in a plane.

The foregoing remarks indicate why we wish to study, in this introductory chapter, the geometry of a normal system having a plane of symmetry. We have already investigated, in previous chapters, some of the qualities of normal systems. We have found that the rays of a normal system envelop a surface, the caustic, to which, in general, each ray is tangential at two points. We shall study in detail in this chapter the differential qualities of wave surfaces and their caustics, that is, their properties in the neighborhood of a *principal* ray, which we shall assume to lie in the meridional plane. In an actual optical system, this ray may be the ray from the object point through the center of the exit pupil, so we shall investigate the light coming from the object point and going through a more or less small aperture of the system. We shall give approximate formulae (1) for the wave surface, (2) for the caustic, (3) for the coordinates of the diapoints, that is, the intersection points of the rays with the meridional plane, and (4) for the coordinates of the intersection points of the rays with a set of planes. These planes, at first, we shall assume to be perpendicular to the principal ray, but later, more appropriately, perpendicular to the system axis, that is, inclined to the principal ray.

We have seen in Chapter 14 that the rays of a normal system can be specified with the help of either one of two characteristic functions. Let us choose, as the initial surface, an arbitrary continuously differentiable surface $\vec{a}\,(u, v)$, the parameters (u, v) being, as yet, undefined. Let $\vec{s}\,(u, v)$ be the vector of length n along the ray passing through the point $\vec{a}\,(u, v)$ of the initial surface.

A system of rays forms a normal system, as we have shown, if and only if there exists a function $g\,(u, v)$ such that

$$\vec{s}d\vec{a} = dg \tag{23.1}$$

[*cf.* (14.21)] or a function $h\,(u, v)$ such that

$$\vec{a}d\vec{s} = dh. \tag{23.2}$$

From this it follows that, neglecting an unessential constant, h and g are connected by

$$g + h = \vec{a}\vec{s}, \tag{23.3}$$

where g can be interpreted as the optical path from a fixed wave surface to the initial surface $\vec{a}\,(u, v)$, and h as the light path to the wave surface from the footpoint of the perpendicular dropped from the origin to the ray.

The most important qualities of the two functions g and h, which we shall call the *principal functions* of the normal system, are that h is invariant against *transition*, that is, it does not depend on the initial manifold chosen, whereas g is invariant against *refraction*, if we choose the initial surface $\vec{a}\,(u, v)$ as the refracting surface. These facts can be shown as follows: Let $\vec{b}\,(u, v)$ be a second surface intersecting the rays, that is,

$$\vec{b} = \vec{a} + l\vec{s}, \tag{23.4}$$

where l may be an arbitrary scalar function of (u, v). From

$$\vec{s}^2 = n^2, \quad \vec{s}d\vec{s} = 0, \tag{23.5}$$

we obtain, again neglecting an unessential constant,

$$\vec{b}d\vec{s} = \vec{a}d\vec{s} \qquad (23.6)$$
$$h(\vec{b}) = h(\vec{a}),$$

proving the first assertion. On the other hand, the vector form of the refraction law, as given by (1.9), is

$$\vec{s}' - \vec{s} = \Gamma\vec{o}, \qquad (23.7)$$

where $\vec{o}$ is normal to the refracting surface, that is, $\vec{o}\ d\vec{a} = 0$. This gives

$$\vec{s}'d\vec{a}' - \vec{s}\ d\vec{a} = 0$$
$$g' = g, \qquad (23.8)$$

which proves the second statement. The wave-surfaces of the optical system are given by

$$\vec{w} = \vec{a} + l_w\vec{s}$$
$$l_w = -(g/n^2) = (h - \vec{a}\vec{s})/n^2, \qquad (23.9)$$

and the caustic by

$$\vec{c} = \vec{a} + l_\varkappa\vec{s},$$

where $l_\varkappa$ is given by (14.28) as the solution of the quadratic equation

$$l_\varkappa^2[\vec{s}_u\vec{s}_v\vec{s}] + l_\varkappa([\vec{s}_u\vec{a}_v\vec{s}] + [\vec{a}_u\vec{s}_v\vec{s}]) + [\vec{a}_u\vec{a}_v\vec{s}] = 0. \qquad (23.10)$$

Let us now assume a Cartesian coordinate system with the origin on the principal ray. We shall at first assume $n = 1$, that is, consider the geometrical qualities of the bundle in air. Moreover, we shall at first use coordinates so that the z-axis coincides with the principal ray and the yz-plane is the plane of symmetry, that is, the x-axis is normal to the plane of symmetry. The intersection of the rays with the plane $x = 0$ are then the diapoints. The direction cosines of the ray with respect to these axes are designated by ξ, η, ζ and, because of symmetry, h can be considered as a function of $v = \eta$ and $w = \frac{1}{2}\xi^2$.

If we choose as initial manifold, the plane $z = 0$, we find

$$dh = \vec{a}d\vec{s} = xd\xi + yd\eta = (x/\xi)\,dw + ydv. \qquad (23.11)$$

In the case that ξ and η determine the ray, this gives the coordinates of its intersection point with the plane $z = 0$ as

$$y = h_v, \quad x = h_w \xi. \tag{23.12}$$

Instead of v and w we can take as coordinates

$$\bar{v} = \eta, \quad \bar{w} = 1 - \zeta \tag{23.13}$$

and take the diapoints as initial points. We then obtain

$$d\bar{h} = \vec{a} d\vec{s} = y_D d\eta + z_D d\zeta = y_D d\bar{v} - z_D d\bar{w} \tag{23.14}$$

or

$$y_D = \bar{h}_{\bar{v}}, \quad z_D = -\bar{h}_{\bar{w}} \tag{23.15}$$

for the coordinates of the diapoint.

Since h is independent of coordinates, we have $h = \bar{h}$. To obtain the transformation equations connecting the coordinates, we observe that the direction cosines of the ray are given by

$$\begin{aligned} \xi &= \sqrt{2w} = \sqrt{2\bar{w} - \bar{v}^2 - \bar{w}^2} \\ \eta &= v = \bar{v} \\ \zeta &= 1 - \bar{w} = \sqrt{1 - v^2 - 2w}\,, \end{aligned} \tag{23.16}$$

which leads to

$$\begin{aligned} v &= \bar{v} & \bar{v} &= v \\ w &= \bar{w} - \tfrac{1}{2}\bar{v}^2 - \tfrac{1}{2}\bar{w}^2 & \bar{w} &= 1 - \sqrt{1 - 2w - v^2}. \end{aligned} \tag{23.17}$$

We shall develop h as a function of v and w or of $\bar{v}$ and $\bar{w}$, respectively, up to the fourth order, keeping in mind that w and $\bar{w}$ are of the second order. The developments can be written

$$\begin{aligned} h &= (\tfrac{1}{2} a_{22} v^2 + a_3 w) + (\tfrac{1}{6} a_{222} v^3 + a_{23} vw) \\ &\quad + (\tfrac{1}{24} a_{2222} v^4 + \tfrac{1}{2} a_{223} v^2 w + \tfrac{1}{2} a_{33} w^2) \\ &= (\tfrac{1}{2} \bar{a}_{22} \bar{v}^2 + \bar{a}_3 \bar{w}) + (\tfrac{1}{6} \bar{a}_{222} \bar{v}^3 + \bar{a}_{23} \bar{v}\bar{w}) \\ &\quad + (\tfrac{1}{24} \bar{a}_{2222} \bar{v}^4 + \tfrac{1}{2} \bar{a}_{223} \bar{v}^2 \bar{w} + \tfrac{1}{2} \bar{a}_{33} \bar{w}^2). \end{aligned} \tag{23.18}$$

The connection between the two sets of coefficients in (23.18) can be obtained by inserting (23.17) into (23.18) and equating. We obtain

$$\bar{a}_{22} = a_{22} - a_3, \quad \bar{a}_{222} = a_{222} - 3a_{23}, \quad \bar{a}_{2222} = a_{2222} - 6a_{223} + 3a_{33}$$
$$\bar{a}_3 = a_3\,, \qquad \bar{a}_{23} = a_{23}\,, \qquad \bar{a}_{223} = a_{223} - a_{33}$$
$$\bar{a}_{33} = a_{33} - a_3 \qquad (23.19)$$

or inversely

$$a_{22} = \bar{a}_{22} + \bar{a}_3, \quad a_{222} = \bar{a}_{222} + 3\bar{a}_{23},$$
$$a_3 = \bar{a}_3, \qquad a_{23} = \bar{a}_{23},$$
$$a_{2222} = \bar{a}_{2222} + 6\bar{a}_{223} + 3\bar{a}_{33} + 3\bar{a}_3$$
$$a_{223} = \bar{a}_{223} + \bar{a}_{33} + \bar{a}_3$$
$$a_{33} = \bar{a}_{33} + \bar{a}_3 \qquad (23.20)$$

These coefficients will be given the following names, which we shall justify later. We shall call a_{22} and a_3 (or $\bar{a}_{22}$ and $\bar{a}_3$) the *astigmatic errors*, a_{222} and a_{23} (or $\bar{a}_{222}$ and $\bar{a}_{23}$) the *asymmetry errors*, and a_{2222}, a_{223}, and a_{33} (or $\bar{a}_{2222}$, $\bar{a}_{223}$, and $\bar{a}_{33}$) the *Gullstrand errors*, the latter named for the Swedish scientist who first drew the attention of the optical designer to their significance. For the coordinates x, y of the intersection point with the plane $z = 0$ we find from (23.12), (23.15), and (23.18),

$$x/\xi = a_3 + a_{23}\, v + (\tfrac{1}{2}\, a_{223}\, v^2 + a_{33}\, w)$$
$$y = a_{22}\, v + (\tfrac{1}{2}\, a_{222}\, v^2 + a_{23} w) + (\tfrac{1}{6}\, a_{2222}\, v^3 + a_{223} v w), \qquad (23.21)$$

and for the coordinates of the diapoint,

$$y = \bar{a}_{22}\, \bar{v} + (\tfrac{1}{2}\, \bar{a}_{222} \bar{v}^2 + \bar{a}_{23} \bar{w}) + (\tfrac{1}{6}\, \bar{a}_{2222}\, \bar{v}^3 + \bar{a}_{223}\, \overline{vw})$$
$$-z = \bar{a}_3 + \bar{a}_{23}\, \bar{v} + (\tfrac{1}{2}\, \bar{a}_{223}\, \bar{v}^2 + \bar{a}_{33}\, \bar{w}), \qquad (23.22)$$

equations which we shall write in the form

	x/ξ	y	z
1	a_3		0
v	a_{23}	a_{22}	0
$\frac{1}{2}v^2$	a_{223}	a_{222}	0
w	a_{33}	a_{23}	0
$\frac{1}{6}v^3$		a_{2222}	0
vw		a_{223}	0

	x	y_D	z_D
1	0		$-\bar{a}_3$
$\bar{v}$	0	$\bar{a}_{22}$	$-\bar{a}_{23}$
$\frac{1}{2}\bar{v}^2$	0	$\bar{a}_{222}$	$-\bar{a}_{223}$
$\bar{w}$	0	$\bar{a}_{23}$	$-\bar{a}_{33}$
$\frac{1}{6}\bar{v}^3$		$\bar{a}_{2222}$	
$\overline{vw}$		$\bar{a}_{223}$	

Since we have the transformation equations (23.17), we can use either of the two coordinate representations, whichever is more convenient for a particular problem.

Lines of Curvature

A neighboring ray intersects the principal ray if and only if

$$i = y\xi - x\eta = 0. \tag{23.23}$$

Since i is invariant along the ray, we can assume x, y to be the coordinates of the intersection point with the plane $z = 0$ or the coordinates $x_D = 0$, y_D of the diapoint. This gives

$$\begin{aligned} i = y_D\xi &= \xi\left[\bar{a}_{22}\,\bar{v} + \tfrac{1}{2}\,\bar{a}_{222}\,\bar{v}^2 + \bar{a}_{23}\,\bar{w} + \tfrac{1}{6}\,\bar{a}_{2222}\,\bar{v}^3 + \bar{a}_{223}\bar{v}\bar{w}\right] \\ = y\xi - x\eta &= \xi[(a_{22} - a_3)\,v + \tfrac{1}{2}\,(a_{222} - 2a_{23})\,v^2 + a_{23}\,w \\ &\qquad + \tfrac{1}{6}\,(a_{2222} - 3a_{223})v^3 + (a_{223} - a_{33})vw]. \end{aligned} \tag{23.24}$$

The curves on the initial surface for which i vanishes will be called *curvature lines*. One of the lines of curvature is given by $\xi = 0$, that is, by the rays in the meridional plane

$$(w = 0,\ \bar{v}^2 = 2\bar{w} - \bar{w}^2).$$

If $a_{22} - a_3 = \bar{a}_{22} \neq 0$, there exists one and only one other line of curvature, and this is given (near the axis) by $v = 0$, that is, a line having a tangent normal to the meridional plane. A normal system with $\bar{a}_{22} \neq 0$ will be called an *astigmatic* system, and $\bar{a}_{22}$ will be taken as a measure of *astigmatism*.

Equation (23.21) shows that we have, to a first approximation,

$$x = a_3\xi, \quad y = a_{22}\,v = a_{22}\eta, \tag{23.25}$$

which means that the nearby rays *in* the meridional plane ($\xi = 0$) meet at a point at the distance $z = -a_{22}$. This point is called the *meridional* focus. The nearby rays in the plane *perpendicular* to the meridional plane intersect at a distance $z = -a_3$; this point is called the *sagittal* focus. The distance $\bar{a}_{22} = a_{22} - a_3$ is called the *astigmatic distance*. We shall soon see that the two foci thus determined give us the two points in which the principal ray is tangential to the *caustic*.

The normal system is called *anastigmatic* if $\bar{a}_{22} = a_{22} - a_3$ vanishes. In this case the ray is tangential to the caustic in only one point.

Equation (23.24) shows that, in an anastigmatic system, we have, besides the meridional line of curvature, two lines of curvature the directions of which are given by equating to zero the second-order members of (23.24). This gives

$$(a_{222} - 2a_{23})\, y^2 + a_{23}\, x^2 = 0$$

or

$$(\bar{a}_{222} + \bar{a}_{23})\, y^2 + \bar{a}_{23}\, x^2 = 0. \qquad (23.26)$$

We shall call these directions the principal *asymmetric directions*. A normal system for which $\bar{a}_{22} = \bar{a}_{222} = \bar{a}_{23} = 0$ or, correspondingly, $a_{22} - a_3 = a_{222} = a_{23} = 0$ will be called an *anasymmetric* system. In this case we have from (23.18)

$$\bar{h} = \bar{a}_3\, \overline{w} + \left(\tfrac{1}{24}\, \bar{a}_{2222}\, \bar{v}^4 + \tfrac{1}{2}\, \bar{a}_{223}\, \bar{v}^2\overline{w} + \tfrac{1}{2}\, \bar{a}_{33}\, \overline{w}^2\right), \qquad (23.27)$$

that is, h is a function of ξ^2 and η^2 only. This is the case in the image of a point of the axis in a system with two symmetry planes if *astigmatism* is corrected.

In an *anasymmetric* system, Equation (23.24) shows that there are four lines of curvature

$$\xi = 0, \quad \eta = 0,$$

and

$$(\tfrac{1}{3}\, a_{2222} - a_{223})\, y^2 + (a_{223} - a_{33})\, x^2 = 0. \qquad (23.28)$$

These latter lines we shall call the *Gullstrand* lines of curvature. The reader may note that neither the *asymmetric* lines of curvature nor the *Gullstrand* lines of curvature are necessarily real.

If $\bar{a}_{22} = \bar{a}_{222} = \bar{a}_{23} = \bar{a}_{2222} = \bar{a}_{223} = 0$, all directions are lines of curvature. In this case, up to the order considered, $\bar{h}$ is a function of $\overline{w}$ alone, that is, a function of $(\xi^2 + \eta^2)$, and so it has *symmetry of rotation* with respect to the principal ray:

$$\bar{h} = \bar{a}_3\, \overline{w} + \tfrac{1}{2}\, \bar{a}_{33}\, \overline{w}^2. \qquad (23.29)$$

Equations (23.22), in this case, give for the coordinates of the diapoint

$$y = 0, \quad -z = \bar{a}_3 + \bar{a}_{33}\,\overline{w}. \tag{23.30}$$

In the case in which $\bar{a}_{33} = 0 = a_{33} - a_3$, we have a *sharp* image. All the rays come to a focus at the distance $z = -a_3$ from the origin: $y = 0$, $-z = a_3$.

We summarize the four types of images:

$$\left.\begin{array}{l} a_{22} - a_3 = 0 \\ \bar{a}_{22} = 0 \end{array}\right\} \text{anastigmatic image.}$$

$$\left.\begin{array}{l} a_{22} - a_3 = 0, \quad a_{222} = a_{23} = 0 \\ \bar{a}_{22} = \bar{a}_{222} = \bar{a}_{23} = 0 \end{array}\right\} \text{anasymmetric image.}$$

$$\left.\begin{array}{l} a_{22} - a_3 = a_{222} = a_{23} \\ \qquad = \frac{1}{3}\, a_{2222} - a_{33} = a_{223} - a_{33} = 0 \\ \bar{a}_{22} = \bar{a}_{23} = \bar{a}_{222} = \bar{a}_{2222} = \bar{a}_{223} = 0 \end{array}\right\} \text{rotation-symmetric image.}$$

$$\left.\begin{array}{l} a_{22} - a_3 = a_{222} = a_{23} \\ \qquad = \frac{1}{3}\, a_{2222} - a_3 = a_{223} - a_3 = a_{33} - a_3 = 0 \\ \bar{a}_{22} = \bar{a}_{23} = \bar{a}_{222} = \bar{a}_{2222} = \bar{a}_{223} = \bar{a}_{33} = 0 \end{array}\right\} \text{sharp image.}$$

We shall now study the caustic surfaces and their dependence on the a_{ik}.

Caustic Surfaces

The distance $l_\varkappa$ of the points of the caustic surfaces from the diapoint is given from Equation (23.10) by inserting from (23.22) the coordinates of the diapoint. If the coordinates $\overline{v}$ and $\overline{w}$ are used, the vector $\vec{s}$ has the coordinates

$$\xi = \sqrt{2\overline{w} - \overline{v}^2 - \overline{w}^2}, \quad \eta = \overline{v}, \quad \zeta = 1 - \overline{w}, \tag{23.31}$$

and the vector $\vec{a}$ (to the diapoint) has the coordinates

$$\begin{aligned} x_D &= 0 \\ y_D &= \bar{a}_{22}\overline{v} + (\tfrac{1}{2}\bar{a}_{222}\overline{v}^2 + \bar{a}_{23}\overline{w}) + (\tfrac{1}{6}\bar{a}_{2222}\overline{v}^3 + \bar{a}_{223}\overline{v}\overline{w}) \\ -z_D &= \bar{a}_3 + \bar{a}_{23}\overline{v} + (\tfrac{1}{2}\bar{a}_{223}\overline{v}^2 + \bar{a}_{33}\overline{w}). \end{aligned} \tag{23.32}$$

Differentiating and inserting these equations into (23.10) then gives for $l_\varkappa$ the equation

$$l_\varkappa^2 + l_\varkappa B + C = 0,$$

with

$$B = \bar{a}_{22} + (\bar{a}_{222} + 2\bar{a}_{23})\bar{v} + \tfrac{1}{2}\bar{v}^2 (\bar{a}_{2222} + 4\bar{a}_{223} - 2\bar{a}_{22})$$
$$+ \bar{w}\,(\bar{a}_{223} + 2\bar{a}_{33}) \qquad (23.33)$$
$$C = (\bar{a}_{22}\bar{a}_{33} - \bar{a}_{23}^{2})\,(2\bar{w} - \bar{v}^2).$$

Considering only the first-order terms in (23.33), which is equivalent to going to third-order terms in the development of h, we obtain

$$B = \bar{a}_{22} + (\bar{a}_{222} + 2\bar{a}_{23})\bar{v}$$
$$C = 0. \qquad (23.34)$$

This leads to

$$l_\varkappa' = 0, \quad - l_\varkappa'' = \bar{a}_{22} + (\bar{a}_{222} + 2\bar{a}_{23})\bar{v} \qquad (23.35)$$

and gives for the coordinates of the first caustic (*sagittal* caustic)

$$x' = 0$$
$$y' = \bar{a}_{22}\bar{v} + \tfrac{1}{2}\,\bar{a}_{222}\bar{v}^2 + \bar{a}_{23}\bar{w} \qquad (23.36)$$
$$-(z' + \bar{a}_3) = \bar{a}_{23}\,\bar{v},$$

that is, up to the third order, the sagittal caustic coincides with the diapoints. The *meridional* caustic is given by

$$x'' = -\,\xi\,[\bar{a}_{22} + (\bar{a}_{222} + 2\bar{a}_{23})\,\bar{v}]$$
$$y'' = -\,\tfrac{1}{2}\,(\bar{a}_{222} + 4\bar{a}_{23})\,\bar{v}^2 + \bar{a}_{23}\bar{w} \qquad (23.37)$$
$$-(z'' + \bar{a}_3 + \bar{a}_{22}) = (\bar{a}_{222} + 3\bar{a}_{23})\bar{v}.$$

The principal ray $\bar{v} = \bar{w} = 0$ is tangential to the sagittal caustic at the point ($z = -a_3 = -\bar{a}_3$), the *sagittal* focus, and to the meridional caustic at the point $z = -(\bar{a}_3 + \bar{a}_{22}) = -a_{22}$, the tangential or *meridional* focus.

The sagittal caustic has a third-order contact with the meridional plane, in which it has a tangent line given by

$$\bar{a}_{23}y' + (z' + \bar{a}_3)\,\bar{a}_{22} = 0$$

or

$$a_{23}y' + (z' + a_3)\,(a_{22} - a_3) = 0, \qquad (23.38)$$

the slope of which is $-\bar{a}_{22}/\bar{a}_{23}$. All the rays of the system go (within second-order accuracy) through this line, which lies in the meridional plane.

This fact was emphasized by *A. Gullstrand*, who fought the erroneous assumption, based on the first-order approximation, that the rays go through a line element in the direction of the

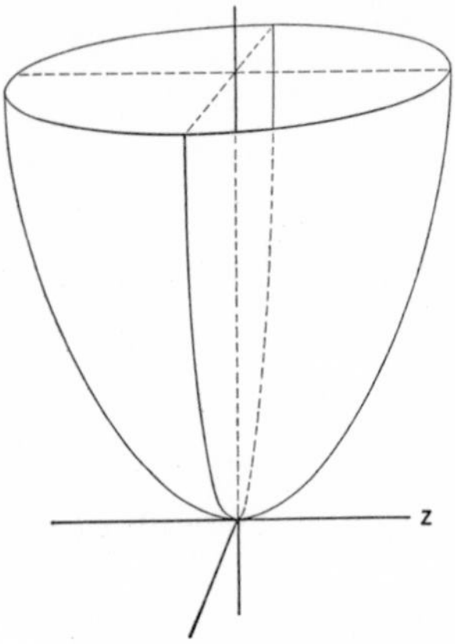

Fig. 23.1. Approximate form of meridional caustic, first case with astigmatism uncorrected.

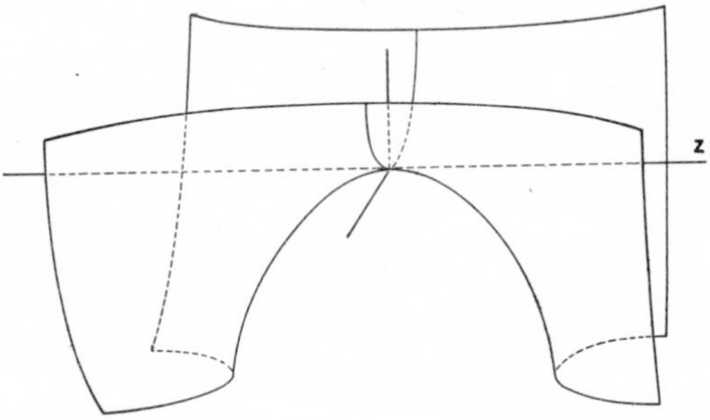

Fig. 23.2. Approximate form of meridional caustic, second case, with astigmatism uncorrected.

y-axis (normal to the principal ray), this being the case only if the asymmetry error a_{23} is zero.

The meridional caustic, as Equations (23.37) show, is tangential to the xz-plane and is approximated by the paraboloid

$$2y'' = \frac{x''^2}{\bar{a}_{22}^2/\bar{a}_{23}} - \frac{(z'' + \bar{a}_{22} + \bar{a}_3)^2}{\bar{a}_{222} + 3\bar{a}_{23}}, \tag{23.39}$$

which is either an elliptic paraboloid (first case) or a hyperbolic paraboloid (second case). This shows that it is a surface of double curvature, with vertex curvatures in the xy-plane and the yz-plane given, respectively, by

$$K_s = \frac{\bar{a}_{23}}{\bar{a}_{22}{}^2} = \frac{a_{23}}{(a_{22} - a_3)^2}, \quad -K_m = \frac{1}{\bar{a}_{222} + 3\bar{a}_{23}} = \frac{1}{a_{222}} \tag{23.40}$$

and a Gaussian curvature of

$$K = K_s K_m = \frac{-\bar{a}_{23}}{(\bar{a}_{222} + 3\bar{a}_{23})\,\bar{a}_{22}{}^2} = \frac{-a_{23}}{a_{222}\,(a_{22} - a_3)^2}, \tag{23.41}$$

these quantities depending on the astigmatism $\bar{a}_{22}$ and the two asymmetry coefficients $\bar{a}_{222}$ and $\bar{a}_{23}$.

Anastigmatic Image Formation

In the case in which $\bar{a}_{22} = 0$, that is, astigmatism is corrected, we have for the first and second caustics (up to the third-order approximation)

$$\begin{aligned} x' &= 0 & x'' &= -\xi\bar{v}\,(\bar{a}_{222} + 2\bar{a}_{23}) \\ y' &= \tfrac{1}{2}\,\bar{a}_{222}\bar{v}^2 + \bar{a}_{23}\bar{w} & y'' &= -\tfrac{1}{2}\,(\bar{a}_{222} + 4\bar{a}_{23})\bar{v}^2 + \bar{a}_{23}\bar{w} \\ -(z' + \bar{a}_3) &= \bar{a}_{23}\bar{v} & -(z'' + \bar{a}_3) &= (\bar{a}_{222} + 3\bar{a}_{23})\bar{v}. \end{aligned} \tag{23.42}$$

To obtain a picture of the two caustics in this case, we first consider the rays which go through a circle in the (infinite) pupil, that is, for which $\xi^2 + \eta^2 = 2\bar{w}$ is constant, and next consider the rays for which $\xi^2/(2\bar{w}) = \varkappa$ is constant. That is, we introduce as variable

$$\begin{aligned} 2\bar{w} &= \xi^2 + \eta^2 \\ \varkappa &= \xi^2/(2\bar{w}) \end{aligned} \quad \text{or} \quad \begin{aligned} 2w &= \xi^2 = 2\bar{w}\varkappa \\ \bar{v}^2 &= 2\bar{w}\,(1 - \varkappa). \end{aligned} \tag{23.43}$$

Eliminating $\bar{w}$ from

$$\begin{aligned} x' &= 0 \\ y' &= \bar{w}\,[\bar{a}_{222}\,(1 - \varkappa) + \bar{a}_{23}] = [\bar{a}_{222} + \bar{a}_{23} - \bar{a}_{222}\varkappa)\,\bar{w} \\ (z' + \bar{a}_3)^2 &= \bar{a}_{23}{}^2 2\bar{w}\,(1 - \varkappa) \end{aligned} \tag{23.44}$$

leads to

$$(z' + \bar{a}_3)^2 [\bar{a}_{222} + \bar{a}_{23} - \bar{a}_{222}\varkappa] = \bar{a}_{23}^2\, 2y' (1 - \varkappa). \quad (23.45)$$

Thus the rays through a given radial direction $\varkappa = \varkappa_o$ in the infinite exit pupil give points of the caustic which form a parabola in the yz-plane, this parabola being tangential to the principal ray and having a vertex curvature equal to

$$K_\varkappa = \frac{\bar{a}_{222} + \bar{a}_{23} - \bar{a}_{222}\varkappa}{\bar{a}_{23}^2 (1 - \varkappa)} = \frac{a_{222} - 2a_{23} - (a_{222} - 3a_{23})\varkappa}{a_{23}^2 (1 - \varkappa)}. \quad (23.46)$$

This means that all these parabolas have the principal ray as a common tangent.

In the same way the meridional caustic can be visualized. Inserting (23.43) into (23.42) leads to

$$\begin{aligned} x''^2 &= (2\bar{w})^2\, \varkappa (1 - \varkappa) (\bar{a}_{222} + 2\bar{a}_{23})^2 \\ y'' &= \bar{w} [\bar{a}_{23} - (1 - \varkappa) (\bar{a}_{222} + 4\bar{a}_{23})] = \bar{w} [- (\bar{a}_{222} + 3\bar{a}_{23}) \\ &\quad + \varkappa (\bar{a}_{222} + 4\bar{a}_{23})] \\ (z'' + \bar{a}_3)^2 &= 2\bar{w} (1 - \varkappa) (\bar{a}_{222} + 3\bar{a}_{23})^2. \end{aligned} \quad (23.47)$$

Equations (23.47), after the elimination of $\bar{w}$, are seen to represent a family of parabolas lying in the planes $\varkappa =$ constant, having the z-axis as a common tangent and having curvatures which are functions of $\varkappa$. In this case, however, the parabolas do not lie in the meridional plane but in the planes through the z-axis with

$$\begin{aligned} \frac{x''}{y''} &= \pm \frac{2\sqrt{\varkappa (1 - \varkappa)}\, (\bar{a}_{222} + 2\bar{a}_{23})}{- (\bar{a}_{222} + 3\bar{a}_{23}) + \varkappa (\bar{a}_{222} + 4\bar{a}_{23})} \\ &= \pm \frac{2\sqrt{\varkappa (1 - \varkappa)}\, (a_{222} - a_{23})}{- a_{222} + \varkappa (a_{222} + a_{23})}. \end{aligned} \quad (23.48)$$

The curvatures of the parabolas are given by

$$K_\varkappa = \frac{1}{(1 - \varkappa)\, a_{222}{}^2}$$

$$\times \sqrt{[\varkappa (a_{222} + a_{23}) - a_{222}]^2 + 4\varkappa (1 - \varkappa)(a_{222} - a_{23})^2} \quad (23.49)$$

$$= \frac{1}{(1 - \varkappa)(\bar{a}_{222} + 3\bar{a}_{23})^2}$$

$$\times \sqrt{[\varkappa (\bar{a}_{222} + 4\bar{a}_{23}) - (\bar{a}_{222} + 3\bar{a}_{23})]^2 + 4\varkappa (1 - \varkappa)(\bar{a}_{222} + 2\bar{a}_{23})^2}.$$

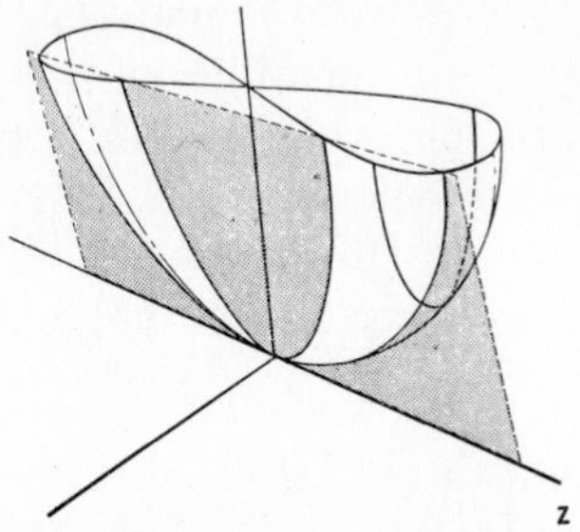

Fig. 23.3. Approximate form of meridional caustic, first anastigmatic case.

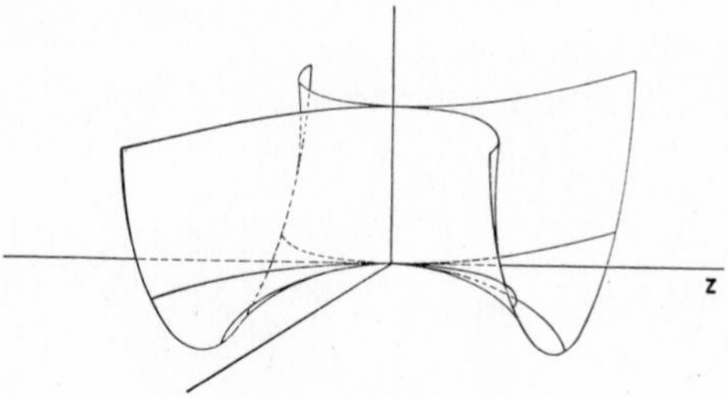

Fig. 23.4. Approximate form of meridional caustic, second anastigmatic case.

We can show by analysis of Equations (23.47) that the meridional caustic surface has at the focus only a tangential line, namely, the principal ray, rather than a tangential plane; that is, the surface has a wedge at that point.

The Caustics in an Anasymmetric System

If the system is anasymmetric, we have from Equation (23.33), since $\bar{a}_{22} = \bar{a}_{222} = \bar{a}_{23} = 0$,

$$\begin{aligned} B &= \tfrac{1}{2}\,\bar{v}^2\,(\bar{a}_{2222} + 4\bar{a}_{223}) + \bar{w}\,(\bar{a}_{223} + 2\bar{a}_{33}) \\ C &= 0, \end{aligned} \qquad (23.50)$$

or

$$l_\varkappa' = 0, \quad -\,l_\varkappa'' = \tfrac{1}{2}\,\bar{v}^2\,(\bar{a}_{2222} + 4\bar{a}_{223}) + \bar{w}\,(\bar{a}_{223} + 2\bar{a}_{33}). \qquad (23.51)$$

We draw the reader's attention to the fact that, though for anasymmetric systems we can calculate $l_\varkappa'$ and $l_\varkappa''$ to the fourth order, this is not generally possible in systems with astigmatic correction owing to the fact that, for $B^2 - 4C = 0$, the solutions $l_\varkappa'$, $l_\varkappa''$ of (23.33) cannot generally be developed into power series with respect to $\bar{v}$ and $\bar{w}$. However, this is possible in the anasymmetric case and we have [*cf.* (23.32)]

$$\begin{aligned} x' &= 0 \\ y' &= \bar{v}\,[\tfrac{1}{2}\,\bar{v}^2\,(\tfrac{1}{3}\,\bar{a}_{2222}) + \bar{a}_{223}\bar{w}], \qquad (23.52) \\ -\,(z' + \bar{a}_3) &= \tfrac{1}{2}\,\bar{a}_{223}\,\bar{v}^2 + \bar{a}_{33}\bar{w}, \\ -\,x'' &= \xi\,[\tfrac{1}{2}\,\bar{v}^2\,(\bar{a}_{2222} + 4\bar{a}_{223}) + \bar{w}\,(\bar{a}_{223} + 2\bar{a}_{33})] \\ -\,y'' &= 2\bar{v}\,[\tfrac{1}{2}\,\bar{v}^2\,(\tfrac{1}{3}\,\bar{a}_{2222} + 2\bar{a}_{223}) + \bar{w}\bar{a}_{33}] \\ -\,(z'' + \bar{a}_3) &= \tfrac{1}{2}\,\bar{v}^2\,(5\bar{a}_{223} + \bar{a}_{2222}) + \bar{w}\,(3\bar{a}_{33} + \bar{a}_{223}). \end{aligned}$$

Again we can visualize the caustic, by considering the rays going through radial lines in the pupil ($\varkappa = \varkappa_o$). Inserting $\varkappa$ and $\bar{w}$ [*cf.* (23.43)] into (23.52) and introducing the abbreviations

$$\begin{aligned} G_m &= \tfrac{1}{3}\,a_{2222} - a_3 & \tfrac{1}{3}\,\bar{a}_{2222} &= G_m - 2G_c + G_s \\ G_c &= a_{223} - a_3 & \bar{a}_{223} &= G_c - G_s \qquad (23.53) \\ G_s &= a_{33} - a_3 & \bar{a}_{33} &= G_s\,, \end{aligned}$$

we find the sagittal caustic to be

$$\begin{aligned} x' &= 0 \\ y'^2 &= 2\bar{w}^3\,(1 - \varkappa)\,[G_m - G_c - \varkappa\,(G_m - 2G_c + G_s)]^2 \\ -\,(z' + a_3) &= \bar{w}\,[G_c - \varkappa\,(G_c - G_s)]. \end{aligned} \qquad (23.54)$$

Eliminating $\bar{w}$, we obtain an equation of the form

$$(z' + a_3)^3 = By'^2, \qquad (23.55)$$

that is, the equation of a semicubical parabola with the principal ray as cusp-tangent and the "beak curvature" B given by

$$B = -\frac{[G_c - \varkappa (G_c - G_s)]^3}{2(1-\varkappa)[G_m - G_c - \varkappa (G_m - 2G_c + G_s)]^2}. \qquad (23.56)$$

These curves have a higher order of contact with the axis than the parabolas described in the anastigmatic case, and they are symmetrical with respect to the principal ray. The meridional caustic can be studied in the same way.

From the second set of Equations (23.52), inserting $\varkappa$ from (23.43) and the abbreviations G_m, G_s, G_c from (23.53), we obtain

$$\begin{aligned} x''^2 &= 2\overline{w}^3 \varkappa [3G_m - G_c - \varkappa (3G_m - 2G_c - G_s)]^2 \\ y''^2 &= 8\overline{w}^3 (1-\varkappa)[G_m - \varkappa (G_m - G_s)]^2 \\ -(z'' + a_3) &= \overline{w}[3G_m - \varkappa (3G_m - G_c - 2G_s)]. \end{aligned} \qquad (23.57)$$

Eliminating $\overline{w}$, we find Equation (23.57) again as the equation of a semi-cubical parabola, which, for a given value of $\varkappa$, lies in the plane

$$\frac{x''}{y''} = \pm \tfrac{1}{2}\sqrt{\frac{\varkappa}{1-\varkappa}}\,\frac{3G_m - G_c - \varkappa (3G_m - 2G_c - G_s)}{G_m - \varkappa (G_m - G_s)} \qquad (23.58)$$

and has a beak curvature $B(\varkappa)$ given by

$$B = -\frac{[3G_m - \varkappa(3G_m - G_c - 2G_s)]^3}{2\varkappa[3G_m - G_c - \varkappa(3G_m - 2G_c - G_s)]^2 + 8(1-\varkappa)[G_m - \varkappa(G_m - G_s)]^2}. \qquad (23.59)$$

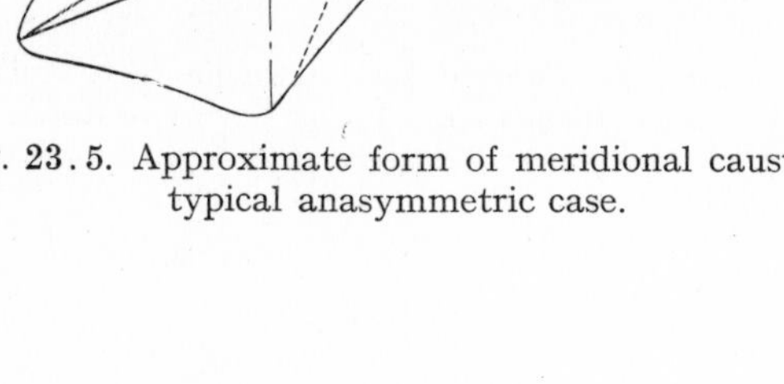

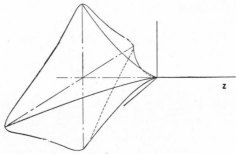

Fig. 23.5. Approximate form of meridional caustic, typical anasymmetric case.

The meridional caustic is a surface of double symmetry with respect to the xz- and yz-planes. Each cross section through the principal ray is a semi-cubical parabola* with the axis as the common tangent. Figure 23.5 will give an idea of its form.

Rotation-Symmetric Systems

In the case of rotational symmetry, we have

$$G_m = G_c = G_s = \bar{a}_{33} = a_{33} - a_3 = a_{223} - a_3 = \tfrac{1}{3}a_{2222} - a_3 = G. \tag{23.60}$$

This gives for the sagittal caustic

$$\begin{aligned} x' &= 0 \\ y' &= 0 \\ -(z' + a_3) &= \overline{w}G. \end{aligned} \tag{23.61}$$

That is, the sagittal caustic is formed by part of the principal ray.

The meridional caustic is given by

$$\begin{aligned} x''^2 &= 8\overline{w}^3\varkappa G^2 \\ y''^2 &= 8\overline{w}^3(1 - \varkappa)G^2 \\ -(z'' + a_3)^3 &= 27\overline{w}^3G^3. \end{aligned} \tag{23.62}$$

The meridional caustic is a rotation-symmetric surface that is generated by rotating a semi-cubical parabola of beak curvature B around the principal ray:

$$(z' + a_3)^3 + \tfrac{27}{8}G(x''^2 + y''^2) = 0, \tag{23.63}$$

that is,

$$B = -\tfrac{27}{8}G.$$

When $G = 0$ the image formation is sharp.

* In some cases, there may be more than one such semi-cubical parabola in a given plane through the z-axis since two different values of $\varkappa$ may lead to the same plane. The same statement applies to the anastigmatic case.

The Wave Surfaces

It is not difficult to calculate the equations of all the wave surfaces up to the desired order. If we form the equation

$$g = \vec{a}\vec{s} - h = -h + x\xi + y\eta \tag{23.64}$$

and insert x and y from (23.21), we find

$$g = (\tfrac{1}{2} v^2 a_{22} + a_3 w) + 2(\tfrac{1}{6} v^3 a_{222} + a_{23} vw) + 3(\tfrac{1}{24} v^4 a_{2222} + \tfrac{1}{2} v^2 w\, a_{223} + \tfrac{1}{2} w^2 a_{33}). \tag{23.65}$$

Since the points of a wave surface are given by

$$\begin{aligned} x_w/\xi &= x/\xi - g \\ y_w &= y - gv \\ z_w &= -g\zeta = -g(1 - \tfrac{1}{2} v^2 - w + \dots), \end{aligned} \tag{23.66}$$

the relations

$$\begin{aligned} x_w/\xi &= a_3 + a_{23} v + \tfrac{1}{2} v^2 (a_{223} - a_{22}) + w(a_{33} - a_3) \\ y_w &= a_{22} v + \tfrac{1}{2} v^2 a_{222} + a_{23} w + \tfrac{1}{6} v^3 (a_{2222} - 3a_{22}) + vw(a_{223} - a_3) \\ -z_w &= \tfrac{1}{2} v^2 a_{22} + a_3 w + \tfrac{1}{6} v^3 (2a_{222}) + 2a_{23} vw \\ &\quad + \tfrac{1}{8} v^4 (a_{2222} - 2a_{22}) + \tfrac{1}{2} v^2 w (3a_{223} - a_3 - a_{22}) \\ &\quad + \tfrac{1}{2} w^2 (3a_{33} - 2a_3) \end{aligned} \tag{23.67}$$

give the equations of the wave surface through the origin. The wave surface through a point at the distance z_o from the origin is obtained by subtracting z_o from g, which gives

$$\begin{aligned} x_w/\xi &= a_3 + z_o + a_{23} v + \tfrac{1}{2} v^2 (a_{223} - a_{22}) + w(a_{33} - a_3) \\ y_w &= (a_{22} + z_o) v + \tfrac{1}{2} v^2 a_{222} + a_{23} w + \tfrac{1}{6} v^3 (a_{2222} - 3a_{22}) \\ &\quad + vw(a_{223} - a_3) \\ -(z_w - z_o) &= \tfrac{1}{2} v^2 (a_{22} + z_o) + w(a_3 + z_o) + \tfrac{1}{6} v^3 (2a_{222}) \\ &\quad + 2 a_{23} vw + \tfrac{1}{8} v^4 (a_{2222} - 2a_{22} + z_o) \\ &\quad + \tfrac{1}{2} v^2 w (3a_{223} - a_3 - a_{22} + z_o) \\ &\quad + \tfrac{1}{2} w^2 (3a_{33} - 2a_3 + z_o). \end{aligned} \tag{23.68}$$

The wave surfaces, in general, are surfaces of double curvature; the paraboloid

$$2\,(z_w - z_o) + \frac{y^2}{a_{22} + z_o} + \frac{x^2}{a_3 + z_o} = 0 \tag{23.69}$$

with principal curvatures given by

$$K_m{}^2 = \frac{1}{z_o + a_{22}}, \quad K_s{}^2 = \frac{1}{z_o + a_3} \tag{23.70}$$

(K_m, meridional curvature; K_s, sagittal curvature) is the osculating surface at the origin, that is, the points at the distance $z_o = -\,a_3$ and $z_o = -\,a_{22}$ from the origin are the centers of curvature of the wave surface. It is interesting to study the behavior of the wave surface going through one of the centers of curvature, for instance, $z_o = -\,a_3$. Equation (23.68) gives

$$\begin{aligned} x_w &= \xi v a_{23} + \ldots \\ y_w &= (a_{22} - a_3)\, v + \ldots \\ -\,(z_w + a_3) &= \tfrac{1}{2}\, v^2\, (a_{22} - a_3) + \ldots \end{aligned} \tag{23.71}$$

Introducing (23.43) as before, we can show that the surface has a wedge (that is, it does not have a tangential plane, but a tangential line) at the origin in the direction of the y-axis. Analogously, setting $z = -\,a_{22}$, we find a surface with a tangential wedge in the sagittal direction (along the x-axis).

The reader may analyze for himself the form of the wave surface through the focus in the case of an anastigmatic, anasymmetric, or rotation-symmetric system. The equations of the wave surface through the focus are given in the *anastigmatic* case as

$$\begin{aligned} x_w/\xi &= a_{23} v \\ y_w &= \tfrac{1}{2}\, v^2\, a_{222} + a_{23}\, w \\ -\,(z_w + a_3) &= 2v\,[(\tfrac{1}{3}\, a_{222})\, \tfrac{1}{2}\, v^2 + a_{23} w], \end{aligned} \tag{23.72}$$

and in the *anasymmetric case as*

$$\begin{aligned} x_w/\xi &= \tfrac{1}{2}\, v^2\, (a_{223} - a_3) + w\, (a_{33} - a_3) \\ y_w &= v\,[\tfrac{1}{2}\, v^2\, (\tfrac{1}{3}\, a_{2222} - a_3) + w\, (a_{223} - a_3)] \\ -\,(z_w + a_3) &= \tfrac{1}{8}\, v^4\, (a_{2222} - 3a_3) + \tfrac{3}{2}\, v^2 w\, (a_{223} - a_3) \\ &\quad + \tfrac{3}{2}\, w^2\, (a_{33} - a_3), \end{aligned} \tag{23.73}$$

or, introducing the G's from (23.53), as

$$\begin{aligned} x_w &= \xi\,[\tfrac{1}{2}\,v^2\,G_c + w\,G_s] \\ y_w &= v\,[\tfrac{1}{2}\,v^2\,G_m + w\,G_c] \\ -\,(z_w + a_3) &= \tfrac{3}{8}\,v^4\,G_m + \tfrac{3}{2}\,v^2 w\,G_c + \tfrac{3}{2}\,w^2\,G_s. \end{aligned} \tag{23.74}$$

In the case of a rotation-symmetric system, this reduces to

$$\begin{aligned} x_w &= \tfrac{1}{2}\,\xi\,(\xi^2 + v^2)\,G \qquad -\,(z_w + a_3) = \tfrac{3}{8}\,(\xi^2 + v^2)^2\,G \\ y_w &= \tfrac{1}{2}\,v\,(\xi^2 + v^2)\,G \end{aligned} \tag{23.75}$$

or

$$(x^2 + y^2)^2 + \tfrac{32}{27}\,G\,(z + a_3)^3 = 0, \tag{23.76}$$

which gives the form of the wave surface through the focus.

CHAPTER TWENTY-FOUR

Light Distribution in a Plane

Light Distribution in a Plane Perpendicular to the Principal Ray

Although the form of the caustic and the wave surface are important in investigating the optical image, what the designer really wants to know is the light distribution in the image plane. The image plane to be investigated is, in general, perpendicular to the optical axis of the system and not to the principal ray. However, we shall at first investigate the intersection of the rays with a plane perpendicular to the principal ray at the distance z from the origin. From (23.32), noting that

$$\frac{x}{\xi} = \frac{x_o}{\xi} + \frac{z}{\zeta}, \quad y = y_o + \frac{zv}{\zeta}, \quad \frac{1}{\zeta} = 1 + \tfrac{1}{2} v^2 + w + \ldots, \tag{24.1}$$

we find from (23.21) for the intersection of the rays with a plane at the distance z

$$\begin{aligned} \frac{x}{\xi} &= a_3 + z + a_{23} v + \tfrac{1}{2} v^2 (a_{223} + z) + w (a_{33} + z) \\ y &= v (a_{22} + z) + \tfrac{1}{2} a_{222} v^2 + a_{23} w + \tfrac{1}{6} v^3 (a_{2222} + 3z) \\ &\qquad + vw (a_{223} + z). \end{aligned} \tag{24.2}$$

To investigate the light distribution in such a plane, we can proceed in one or more of the following ways:

(*a*) We can investigate the rays going through a system of concentric circles and radial lines in the exit pupil (which in this chapter is assumed to be at infinity) and study the corresponding curves in the image planes.

(*b*) We can calculate the density of light at every point of the image plane.

(*c*) We can choose a number of points evenly spaced over the exit pupil and plot the corresponding points of intersection with the image plane. These *spot diagrams,* as the author has called them, give a clear intuitive picture of the light distribution in the image plane and will be extensively used in the future course of the book.

In general we shall again investigate the second-, third-, and fourth-order coefficients *separately* and then study their *interaction.*

In first order, we have

$$x = \xi\,(a_3 + z), \quad y = v\,(a_{22} + z). \tag{24.3}$$

Inserting

$$\xi^2 = \varkappa\, 2\overline{w}, \quad v^2 = (1 - \varkappa)\, 2\overline{w} \tag{24.4}$$

we obtain

$$\begin{aligned} x^2 &= 2\overline{w}\varkappa\,(a_3 + z)^2 \\ y^2 &= 2\overline{w}\,(1 - \varkappa)\,(a_{22} + z)^2, \end{aligned} \tag{24.5}$$

whence, eliminating $2\overline{w}$,

$$x^2\,(1 - \varkappa)\,(a_{22} + z)^2 = y^2\varkappa\,(a_3 + z)^2 \tag{24.6}$$

or, eliminating $\varkappa$,

$$\frac{x^2}{2\overline{w}\,(a_3 + z)^2} + \frac{y^2}{2\overline{w}\,(a_{22} + z)^2} = 1\,. \tag{24.7}$$

Thus, in first order, the rays through a set of circles in the exit pupil intersect the plane at the distance z from the origin in a set of ellipses, the axes of these ellipses being proportional to the distances from the two foci and to the diameter of the exit pupil. (Here the "apparent" diameter is $2\sqrt{2\overline{w}} = 2\sqrt{\xi^2 + \eta^2}$.)

The Image in the Plane through the Focus of an Anastigmatic System

Up to the third order, we have in this case

$$\begin{aligned} x &= \xi\, a_{23} v \\ y &= \tfrac{1}{2}\, a_{222}\, v^2 + a_{23}\, w, \end{aligned} \tag{24.8}$$

or, introducing $\varkappa$ and $\overline{w}$,

$$x = \pm\, 2\overline{w}a_{23}\sqrt{\varkappa(1-\varkappa)}$$
$$y = \overline{w}\,[a_{222} + \varkappa(a_{23} - a_{222})]. \qquad (24.9)$$

Eliminating $\varkappa$, we find

$$\frac{x^2}{a_{23}{}^2\overline{w}^2} + \frac{[y - \frac{1}{2}\overline{w}(a_{23} + a_{222})]^2}{\frac{1}{4}(a_{23} - a_{222})^2\overline{w}^2} = 1, \qquad (24.10)$$

which means that the rays going through a set of concentric circles in the infinite pupil go through a series of eccentric ellipses the centers of which lie along the y-axis and are given by

$$x = 0, \quad y = \tfrac{1}{2}\overline{w}(a_{23} + a_{222})$$

and the semiaxes of which are proportional (numerically) to $\overline{w}a_{23}$ and $\overline{w}(a_{23} - a_{222})$, respectively.

The rays through a radial direction $\varkappa$ go through a pair of straight lines whose directions are given by

$$\frac{x}{y} = \pm\frac{2a_{23}\sqrt{\varkappa(1-\varkappa)}}{a_{222} + (a_{23} - a_{222})\varkappa}, \qquad (24.11)$$

which for $\varkappa = 0$ (meridional rays) and $\varkappa = 1$ (sagittal rays) both have the direction of the y-axis.

We have to distinguish two cases.

(*a*) $a_{23}\,a_{222} > 0$ may be called *outside asymmetry*. In this case we find that all the ellipses given by (24.10) have two common tangents as envelopes, these being given by

$$a_{222}\,x^2 = a_{23}\,y^2. \qquad (24.12)$$

All the ellipses described in (24.10) have the same power with respect to the point $x = y = 0$, and the lines given by (24.12) as common tangent. (See the left-hand diagram in Figure 24.5).

Calling a_{23} the *sagittal asymmetry coefficient* C_s, and a_{222} the *meridional asymmetry coefficient* C_m, that is,

$$C_s = a_{23} = \bar{a}_{23} \qquad \bar{a}_{23} = C_s = a_{23}$$
$$\bar{a}_{222} = C_m - 3C_s \qquad (24.13)$$
$$C_m = a_{222} = \bar{a}_{222} + 3\bar{a}_{23} \qquad a_{222} = C_m$$

we can rewrite (24.9) and (24.10) in the form

$$\begin{aligned} x^2 &= 4C_s^2\,\overline{w}^2\,\varkappa\,(1-\varkappa) \\ y &= \overline{w}\,[C_m + (C_s - C_m)\,\varkappa] \\ \frac{x^2}{C_s^2\overline{w}^2} &+ \frac{[y - \frac{1}{2}\overline{w}\,(C_m + C_s)]^2}{\frac{1}{4}\overline{w}^2\,(C_s - C_m)^2} = 1 \end{aligned} \tag{24.14}$$

(*b*) $a_{23}a_{222} = C_s\,(C_m) < 0.$

The point $x = y = 0$ lies inside all the ellipses in question. We speak in this case of "inside asymmetry." The ellipses are eccentric but inside one another. Again the point $x = y = 0$ has the same power for all the ellipses, which in this case, however, is negative.

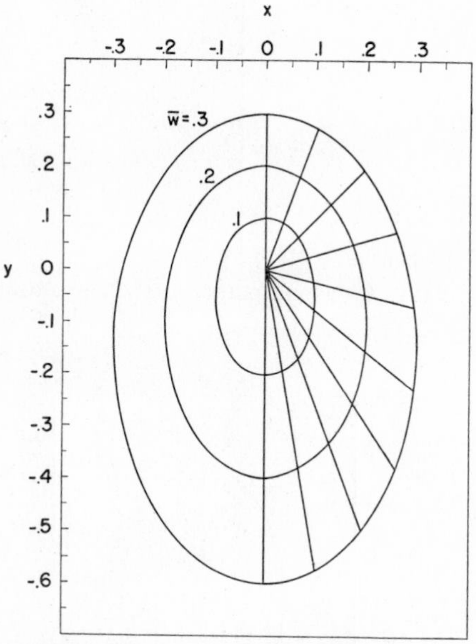

Fig. 24.1. Inside asymmetry figures, curves $\overline{w}$ = const.

The light distribution in the image plane in this case becomes clear if we calculate the spot diagrams. For a number of evenly distributed points situated in a circle of the exit pupil, these being given, for instance, by the coordinates designated in Figure 24.2, we compute from (24.8) the intersection points in the image plane. Figures 24.3, 24.4 and 24.5 show the spot diagrams for several values of C_m and C_s compared with the corresponding curves $\overline{w} =$ const.

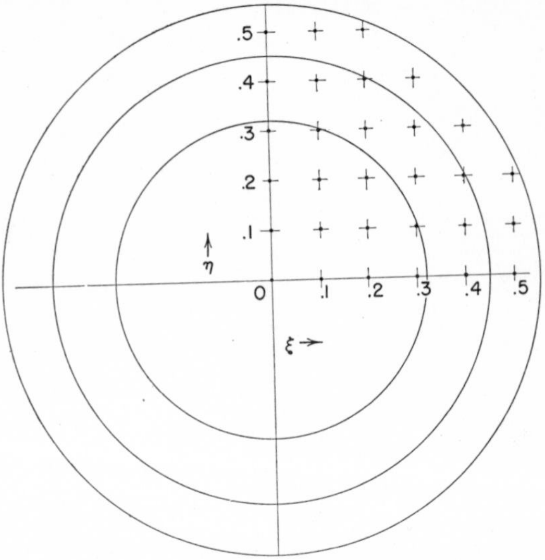

Fig. 24.2. Choice of points in the exit pupil.

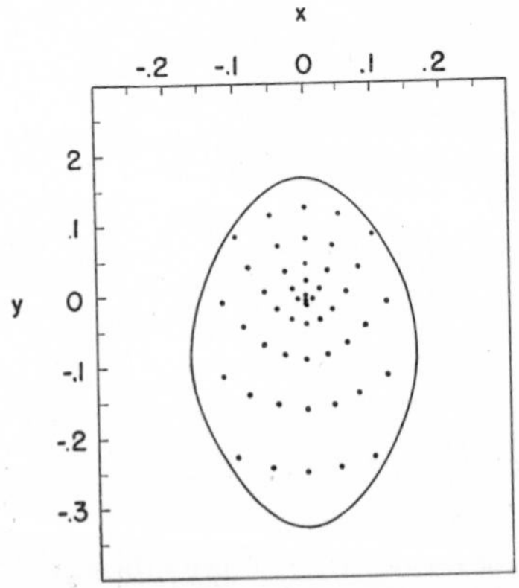

Fig. 24.3. Typical spot diagram in anastigmatic case, intersection of rays with focal plane.

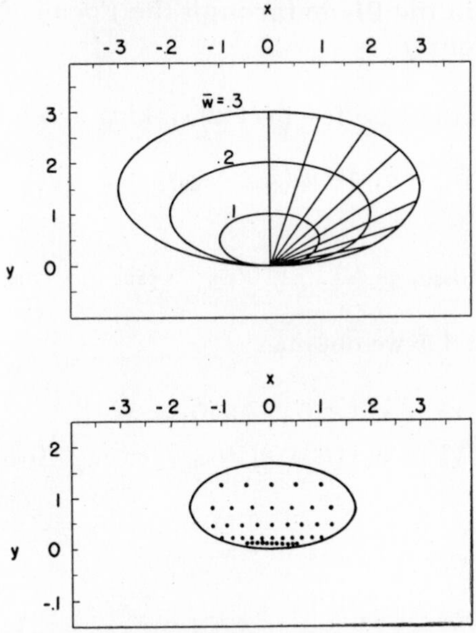

Fig. 24.4. Second example of anastigmatic case, curves $\overline{w}$ = const. and corresponding spot diagram.

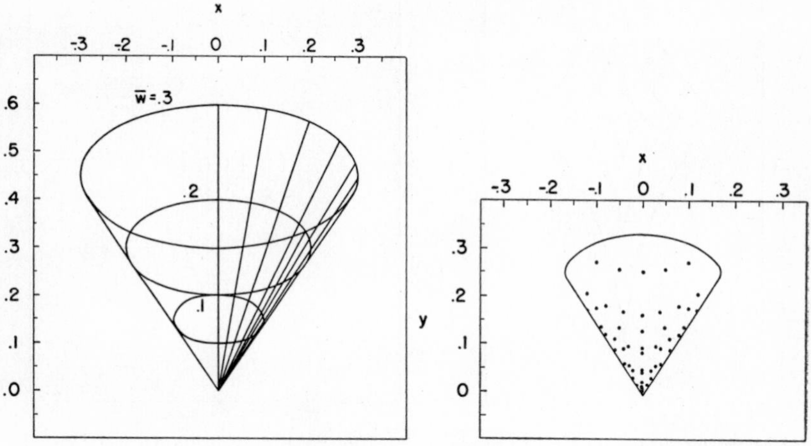

Fig. 24.5. Third example of anastigmatic case, curves $\overline{w}$ = const. and corresponding spot diagram.

The Image in the Plane through the Focus of an Anasymmetric System

We have in this case from (24.2), taking account of (23.53),

$$x = \xi \left[\tfrac{1}{2} v^2 (a_{223} - a_3) + w (a_{33} - a_3)\right] = \xi \left[G_c \left(\tfrac{1}{2} v^2\right) + G_s w\right] \tag{24.15}$$

$$y = v \left[\tfrac{1}{2} v^2 \left(\tfrac{1}{3} a_{2222} - a_3\right) + w (a_{223} - a_3)\right] = v \left[G_m \left(\tfrac{1}{2} v^2\right) + G_c w\right].$$

Inserting $\varkappa$ and $\overline{w}$ we obtain

$$\begin{aligned} x^2 &= 2\overline{w}^3 \varkappa \left[G_c + \varkappa (G_s - G_c)\right]^2 \\ y^2 &= 2\overline{w}^3 (1 - \varkappa) \left[G_m + \varkappa (G_c - G_m)\right]^2, \end{aligned} \tag{24.16}$$

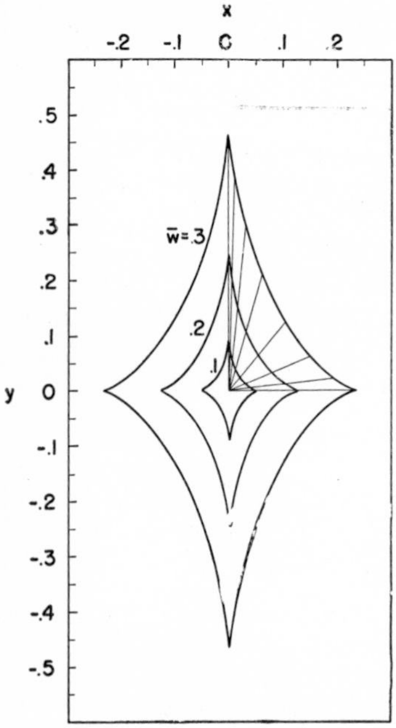

Fig. 24.6a. Typical figure in anasymmetric case, curves $\overline{w}$ = const.

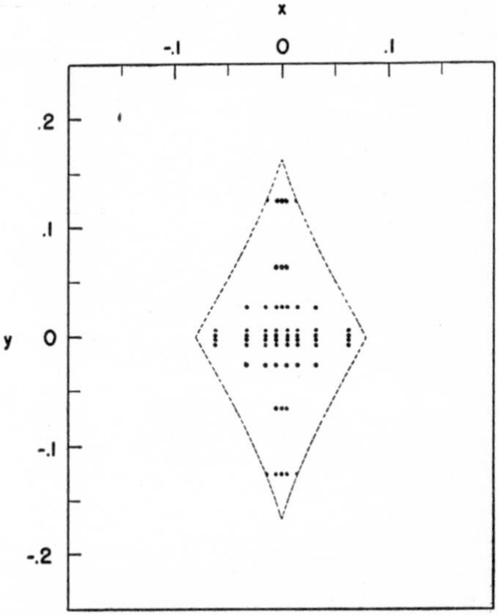

Fig. 24.6b. Spot diagram corresponding to Figure 24.6a.

and the elimination of $\overline{w}$ gives

$$\frac{x}{y} = \pm \sqrt{\frac{\varkappa}{1-\varkappa}\,\frac{G_c + \varkappa\,(G_s - G_c)}{G_m + \varkappa\,(G_c - G_m)}}\,, \tag{24.17}$$

that is, the rays through a radial line in the pupil go through a radial line in the image plane. Figures 24.6a, 24.6b, 24.7a, 24.7b, etc. show the curves which correspond to the circles $\overline{w} = \overline{w}_o$ and the corresponding spot diagrams, respectively.

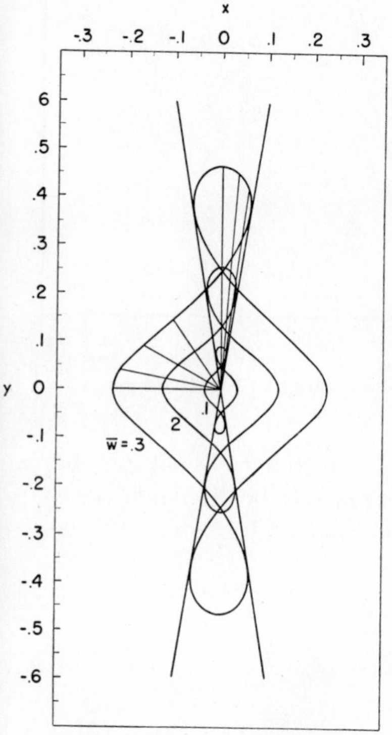

Fig. 24.7a. Second example of anasymmetric case.

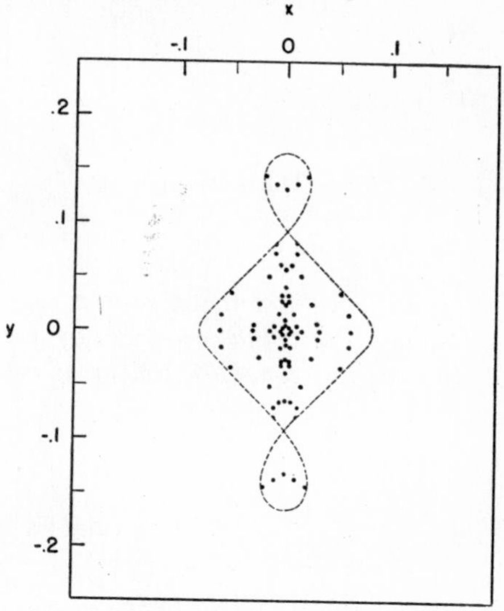

Fig. 24.7b. Spot diagram corresponding to Figure 24.7a.

To understand the geometrical meaning of the three coefficients G_m, G_s, G_c, we shall assume for the moment that all but one are zero. If $G_m = G_c = 0$, we find

$$x^2 = 2\bar{w}^3 \varkappa^3 G_s^2$$
$$y^2 = 0, \qquad (24.18)$$

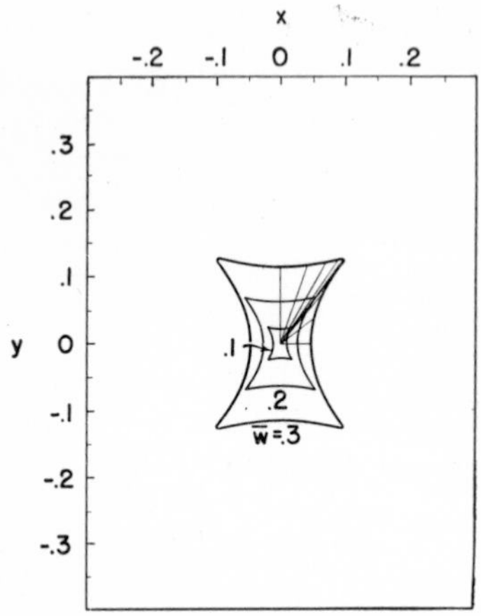

Fig. 24.8a. Third example of anasymmetric case

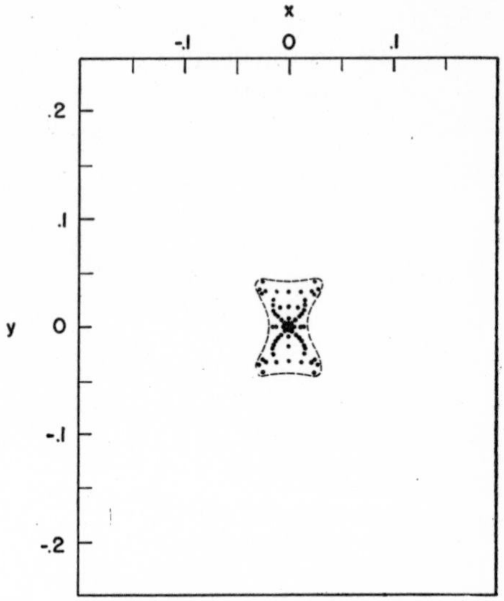

Fig. 24.8b. Spot diagram corresponding to Figure 24.8a.

giving a line element in the sagittal direction. We call G_s the *sagittal Gullstrand coefficient* or, for a reason to be discussed later, the *sagittal zonal coefficient of astigmatism.* If $G_s = G_c = 0$, we find

$$x^2 = 0$$
$$y^2 = 2\bar{w}^3 (1 - \varkappa)^3 G_m^2, \qquad (24.19)$$

giving a line element in the *meridional* direction. Thus G_m is called the *meridional Gullstrand coefficient* or *meridional zonal coefficient of astigmatism.*

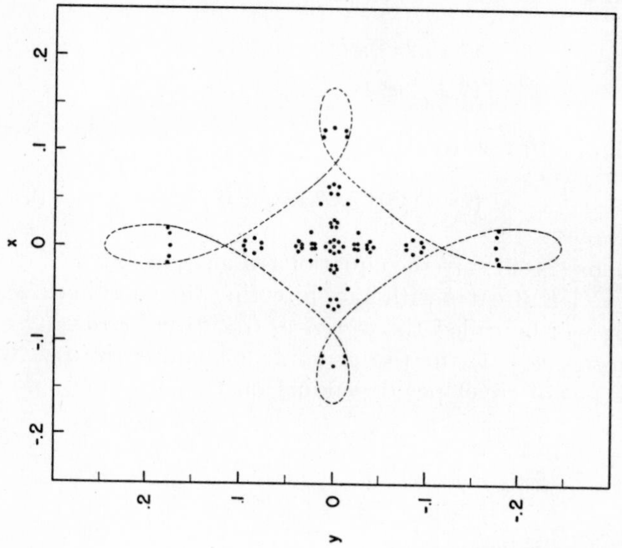

Fig. 24.9b. Spot diagram corresponding to Figure 24.9a.

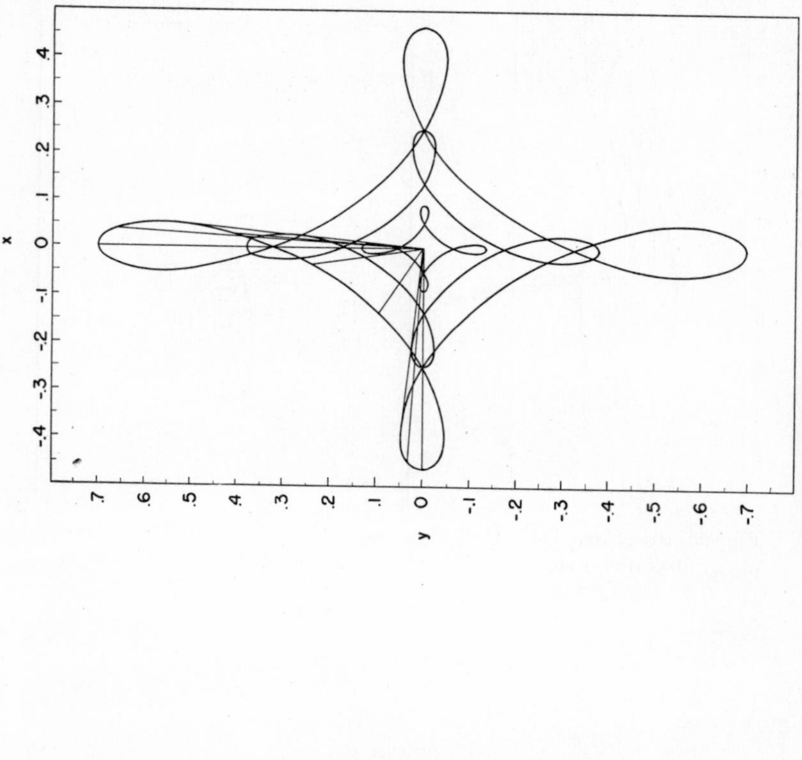

Fig. 24.9a. Fourth example of anasymmetric case.

We now assume $G_m = G_s = 0$. This leads to

$$x^2 = 2\overline{w}^3 \varkappa (1 - \varkappa)^2 G_c^2$$
$$y^2 = 2\overline{w}^3 (1 - \varkappa) \varkappa^2 G_c^2, \qquad (24.20)$$

and by eliminating $\varkappa$, to

$$(x^2 + y^2)^3 = 2\overline{w}^3 G_c^2 x^2y^2. \qquad (24.21)$$

Equations (24.21) are the equations of a set of four-leaf clover figures (two lemniscates with axes bisecting the coordinate axes). This error will be called the *cloverleaf Gullstrand error.*

The curves $\overline{w} = \overline{w}_o$ in the general anasymmetric case have various types of envelopes depending on the size of G_s and G_m.

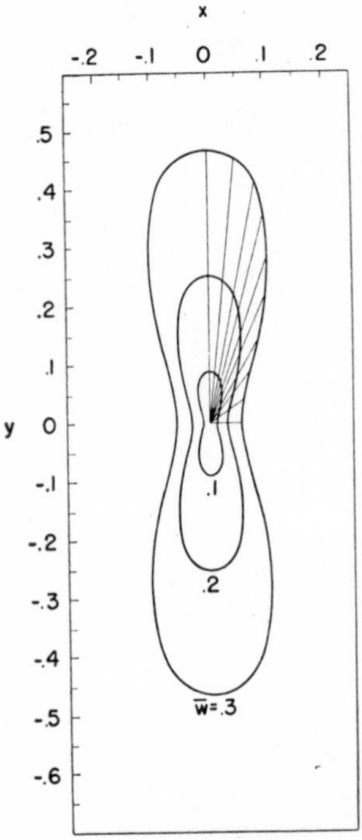

Fig. 24.10a. Fifth example of anasymmetric case

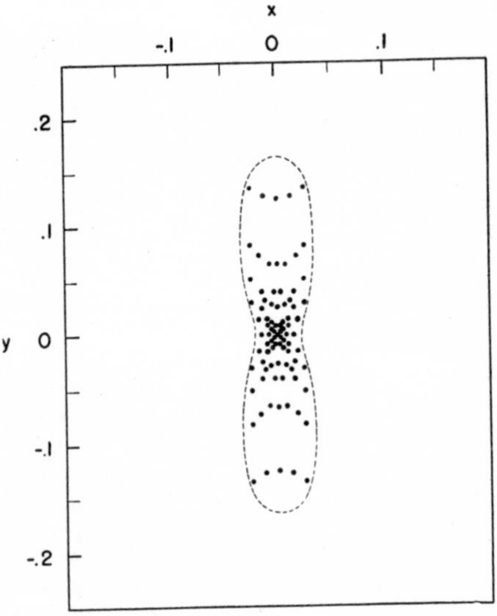

Fig. 24.10b. Spot diagram corresponding to figure 24.10a.

We find the envelopes by setting the functional determinant of (24.16) equal to zero. This gives

$$\varkappa^2 (G_s G_c - 3G_s G_m + G_c^2 + G_c G_m) + \varkappa (3\, G_m G_s - 2G_m G_c - G_c^2) + G_c G_m = 0. \quad (24.22)$$

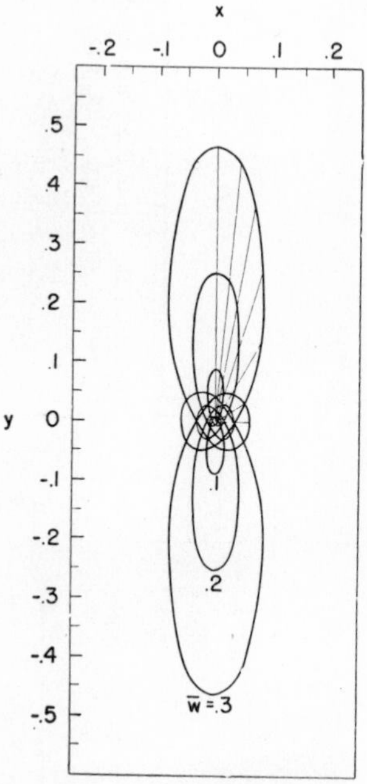

Fig. 24.11a. Sixth example of anasymmetric case.

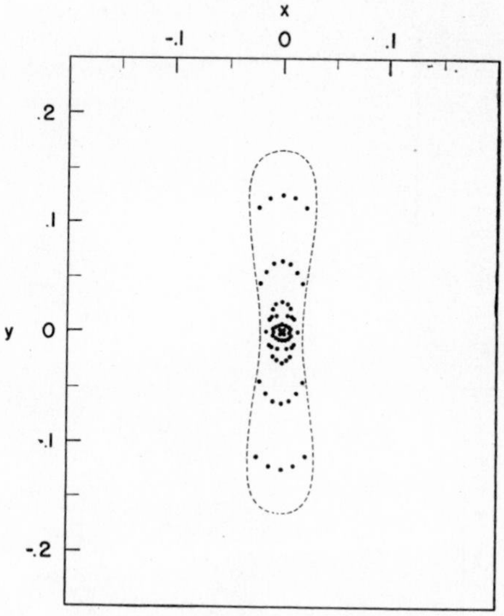

Fig. 24.11b. Spot diagram corresponding to Figure 24.11a.

The quantity $\varkappa$ must be positive by definition [see (23.43)]. Equation (23.22) has a discriminant equal to

$$(G_s G_m - G_c^2)\,(9\, G_m G_s - G_c^2). \quad (24.23)$$

An easy analysis shows the number of admissible values of $\varkappa$ in various cases to be as follows:

$G_s\, G_m < 0$, one positive value of $\varkappa$ fulfilling (23.22)
$0 < G_s\, G_m < \frac{1}{9} G_c^2$, two positive values of $\varkappa$,
$\frac{1}{9} G_c^2 < G_s\, G_m < G_c^2$, no positive values of $\varkappa$,
$G_c^2 < G_s G_m$, one positive value of $\varkappa$.

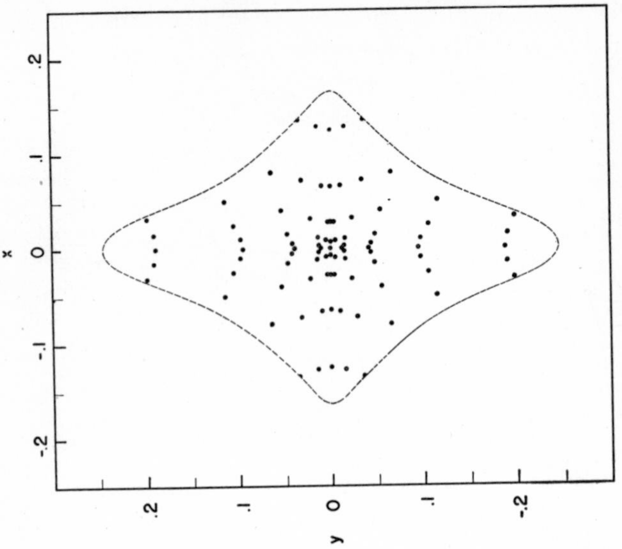

Fig. 24.12b. Spot diagram corresponding to Figure 24.12a.

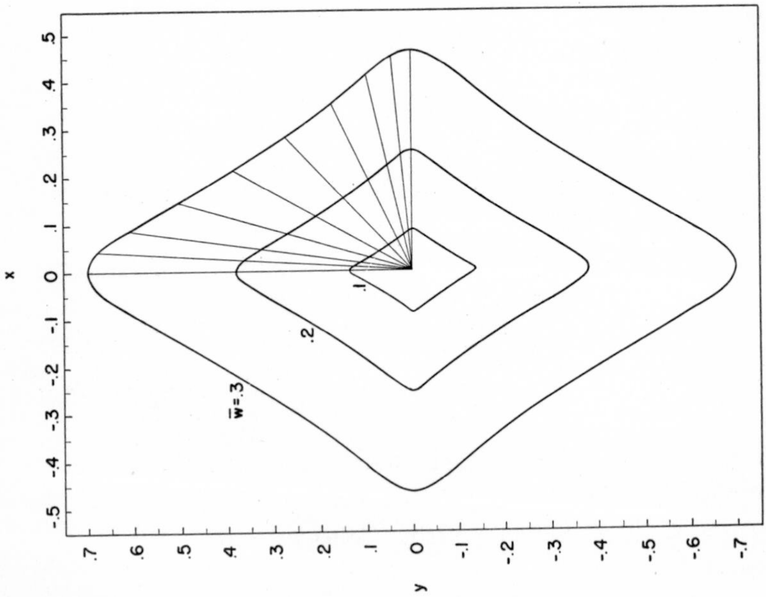

Fig. 24.12a. Seventh example of anasymmetric case.

In this analysis one has to consider that, to each value of $\varkappa$, there correspond two directions, which means that the number of enveloping straight lines in the above cases is two, four, none, and two, respectively, as the corresponding figures verify.

Light Density in the Image Plane

If we assume the pupil (at infinity) to be uniformly illuminated, we can judge the density of the light in the image plane by the reciprocal value of the functional determinant D of (24.2). At the points where $(1/D)$ vanishes, we should, theoretically, obtain an infinite value of the light intensity. Owing to the presence of diffraction, there is no such infinite intensity, but still the points where D vanishes are points of maximum concentration. We have

$$1/D = \begin{vmatrix} \frac{\partial x}{\partial v} & \frac{\partial x}{\partial w} \\ \frac{\partial y}{\partial v} & \frac{\partial y}{\partial w} \end{vmatrix} = \frac{-1}{\sqrt{2w}} \begin{vmatrix} A & 2wB \\ B & C \end{vmatrix} = 0\,,$$

where

$$\begin{aligned} A &= a_3 + z + a_{23}v + \tfrac{1}{2}(a_{223} + z)v^2 + 3(a_{33} + z)w \\ B &= a_{23} + (a_{223} + z)v \\ C &= a_{22} + z + a_{222}v + \tfrac{3}{2}(\tfrac{1}{3}a_{2222} + z)v^2 + (a_{223} + z)w. \end{aligned}$$

In first order, this produces again the focal points, since

(24.24)

$$1/D = (-1/\sqrt{2w})\,(a_3 + z)\,(a_{22} + z), \tag{24.25}$$

which vanishes only at the foci, $z = -a_3$, $z = -a_{22}$. In case astigmatism is corrected (anastigmatic case), if we investigate the single plane through the focus, we find, up to the third order,

$$\begin{vmatrix} a_{23}v & a_{23}2w \\ a_{23} & a_{222}v \end{vmatrix} = 0, \tag{24.26}$$

which gives the lines

$$a_{222}v^2 = a_{23}\,2w$$

or

$$a_{222}y^2 = a_{23}\,x^2, \tag{24.27}$$

which are the lines of strongest light concentration in the focal plane when astigmatism is corrected. In an *anasymmetric* system, Equation (24.24), for the plane passing through the focus ($z = -a_{22} = -a_3$) and perpendicular to the principal ray, leads to

$$\begin{vmatrix} G_c\,\frac{1}{2}v^2 + G_s\,3w & G_c\,v\,2w \\ G_c\,v & G_m\,\frac{3}{2}v^2 + G\,w \end{vmatrix} = 0 \tag{24.28}$$

or $\frac{1}{4}\,G_cG_m\,v^4 + \frac{1}{2}\,v^2w\,(3\,G_sG_m - G_c{}^2) + G_sG_c\,w^2 = 0,$

which is identical with (24.22), as the reader may verify.

Intersection with a Plane Inclined to the Axis

Let us intersect the rays with a plane

$$\bar{z} - z_o = \bar{y}\tan\sigma \tag{24.29}$$

inclined against the principal ray but perpendicular to the meridional plane. The coordinates $\bar{x}$ and $\bar{y}$ of the point of intersection of a ray with the plane are given by

$$\begin{aligned} \bar{x} &= x + l\xi \\ \bar{y} &= y + l\eta \\ \bar{z} &= l\zeta = z_o + (y + lv)\tan\sigma, \end{aligned} \tag{24.30}$$

which leads to

$$l = \frac{z_o + y\tan\sigma}{\zeta - v\tan\sigma}\,. \tag{24.31}$$

Development of l in a series of powers of v and w, keeping in mind the development of y in (23.21), gives

$$\begin{aligned} l = z_o + v\tan\sigma\,(z_o + a_{22}) + \tfrac{1}{2}\,v^2\,[z_o\,(2\tan^2\sigma + 1) \\ + 2a_{22}\tan^2\sigma + a_{222}\tan\sigma] + w\,(z_o + a_{23}\tan\sigma). \end{aligned} \tag{24.32}$$

Inserting this into (24.30) leads to

$$\bar{x}/\xi = a_3 + z_o + v\,[a_{23} + (z_o + a_{22})\tan\sigma] + \tfrac{1}{2}\,v^2\,[a_{223} + z_o\,(2\tan^2\sigma + 1) + 2\,a_{22}\tan^2\sigma + a_{222}\tan\sigma] + w\,(a_{33} + z_o + a_{23}\tan\sigma)$$

$$\bar{y} = v\,(a_{22} + z_o) + \tfrac{1}{2}\,v^2\,[a_{222} + 2\,(z_o + a_{22})\tan\sigma] + w\,a_{23} + \tfrac{1}{6}\,v^3\,[a_{2222} + 3z_o\,(2\tan^2\sigma + 1) + 6a_{22}\tan^2\sigma + 3a_{222}\tan\sigma] + vw\,(a_{223} + z_o + a_{23}\tan\sigma). \tag{24.33}$$

These formulae are a generalization of (23.68). For a plane through the focus of an anastigmatic system, setting $z_o = -a_{22} = -a_3$ gives, up to the third order,

$$\bar{x}/\xi = a_{23}v$$

$$\bar{y} = \tfrac{1}{2}\,a_{222}\,v^2 + a_{23}w, \tag{24.34}$$

that is, equations of the same type as before, giving a series of eccentric ellipses.

In the *anasymmetric* case we have

$$\bar{x} = \xi\,[\tfrac{1}{2}\,v^2\,(G_c) + G_s w]$$

$$\bar{y} = v\,[\tfrac{1}{2}\,v^2\,(G_m) + G_c w], \tag{24.35}$$

equations identical with (24.15).

It should be emphasized that all three methods described at the beginning of this chapter are useful for analyzing the light distribution in various planes. The figures obtained from radial and circular curves in the aperture as well as the curves of maximum density are in good agreement with the spot diagrams. The spot diagrams have been used for some time by the author in analyzing practical optical systems, and they have proved of great value in predicting and describing the performance of various lenses since, as we shall show later, they give a graphic picture of the light intensity in a plane.

CHAPTER TWENTY-FIVE

Tracing a Normal Bundle through an Optical System

In the last chapter we discussed the neighborhood of a principal ray. Taking the principal ray as z-axis of a coordinate system, we chose as coordinates

$$\bar{v} = \bar{\eta}, \quad \bar{w} = 1 - \bar{\zeta}. \tag{25.1}$$

These coordinates will be called the *intrinsic* coordinates. Developing h with respect to these variables, we wrote [*cf.* (23.18)]

$$h = \tfrac{1}{2}\,\bar{a}_{22}\bar{v}^2 + \bar{a}_3\bar{w} + \tfrac{1}{6}\,\bar{a}_{222}\bar{v}^3 + \bar{a}_{23}\bar{v}\bar{w} + \tfrac{1}{24}\,\bar{a}_{2222}\bar{v}^4 + \tfrac{1}{2}\,\bar{a}_{223}\bar{v}^2\bar{w} + \tfrac{1}{2}\,\bar{a}_{33}\bar{w}^2 \tag{25.2}$$

and studied the effect of each coefficient on the image formation, first in a plane perpendicular to the ray and finally in a plane inclined to the principal ray.

It is the object of this chapter to give an approximate method for tracing a bundle through an optical system. We assume that we know the trace of the principal ray, which we have traced with the help of the ray-tracing formulae in Chapter 4. This means that we know the distances $e_\varkappa$, $e_{\varkappa+1}$ on the ray between the points of intersection with a given surface and the preceding and following surfaces; we know the angles of inclination $i_\varkappa$, $i_\varkappa'$ of the ray with respect to the surface normal before and after refraction; and we know the equation of the refracting surface.

We shall divide the calculation procedure into specific parts.

(*a*) If the characteristic function h is known as a function of $\bar{v}$ and $\bar{w}$, we find its value when the origin is shifted a distance e along the principal ray. From the definition of h as the distance to a wave surface from the footpoint of the perpendicular to the ray from the origin, we find that

$$\tilde{h} = h - e\bar{\zeta} = h - e\,(1 - \bar{w}), \tag{25.3}$$

which shows that all the coefficients of h in (25.2) remain invariant with the exception of a_3, which changes to

$$\tilde{a}_3 = a_3 + e. \tag{25.4}$$

(*b*) If h is known as a function of $\bar{v}$ and $\bar{w}$ relative to a coordinate system connected with the principal ray, which forms its z-axis, we shall find h relative to a new coordinate system, in which the z-axis lies in the meridional plane at an angle i with the principal ray. For this purpose we take as coordinates V and W determined by

$$\xi^2 = 2W, \quad \eta = V + n \sin i\,. \tag{25.5}$$

We now drop the assumption that n is equal to unity and take h as the optical distance, which is n times the geometrical distance. In this case, ξ, η, and ζ become the *optical* direction cosines with respect to the inclined coordinate system, that is,

$$\begin{aligned} \eta/n &= \bar{v} \cos i + (1 - \bar{w}) \sin i \\ \zeta/n &= -\bar{v} \sin i + (1 - \bar{w}) \cos i. \end{aligned} \tag{25.6}$$

From (25.6) we obtain

$$\xi^2/n^2 = 2W/n^2 = 1 - \bar{v}^2 - (1 - \bar{w})^2 = 2\bar{w} - \bar{v}^2 - \bar{w}^2$$

or

$$\begin{aligned} W/n^2 &= \bar{w} - \tfrac{1}{2}\bar{v}^2 - \tfrac{1}{2}\bar{w}^2 \\ V/n &= \bar{v} \cos i - \bar{w} \sin i. \end{aligned} \tag{25.7}$$

Since h is independent of the choice of coordinates, that is,

$$\begin{aligned} h &= \tfrac{1}{2}A_{22}V^2 + A_3W + \tfrac{1}{6}A_{222}V^3 + A_{23}VW \\ &\quad + \tfrac{1}{24}A_{2222}V^4 + \tfrac{1}{2}A_{223}V^2W + \tfrac{1}{2}A_{33}W^2 \\ h/n &= \tfrac{1}{2}\bar{a}_{22}\bar{v}^2 + \bar{a}_3\bar{w} + \tfrac{1}{6}\bar{a}_{222}\bar{v}^3 + \bar{a}_{23}\bar{v}\bar{w} + \tfrac{1}{24}\bar{a}_{2222}\bar{v}^4 \\ &\quad + \tfrac{1}{2}\bar{a}_{223}\bar{v}^2\bar{w} + \tfrac{1}{2}\bar{a}_{33}\bar{v}^2, \end{aligned} \tag{25.8}$$

we find by inserting (25.7) and abbreviating $c = \cos i$, $s = \sin i$:

$$\begin{aligned} \bar{a}_{22} &= n\,(c^2A_{22} - A_3) & \bar{a}_{222} &= n^2c\,(c^2A_{222} - 3A_{23}) \\ \bar{a}_3 &= nA_3 & \bar{a}_{23} &= nc\,(nA_{23} - sA_{22}) \end{aligned} \tag{25.9}$$

$$\bar{a}_{2222} = n^3 (c^4 A_{2222} - 6c^2 A_{223} + 3A_{33})$$
$$\bar{a}_{223} = n^3 (c^2 A_{223} - A_{33}) + n^2 s (A_{23} - c^2 A_{222})$$
$$\bar{a}_{33} = n^3 A_{33} - nA_3 - 2n^2 s A_{23} + ns^2 A_{22}.$$

For $c = 1$, $s = 0$, $n = 1$, these formulae reduce to (23.19).

Reversing (25.9) we find

$$nA_{22} = \frac{1}{c^2} (\bar{a}_{22} + \bar{a}_3), \quad n^2 A_{222} = \frac{1}{c^3} \left[\bar{a}_{222} + 3\bar{a}_{23} + 3\frac{s}{c} (\bar{a}_{22} + \bar{a}_3) \right]$$

$$nA_3 = \bar{a}_3, \qquad n^2 A_{23} = \frac{1}{c} \left[\bar{a}_{23} + \frac{s}{c} (\bar{a}_{22} + \bar{a}_3) \right] \tag{25.10}$$

$$n^3 A_{2222} = \frac{1}{c^4} \left[\bar{a}_{2222} + 6\bar{a}_{223} + 3(\bar{a}_{33} + \bar{a}_3) + 6\frac{s}{c} (\bar{a}_{222} + 3\bar{a}_{23}) + 15\frac{s^2}{c^2} (\bar{a}_{22} + \bar{a}_3) \right]$$

$$n^3 A_{223} = \frac{1}{c^2} \left[\bar{a}_{223} + \bar{a}_{33} + \bar{a}_3 + \frac{s}{c} (\bar{a}_{222} + 4\bar{a}_{23}) + 3\frac{s^2}{c^2} (\bar{a}_{22} + \bar{a}_3) \right]$$

$$n^3 A_{33} = \bar{a}_{33} + \bar{a}_3 + 2\frac{s}{c} \bar{a}_{23} + \frac{s^2}{c^2} (\bar{a}_{22} + \bar{a}_3),$$

formulae containing (23.20) as a special case.

(*c*) Let us now assume h to be known as a function of V and W in the case in which the origin is at the point of intersection of the principal ray with a refracting (or reflecting) surface and the z-axis has the direction of the surface normal, and let us assume the refracting surface to be given with respect to this coordinate system by

$$z^* = f(u^*, y^*) = \tfrac{1}{2} B_{22} y^{*2} + B_3 u^* + \tfrac{1}{6} B_{222} y^{*3} + B_{23} y^* u^* + \tfrac{1}{24} B_{2222} y^{*4} + \tfrac{1}{2} B_{223} y^{*2} u^* + \tfrac{1}{2} B_{33} u^{*2} \tag{25.11}$$

with x^*, y^*, z^* the coordinates of the points of the surface and

$$u^* = \tfrac{1}{2} x^{*2}.$$

Here we assume h to be given, according to (25.8), as a function of V and W. It is our problem to compute the corresponding characteristic function g as a function of u^* and y^*, that is,

$$g^* = \tfrac{1}{2}b_{22}y^{*2} + b_3u^* + \tfrac{1}{6}b_{222}y^{*3} + \tfrac{1}{24}b_{2222}y^{*4} + \tfrac{1}{2}b_{223}y^{*2}u^* + \tfrac{1}{2}b_{33}u^{*2}. \qquad (25.12)$$

Equation (23.2) shows that we obtain the coordinates x, y of the point of intersection of a ray with the plane $z = 0$ by

$$\begin{aligned} x/\xi &= h_W = A_3 + A_{23}V + \tfrac{1}{2}A_{223}V^2 + A_{33}W \\ y &= h_V = A_{22}V + \tfrac{1}{2}A_{222}V^2 + A_{23}W + \tfrac{1}{6}A_{2222}V^3 + A_{223}VW. \end{aligned} \qquad (25.13)$$

Let λ be the (hitherto unknown) distance from the plane to the refracting surface. Then

$$\begin{aligned} x^*/\xi &= x/\xi + \lambda \\ y^* &= y + \lambda\eta = y + \lambda(V + ns), \quad z^* = \lambda\zeta. \end{aligned} \qquad (25.14)$$

On the other hand, from (23.3), we find the characteristic function g for the plane $z = 0$ to be

$$g = \vec{a}\vec{s} - h = x\xi + y\eta - h = 2Wh_W + h_V(V + ns) - h \qquad (25.15)$$

and the light path to the surface to be

$$g^* = g + n^2\lambda. \qquad (25.16)$$

In the calculations as outlined above, g^* and λ will be found as functions of V *and* W. In order to find them as functions of u^* *and* y^*, we shall have to obtain the transformation formulae between these two sets of coordinates. Equations (25.13) and (25.14) give

$$\begin{aligned} u^* &= \tfrac{1}{2}x^{*2} = \tfrac{1}{2}(x + \lambda\xi)^2 = W(h_W + \lambda)^2 \\ y^* &= h_V + \lambda(V + ns) \\ z^* &= \lambda\zeta = \lambda\sqrt{n^2c^2 - 2nsV - V^2 - 2W}. \end{aligned} \qquad (25.17)$$

Developing λ formally as a function of V and W leads to

$$\lambda = \tfrac{1}{2}\lambda_{22}V^2 + \lambda_3W + \tfrac{1}{6}\lambda_{222}V^3 + \lambda_{23}VW + \tfrac{1}{24}\lambda_{2222}V^4 + \tfrac{1}{2}\lambda_{223}V^2W + \tfrac{1}{2}\lambda_{33}W^2. \qquad (25.18)$$

Inserting this function into (27.17) and using (25.13) leads by comparison with (25.11) to

$$nc\lambda_{22} = A_{22}{}^2B_{22}, \quad nc\lambda_3 = A_3{}^2B_3$$

$$nc\lambda_{222} = A_{22}{}^3B_{222} + 3A_{22}B_{22}\,(A_{222} + ns\lambda_{22}) + 3\frac{s}{c}\,\lambda_{22}$$

$$nc\lambda_{23} = A_{22}A_3{}^2B_{23} + 2B_3A_3A_{23} + A_{22}B_{22}\,(A_{23} + ns\lambda_3) + \frac{s}{c}\lambda_3$$

$$\begin{aligned} nc\lambda_{2222} = {} & B_{2222}A_{22}{}^4 + 6B_{222}A_{22}{}^2\,(A_{222} + ns\lambda_{22}) \\ & + 3B_{22}\,(A_{22} + ns\lambda_{22})^2 + 4B_{22}A_{22}\,(A_{2222} + ns\lambda_{222} + 3\lambda_{22}) \\ & + 6\lambda_{22}\frac{1}{nc}\frac{1}{c^2} + 4\frac{s}{c}\lambda_{222} \end{aligned} \qquad (25.19)$$

$$\begin{aligned} nc\lambda_{223} = {} & B_{222}A_{22}{}^2A_3{}^2 + 4B_{23}A_{23}A_3A_{22} + 2B_3A_{23}{}^2 \\ & + B_{23}A_3{}^2\,(A_{222} + ns\lambda_{22}) + B_{222}A_{22}{}^2\,(A_{23} + ns\lambda_3) \\ & + 2B_3A_3\,(A_{223} + \lambda_{22}) + B_{22}\,(A_{23} + ns\lambda_3)\,(A_{222} + ns\lambda_{22}) \\ & + 2B_{22}A_{22}(A_{223} + ns\lambda_{23} + \lambda_3) + \lambda_3\frac{1}{n}\frac{1}{c^3} + \lambda_{22}\frac{1}{nc} + 2\frac{s}{c}\lambda_{23} \end{aligned}$$

$$\begin{aligned} nc\lambda_{33} = {} & B_{33}A_3{}^4 + 2B_{23}A_3{}^2\,(A_{23} + ns\lambda_3) + 4B_3A_3\,(A_{33} + \lambda_3) \\ & + B_{22}\,(A_{23} + ns\lambda_3)^2 + 2\lambda_3\frac{1}{nc}. \end{aligned}$$

In this calculation we have made use of the fact that ζ, if developed with respect to V and W, gives

$$\zeta = nc + \zeta_2V + \tfrac{1}{2}\zeta_{22}V^2 + \zeta_3W + \tfrac{1}{6}\zeta_{222}V^3 + \zeta_{23}VW,$$

with

$$\zeta_2 = -\frac{s}{c} \qquad \zeta_3 = -\frac{1}{nc} \qquad \zeta_{23} = -\frac{s}{n^2c^3}$$

$$\zeta_{22} = -\frac{1}{n}\frac{1}{c^3} \quad \zeta_{222} = -\frac{3s}{n^2c^5}. \qquad (25.20)$$

We now find g^* from (25.15) and (25.16) to be

$$\begin{aligned} g^* = {} & g_2V + \tfrac{1}{2}g_{22}V^2 + g_3W + \tfrac{1}{6}g_{222}V^3 + g_{23}VW + \tfrac{1}{24}g_{2222}V^4 \\ & + \tfrac{1}{2}g_{223}V^2W + \tfrac{1}{2}g_{33}W^2, \end{aligned}$$

with

$$
\begin{aligned}
g_2 &= nsA_{22} \\
g_{22} &= A_{22} + nsA_{222} + n^2\lambda_{22}, \quad g_{222} = 2A_{222} + nsA_{2222} + n^2\lambda_{222} \\
g_3 &= A_3 + nsA_{23} + n^2\lambda_3, \qquad g_{23} = 2A_{23} + nsA_{223} + n^2\lambda_{23} \\
g_{2222} &= 3A_{2222} + nsA_{22222} + n^2\lambda_{2222} \\
g_{223} &= 3A_{223} + nsA_{2223} + n^2\lambda_{223} \\
g_{33} &= 3A_{33} + nsA_{233} + n^2\lambda_{33},
\end{aligned} \tag{25.21}
$$

where the λ_{ik} must be inserted from (25.19).

The transformation formulae connecting the coordinates y^*, u^* and the coordinates V, W can be obtained from

$$
\begin{aligned}
y^* &= y_2V + \tfrac{1}{2}y_{22}V^2 + y_3W + \tfrac{1}{6}y_{222}V^3 + y_{23}VW + \tfrac{1}{24}y_{2222}V^4 \\
&\quad + \tfrac{1}{2}y_{223}V^2W + \tfrac{1}{2}y_{33}W^2 \\
u^* &= u_3W + u_{23}VW + \tfrac{1}{2}u_{223}V^2W + \tfrac{1}{2}u_{33}W^2,
\end{aligned}
$$

with [from (25.17)]

$$
\begin{aligned}
y_2 &= A_{22} \qquad\qquad\qquad y_{222} = A_{2222} + ns\lambda_{222} + 3\lambda_{22} \\
y_{22} &= A_{222} + ns\lambda_{22} \qquad y_{23} = A_{223} + ns\lambda_{23} + \lambda_3 \\
y_3 &= A_{23} + ns\lambda_3 \\
y_{2222} &= A_{22222} + ns\lambda_{2222} + 4\lambda_{222} \\
y_{223} &= A_{2223} + ns\lambda_{223} + 2\lambda_{23} \\
y_{33} &= A_{233} + ns\lambda_{33}
\end{aligned} \tag{25.22}
$$

and

$$
\begin{aligned}
u_3 &= A_3^2 \\
u_{23} &= 2A_3A_{23} \\
u_{223} &= 2A_{23}^2 + 2A_3(A_{223} + \lambda_{22}) \\
u_{33} &= 4A_3(A_{33} + \lambda_3),
\end{aligned} \tag{25.23}
$$

where the λ_{ik} can, of course, be inserted from (25.19).

Substitution of the values for y^* and u^* into (25.12) and comparison with (25.21) gives finally the equations needed to calculate the b_{ik}.

The results are

$$b_{22} = ncB_{22} + \frac{1}{A_{22}}, \quad b_{222} = ncB_{222} - 3\frac{s}{c}\frac{B_{22}}{A_{22}} - \frac{A_{222}}{A_{22}{}^3}$$

$$b_3 = ncB_3 + \frac{1}{A_3}, \quad b_{23} = ncB_{23} - \frac{s}{c}\frac{B_3}{A_{22}} - \frac{A_{23}}{A_{22}A_3{}^2} \tag{25.24}$$

$$b_{2222} = ncB_{2222} - 4\frac{s}{c}\frac{B_{222}}{A_{22}} + \frac{3}{A_{22}{}^5}\left(A_{222} + \frac{s}{c}B_{22}A_{22}{}^2\right)^2 - \frac{A_{2222}}{A_{22}{}^4} - \frac{6}{nc^3}\frac{B_{22}}{A_{22}{}^2}$$

$$b_{223} = ncB_{223} - 2\frac{s}{c}\frac{B_{23}}{A_{22}} + \frac{1}{A_{22}{}^3A_3{}^2}\left(A_{23} + \frac{s}{c}B_3A_3{}^2\right) \times\left(A_{222} + \frac{s}{c}B_{22}A_{22}{}^2\right) - \frac{A_{223}}{A_{22}{}^2A_3{}^2} + \frac{2A_{23}{}^2}{A_{22}{}^2A_3{}^3} - \frac{1}{nc}\frac{B_{22}}{A_3{}^2} - \frac{1}{nc^3}\frac{B_3}{A_{22}{}^2}$$

$$b_{33} = nc\,B_{33} + \frac{1}{A_3{}^4A_{22}}\left(A_{23} + \frac{s}{c}B_3A_{22}{}^2\right)^2 - \frac{A_{33}}{A_3{}^4} - \frac{2}{nc}\frac{B_3}{A_3{}^2}.$$

We may introduce the intrinsic coefficients $\bar{a}_{ik}$ into (23.24), using (25.10) and making use of the abbreviations in Chapter 24 together with two new ones, l_m and l_s, so that we have

$$\begin{aligned} l_m &= -(\bar{a}_{22} + \bar{a}_3),\ l_s = -\bar{a}_3 \\ C_m &= \bar{a}_{222} + 3\bar{a}_{23},\ C_s = \bar{a}_{23} \\ 3\,G_m &= \bar{a}_{2222} + 6\bar{a}_{223} + 3\bar{a}_{33} \\ G_c &= \bar{a}_{223} + \bar{a}_{33} \\ G_s &= \bar{a}_{33}. \end{aligned} \tag{25.25}$$

Equations (25.24) then assume the form

$$b_{22} = ncB_{22} - \frac{nc^2}{l_m}, \quad b_{222} = ncB_{222} + 3ns\left[B_{22}\frac{c}{l_m} - \frac{c^2}{l_m{}^2}\right] + \frac{nc^3}{l_m{}^3}C_m$$

$$b_3 = ncB_3 - \frac{n}{l_s}, \quad b_{23} = ncB_{23} + ns\left[B_3\frac{c}{l_m} - \frac{1}{l_s{}^2}\right] + \frac{nc}{l_ml_s{}^2}C_s$$

$$b_{2222} = ncB_{2222} + 4nsB_{222}\frac{c}{l_m} - 6B_{22}\frac{nc}{l_m{}^2} - \frac{3\,nc^4}{l_m{}^5}\left[C_m - 3ns\frac{l_m}{nc} + nsB_{22}\frac{l_m{}^2}{nc^2}\right]^2 \tag{25.26}$$

$$- \frac{c^4}{l_m{}^4}\left[3nG_m + 6ns\frac{C_m}{c} - 15n^2s^2\frac{l_m}{nc^2} - 3nl_s\right]$$

$$b_{223} = ncB_{223} + 2nsB_{23}\frac{c}{l_m} - B_{22}\frac{n}{cl_s{}^2} - B_3\frac{nc}{l_m{}^2}$$

$$- \frac{2nc^2}{l_m{}^2l_s{}^3}\left[C_s - ns\frac{l_m}{nc}\right]^2$$

$$- \frac{nc^2}{l_m{}^3l_s{}^2}\left[C_s - ns\frac{l_m}{nc} + nsB_3\frac{l_s{}^2}{n}\right]\left[C_m - 3ns\frac{l_m}{nc} + nsB_{22}\frac{l_m{}^2}{nc^2}\right]$$

$$- \frac{nc^2}{l_m{}^2l_s{}^2}\left[G_c + (C_m + C_s)\frac{ns}{nc} - 3l_m\frac{s^2}{c^2} - l_s\right]$$

$$b_{33} = ncB_{33} - 2B_3\frac{n}{cl_s{}^2} - \frac{n}{l_s{}^4l_m}\left[C_s - \frac{s}{c}\left(l_m - B_3\frac{l_m{}^2}{c^3}\right)\right]^2$$

$$- \frac{n}{l_s{}^4}\left[G_s + 2\frac{s}{c}C_s - \frac{s^2}{c^2}l_m - l_s\right].$$

Equations (25.26) can be used to trace a congruence through an optical system if the trace of the principal ray is known. If the congruence is given by l_s, l_m (these representing distances from the point of intersection with the first surface) and the angle i with the surface normal is known, we can then compute the $b_{i\varkappa}$ according to Formulae (25.26). The $b_{i\varkappa}$ are invariant against refraction. Therefore replacing in (25.26) n, s, c by the corresponding quantities n', s', c' for the refracted ray, one can compute in order

$$l_m', l_s', C_m', C_s', G_m', G_c', G_s',$$

that is, the intrinsic coefficients of the refracted bundle. The reader may recognize that (25.25) can be used to express $1/l_m$, $1/l_s$, C_m, C_s, G_m, G_c, G_s directly in terms of known quantities.

These coefficients having been obtained, transition to the next surface is simply given by

$$l_{s+} = l_{s-} - e, \quad l_{m+} = l_{m-} - e, \tag{25.27}$$

where e is the distance along the ray between two consecutive points of intersection, whereas the quantities C_s, C_m, G_s, G_c, G_m remain invariant. A second application of Formulae (25.26) with the corresponding new values n', c', s' in place of n, c, s, respectively, gives the values of the above quantities after the second refraction. The reader can easily prove that, in the case of reflection, the above formulae can be applied by setting formally $n' = -n$.

Formulae (25.25) can be specialized to the case of a sphere by specializing the quantities $B_{i\varkappa}$. We have

$$z = \frac{1}{2r}(x^2 + y^2) + \left(\frac{1}{2r}\right)^3 (x^2 + y^2)^2$$

or

$$\begin{aligned} B_{22} &= 1/r = B_3 \\ B_{222} &= B_{23} = 0 \\ B_{2222} &= 3/r^3, \quad B_{223} = 1/r^3 = B_{33}. \end{aligned} \tag{25.28}$$

If we designate the difference of a quantity x before and after refraction by Δx, we find for the first order the well-known formulae used for tracing astigmatism,

$$(1/r)\Delta nc = \Delta(nc^2/lm) = \Delta(n/l_s). \tag{25.29}$$

For the second-order terms (keeping in mind the refraction law $n's' = ns$), we find

$$\begin{aligned} \Delta \frac{nc^3}{l_m{}^3} C_m &= 3ns\,\Delta\left(\frac{c^2}{l_m{}^2} - \frac{1}{r}\frac{c}{l_m}\right) \\ \Delta \frac{nc}{l_m l_s{}^2} C_s &= ns\,\Delta\left(\frac{1}{l_s{}^2} - \frac{1}{r}\frac{c}{l_m}\right). \end{aligned} \tag{25.30}$$

For a plane surface (a special case of a sphere) we have $B_{22} = B_3 = B_{222} = B_{23} = B_{2222} = B_{223} = B_{33} = 0$ in (25.28), or

$$\begin{aligned} \Delta \frac{nc^2}{l_m} &= \Delta \frac{n}{l_s} = 0 \\ \Delta \frac{nc^3}{l_m{}^3} C_m &= 3ns\,\Delta \frac{c^2}{l_m{}^2} \\ \Delta \frac{nc}{l_m l_s{}^2} C_s &= ns\,\Delta \frac{1}{l_s{}^2}. \end{aligned} \tag{25.31}$$

Starting the rays at a point whose distance from the first surface measured along the ray is S, we have

$$l_s = l_m = S, \quad C_m = C_s = G_s = G_c = G_m = 0.$$

PART VII. THIRD- AND FIFTH-ORDER IMAGE-ERROR THEORY

CHAPTER TWENTY-SIX

Relations between the Coefficients of the Characteristic Functions

In the last chapter, we studied the image errors of a normal system, which is equivalent to studying the image errors of a single point. In this part, we shall investigate the image errors for all the points of a plane, for all the points of a surface that are rotationally symmetric, and finally, for all the points in space. We develop the various characteristic functions up to the sixth-order terms, that is, up to the third order in its quadratic variables. We shall consider the angle characteristic W, the mixed characteristic V', and the point characteristic E.

It is the object of this introductory chapter to show how to compute the coefficients of any one of these functions up to the sixth order from those of any one of the others. In the following chapter we shall compute the classical image errors and the intrinsic image errors discussed in Part VI as a function of the coefficients of the various characteristic functions and give a geometric interpretation of the results.

Let us assume an optical system given with symmetry of rotation about the z, z' axis. We assume arbitrary origins O, O' in object and image spaces. The light path E between the planes $z = 0$, $z' = 0$ is a function of

$$2e_1 = x^2 + y^2, \quad e_2 = xx' + yy', \quad 2e_3 = x'^2 + y'^2, \qquad (26.1)$$

and the optical direction cosines of an object ray and its image ray are given by (20.5) as

$$\begin{aligned} -\xi &= \bar{E}_1 x + \bar{E}_2 x' & \quad -\eta &= \bar{E}_1 y + \bar{E}_2 y' \\ \xi' &= \bar{E}_2 x + \bar{E}_3 x' & \quad \eta' &= \bar{E}_2 y + \bar{E}_3 y', \end{aligned} \qquad (26.2)$$

where $\bar{E}_i$ is an abbreviation for $\partial E/\partial e_i$.*

* The symbol $\bar{E}_i$ is adopted to distinguish these derivatives from the constant coefficients E_1, E_2, E_3 in the series expansion.

The light path V' from an object point lying on the plane $z = 0$ to the footpoint of the perpendicular from the image origin to the image ray is a function of

$$2v_1 = x^2 + y^2, \quad v_2 = x\xi' + y\eta', \quad 2v_3 = \xi'^2 + \eta'^2 \qquad (26.3)$$

and we have from (20.7)

$$\begin{aligned} -\xi &= \overline{V}_1 x + \overline{V}_2 \xi' & -\eta &= \overline{V}_1 y + \overline{V}_2 \eta' \\ -x' &= \overline{V}_2 x + \overline{V}_3 \xi' & -y' &= \overline{V}_2 y + \overline{V}_3 \eta', \end{aligned} \qquad (26.4)$$

with $\overline{V}_i = \partial V'/\partial v_i$. Analogously W is a function of

$$2w_1 = \xi^2 + \eta^2, \quad w_2 = \xi\xi' + \eta\eta', \quad 2w_3 = \xi'^2 + \eta'^2, \qquad (26.5)$$

with (20.8) giving

$$\begin{aligned} x &= \overline{W}_1 \xi + \overline{W}_2 \xi' & y &= \overline{W}_1 \eta + \overline{W}_2 \eta' \\ -x' &= \overline{W}_2 \xi + \overline{W}_3 \xi' & -y' &= \overline{W}_2 \eta + \overline{W}_3 \eta'. \end{aligned} \qquad (26.6)$$

We now assume W, V', and E each to be developed into a power series according to its variables, all terms of order higher than the third in these variables being neglected. Thus

$$\begin{aligned} W = W_o &+ W_1 w_1 + W_2 w_2 + W_3 w_3 + \tfrac{1}{2}(W_{11} w_1^2 + 2W_{12} w_1 w_2 \\ &+ 2W_{13} w_1 w_3 + W_{22} w_2^2 + 2W_{23} w_2 w_3 + W_{33} w_3^2) \\ &+ \tfrac{1}{6}(W_{111} w_1^3 + 3W_{112} w_1^2 w_2 + 3W_{113} w_1^2 w_3 \\ &+ 3W_{122} w_1 w_2^2 + 6W_{123} w_1 w_2 w_3 + 3W_{133} w_1 w_3^2 \\ &+ W_{222} w_2^3 + 3W_{223} w_2^2 w_3 + 3W_{233} w_2 w_3^2 + W_{333} w_3^3) \end{aligned} \qquad (26.7)$$

and analogously for V' and E, each being developed with respect to its own variables.

It is now our intention to derive formulae for computing the coefficient $V_{i\varkappa}$ (and $V_{i\varkappa\lambda}$) if the corresponding $W_{i\varkappa}$ (and $W_{i\varkappa\lambda}$) are given, and *vice versa*, and similar formulae for computing the $E_{i\varkappa}$ ($E_{i\varkappa\lambda}$) when the $V_{i\varkappa}$ ($V_{i\varkappa\lambda}$) are given, and *vice versa*. These formulae will be used later to compute the dependence of the image errors on the object and stop positions. At present we simply make the necessary preliminary calculations.

There are two ways of making these calculations.

(1) We know, from (16.3) with $z = z' = 0$, that

$$\begin{aligned} V' &= W - \vec{a}\vec{s} = W - (x\xi + y\eta) = W - (2\overline{W}_1 w_1 + \overline{W}_2 w_2) \\ E &= V' + \vec{a}'\vec{s}' = V' + x'\xi' + y'\eta' = W - (\overline{V}_2 v_2 + 2\overline{V}_3 v_3). \end{aligned} \tag{26.8}$$

In the upper equation V' is given as a function of the w's. In order to compare the series expansions on the right and left sides, we have to express the v's as functions of the w's, or *vice versa*. This can be done by using the equations

$$\begin{aligned} v_1 &= \overline{W}_1{}^2 w_1 + \overline{W}_1 \overline{W}_2 w_2 + \overline{W}_2{}^2 w_3 \\ v_2 &= \overline{W}_1 w_2 + 2\overline{W}_2 w_3 \\ v_3 &= w_3, \end{aligned} \tag{26.9}$$

expanding each of these into a power series, and then obtaining the corresponding series expansion of $v_1{}^2$, $v_1 v_2$, etc.

Analogously we can deal with the transformation from V' to E by taking account of the formulae

$$\begin{aligned} e_1 &= v_1 \\ e_2 &= -(2\overline{V}_2 v_1 + \overline{V}_3 v_2) \\ e_3 &= \overline{V}_2{}^2 v_1 + \overline{V}_2 \overline{V}_3 v_2 + \overline{V}_3{}^2 v_3. \end{aligned} \tag{26.10}$$

However, since we want to know V' and E up to their third-order terms, Formulae (26.9) and (26.10) must be developed up to the third-order terms, which requires an elaborate calculation. This can be speeded up by the second method.

(2) Inserting (26.6) into (26.4) and (26.4) into (26.2) leads to the functional relationships

$$\begin{aligned} \overline{V}_1 &= -1/\overline{W} & \bar{E}_1 &= \overline{V}_1 - \overline{V}_2{}^2/\overline{V}_3 \\ \overline{V}_2 &= \overline{W}_2/\overline{W}_1 & \bar{E}_2 &= -\overline{V}_2/\overline{V}_3 \\ \overline{V}_3 &= \overline{W}_3 - \overline{W}_2{}^2/\overline{W}_1 & \bar{E}_3 &= -1/\overline{V}_3. \end{aligned} \tag{26.11}$$

In these equations, the left-hand sides are functions of the v_i and e_i, respectively, whereas the right-hand sides are functions of the w_i and v_i, respectively. The necessary changes of coordinates can be carried out with the help of (26.9) and (26.10) as described in method (1) above, but, since we develop the V_i and not V', we have only to develop (26.9) and (26.10) to the *second* order in w_i and v_i, respectively, and the coefficients $\overline{W}_1^2$, $\overline{W}_1$, $\overline{W}_2$, etc. of w_i and v_i only to the *first* order. We first obtain

$$\begin{aligned}
\overline{W}_1^2 &= W_1^2 + 2W_1W_{11}w_1 + 2W_1W_{12}w_2 + 2W_1W_{13}w_3 \\
\overline{W}_1\overline{W}_2 &= W_1W_2 + (W_1W_{12} + W_2W_{11})\,w_1 \\
&\quad + (W_1W_{22} + W_2W_{12})w_2 + (W_1W_{23} + W_2W_{13})w_3 \\
\overline{W}_2^2 &= W_2^2 + 2W_2W_{12}w_1 + 2W_2W_{22}w_2 + 2W_2W_{23}w_3 \qquad (26.12)
\end{aligned}$$

and analogously for the transformation between the v's and the e's.

Inserting these developments into (26.9) and substituting (26.9) into (26.11) gives finally the important results:

$$\begin{aligned}
W_1^4V_{11} &= W_{11} & W_1V_1 &= -1 \\
W_1^4V_{12} &= W_1W_{12} - W_2W_{11} & W_1V_2 &= W_2 \\
W_1^4V_{13} &= W_1^2W_{13} - 2W_1W_2W_{12} + W_2^2W_{11}, & W_1V_3 &= W_1W_3 - W_2^2 \\
W_1^4V_{22} &= W_1^2W_{22} - 2W_1W_2W_{12} + W_2^2W_{11} & & (26.13) \\
W_1^4V_{23} &= W_1^3W_{23} - W_1^2W_2(W_{13} + 2W_{22}) \\
&\quad + 3W_1W_2^2W_{12} - W_2^3W_{11} \\
W_1^4V_{33} &= W_1^4W_{33} - 4W_1^3W_2W_{23} + 2W_1^2W_2^2(W_{13} + 2W_{22}) \\
&\quad - 4W_1W_2^3W_{12} + W_2^4W_{11}
\end{aligned}$$

for the first- and third-order image coefficients, and for the fifth-order coefficients

$$\begin{aligned}
W_1^6V_{111} &= W_{111} - 6W_1^7V_{11}^2 \\
W_1^6V_{112} &= W_1W_{112} - W_2W_{111} - 6W_1^7V_{11}V_{12} \qquad (26.14) \\
W_1^6V_{113} &= W_1^2W_{113} - 2W_1W_2W_{112} + W_2^2W_{111} \\
&\quad - 2W_1^7(2V_{11}V_{13} + V_{12}^2) \\
W_1^6V_{122} &= W_1^2W_{122} - 2W_1W_2W_{112} + W_2^2W_{111} \\
&\quad - 2W_1^7(V_{11}V_{22} + 2V_{12}^2) \\
W_1^6V_{123} &= W_1^3W_{123} - W_1^2W_2(2W_{122} + W_{113}) + 3W_1W_2^2W_{112} \\
&\quad - W_2^3W_{111} - W_1^7[V_{11}V_{23} + V_{12}(3V_{13} + 2V_{22})] \\
W_1^6V_{222} &= W_1^3W_{222} - 3W_1^2W_2W_{122} + 3W_1W_2^2W_{112} \\
&\quad - W_2^3W_{111} - 6W_1^7V_{12}V_{22}
\end{aligned}$$

$$\begin{aligned}
W_1^6V_{223} &= W_1^4W_{223} - 2W_1^3W_2(W_{222} + W_{123}) \\
&\quad + W_1^2W_2^2(5W_{122} + W_{113}) - 4W_1W_2^3W_{112} + W_2^4W_{111} \\
&\quad - 2W_1^7[V_{12}V_{23} + V_{22}(V_{22} + V_{13})] \\
W_1^6V_{133} &= W_1^4W_{133} - 4W_1^3W_2W_{123} + 2W_1^2W_2^2(2W_{122} + W_{113}) \\
&\quad - 4W_1W_2^3W_{112} + W_2^4W_{111} - 2W_1^7(V_{13}^2 + 2V_{12}V_{23}) \\
W_1^6V_{233} &= W_1^5W_{233} - W_1^4W_2(W_{133} + 4W_{223}) \\
&\quad + 2W_1^3W_2^2(3W_{123} + 2W_{222}) - 2W_1^2W_2^3(4W_{122} + W_{113}) \\
&\quad + 5W_1W_2^4W_{112} - W_2^5W_{111} - 2W_1^7V_{23}(V_{13} + 2V_{22}) \\
W_1^6V_{333} &= W_1^6W_{333} - 6W_1^5W_2W_{233} + 3W_1^4W_2^2(W_{133} + 4W_{223}) \\
&\quad - 4W_1^3W_2^3(3W_{123} + 2W_{222}) + 3W_1^2W_2^4(W_{113} + 4W_{122}) \\
&\quad - 6W_1W_2^5W_{112} + W_2^6W_{111} - 6W_1^7V_{23}^2.
\end{aligned}$$

The reader will note the symmetrical structure of these formulae. The transition formulae between the V_i and the E_i are of essentially the same form, to wit:

$$\begin{aligned}
V_3^4E_{11} &= V_2^4V_{33} - 4V_2^3V_3V_{23} + 2V_2^2V_3^2(V_{13} + 2V_{22}) \\
&\quad - 4V_2V_3^3V_{12} + V_3^4V_{11} \\
V_3^4E_{12} &= V_2^3V_{33} - 3V_2^2V_3V_{23} + V_2V_3^2(V_{13} + 2V_{22}) - V_3^3V_{12} \\
V_3^4E_{13} &= V_2^2V_{33} - 2V_2V_3V_{23} + V_3^2V_{13} \\
V_3^4E_{22} &= V_2^2V_{33} - 2V_2V_3V_{23} + V_3^2V_{22} \qquad V_3E_1 = V_1V_3 - V_2^2 \\
V_3^4E_{23} &= V_2V_{33} - V_3V_{23} \qquad V_3E_2 = -V_2 \qquad (26.15) \\
V_3^4E_{33} &= V_{33} \qquad V_3E_3 = -1
\end{aligned}$$

for the so-called first- and third-order image coefficients. For the fifth-order coefficients, we find

$$\begin{aligned}
V_3^6E_{111} &= V_2^6V_{333} - 6V_2^5V_3V_{233} + 3V_2^4V_3^2(V_{133} + 4V_{223}) \\
&\quad - 4V_2^3V_3^3(3V_{123} + 2V_{222}) + 3V_2^2V_3^4(V_{113} + 4V_{122}) \\
&\quad - 6V_2V_3^5V_{112} + V_3^6V_{111} - 6V_3^7E_{12}^2 \\
V_3^6E_{112} &= V_2^5V_{333} - 5V_2^4V_3V_{233} + 2V_2^3V_3^2(V_{133} + 4V_{223}) \\
&\quad - 2V_2^2V_3^3(3V_{123} + 2V_{222}) + V_2V_3^4(V_{113} + 4V_{122}) \\
&\quad - V_3^5V_{112} - 2V_3^7E_{12}(E_{13} + 2E_{22})
\end{aligned}$$

$$
\begin{aligned}
V_3{}^6E_{113} &= V_2{}^4V_{333} - 4V_2{}^3V_3V_{233} + 2V_2{}^2V_3{}^2(2V_{223} + V_{133}) \\
&\quad - 4V_2V_3{}^3V_{123} + V_3{}^4V_{113} - 2V_3{}^7(E_{13}{}^2 + 2E_{23}E_{12}) \\
V_3{}^6E_{122} &= V_2{}^4V_{333} - 4V_2{}^3V_3V_{233} + V_2{}^2V_3{}^2(5V_{223} + V_{133}) \\
&\quad - 2V_2V_3{}^3(V_{123} + V_{222}) + V_3{}^4V_{122} \\
&\quad - 2V_3{}^7[E_{22}(E_{13} + E_{22}) + E_{12}E_{23}] \\
V_3{}^6E_{123} &= V_2{}^3V_{333} - 3V_2{}^2V_3V_{233} + V_2V_3{}^2(V_{133} + 2V_{223}) \\
&\quad - V_3{}^3V_{123} - V_3{}^7[E_{33}E_{12} + E_{23}(3E_{13} + 2E_{22})] \\
V_3{}^6E_{222} &= V_2{}^3V_{333} - 3V_2{}^2V_3V_{233} + 3V_2V_3{}^2V_{223} - V_3{}^3V_{222} \\
&\quad - 6V_3{}^7E_{22}E_{23} \\
V_3{}^6E_{133} &= V_2{}^2V_{333} - 2V_2V_3V_{233} + V_3{}^2V_{133} \\
&\quad - 2V_3{}^7(E_{23}{}^2 + 2E_{13}E_{33}) \\
V_3{}^6E_{223} &= V_2{}^2V_{333} - 2V_2V_3V_{233} + V_3{}^2V_{223} \\
&\quad - 2V_3{}^7(2E_{23}{}^2 + E_{22}E_{33}) \\
V_3{}^6E_{233} &= V_2V_{333} - V_3V_{233} - 6V_3{}^7E_{23}E_{33} \\
V_3{}^6E_{333} &= V_{333} - 6V_3{}^7E_{33}{}^2.
\end{aligned}
\tag{26.16}
$$

The basic structure of these formulae will become more obvious still if we separate them into groups. The so-called *meridional errors* or zero-rank errors (the geometrical meaning will be discussed in the next chapter) transform by themselves, giving at the third-order level

$$
\begin{aligned}
W_1{}^4V_{11} &= W_{11} \\
W_1{}^4V_{12} &= -W_2W_{11} + W_1W_{12} \\
\tfrac{1}{3}W_1{}^4(V_{13} + 2V_{22}) &= W_2{}^2W_{11} - 2W_1W_2W_{12} + \tfrac{1}{3}W_1{}^2(W_{13} + 2W_{22}) \\
W_1{}^4V_{23} &= -W_2{}^3W_{11} + 3W_2{}^2W_1W_{12} - 3W_2W_1{}^2\tfrac{1}{3}(W_{13} + 2W_{22}) \\
&\quad + W_1{}^3W_{23} \\
W_1{}^4V_{33} &= W_2{}^4W_{11} - 4W_2{}^3W_1W_{12} + 6W_2{}^2W_1{}^2\tfrac{1}{3}(W_{13} + 2W_{22}) \\
&\quad - 4W_2W_1{}^3W_{23} + W_1{}^4W_{33}
\end{aligned}
$$

and at the fifth-order level (26.17)

$$
\begin{aligned}
W_1{}^6V_{111} &= W_{111} - 6W_1{}^7V_{11}{}^2 \\
W_1{}^6V_{112} &= -W_2W_{111} + W_1W_{112} - 6W_1{}^7V_{11}V_{12}
\end{aligned}
$$

$$\tfrac{1}{5}W_1^6(V_{113}+4V_{122}) = W_1^2\,\tfrac{1}{5}(W_{113}+4W_{122}) - 2W_1W_2W_{112} + W_2^2W_{111} - \tfrac{2}{5}W_1^7[2V_{11}(V_{13}+2V_{22})+9V_{12}^2]$$

$$\tfrac{1}{5}W_1^6(3V_{123}+2V_{222}) = W_1^3\,\tfrac{1}{5}(3W_{123}+2W_{222}) - 3W_1^2W_2\,\tfrac{1}{5}(W_{113} + 4W_{122}) + 3W_1W_2^2W_{112} - W_2^3W_{111} - \tfrac{3}{5}W_1^7[V_{11}V_{23}+3V_{12}(V_{13}+2V_{22})]$$

$$\tfrac{1}{5}W_1^6(V_{133}+4V_{223}) = W_1^4\,\tfrac{1}{5}(W_{133}+4W_{223}) - 4W_1^3W_2\,\tfrac{1}{5}(3W_{123}+2W_{222}) + 6W_1^2W_2^2\,\tfrac{1}{5}(W_{113}+4W_{122}) - 4W_1W_2^3W_{112} + W_2^4W_{111} - \tfrac{2}{5}W_1^7[6V_{12}V_{23}+(V_{13}+2V_{22})^2]$$

$$W_1^6V_{233} = W_1^5W_{233} - 5W_1^4W_2\,\tfrac{1}{5}(W_{133}+4W_{223}) + 10W_1^3W_2^2\,\tfrac{1}{5}(3W_{123}+2W_{222}) - 10W_1^2W_2^3\,\tfrac{1}{5}(W_{113}+4W_{122}) + 5W_1W_2^4W_{112} - W_2^5W_{111} - 2W_1^7V_{23}(V_{13}+2V_{22})$$

$$W_1^6V_{333} = W_1^6W_{333} - 6W_1^5W_2W_{233} + 15W_1^4W_2^2\,\tfrac{1}{5}(W_{133}+4W_{223}) - 20W_1^3W_2^3\,\tfrac{1}{5}(3W_{123}+2W_{222}) + 15W_1^2W_2^4\,\tfrac{1}{5}(W_{113}+4W_{122}) - 6W_1W_2^5W_{112} + W_2^6W_{111} - 6W_1^7V_{23}^2.$$

For the Petzval or first-rank errors of third order, we find the formula

$$W_1^2\,(V_{22} - V_{13}) = W_{22} - W_{13} \tag{26.18}$$

and for the corresponding fifth-order values, the equations

$$W_1^4(V_{122}-V_{113}) = (W_{122}-W_{113}) - 2W_1^5[V_{11}(V_{22}-V_{13})+V_{12}^2-V_{11}V_{13}]$$

$$W_1^4(V_{222}-V_{123}) = W_1(W_{222}-W_{123}) - W_2(W_{122}-W_{113}) - W_1^5[3V_{12}(V_{22}-V_{13})+V_{12}V_{22}-V_{11}V_{23}]$$

$$W_1^4(V_{223}-V_{133}) = W_1^2(W_{223}-W_{133}) - 2W_1W_2(W_{222}-W_{123}) + W_2^2(W_{122}-W_{113}) - 2W_1^5[V_{13}(V_{22}-V_{13})+V_{22}^2-V_{12}V_{23}]. \tag{26.19}$$

Analogous formulae are found for the transformation of the E's into the V's.

It will be important to investigate the changes in the E_i, V_i, and W_i resulting from a shifting of the object or the image origin. For this purpose it will be useful to introduce new variables into W. As these new variables we shall choose

$$\tau_1 = 1 - \zeta/n = 1 - \sqrt{1 - 2w_1/n^2}$$

$$\tau_2 = \frac{1}{nn'}(\xi\xi' + \eta\eta' + \zeta\zeta' - nn') = \frac{w_2}{nn'} - 1 + \sqrt{1 - \frac{2w_1}{n^2}}\sqrt{1 - \frac{2w_3}{n'^2}}$$

$$\tau_3 = 1 - \zeta'/n' = 1 - \sqrt{1 - 2w_3/n'^2}. \tag{26.20}$$

Setting $W(w_1, w_2, w_3) = T(\tau_1, \tau_2, \tau_3)$ we obtain

$$\overline{W}_1 = \frac{1}{n^2(1-\tau_1)}[\overline{T}_1 - \overline{T}_2(1-\tau_3)]$$

$$\overline{W}_2 = \frac{1}{nn'}\overline{T}_2 \tag{26.21}$$

$$\overline{W}_3 = \frac{1}{n'^2(1-\tau_3)}[\overline{T}_3 - \overline{T}_2(1-\tau_1)]$$

or in the reverse form

$$\overline{T}_1 = n^2(1-\tau_1)\overline{W}_1 + nn'\overline{W}_2(1-\tau_3)$$
$$\overline{T}_2 = nn'\overline{W}_2 \tag{26.22}$$
$$\overline{T}_3 = n'^2(1-\tau_3)\overline{W}_3 + nn'\overline{W}_2(1-\tau_1).$$

The above choice of variables is made for two reasons. A change of coordinate origins of k, k', respectively, in the object and image spaces leads, as is geometrically evident, to

$$\tilde{T} = T - nk(1-\tau_1) + n'k'(1-\tau_3), \tag{26..23}$$

that is, $\overline{T}_1$ and $\overline{T}_2$ change by a constant if the origin is shifted, while all other derivatives remain unchanged. Moreover, comparison with Chapter 18 shows that, for a concentric system with the origins at the center, T is a function of τ_2 alone (for arbitrary origins, only a linear function of τ_1 and τ_3 is added) as is seen from (26.23). Equations (26.21) can be used to compute the coefficients of T as functions of the coefficients of W, and *vice versa*.

We find by a straightforward calculation the equations:

$$n^2W_1 = T_1 - T_2 \qquad nn'W_2 = T_2 \qquad n'^2W_3 = T_3 - T_2$$

$$\begin{aligned}
n^4W_{11} &= T_1 - T_2 + T_{11} - 2T_{12} + T_{22}\\
n^3n'W_{12} &= T_{12} - T_{22}\\
n^2n'^2W_{13} &= T_2 - T_{12} + T_{13} + T_{22} - T_{23}\\
n^2n'^2W_{22} &= T_{22}\\
nn'^3W_{13} &= T_{23} - T_{22}\\
n'^4W_{33} &= T_3 - T_2 + T_{22} - 2T_{23} + T_{33}\\
n^6W_{111} &= 3(T_1 - T_2) + 3\,(T_{11} - 2T_{12} + T_{22})\\
&\quad + T_{111} - 3T_{112} + 3T_{122} - T_{222}\\
n^5n'W_{112} &= T_{12} - T_{22} + T_{112} - 2T_{122} + T_{222}\\
n^4n'^2W_{113} &= T_{12} + T_{13} - T_{22} - T_{23} - T_{112} + T_{113}\\
&\quad + 2(T_{122} - T_{123}) - T_{222} + T_{223}\\
n^4n'^2W_{122} &= T_{122} - T_{222}\\
n^3n'^3W_{123} &= T_{22} - T_{122} + T_{123} + T_{222} - T_{223}\\
n^2n'^4W_{133} &= T_{13} - T_{22} - T_{12} + T_{23} + T_{122} - 2T_{123}\\
&\quad + T_{133} - T_{222} + 2T_{223} - T_{233}\\
n^2n'^4W_{223} &= T_{223} - T_{222}\\
nn'^5W_{233} &= T_{23} - T_{22} + T_{233} - 2T_{223} + T_{222}\\
n'^6W_{333} &= 3(T_3 - T_2 + T_{33} - 2T_{23} + T_{22})\\
&\quad + T_{333} - 3(T_{233} + T_{223}) - T_{222}.
\end{aligned} \tag{26.24}$$

CHAPTER TWENTY-SEVEN

The Image Errors and Their Geometrical Significance

The coefficients of the characteristic function expansions described in the last chapter can be used for coordinating object and image rays in the neighborhood of the axis to the desired degree of approximation. This is done with the help of Equations (26.2), (26.4), and (26.6).

It is the aim of this chapter to give a geometrical interpretation of the coefficients involved and to study the theory of image errors, restricting ourselves here to a simultaneous investigation of the third- and fifth-order errors.

At first we shall investigate the rays coming from all the points of a plane perpendicular to the axis, this plane being either at a finite distance (for instance, the xy-plane of our coordinate system) or at infinity (a bundle of mutually parallel rays entering with the same values of ξ, η is considered as a point of the infinite plane). Later we shall investigate the change of image errors for different positions of the object.

The rays from an object point form a normal system. In Chapter 25 we studied the rays of a normal system in the neighborhood of a principal ray. In applying this theory to our problem, we have to choose a bundle of principal rays, one from each object point. To simplify our investigations, we assume all these principal rays to pass through a fixed point in the image space, and this point, for lack of a better name, we shall call the *exit pupil*. The exit pupil can be finite, (for instance, the image-side origin of our coordinate system) or infinite (in this case the principal rays in the image space are parallel to the axis: $\xi' = \eta' = 0$). We shall at first assume a *fixed* exit pupil and later investigate the change of image errors arising when the exit pupil is shifted.

The name *exit pupil* is chosen because of its significance for a system with finite aperture and field. Such systems frequently have a diaphragm which can be stopped down. If this is done, only the rays passing near the center of the pupil, that is, lying near the principal rays, traverse the lens. Thus, by investigating the stopped-down system, we can actually visualize in a practical situation the geometrical facts discussed here.

In introducing the name *image errors*, we must ask ourselves what we should call a system which is *free* of image errors, that is, we must specify an ideal image formation, the deviations from which will be called *errors*.

This is easy for a point object. The ideal image is a sharp image. All the rays from the point go through the image point. As in Chapter 25, we can determine the diapoint on the principal ray and on each of the rays coming from the object point. If the image is sharp, all the diapoints coincide with the one on the principal ray. The coefficients $\bar{a}_{i\varkappa}$ of the angle characteristic can be considered as intrinsic errors, and we can compute, for each object point, its caustic surfaces. The corresponding errors can be considered as *image-forming errors*.

But let us assume that every point of the object plane has a sharp image. Even then, we may not be satisfied, for the reason that the image may be formed on a curved surface and we want to record it on a plane. Since the surface, if it exists, coincides with the diapoint-surface (the surface formed by all the diapoints on the principal rays), we shall call the coefficients of the equation of this surface, which is the best possible surface for image formation, the *errors of curvature*. The reader should keep in mind that, if we do not have sharp image formation, this "*best surface*" may change when we change the pupil, since the principal rays, and with them the diapoints on the principal rays, also change. If we have a sharp image of all points of the object plane, the "best image" is independent of the pupil position and is referred to as the *image surface*.

However, even if the image is on a plane and sharp, it might not be completely satisfactory if it is not similar to the object, that is, if the magnification, the ratio of image height to object height, is not constant for all points of the object. In this case, we speak of a *distorted* image and of *errors of distortion*. For an infinite object, the ratio of object height divided by the tangent of the incidence angle takes the place of magnification, and variations in this ratio are the errors of distortion in this case.

Having analyzed these "intrinsic errors," we shall compute the points of intersection of the image rays *(1)* with a *fixed* plane through the paraxial focus and perpendicular to the axis, *(2)* with an *arbitrary* plane perpendicular to the axis, and *(3)* with the *meridional* plane (the plane through the object point and the axis), that is, calculate the *diapoints*.

Assuming a given optical system, we shall investigate all these problems as well as the intrinsic errors discussed in Part VI.

Let us first investigate the image of a plane object, assuming the exit pupil to be at infinity, that is, assuming that the principal rays emerge parallel to the axis.

Considering the characteristic function V' and choosing the object-side origin at the object plane and the image origin arbitrarily, we find from (20.7)

$$\begin{aligned} -\xi &= \overline{V}_1 x + \overline{V}_2 \xi' & \qquad -x' &= \overline{V}_2 x + \overline{V}_3 \xi' \\ -\eta &= \overline{V}_1 y + \overline{V}_2 \eta' & \qquad -y' &= \overline{V}_2 y + \overline{V}_3 \eta', \end{aligned} \tag{27.1}$$

where V' is a function of v_1, v_2, v_3 and

$$2v_1 = x^2 + y^2, \quad v_2 = x\xi' + y\eta', \quad 2v_3 = \xi'^2 + \eta'^2, \quad \overline{V}_i = \partial V'/\partial v_i. \tag{27.2}$$

The rays through the object axis point (the aperture rays) are given by $x = y = 0$, which is equivalent to $v_1 = v_2 = 0$; that is, for the aperture rays, V' is a function of v_3 alone. The principal rays (the rays through the center of the exit pupil) are given by $\xi' = \eta' = 0$, which corresponds to $v_2 = v_3 = 0$; that is, for the principal rays, V' is a function of v_1 alone. The last two equations of (27.1) can be written

$$\begin{aligned} x' &= \mu x + \nu n'\xi'/\zeta' \\ y' &= \mu y + \nu n'\eta'/\zeta' \end{aligned} \quad \text{where} \quad \begin{aligned} \mu &= -\overline{V}_2 \\ \nu &= -\overline{V}_3\zeta'/n'. \end{aligned} \tag{27.3}$$

Developing ζ' into a series, we find

$$\zeta'/n' = \sqrt{1 - 2v_3/n'^2} = 1 - (v_3/n'^2) - (\tfrac{1}{2}v_3^2/n'^4). \tag{27.4}$$

The intersection of the rays with a plane at the distance z' from the image origin is given by

$$x'_{z'} = \mu x + (\nu + z'/n')\, n'\xi'/\zeta'$$
$$y'_{z'} = \mu y + (\nu + z'/n')\, n'\eta'/\zeta'. \qquad (27.5)$$

We find the points of intersection with the Gaussian plane by setting $z'/n' = -\nu_o$, giving

$$x'_o = \mu x + (\nu - \nu_o)\, n'\xi'/\zeta'$$
$$y'_o = \mu y + (\nu - \nu_o)\, n'\eta'/\zeta'. \qquad (27.6)$$

The diapoint of a ray, that is, the intersection of the image ray with the meridional plane, is found by inserting $z'/n' = -\nu$ into (27.5), giving

$$x_D' = \mu x$$
$$y_D' = \mu y \qquad (27.7)$$
$$-z_D'/n' = \nu.$$

If the object plane ($z = 0$) has a sharp, plane, and undistorted image, μ and ν must be constant, $\mu = \mu_o$ being equal to the Gaussian magnification, and $\nu = \nu_o$ being equal to the ordinary distance of the image-side coordinate plane from the Gaussian plane divided by n'.

If the optical system has a sharp image which is plane but not undistorted, μ and ν are independent of v_2 and v_3 but μ is a function of v_1. We therefore call the deviation of m, where

$$m = \mu_o + \mu_1 v_1 + \tfrac{1}{2}\, \mu_{11} v_1^2,$$

from its constant value the *error of distortion.*

If the system has a sharp image which is on a surface, ν is still a function of v_1. We therefore call the deviation

$$\nu - \nu_o = \nu_1 v_1 + \tfrac{1}{2} \nu_{11} v_1^2$$

the *diapoint curvature or sagittal curvature error*. The constants μ_1 and ν_1 are called the *Seidel errors of distortion* and of *sagittal (diapoint) curvature,* respectively, whereas μ_{11} and ν_{11} will be called the *aperture coefficients* of these respective errors.

Equations (27.7) suggest calling the coefficients of μ *lateral errors* (or *errors of magnification*) and the coefficients of ν *longitudinal errors*. Developing μ and ν into series with respect to the v_i, we write

$$\mu = \mu_o + \mu_1 v_1 + \mu_2 v_2 + \mu_3 v_3 + \tfrac{1}{2}(\mu_{11} v_1^2 + 2\mu_{12} v_1 v_2 + 2\mu_{13} v_1 v_3 + \mu_{22} v_2^2 + 2\mu_{23} v_2 v_3 + \mu_{33} v_3^2), \tag{27.8}$$

$$\nu = \nu_o + \nu_1 v_1 + \nu_2 v_2 + \nu_3 v_3 + \tfrac{1}{2}(\nu_{11} v_1^2 + 2\nu_{12} v_1 v_2 + 2\nu_{13} v_1 v_3 + \nu_{22} v_2^2 + 2\nu_{23} v_2 v_3 + \nu_{33} v_3^2).$$

From (27.3) and (27.4) it follows that

$$\begin{array}{lll}
\mu_o = -V_2 & \mu_{11} = -V_{112} & \nu_{11} = -V_{113} \\
\mu_1 = V_{12} & \mu_{12} = -V_{122} & \nu_{12} = -V_{123} \\
\mu_2 = -V_{22},\ \nu_1 = -V_{13} & \mu_{13} = -V_{123} & \nu_{13} = -\left(V_{133} - \dfrac{V_{13}}{n'^2}\right) \\
\mu_3 = -V_{23} = \nu_2 & \mu_{22} = -V_{222} & \nu_{22} = -V_{223} \\
-\left(V_{33} - \dfrac{V_3}{n'^2}\right) = \nu_3 & \mu_{23} = -V_{223} & \nu_{23} = -\left(V_{233} - \dfrac{V_{23}}{n'^2}\right) \\
 & \mu_{33} = -V_{233} & \nu_{33} = -\left(V_{333} - \dfrac{2V_{33}}{n'^2} - \dfrac{V_3}{n'^4}\right)
\end{array} \tag{27.9}$$

with the following equalities between the μ_i and the ν_i:

$$\begin{array}{ll}
 & \mu_{13} - \nu_{12} = 0 \\
\mu_3 - \nu_2 = 0 & \mu_{23} - \nu_{22} = 0 \\
 & \mu_{33} - \nu_{23} = \nu_2/n'^2.
\end{array} \tag{27.10}$$

We shall now give names to certain groups of these coefficients and investigate these groups by themselves, thus coordinating the results in this chapter with the analysis of normal systems given in Part VI.

We call

		$\mu_1,$	μ_{11}		*distortion coefficients,*
ν_1	ν_{11}	μ_2	μ_{12}		*astigmatic coefficients,*
ν_2	ν_{12}	μ_3	μ_{22}	μ_{13}	*asymmetry coefficients,*
and ν_3	ν_{13}	ν_{22}	μ_{23}		*Gullstrand coefficients.*

These names will be shown to agree with the corresponding terms in Chapter 24, and we shall investigate these four types of coefficients in their relation to the field variable v_1.

Two other groups of coefficients will be investigated in their relation to the aperture variable v_3. We shall call

ν_3 ν_{33} *spherical aberration coefficients*

and μ_3 μ_{33} *coma coefficients.*

Let us study the basic errors in turn.

(*a*) *Spherical Aberration*

The rays coming from the axis point ($x = y = v_1 = v_2 = 0$) are functions of v_3 alone. Therefore Equations (27.6) give for the intersection with the Gaussian plane

$$x_o' = (\nu_3 v_3 + \tfrac{1}{2}\nu_{33} v_3^2)\, n'\xi'/\zeta'$$
$$y_o' = (\nu_3 v_3 + \tfrac{1}{2}\nu_{33} v_3^2)\, n'\eta'/\zeta', \qquad (27.11)$$

and Equations (27.7) give for the diapoint

$$x_D' = 0$$
$$y_D' = 0$$
$$-(z_D'/n' + \nu_o) = \nu_3 v_3 + \tfrac{1}{2}\nu_{33} v_3^2. \qquad (27.12)$$

Equations (27.12) give the intersection points of the "aperture" rays with the axis. The quantity $(z_D'/n' + \nu_o)$ in optics is called the *longitudinal spherical aberration.* Equations (27.11) give the intersection point of each ray with the Gaussian plane. We see that the rays passing through a fixed point of the axis and through a circle in the infinite aperture (v_3 = constant) go through a circle in the Gaussian plane with a radius given by

$$r^2(v_3) = x_o'^2 + y_o'^2 = (\nu_3 v_3 + \tfrac{1}{2}\nu_{33} v_3^2)^2 \frac{2v_3}{1 - (2v_3/n'^2)}$$
$$\approx 2\nu_3 v_3^3 \left[\nu_3 + \left(\nu_{33} + \frac{2\nu_3}{n'^2}\right) v_3\right], \qquad (27.13)$$

neglecting higher order terms. The sagittal caustic for the axis point is given by the diapoint equations, (27.12), if we vary v_3 from zero to its maximum value. The meridional caustic [*cf.* (14.28)] is found approximately by

$$x'^2 + y'^2 = 8\nu_3 v_3^3 [\nu_3 + 2(\nu_{33} - \nu_3/n'^2)\, v_3]$$
$$-(z'/n' + \nu_o) = 3\nu_3 v_3 + \tfrac{1}{2} v_3^2 (5\nu_{33} - 8\nu_3/n'^2). \qquad (27.14)$$

Eliminating v_3 we obtain, as an approximate equation for the caustic,

$$x'^2 + y'^2 = -\frac{8}{27\nu_3}(z'/n' + \nu_o) - \frac{4}{81\nu_3{}^3}\left(\nu_{33} - \frac{4\nu_3}{n'^2}\right)(z'/n' + \nu_o)^4. \tag{27.15}$$

This equation shows that the caustic has a cusp at the Gaussian focus

$$x' = y' = 0, \quad -z'/n' = \nu_o.$$

(b) Coma and Sine Condition

To investigate a point near the axis, we may assume without loss of generality that the point lies in the yz-plane ($x = 0$). Neglecting second and higher powers of y in (27.6) then leads to the equations

$$\begin{aligned} x' &= (\nu_2 v_2 + \nu_3 v_3 + \nu_{23} v_2 v_3 + \tfrac{1}{2}\nu_{33} v_3{}^2)\, n'\xi'/\zeta' \\ y' - \mu_o y &= (\mu_3 v_3 + \tfrac{1}{2}\mu_{33} v_3{}^2) y \\ &\quad + (\nu_2 v_2 + \nu_3 v_3 + \nu_{23} v_2 v_3 + \tfrac{1}{2}\nu_{33} v_3{}^2)\, n'\eta'/\zeta' \end{aligned} \tag{27.16}$$

for the intersection at the Gaussian plane, and likewise Equations (27.7) lead to the diapoint equations

$$\begin{aligned} x_D' &= 0 \\ y_D' - \mu_o y &= (\mu_3 v_3 + \tfrac{1}{2}\mu_{33} v_3{}^2) y \\ -(z_D'/n' + \nu_o) &= \nu_2 v_2 + \nu_3 v_3 + \nu_{23} v_2 v_3 + \tfrac{1}{2}\nu_{33} v_3{}^2, \end{aligned} \tag{27.17}$$

with

$$\mu_3 = \nu_2, \quad \mu_{33} = \nu_{23} + \nu_2/n'^2.$$

If $\mu_3 = \mu_{33} = 0$, we find that the caustic of the near-axis point is symmetrical with respect to the principal ray, which at present we are assuming to be parallel to the axis in the image space.

Let us assume the spherical aberration to be corrected and accordingly insert $\nu_3 = \nu_{33} = 0$ into (27.16). Since $v_2 = y\eta'$ and

$$\frac{n'}{\zeta'} = \frac{1}{\sqrt{1 - 2v_3/n'^2}} = 1 + \frac{v_3}{n'^2} + \frac{3v_3{}^2}{2n'^4},$$

it follows that the intersection at the Gaussian plane is given by

$$x' = [\nu_2 + (\nu_{23} + \nu_2/n'^2)v_3]\xi'\eta' y = (\mu_3 + \mu_{33}v_3)\xi'\eta' y$$
$$y' - \mu_o y = (\mu_3 v_3 + \tfrac{1}{2}\mu_{33}v_3^2)\, y + (\mu_3 + \mu_{33}v_3)\, \eta'^2 y. \qquad (27.18)$$

Eliminating ξ' and η' from (27.18) by using the relation

$$2v_3 = \xi'^2 + \eta'^2,$$

we find that the rays through a set of concentric circles in the exit pupil (constant values of v_3) go through a series of eccentric circles in the Gaussian image plane, their equations being given by

$$x'^2 + [y' - \mu_o y - \tfrac{1}{2}y\,(4\mu_3 v_3 + 3\mu_{33}v_3^2)]^2 = (\mu_3 + \mu_{33}v_3)^2 v_3^2 y^2. \qquad (27.19)$$

The envelopes of these eccentric circles are two curves passing through the Gaussian focus, and these form an angle of 60° with each other and are given approximately by

$$3x'^2 = (y' - \mu_o y)^2 - (\mu_{33}/\mu_3^2 y)\,(y' - \mu_o y)^3. \qquad (27.20)$$

The presence of the comet-like figure formed by the circles described above led opticians to call this error the *coma* error. We shall distinguish it from the asymmetry error described later.

It is interesting that one can obtain the coma coefficients μ_3 and μ_{33} for an infinite exit pupil by the trace of the aperture rays alone. Equations (27.1) give for the aperture rays ($x = y = v_1 = v_2 = 0$)

$$-\xi = \overline{V}_2\xi' = (V_2 + V_{23}v_3 + \tfrac{1}{2}V_{233}v_3^2)\,\xi'$$
$$-\eta = \overline{V}_2\eta' = (V_2 + V_{23}v_3 + \tfrac{1}{2}V_{233}v_3^2)\,\eta' \qquad (27.21)$$

or, because of (27.9),

$$\xi = (\mu_o + \mu_3 v_3 + \tfrac{1}{2}\mu_{33}v_3^2)\,\xi'$$
$$\eta = (\mu_o + \mu_3 v_3 + \tfrac{1}{2}\mu_{33}v_3^2)\,\eta'. \qquad (27.22)$$

The ratio of the direction cosines is equal to the ratio of the sines of the angles (σ, σ') formed by the rays with the axis. Since from (27.22)

$$\xi/\xi' = \eta/\eta'$$

and

$$n^2 \sin^2\sigma = \xi^2 + \eta^2, \quad n'^2 \sin^2\sigma' = \xi'^2 + \eta'^2, \qquad (27.23)$$

it follows that

$$\overline{m}n' \sin \sigma' = n \sin \sigma,$$

where

$$\overline{m} = \mu_o + \mu_3 v_3 + \tfrac{1}{2}\mu_{33} v_3^2. \qquad (27.24)$$

If $\overline{m} = \mu_o$ (that is, $\mu_3 = \mu_{33} = 0$), we say that the *sine condition* is fulfilled. For the case of an infinite exit pupil, which we are assuming, the fulfillment of the sine condition is therefore identical with freedom from coma.

Spherical aberration and coma are functions of the aperture (v_3). We shall investigate the remaining image errors as functions of the field (v_1).

(*c*) *Distortion*

The principal rays ($v_2 = v_3 = \xi' = \eta' = 0, \zeta' = n'$) intersect the Gaussian plane at the point

$$x' = (\mu_o + \mu_1 v_1 + \tfrac{1}{2}\mu_{11} v_1^2)\, x = mx$$
$$y' = (\mu_o + \mu_1 v_1 + \tfrac{1}{2}\mu_{11} v_1^2)\, y = my. \qquad (27.25)$$

If m is constant (equal to μ_o), we find that the principal rays intersect the Gaussian image plane in a figure which is similar to the object. For instance, to the four sides of a square $x = \pm x_o$, $y = \pm y_o$ in the object plane correspond the four sides of the image figure $x' = \pm mx_o$, $y' = \pm my_o$.

If m is not constant, we find that the image figure has curved sides. We say that the image is *distorted*. If m is a positive monotonic *increasing* function of v_1, then the points farther from the center are projected with higher magnification. This behavior is called *pin-cushion distortion,* since the figure corresponding to a square in the object space resembles a pin cushion. If m is a monotonic *decreasing* function, it produces *barrel* distortion.

(*d*) *Astigmatism*

Neglecting second-order and higher order terms in the aperture variables ξ', η' and assuming the object point to lie in the meridional plane ($x = 0$), $v_1 = \frac{1}{2}y^2$, $v_2 = y\eta'$, $v_3 = \frac{1}{2}(\xi'^2 + \eta'^2)$, we find from (27.6)

$$\begin{aligned} x' &= (\nu_1 v_1 + \tfrac{1}{2}\nu_{11}v_1^2)n'\xi'/\zeta' = (\nu_1 v_1 + \tfrac{1}{2}\nu_{11}v_1^2)\,\xi' \\ y' - my &= (\mu_2 + \mu_{12}v_1)v_2 y + (\nu_1 v_1 + \tfrac{1}{2}\nu_{11}v_1^2)\,\eta' \qquad (27.26) \\ &= [(\nu_1 + 2\mu_2)v_1 + \tfrac{1}{2}(\nu_{11} + 4\mu_{12})v_1^2]\,\eta'. \end{aligned}$$

Equation (27.26) shows that the rays through a small aperture intersect the image plane in an ellipse around the intersection point of the (distorted) principal ray, the equation of this ellipse being

$$\frac{\bar{x}'^2}{(\nu_1 + \tfrac{1}{2}\nu_{11}v_1)^2} + \frac{\bar{y}'^2}{[\nu_1 + 2\mu_2 + \tfrac{1}{2}(\nu_{11} + 4\mu_{12})\,v_1]^2} = 2v_1^2 v_3. \qquad (27.27)$$

A comparison of (27.26) and (27.5) shows that the ellipse reduces to a vertical line $x' = 0$ if one intersects the rays with a plane at the distance z_s' from the Gaussian plane given by

$$z_s'/n' + \nu_1 v_1 + \tfrac{1}{2}\nu_{11}v_1^2 = 0$$

and into a horizontal line for

$$z_m'/n' + (\nu_1 + 2\mu_2)\,v_1 + \tfrac{1}{2}(\nu_{11} + 4\mu_{12})\,v_1^2. \qquad (27.28)$$

We call z_s' the *sagittal focal distance* from the Gaussian plane and z_m' the *meridional focal distance* from the Gaussian plane.

The difference $z_m' - z_s'$ given by

$$z_m' - z_s' + 2v_1(\mu_2 + \mu_{12}v_1)\,n' = 0 \qquad (27.29)$$

is called the *astigmatic* distance. A principal ray is called *anastigmatic* if μ_2 and μ_{12} vanish (*cf.* Chapter 23). In this case, Equation (27.27) becomes a circle, all the rays within the assumed approximation passing through the point at the distance $z_s' = z_m'$ from the Gaussian focal plane.

We summarize the above discussion of astigmatism. We shall call $2v_1(\mu_2 + \mu_{12}v_1)$ the *astigmatic error* for the field distance v_1. In particular, we shall call μ_2 the *Seidel coefficient* of *astigmatism* and μ_{12} its *field coefficient*. We shall call $v_1(\nu_1 + \tfrac{1}{2}\nu_{11}v_1)$ the *sagittal* or *diapoint curvature* and, in particular, ν_1, the *Seidel sagittal astigmatic coefficient* and ν_{11} its *field coefficient*. We shall call $v_1[\nu_1 + 2\mu_2 + \tfrac{1}{2}v_1(\nu_{11} + 4\mu_{12})]$ the *meridional astigmatic error* and in particular $\nu_1 + 2\mu_2$ the *Seidel meridional astigmatic coefficient and* $\nu_{11} + 4\mu_{12}$ its *field coefficient.*

(e) Asymmetry Errors

Let us assume astigmatism to be corrected. The next higher order terms give us for a point in the meridional plane ($x = 0$, $v_1 = \frac{1}{2}y^2$, $v_2 = y\eta'$, $2v_3 = \xi'^2 + \eta'^2$) and the corresponding intersection with the Gaussian image plane:

$$\begin{aligned} x' &= (\nu_2 + \nu_{12}v_1)\, v_2 n'\xi'/\zeta' = (\nu_2 + \nu_{12}v_1)\xi'\eta' y, \\ y' - my &= (\nu_2 + \nu_{12}v_1)\, v_2 n'\eta'/\zeta' + [(\mu_3 + \mu_{13}v_1)v_3 + \tfrac{1}{2}\mu_{22}v_2^2)]y \\ &= (\nu_2 + \nu_{12}v_1)\, \eta'^2 y + (\mu_3 v_3 + \mu_{13}v_1 v_3 + \tfrac{1}{2}\mu_{22}v_2^2)y \\ &= [\nu_2 + (\nu_{12} + \mu_{22})\, v_1]\, \eta'^2 y + (\mu_3 + \mu_{13}v_1)v_3 y, \end{aligned} \qquad (27.30)$$

or, considering that $\nu_2 = \mu_3$ and $\nu_{12} = \mu_{13}$,

$$\begin{aligned} x' &= (\mu_3 + \mu_{13}v_1)\, \xi'\eta' y \\ y' - my &= [\mu_3 + (\mu_{13} + \mu_{22})\, v_1]\, \eta'^2 y + (\mu_3 + \mu_{13}v_1)\, v_3 y. \end{aligned} \qquad (27.30a)$$

Eliminating ξ' and η' from (27.30) and $2v_3 = \xi'^2 + \eta'^2$, we find that the rays through a set of concentric circles in the infinite aperture plane pass through a series of eccentric ellipses in the Gaussian image plane, the equations being given by

$$\frac{x'^2}{[(\mu_3 + \mu_{13}v_1)v_3 y]^2} + \frac{\{y' - my - [2\mu_3 + (\mu_{22} + 2\mu_{13})\, v_1]\, v_3 y\}^2}{[(\mu_3 + (\mu_{22} + \mu_{13})\, v_1)\, v_3 y]^2} = 1. \qquad (27.31)$$

These ellipses have as envelopes two straight lines given by

$$\bar{y}'^2\, (\mu_3 + \mu_{13}v_1) = 3x'^2\, [\mu_3 + (\mu_{13} + \tfrac{2}{3}\mu_{22})\, v_1]. \qquad (27.32)$$

Comparison with (24.14) shows that (aside from an unessential constant of proportionality) the coefficients in (27.31) and (27.32) give the asymmetry coefficient C_s and C_m of Chapter 24:

$$\begin{aligned} C_s &= \varkappa\, (\mu_3 + \mu_{13}v_1) \\ C_m &= 3\varkappa\, [\mu_3 + (\mu_{13} + \tfrac{2}{3}\mu_{22})\, v_1]. \end{aligned} \qquad (27.33)$$

Equations (27.33) permit us to call $\mu_3 + \mu_{13}v_1$ the *sagittal* asymmetry error and $3\mu_3 + (3\mu_{13} + 2\mu_{22})\, v_1$ the *meridional* asymmetry error.

We see that the third-order (Seidel) part of the asymmetry error is equivalent to the coma coefficient in Seidel theory, the meridional asymmetry error being equal to three times the sagittal asymmetry error.

The coefficient μ_{13} may be called the *field coefficient* of the sagittal asymmetry error, and $3\mu_{13} + 2\mu_{22}$ the *field coefficient* of the meridional asymmetry error. These coefficients show the change of the asymmetry image errors with the field angle.

If $\mu_{22} = 0$, (27.31) denotes a series of eccentric circles with two straight lines at a sixty-degree angle as envelopes. In this case we have $C_m = 3\, C_s$ regardless of the field angle. We shall call μ_{22} the *asymmetric deformation coefficient.*

(f) Gullstrand Errors

If astigmatism and asymmetry are assumed to be corrected, Equations (27.6) give for the intersection with the Gaussian plane (retaining terms of third order in the aperture):

$$x' = (\nu_3 v_3 + \nu_{13} v_1 v_3 + \tfrac{1}{2}\nu_{22} v_2{}^2)\, n'\xi'/\zeta'$$
$$y' - my = (\mu_{23} v_2 v_3)\, y + (\nu_3 v_3 + \nu_{13} v_1 v_3 + \tfrac{1}{2}\nu_{22} v_2{}^2)\, n'\eta'/\zeta', \quad (27.34)$$

which, for the order considered, since $\mu_{23} = \nu_{22}$, is equivalent to

$$x' = \xi' \{\tfrac{1}{2}(\nu_3 + \nu_{13} v_1)\, \xi'^2 + \tfrac{1}{2}\eta'^2 (\nu_3 + [\nu_{13} + 2\nu_{22})\, v_1]\}$$
$$y' - my = \eta' \{\tfrac{1}{2}\, \xi'^2 [\nu_3 + (\nu_{13} + 2\nu_{22})\, v_1] + \tfrac{1}{2}\, \eta'^2 [\nu_3 + (\nu_{13} + 4\nu_{22})\, v_1]\}. \quad (27.35)$$

Comparison of (27.35) with (23.74) shows that these are Gullstrand errors with

$G_s = \nu_3 + \nu_{13} v_1$ sagittal Gullstrand error
$G_c = \nu_3 + (\nu_{13} + 2\nu_{22})\, v_1$ cloverleaf Gullstrand error
$G_m = \nu_3 + (\nu_{13} + 4\nu_{22})\, v_1$. meridional Gullstrand error.

For $v_1 = 0$, we note that $G_s = G_c = G_m = \nu_3$, that is, the caustic is rotation-symmetric and the Gullstrand error coincides with the spherical aberration of Seidel theory. If $\nu_{22} = 0$, the caustic remains rotation-symmetric but the spherical aberration changes from point to point. We therefore call ν_{22} the *Gullstrand deformation coefficient.* In this way, we have found the geometrical significance of all the coefficients of the development of μ and ν. We repeat:

$$\begin{array}{rl}
\mu_1 & \text{distortion (Seidel)} \\
\mu_2 & \text{astigmatism (Seidel)} \\
\mu_3 = \nu_2 & \text{coma and asymmetry (Seidel)} \\
\nu_1 & \text{sagittal curvature (Seidel)} \\
\nu_3 & \text{spherical aberration} = \text{Gullstrand error (Seidel)} \\
\mu_{11} & \text{distortion (field coefficient)} \\
\mu_{12} & \text{astigmatism (field coefficient)} \\
\mu_{13} = \nu_{12} & \text{sagittal asymmetry (field coefficient)} \\
\mu_{22} & \text{asymmetry (deformation coefficient)} \\
\mu_{23} = \nu_{22} & \text{Gullstrand error (deformation coefficient)} \\
\mu_{33} = \nu_{23} + \nu_2/n'^2 & \text{coma error (aperture coefficient)} \\
\nu_{11} & \text{sagittal curvature (field coefficient)} \\
\nu_{12} & \text{sagittal asymmetry (field coefficient)} \\
\nu_{13} & \text{sagittal Gullstrand error (field coefficient)} \\
\nu_{22} & \text{Gullstrand error (deformation coefficient)} \\
\nu_{23} = \mu_{33} - \mu_3/n'^2 & (\textit{cf.}\ \text{coma error, above}) \\
\nu_{33} & \text{spherical aberration (aperture coefficient).}
\end{array} \tag{27.36}$$

In practical optical calculations, lens designers have (unfortunately) almost exclusively computed rays in the meridional plane. Let us see what information we can obtain from these rays.

We assume the object point to lie in the yz-plane ($x = 0$). Then setting $\xi' = 0$ gives the meridional rays, that is,

$$2v_1 = y^2, \quad v_2 = y\eta', \quad v_3 = \tfrac{1}{2}\eta'^2, \tag{27.37}$$

and for the diapoint coordinates (27.7) ordered with respect to powers of η', we have

$$\begin{aligned}
y_D' = y\,\{&(\mu_o + \mu_1 v_1 + \tfrac{1}{2}\mu_{11} v_1^2) + (\mu_2 + \mu_{12} v_1)\, y\eta' \\
&+ \tfrac{1}{2}\eta'^2 [\mu_3 + (\mu_{13} + 2\mu_{22})\, v_1] + \tfrac{1}{6}\eta'^3 (3\mu_{23})\, y + \tfrac{1}{24}\eta'^4 (3\mu_{33})\} \\
-\left(\frac{z_D'}{n'} + \nu_o\right) = &(\nu_1 v_1 + \tfrac{1}{2}\nu_{11} v_1^2) + (\nu_2 + \nu_{12} v_1)\, y\eta' \\
&+ \tfrac{1}{2}\eta'^2 [\nu_3 + (\nu_{13} + 2\nu_{22}) v_1] + \tfrac{1}{6}\eta'^3 (3\nu_{23} y) \\
&+ \tfrac{1}{24}\,\eta'^4 (3\nu_{33}).
\end{aligned} \tag{27.38}$$

For the intersection point in the Gaussian plane, we find from (27.6):

$$x' = 0$$

$$\begin{aligned} y' - my = \eta' &[(\nu_1 + 2\mu_2)\, v_1 + \tfrac{1}{2}v_1{}^2\,(\nu_{11} + 4\mu_{12})] \\ &+ \tfrac{1}{2}\eta'^2 y\,[3\mu_3 + v_1\,(3\mu_{13} + 2\mu_{22})] \\ &+ \tfrac{1}{6}\eta'^3\,[3\nu_3 + 3v_1\,(\nu_{13} + 4\nu_{22} + \nu_1/n'^2)] \\ &+ \tfrac{1}{24}\eta'^4\,(15y\mu_{33}) + \tfrac{1}{120}\eta'^5\, 15\left(\nu_{33} + \frac{2\nu_3}{n'^2}\right), \end{aligned} \qquad (27.39)$$

which is in agreement with the former designation of meridional errors:

$(\nu_1 + 2\mu_2)\, v_1 + \tfrac{1}{2}v_1{}^2\,(\nu_{11} + 4\mu_{12})$	meridional astigmatism
$3\mu_3 + v_1\,(3\mu_{13} + 2\mu_{22})$	meridional asymmetry
$\nu_3 + v_1\,(\nu_{13} + 4\nu_{22})$	meridional Gullstrand errors
μ_{33}	sine condition
ν_{33}	spherical aberration.

The treatment of the image errors of an infinite object with infinite pupil follows the same pattern. Using the angle characteristic W, we derive from (26.6)

$$\begin{aligned} x' &= -\,\overline{W}_2(\zeta/n)\,(n\xi/\zeta) - \overline{W}_3\,(\zeta'/n')\,(n'\xi'/\zeta') = \tilde{\mu}n\xi/\zeta + \tilde{\nu}n'\xi'/\zeta' \\ y' &= -\,\overline{W}_2\,(\zeta/n)\,(n\eta/\zeta) - \overline{W}_3\,(\zeta'/n')\left(\frac{n'\eta'}{\zeta'}\right) = \tilde{\mu}n(\eta/\zeta) + \tilde{\nu}n'(\eta'/\zeta'), \end{aligned} \qquad (27.40)$$

with

$$\begin{aligned} \tilde{\mu} &= -\,\overline{W}_2\frac{\zeta}{n} = -\,\overline{W}_2\left(1 - \frac{w_1}{n^2} - \frac{1}{2}\,\frac{w_1{}^2}{n^4}\right) \\ \tilde{\nu} &= -\,\overline{W}_3\frac{\zeta'}{n'} = -\,\overline{W}_3\left(1 - \frac{w_3}{n'^2} - \frac{1}{2}\,\frac{w_3{}^2}{n'^4}\right). \end{aligned} \qquad (27.41)$$

The intersection point with an arbitrary plane at the distance k' from the image origin is given by

$$x' = \tilde{\mu}n\xi/\zeta + (\tilde{\nu} + k'/n')\, n'\xi'/\zeta'$$
$$y' = \tilde{\mu}n\eta/\zeta + (\tilde{\nu} + k'/n')\, n'\eta'\ \zeta'. \tag{27.42}$$

In particular we find for the Gaussian plane

$$x' = \tilde{\mu}n\xi/\zeta + (\tilde{\nu} - \tilde{\nu}_o)\, n'\xi'/\zeta'$$
$$y' = \tilde{\mu}n\eta/\zeta + (\tilde{\nu} - \tilde{\nu}_o)\, n'\eta'/\zeta'. \tag{27.43}$$

Similarly the diapoints are found to be

$$x_D' = \tilde{\mu}n\xi/\zeta$$
$$y_D' = \tilde{\mu}n\eta/\zeta \tag{27.44}$$
$$-\,z_D'/n' = \tilde{\nu}.$$

In this case, $\tilde{\mu}$ is not the *diamagnification* but the *diafocal length,* whereas $n'\tilde{\nu}$ is the distance of the image origin from the diafocal point. The same consideration leads us to examine the field-error functions

$\tilde{\mu}_o + \tilde{\mu}_1 w_1 + \frac{1}{2}\,\tilde{\mu}_{11} w_1^2$	distortion
$\tilde{\nu}_1 w_1 + \frac{1}{2}\,\tilde{\nu}_{11} w_1^2$	sagittal astigmatism
$(2\tilde{\mu}_2 + 2\tilde{\mu}_{12} w_1) w_1$	astigmatism
$\tilde{\mu}_3 + \tilde{\mu}_{13} w_1$	sagittal asymmetry
$3\tilde{\mu}_3 + (3\tilde{\mu}_{13} + 2\tilde{\mu}_{22}) w_1$	meridional asymmetry
$\tilde{\nu}_3 + \tilde{\nu}_{13} w_1$	sagittal Gullstrand error
$\tilde{\nu}_3 + (\tilde{\nu}_{13} + 2\tilde{\nu}_{22}) w_1$	cloverleaf Gullstrand error
$\tilde{\nu}_3 + (\tilde{\nu}_{13} + 4\tilde{\nu}_{22}) w_1$	meridional Gullstrand error

and the aperture-dependent errors

$\tilde{\mu}_3 w_3 + \frac{1}{2}\,\tilde{\mu}_{33} w_3^2$	coma error
$\tilde{\nu}_3 w_3 + \frac{1}{2}\,\tilde{\nu}_{33} w_3^2$	spherical aberration.

Expressed by W, the coefficients of $\tilde{\mu}$ and $\tilde{\nu}$ are

$$\tilde{\mu}_o = -\,W_2 \qquad \tilde{\nu}_o = -\,W_3$$
$$\tilde{\mu}_1 = -\left(W_{12} - \frac{W_2}{n^2}\right) \qquad \tilde{\nu}_1 = -\,W_{13}$$
$$\tilde{\mu}_2 = -\,W_{22} \qquad \tilde{\nu}_2 = -\,W_{23}$$

$$\tilde{\mu}_3 = -W_{23} \qquad \tilde{\nu}_3 = -\left(W_{33} - \frac{W_3}{n'^2}\right)$$

$$\tilde{\mu}_{11} = -\left(W_{112} - \frac{2W_{12}}{n^2} - \frac{W_2}{n^4}\right) \qquad \tilde{\nu}_{11} = -W_{113}$$

$$\tilde{\mu}_{12} = -\left(W_{122} - \frac{W_{22}}{n^2}\right) \qquad \tilde{\nu}_{12} = -W_{123}$$

$$\tilde{\mu}_{13} = -\left(W_{123} - \frac{W_{23}}{n^2}\right) \qquad \tilde{\nu}_{13} = -\left(W_{133} - \frac{W_{13}}{n'^2}\right)$$

$$\tilde{\mu}_{22} = -W_{222} \qquad \tilde{\nu}_{22} = -W_{223}$$

$$\tilde{\mu}_{23} = -W_{223} \qquad \tilde{\nu}_{23} = -\left(W_{233} - \frac{W_{23}}{n'^2}\right)$$

$$\tilde{\mu}_{33} = -W_{233} \qquad \tilde{\nu}_{33} = -\left(W_{333} - \frac{2W_{33}}{n'^2} - \frac{W_3}{n'^4}\right), \tag{27.45}$$

where

$$\tilde{\mu}_3 = \tilde{\nu}_2 \qquad \tilde{\mu}_{13} - \tilde{\nu}_{12} = \frac{W_{23}}{n^2} = -\frac{\tilde{\mu}_3}{n^2}$$

$$\tilde{\mu}_{23} - \tilde{\nu}_{22} = 0$$

$$\tilde{\mu}_{33} - \tilde{\nu}_{23} = -\frac{W_{23}}{n'^2} = \frac{\tilde{\mu}_3}{n'^2} \tag{27.46}$$

with corresponding geometrical meanings.

Again coma correction for the infinite pupil corresponds to the fulfillment of the sine condition, this time for an infinite object. Considering the aperture rays ($\xi = \eta = w_1 = w_2 = 0$), we find from the first equations of (26.6)

$$x = \overline{W}_2\xi' = -(\tilde{\mu}_o + \tilde{\mu}_3 w_3 + \tfrac{1}{2}\,\tilde{\mu}_{33} w_3^2)\,\xi'$$
$$y = \overline{W}_2\eta' = -(\tilde{\mu}_o + \tilde{\mu}_3 w_3 + \tfrac{1}{2}\,\tilde{\mu}_{33} w_3^2)\,\eta', \tag{27.47}$$

which shows that the ratio of entrance height divided by the sine of the outgoing angle (the sine condition for an infinite object) gives the coma error.

Image Errors for a Finite Stop

The geometrical interpretation of the image-error coefficients is slightly different if we assume a finite stop in an optical system. The reason is that, while we can consider either of the characteristic functions V' or W as an *angle* characteristic with v_1 as a parameter, the characteristic function E must be considered as a *point* characteristic with the coordinate e_1 of the object point as a parameter. The connection between the coefficients of the point of intersection with a plane and with the diapoint coordinates will be slightly different, though still very simple.

We shall therefore give the same names to the coefficients of the corresponding series developments, but sketch anew, if perfunctorily, the geometrical significance.

Equations (26.2) give

$$-\xi = \bar{E}_1 x + \bar{E}_2 x_P' \qquad \xi' = \bar{E}_2 x + \bar{E}_3 x_P'$$
$$-\eta = \bar{E}_1 y + \bar{E}_2 y_P' \qquad \eta' = \bar{E}_2 y + \bar{E}_3 y_P', \qquad (27.48)$$

with coordinate origins at the object plane and at the exit pupil and with E as a function of

$$e_1 = \tfrac{1}{2}(x^2 + y^2), \quad e_2 = x x_P' + y y_P', \quad e_3 = \tfrac{1}{2}(x_P'^2 + y_P'^2) \qquad (27.49)$$

or, in case the object point is assumed to lie in the meridional plane ($x = 0$),

$$2e_1 = y^2, \quad e_2 = y y_P', \quad 2e_3 = x_P'^2 + y_P'^2. \qquad (27.49a)$$

From (27.48) we derive

$$n'\xi'/\zeta' = Mx + Nx_P'$$
$$n'\eta'/\zeta' = My + Ny_P', \qquad (27.50)$$

with

$$M = \bar{E}_2 n'/\zeta' = \bar{E}_2 \Big/ \sqrt{1 - \frac{2}{n'^2}(\bar{E}_2{}^2 e_1 + \bar{E}_2\bar{E}_2 e_2 + \bar{E}_3{}^2 e_3)}$$

$$N = \bar{E}_3 n'/\zeta' = \bar{E}_3 \Big/ \sqrt{1 - \frac{2}{n'^2}(\bar{E}_2{}^2 e_1 + \bar{E}_2\bar{E}_3 e_2 + \bar{E}_3{}^2 e_3)}. \qquad (27.51)$$

The coordinate of intersection of the rays with a plane at the distance z' from the exit pupil is then given by

$$x'_{z'} = \left(\frac{z'}{n'}\right) Mx + \left(1 + \frac{z'}{n'} N\right) x_P'$$

$$y'_{z'} = \left(\frac{z'}{n'}\right) My + \left(1 + \frac{z'}{n'} N\right) y_P'. \qquad (27.52)$$

In particular, the intersection points with the Gaussian plane are obtained by setting $z'/n' = -1/N_0$ in (27.52), the result being

$$-N_0 x_o' = Mx + (N - N_0)\, x_P'$$

$$-N_0 y_o' = My + (N - N_0)\, y_P'. \qquad (27.53)$$

The diapoint coordinates can be computed from (27.52) as

$$x_D' = -(M/N)\, x, \quad y_D' = -(M/N)\, y$$

$$-z_D'/n' = 1/N. \qquad (27.54)$$

Developing M and N as functions of e_1, e_2, e_3, we see that we can consider their deviations from constants as image errors. We shall divide the errors into groups analogous to our former ones and investigate these groups by themselves. We call

N_3, N_{33}	spherical aberration coefficients,
and $M_3 = N_2$, M_{33}, N_{23}	coma-error coefficients,

these errors being functions of the aperture. As functions of the field position, we call

M_1, M_{11}	errors of distortion (zero order in the pupil coordinates)
N_1, M_2, N_{11}, M_{12}	astigmatic errors (first order in the pupil coordinates)
$M_3 = N_2$, M_{13}, N_{12}, M_{22}	asymmetry errors (second order in the pupil coordinates)
N_3, N_{13}, N_{22}, M_{23}	Gullstrand errors (third order in the pupil coordinates)

As functions of the coefficients of the development of E, the image-error coefficients are more complex. We find from (27.51)

$$M_o = E_2$$

$$M_1 = E_{12} + \frac{1}{n'^2} E_2^3$$

$$M_2 = E_{22} + \frac{1}{n'^2} E_2^2 E_3$$

$$M_3 = E_{23} + \frac{1}{n'^2} E_2 E_3^2$$

$$M_{11} = \left(E_{112} - \frac{3}{n'^4} E_2^5\right) + \frac{6}{n'^2} E_2^2 M_1$$

$$M_{12} = \left(E_{122} - \frac{3}{n'^4} E_2^4 E_3\right) + \frac{1}{n'^2} (E_2^2 (N_1 + 3M_2) + 2E_2E_3M_1)$$

$$M_{13} = \left(E_{123} - \frac{3}{n'^4} E_2^3 E_3^2\right) + \frac{1}{n'^2} (3E_2^2M_3 + 2E_2E_3N_1 + E_3^2M_1)$$

$$M_{22} = \left(E_{222} - \frac{3}{n'^4} E_2^3 E_3^2\right) + \frac{2}{n_1^2} (E_2^2M_3 + 2E_2E_3M_2)$$

$$M_{23} = \left(E_{223} - \frac{3}{n'^4} E_2^2 E_3^3\right) + \frac{1}{n'^2} (E_2^2N_3 + 4E_2E_3M_3 + E_3^2M_2)$$

$$M_{33} = \left(E_{233} - \frac{3}{n'^4} E_2 E_3^4\right) + \frac{2}{n'^2} (2E_2E_3N_3 + E_3^2M_3) \qquad (27.55)$$

and

$$N_o = E_3$$

$$N_1 = \left(E_{13} + \frac{1}{n'^2} E_2^2 E_3\right)$$

$$N_2 = \left(E_{23} + \frac{1}{n'^2} E_2 E_3^2\right)$$

$$N_3 = \left(E_{33} + \frac{1}{n'^2} E_3^3\right)$$

$$N_{11} = \left(E_{113} - \frac{3}{n'^4} E_2^4 E_3\right) + \frac{2}{n'^2} (E_2^2N_1 + 2E_2E_3M_1)$$

$$N_{12} = \left(E_{123} - \frac{3}{n'^4} E_2^3 E_3^2\right) + \frac{1}{n'^2}[E_2^2 M_3 + 2E_2 E_3 (N_1 + M_2) + E_3^2 M_1]$$

$$N_{13} = \left(E_{133} - \frac{3}{n'^4} E_2^2 E_3^3\right) + \frac{1}{n'^2}(E_2^2 N_3 + 2E_2 E_3 M_3 + 3E_3^2 N_1)$$

$$N_{22} = \left(E_{223} - \frac{3}{n'^4} E_2^2 E_3^3\right) + \frac{2}{n'^2}(2E_2 E_3 M_3 + E_3^2 M_2)$$

$$N_{23} = \left(E_{233} - \frac{3}{n'^4} E_2 E_3^4\right) + \frac{2}{n'^2}(E_2 E_3 N_3 + 2E_3^2 M_3)$$

$$N_{33} = \left(E_{333} - \frac{3}{n'^4} E_3^5\right) + \frac{6}{n'^2} E_3^2 N_3, \tag{27.56}$$

from which we derive the connecting equations

$$N_2 - M_3 = 0$$

$$N_{12} - M_{13} = \frac{2E_2}{n'^2}(E_3 M_2 - E_2 M_3)$$

$$N_{22} - M_{23} = \frac{1}{n'^2}[E_3 (E_3 M_2 - E_2 M_3) + E_2 (E_3 N_2 - E_2 N_3)]$$

$$N_{23} - M_{33} = \frac{2E_3}{n'^2}(E_3 N_2 - E_2 N_3). \tag{27.57}$$

We now discuss the various groups of errors specified above for a finite object.

(a) Spherical Aberration

From (27.53) we derive for the rays from the axis point ($x = y = e_1 = e_2 = 0$)

$$-N_o x_o' = (N_3 e_3 + \tfrac{1}{2} N_{33} e_3^2)\, x_P'$$
$$-N_o y_o' = (N_3 e_3 + \tfrac{1}{2} N_{33} e_3^2)\, y_P', \tag{27.58}$$

that is, the rays from an axial object point and circular apertures, $2e_3 = x_P'^2 + y_P'^2 =$ const., go through a series of concentric circles with

$$\tfrac{1}{2} N_o^2 (x_o'^2 + y_o'^2) = (N_3 e_3 + \tfrac{1}{2} N_{33} e_3^2)^2 e_3, \tag{27.59}$$

analogously to Equation (27.13). However, the longitudinal spherical aberration is given by (27.54), which may be written

$$-\frac{z_D'}{n'} = \frac{1}{N} = \frac{1}{N_o + N_3 e_3 + \frac{1}{2} N_{33} e_3^2}$$
$$= \frac{1}{N_o}\left[1 - \frac{N_3}{N_o} e_3 - \frac{1}{2}\left(\frac{N_{33}N_o - 2N_3^2}{N_o^2}\right) e_3^2\right]. \quad (27.60)$$

(*b*) *Coma Correction*

An object point near the axis, assumed in the yz-plane (no loss of generality), leads to the equations:

$$- N_o x_o' = (N_2 e_2 + N_3 e_3 + N_{23} e_2 e_3 + \tfrac{1}{2} N_{33} e_3^2)\, x_P'$$
$$- N_o y_o' - M_o y = (M_3 e_3 - \tfrac{1}{2} M_{33} e_3^2)\, y \quad (27.61)$$
$$+ (N_2 e_2 + N_3 e_3 + N_{23} e_2 e_3 + \tfrac{1}{2} N_{33} e_3^2)\, y_P'.$$

With $x = 0$, $e_1 = \frac{1}{2} y^2$, $e_2 = yy_P'$, and assuming y^2 negligible, we obtain, assuming for the moment that spherical aberration is corrected ($N_3 = N_{33} = 0$),

$$- N_o x_o' = (N_2 + N_{23} e_3)\, x_P' y_P' y$$
$$- (N_o y_o' + M_o y) = (M_3 e_3 + \tfrac{1}{2} M_{33} e_3^2 + N_2 y_P'^2 + N_{23} e_3 y_P'^2)\, y. \quad (27.62)$$

Equations (27.62) give again a series of eccentric circles for the rays going through a series of concentric circles in the finite exit pupil (e_3 = const.). The equation of the circles is

$$\frac{N_o^2 x_o'^2}{e_3^2 y^2 (N_2 + N_{23} e_3)^2} + \frac{[N_o y_o' + M_o y + (M_3 + N_2)\, e_3 + \frac{1}{2} e_3^2 (M_{33} + 2N_{23})]^2}{e_3^2 y^2 (N_2 + N_{23} e_3)^2} = 1, \quad (27.63)$$

in which we can write from (27.57) $N_2 = M_3$, and, since $N_3 = 0$,

$$N_{23} = M_{33} + 2E_3^2 M_3 / n'^2.$$

In case spherical aberration is uncorrected, Equation (26.61) shows that, only if $M_3 = M_{33} = 0$, is the image of a near-axis point symmetrical, that is, to a series of concentric circles in the aperture plane corresponds a series of concentric circles in the image plane. We see that in this case the system is corrected for coma.

In the case of a finite exit pupil, coma is not identical with the fulfillment of the sine condition but is determined by it and the spherical aberration curve. For the aperture rays ($x = y = e_1 = e_2 = 0$) we have from (27.48),

$$-\xi = \bar{E}_2 x_P' \qquad \xi' = \bar{E}_3 x_P'$$
$$-\eta = \bar{E}_2 y_P' \qquad \eta' = \bar{E}_3 y_P', \tag{27.64}$$

and from (27.51),

$$\frac{n \sin \sigma}{n' \sin \sigma'} = \frac{\xi}{\xi'} = \frac{\eta}{\eta'} = -\left[\frac{M_o}{N_o} + \frac{M_3 N_o - N_3 M_o}{N_o^2} e_3 + \tfrac{1}{2} e_3^2 \frac{(M_{33} N_o - N_{33} M_o) N_o + 2N_3 (N_3 M_o - M_3 N_o)}{N_o^3}\right]. \tag{27.65}$$

We find from (27.54),

$$-\frac{M_o z_D'}{n'} = \frac{M_o}{N_o} - \frac{M_o N_3}{N_o^2} e_3 - \tfrac{1}{2} \frac{M_o (N_{33} N_o - 2N_3^2)}{N_o^3} e_3^2. \tag{27.66}$$

Combining the last two equations, we obtain

$$\frac{n \sin \sigma}{n' \sin \sigma'} - \frac{M_o z_D'}{n'} = -\frac{M_3}{N_o} e_3 - \tfrac{1}{2} e_3^2 \frac{1}{N_o^2} \left[M_{33} - 2 \frac{N_3}{N_o} M_3\right]. \tag{27.67}$$

Equation (27.67) is the Staeble-Lihotzky condition stating that the coma error is corrected in an optical system if the spherical aberration and sine condition are proportional to each other.

We now discuss the errors arranged in groups corresponding to powers of the aperture. We have first:

(*c*) *Distortion*

The principal rays ($x_P' = y_P' = e_2 = e_3 = 0$) intersect the Gaussian plane in the points given by

$$- N_o x_o' = (M_o + M_1 e_1 + \tfrac{1}{2} M_{11} e_1^2)\, x = \tilde{M} x$$
$$- N_o y_o' = (M_o + M_1 e_1 + \tfrac{1}{2} M_{11} e_1^2)\, y = \tilde{M} y. \quad (27.68)$$

The values M_1 and M_{11} therefore give a measure for the distortion, M_1 being the Seidel error and M_{11} its field coefficient.

The first-order terms lead to the error group entitled

(*d*) *Astigmatism*

Considering a small aperture (neglecting second-order terms in x_P' and y_P') we find

$$- N_o x_o' - \tilde{M} x = (M_2 + M_{12} e_1) e_2 x + (N_1 e_1 + \tfrac{1}{2} N_{11} e_1^2)\, x_P'$$
$$- N_o y_o' - \tilde{M} y = (M_2 + M_{12} e_1)\, e_2 y + (N_1 e_1 + \tfrac{1}{2} N_{11} e_1^2)\, y_P'. \quad (27.69)$$

Taking the object point in the meridional plane ($x = 0$, $e_1 = \frac{1}{2} y^2$, $e_2 = y y_P'$) we find, therefore,

$$- N_o x_o' = (N_1 e_1 + \tfrac{1}{2} N_{11} e_1^2)\, x_P' \quad (27.70)$$
$$- N_o y_o' - \tilde{M} y = [(N_1 + 2M_2)\, e_1 + \tfrac{1}{2} (N_{11} + 4M_{12})\, e_1^2]\, y_P'.$$

This shows that the rays go through ellipses whose axes are proportional to

$$N_1 e_1 + \tfrac{1}{2} N_{11} e_1^2 \qquad \text{sagittal astigmatism}$$

and $$(N_1 + 2M_2)\, e_1 + \tfrac{1}{2}(N_{11} + 4M_{12})\, e_1^2 \qquad \text{meridional astigmatism,} \quad (27.71)$$

respectively. The reader should keep in mind, however, that, because of (27.54), the above values are proportional to the reciprocal distances of the image planes from the Gaussian focus. The second-order errors with respect to aperture, considered by themselves, lead to the

(*e*) *Asymmetry Errors*

We find for the asymmetry errors of a point in the meridional plane

$$- N_o x_o' = (N_2 + N_{12} e_1)\, x_P' y_P' y$$
$$- N_o y_o' - \tilde{M} y = (N_2 + N_{12} e_1)\, y_P'^2 y$$
$$+ (M_3 e_3 + M_{13} e_1 e_3 + \tfrac{1}{2} M_{22} e_2^2)\, y. \quad (27.72)$$

The rays go through a series of eccentric ellipses given by

$$\frac{N_o{}^2 x_o{}'^2}{(N_2 + N_{12}e_1)^2 y^2 e_3{}^2} + \frac{\{N_o' y_o' + \tilde{M}y + [M_3 + N_2 + (M_{13} + M_{22} + N_{12})e_1]\, e_3 y\}^2}{[N_2 + (N_{12} + M_{22})\, e_1]^2 y^2 e_3{}^2} = 1. \tag{27.73}$$

The third-order errors, again considered by themselves, consist of the

(*f*) *Gullstrand Errors*

We find for the figure formed by the Gullstrand errors in the image plane

$$\begin{aligned} -N_o x_o' &= (N_3 e_3 + N_{13} e_1 e_3 + \tfrac{1}{2} N_{22} e_2{}^2)\, x_P' \\ -N_o y_o' - \tilde{M}y &= (N_3 e_3 + N_{13} e_1 e_3 + \tfrac{1}{2} N_{22} e_2{}^2)\, y_P' + M_{23} e_2 e_3 y, \end{aligned} \tag{27.74}$$

or, inserting $e_1 = \frac{1}{2}\, y^2$, $e_2 = yy_p'$, $e_3 = \frac{1}{2}\,(x_p'^2 + y_p'^2)$,

$$\begin{aligned} -N_o x_o' &= \tfrac{1}{2}\, x_P' \{ (N_3 + N_{13} e_1)\, x_P'^2 \\ +[N_3 &\quad + (N_{13} + 2N_{22})\, e_1]\, y_P'^2\} \\ -N_o y_o' - \tilde{M}y &= \tfrac{1}{2}\, y_P' \{[N_3 + (N_{13} + 2M_{23})\, e_1]\, x_P'^2 \\ &\quad + [N_3 + (N_{13} + 2N_{22} + 2M_{23})\, e_1]\, y_P'^2\}, \end{aligned} \tag{27.75}$$

with

$$M_{23} = N_{22} + (1/n'^2)\,(E_2{}^2 N_3 - E_3{}^2 M_2) \tag{27.76}$$

in accordance with the investigation in Chapter 24.

CHAPTER TWENTY-EIGHT

Dependence of Image Errors on Object and Stop Position

In Chapter 27 we defined the image errors for a fixed (finite or infinite) object and a fixed (finite or infinite) stop. In this chapter we shall investigate the image errors as functions of the stop position. We have Equations (27.50) of the direction cosines ξ', η', ζ' given by

$$\begin{aligned} n'\xi'/\zeta' &= Mx + Nx_P' \\ n'\eta'/\zeta' &= My + Ny_P', \end{aligned} \tag{28.1}$$

while the coordinates of the intersection with the Gaussian plane are given by (27.53) as

$$\begin{aligned} -N_o x_o' &= Mx + (N - N_o)\, x_P' \\ -N_o y_o' &= My + (N - N_o)\, y_P', \end{aligned} \tag{28.2}$$

where $-n'/N_o = z_F'$ is the distance between the exit pupil and the image plane.

Let us now shift the exit pupil a distance k'. We then have for the intersection coordinates $\tilde{x}_P', \tilde{y}_P'$ at the new exit pupil

$$\begin{aligned} \tilde{x}_P' &= x_P' + \frac{k'}{n'} n'\xi'/\zeta' = M\frac{k'}{n'}x + \left(1 + N\frac{k'}{n'}\right) x_P' \\ \tilde{y}_P' &= y_P' + \frac{k'}{n'} n'\eta'/\zeta' = M\frac{k'}{n'}y + \left(1 + N\frac{k'}{n'}\right) y_P'. \end{aligned} \tag{28.3}$$

Inserting (28.3) into the relations

$$\begin{aligned} n'\xi'/\zeta' &= \tilde{M}x + \tilde{N}\tilde{x}_P = Mx + Nx_P' \\ n'\eta'/\zeta' &= \tilde{M}y + \tilde{N}\tilde{y}_P' = My + Ny_P' \end{aligned} \tag{28.4}$$

leads to the simple transforming equations

$$\tilde{M} = \frac{M}{1 + (Nk'/n')}, \quad \tilde{N} = \frac{N}{1 + (Nk'/n')}. \tag{28.5}$$

However, in these equations the right-hand sides are functions of x, y and x_P', y_P', or of their symmetric functions e_1, e_2, e_3, whereas we want the left-hand sides as functions of $\tilde{e}_1, \tilde{e}_2, \tilde{e}_3$ given by

$$\begin{aligned} \tilde{e}_1 &= \tfrac{1}{2}(x^2 + y^2) = e_1 \\ \tilde{e}_2 &= x\tilde{x}_P' + y\tilde{y}_P' = 2M\frac{k'}{n'}e_1 + \left(1 + N\frac{k'}{n'}\right)e_2 \\ \tilde{e}_3 &= \tfrac{1}{2}(\tilde{x}_p'^2 + \tilde{y}_P'^2) = \left(M\frac{k'}{n'}\right)^2 e_1 + M\frac{k'}{n'}\left(1 + N\frac{k'}{n'}\right)e_2 \\ &\quad + \left(1 + N\frac{k'}{n'}\right)^2 e_3. \end{aligned} \tag{28.6}$$

If we develop M and N and abbreviate with

$$\alpha = \frac{1}{1 + (k'/n')\,N_o}, \quad \beta = \frac{(k'/n')\,M_o}{1 + (k'/n')N_o}, \tag{28.7}$$

we obtain

	$\tilde{e}_1$	$\tilde{e}_2$	$\tilde{e}_3$
e_1	1	$2\beta/\alpha$	β^2/α^2
e_2		$1/\alpha$	β/α^2
e_3			$1/\alpha^2$
$\frac{1}{2}e_1^2$		$\frac{k'}{n'}(4M_1)$	$4\frac{k'}{n'}(\beta/\alpha)M_1$
e_1e_2		$\frac{k'}{n'}(2M_2 + N_1)$	$\frac{k'}{n'}(\beta/\alpha)(2M_2 + N_1) + \frac{k'}{n'\alpha}M_1$
e_1e_3		$2\frac{k'}{n'}M_3$	$2\frac{k'}{n'}(\beta/\alpha)M_3 + 2\frac{k'}{n'\alpha}N_1$
$\frac{1}{2}e_2^2$		$2\frac{k'}{n'}N_2$	$2\frac{k'}{n'}(\beta/\alpha)N_2 + 2\frac{k'}{n'\alpha}M_2$
e_2e_3		$\frac{k'}{n'}N_3$	$\frac{k'}{n'}(\beta/\alpha)N_3 + \frac{k'}{n'\alpha}(M_3 + 2N_2)$
$\frac{1}{2}e_3^2$			$\frac{4k'}{n'\alpha}N_3$ (28.8)

Equation (28.5) gives us $\tilde{M}$ and $\tilde{N}$ as function of the e_i, that is,

	$\tilde{M}$	$\tilde{N}$
1	aM_o	aN_o
e_1	$a(M_1-\beta N_1)$	a^2N_1
e_2	$a(M_2-\beta N_2)$	a^2N_2
e_3	$a(M_3-\beta N_3)$	a^2N_3
$\frac{1}{2}e_1^2$	$a(M_{11}-\beta N_{11})-2\frac{k'}{n'}a^2N_1(M_1-\beta N_1)$	$a^2\left(N_{11}-2\frac{k'}{n'}aN_1^2\right)$
e_1e_2	$a(M_{12}-\beta N_{12})-\frac{k'}{n'}a^2N_1(M_2-\beta N_2)$ $-\frac{k'}{n'}a^2N_2(M_1-\beta N_1)$	$a^2\left(N_{12}-2\frac{k'}{n'}aN_1N_2\right)$
e_1e_3	$a(M_{13}-\beta N_{13})-\frac{k'}{n'}a^2N_1(M_3-\beta N_3)$ $-\frac{k'}{n'}a^2N_3(M_1-\beta N_1)$	$a^2\left(N_{13}-2\frac{k'}{n'}aN_1N_3\right)$
$\frac{1}{2}e_2^2$	$a(M_{22}-\beta N_{22})-2\frac{k'}{n'}a^2N_2(M_2-\beta N_2)$	$a^2\left(N_{22}-2\frac{k'}{n'}aN_2^2\right)$
e_2e_3	$a(M_{23}-\beta N_{23})-\frac{k'}{n'}a^2N_2(M_3-\beta N_3)$ $-\frac{k'}{n'}a^2N_3(M_2-\beta N_2)$	$a^2\left(N_{23}-2\frac{k'}{n}aN_2N_3\right)$
$\frac{1}{2}e_3^2$	$a(M_{33}-\beta N_{33})-2\frac{k'}{n'}a^2N_3(M_3-\beta N_3)$	$a^2\left(N_{33}-2\frac{k'}{n'}aN_3^2\right)$.

(28.9)

If we convert (28.9) to the coordinates given by (28.8), we finally find for the image errors with shifted pupil:

$$\tilde{M}_o = aM_o = M_o - \beta N_0, \quad \tilde{N}_0 = aN_o$$
$$\tilde{N}_1 = a^2(N_1 - 2\beta N_2 + \beta^2 N_3)$$
$$\tilde{N}_2 = a^3(N_2 - \beta N_3)$$
$$\tilde{N}_3 = a^4 N_3$$
$$\tilde{M}_1 = a[M_1 - \beta(2M_2 + N_1) + \beta^2(2N_2 + M_3) - \beta^3 N_3]$$

$$\tilde{M}_2 = \alpha^2 [M_2 - \beta (N_2 + M_3) + \beta^2 N_3] \tag{28.10}$$
$$\tilde{M}_3 = \alpha^3 [M_3 - \beta N_3],$$

and for the fifth-order errors

$$\alpha \tilde{N}_{11} = \alpha^3 [N_{11} - 4\beta N_{12} + 2\beta^2 (N_{13} + 2N_{22}) - 4\beta^3 N_{23} + \beta^4 N_{33}] - 2 \frac{k'}{n'} (\tilde{N}_1{}^2 + 2\tilde{N}_2 \tilde{M}_1)$$

$$\alpha \tilde{N}_{12} = \alpha^4 [N_{12} - \beta (N_{13} + 2N_{22}) + 3\beta^2 N_{23} - \beta^3 N_{33}] - \frac{k'}{n'} (3\tilde{N}_1 \tilde{N}_2 + 2\tilde{N}_2 \tilde{M}_2 + \tilde{N}_3 \tilde{M}_1)$$

$$\alpha \tilde{N}_{13} = \alpha^5 [N_{13} - 2\beta N_{23} + \beta^2 N_{33}] - \frac{k'}{n'} (4\tilde{N}_3 \tilde{N}_1 + 2\tilde{N}_2 \tilde{M}_3)$$

$$\alpha \tilde{N}_{22} = \alpha^5 [N_{22} - 2\beta N_{23} + \beta^2 N_{33}] - \frac{k'}{n'} (2\tilde{N}_3 \tilde{M}_2 + 4\tilde{N}_2{}^2)$$

$$\alpha \tilde{N}_{23} = \alpha^6 [N_{23} - \beta N_{33}] - 6 \frac{k'}{n'} \tilde{N}_3 \tilde{M}_3$$

$$\alpha \tilde{N}_{33} = \alpha^7 N_{33} - 6 \frac{k'}{n'} \tilde{N}_3{}^2 \tag{28.11}$$

and analogously

$$\alpha \tilde{M}_{11} = \alpha^2 [M_{11} - \beta (4M_{12} + N_{11}) + 2\beta^2 (2N_{12} + M_{13} + 2M_{22}) - 2\beta^3 (N_{13} + 2N_{22} + 2M_{23}) + \beta^4 (4N_{23} + M_{33}) - \beta^5 N_{33}] - 2 \frac{k'}{n'} \tilde{M}_1 (\tilde{N}_1 + 2\tilde{M}_2)$$

$$\alpha \tilde{M}_{12} = \alpha^3 [M_{12} - \beta (3M_{13} + N_{12}) + \beta^2 (3N_{13} + 3M_{23}) - \beta (3N_{23} + M_{33}) + \beta^4 N_{33}] - \frac{k'}{n'} [2\tilde{M}_3 \tilde{M}_1 + 2\tilde{M}_2 (\tilde{M}_2 + \tilde{N}_1)]$$

$$\alpha \tilde{M}_{13} = \alpha^4 [M_{13} - \beta (N_{13} + 2M_{23}) + \beta^2 (2N_{23} + M_{33}) - \beta_3 N_{33}] - \frac{k'}{n'} [3\tilde{M}_3 \tilde{N}_1 + \tilde{N}_3 \tilde{M}_1 + 2\tilde{M}_2 \tilde{M}_3]$$

$$a\tilde{M}_{22} = \alpha^4 [M_{22} - \beta (N_{22} + 2M_{23}) + \beta^2 (M_{33} + 2N_{23}) - \beta^3 N_{33}] - \frac{k'}{n'} [6\tilde{N}_2 \tilde{M}_2]$$

$$a\tilde{M}_{23} = \alpha^5 [M_{23} - \beta (N_{23} + M_{33}) + \beta^2 N_{33}] - 2\frac{k'}{n'} [\tilde{N}_3 \tilde{M}_2 + 2\tilde{N}_2 \tilde{M}_3]$$

$$a\tilde{M}_{33} = \alpha^6 [M_{33} - \beta N_{33}] - 6\frac{k'}{n'} \tilde{N}_3 \tilde{M}_3. \qquad (28.12)$$

These equations suggest dividing the image errors into groups signifying their dependence on the field rather than on the aperture. Ordering the basic equations as functions of the field, that is, as functions of x and y, we find from (27.53), again assuming the object point to lie in the meridional plane ($x = 0$, $e_1 = \frac{1}{2}y^2$, $e_2 = yy_P'$, $2e_3 = x_P'^2 + y_P'^2$), that

$$x_o' = (1 - N/N_o)\, x_P'$$
$$y_o' = (1 - N/N_o)\, y_P' - (M/N_o)\, y. \qquad (28.13)$$

We find that, with respect to field, we can order these errors in the same way as we previously did with respect to aperture. We find as errors of zero order with respect to field (spherical aberration) N_3, N_{33}, as first-order errors (coma) N_2, N_{23}, M_{33}, and as second-order errors (astigmatism) N_1, M_2, N_{13}, N_{22}, M_{23}, etc.

A system in which the axis point is corrected is said to be free from spherical aberration. We shall call a system in which the first two groups (spherical aberration and coma) are corrected an *aplanatic* system.

A system in which the second-order errors are corrected will also be called a near-field-plane system, etc.

Equations (28.10) to (28.12) show that a system which is corrected "spherical-aplanatic" or "near-field-plane" has this correction independent of the position of the stop, although the single errors depend on the stop position.

Equations (28.10) to (28.12) show, furthermore, how Equations (27.57) depend on the stop position. We obtain

$$\begin{aligned}
\tilde{N}_2 - \tilde{M}_3 &= 0 \\
\tilde{N}_{12} - \tilde{M}_{13} &= \alpha^3 [N_{12} - M_{13} - 2\beta (N_{22} - M_{23}) + \beta^2 (N_{23} - M_{33})] \\
\tilde{N}_{22} - \tilde{M}_{23} &= \alpha^4 [N_{22} - M_{23} - \beta (N_{23} - M_{33})] \\
\tilde{N}_{23} - \tilde{M}_{33} &= \alpha^5 [N_{23} - M_{33}].
\end{aligned} \tag{28.14}$$

CHAPTER TWENTY-NINE

Dependence of Image Errors on Object Position and Object Curvature

Up to now we have considered only the image of the points of a fixed object plane. In this chapter, we shall investigate the changes of M and N if we replace the object plane (*a*) by a different object plane or (*b*) by a curved object surface. To do so we must investigate, besides the functions M and N given by Equations (28.1), the new functions K and Λ given by

$$-n\,\Xi = -n\xi/\zeta = Kx + \Lambda x'_P$$
$$-n\,H = -n\eta/\zeta = Ky + \Lambda y_P' \qquad (29.1)$$

where, analogously to (27.51),

$$K = \bar{E}_1/\sqrt{1 - (2/n^2)(\bar{E}_1{}^2 e_1 + \bar{E}_1\bar{E}_2 e_2 + \bar{E}_2{}^2 e_3)} \qquad (29.2)$$
$$\Lambda = \bar{E}_2/\sqrt{1 - (2/n^2)(\bar{E}_1{}^2 e_1 + \bar{E}_1\bar{E}_2 e_2 + \bar{E}_2{}^2 e_3)}.$$

Developing Equations (29.2) as functions of the e_i, we find

$$\begin{aligned}
K_o &= E_1 & \Lambda_o &= E_2 \\
K_1 &= E_{11} + (1/n^2)\,E_1{}^3 & \Lambda_1 &= E_{12} + (1/n^2)\,E_1{}^2E_2 \\
K_2 &= E_{12} + (1/n^2)\,E_1{}^2E_2 & \Lambda_2 &= E_{22} + (1/n^2)\,E_1E_2{}^2 \qquad (29.3)\\
K_3 &= E_{13} + (1/n^2)\,E_1E_2{}^2 & \Lambda_3 &= E_{23} + (1/n^2)\,E_2{}^3
\end{aligned}$$

and

$$K_{11} = E_{111} + \frac{3}{n^4}E_1{}^5 + \frac{1}{n^2}(6E_1{}^2E_{11})$$

$$K_{12} = E_{112} + \frac{3}{n^4}E_1{}^4E_2 + \frac{1}{n^2}(4E_1{}^2E_{12} + 2E_1E_2E_{11})$$

$$K_{13} = E_{113} + \frac{3}{n^4}E_1{}^3E_2{}^2 + \frac{1}{n^2}(3E_1{}^2E_{13} + 2E_1E_2E_{12} + E_2{}^2E_{11})$$

$$K_{22} = E_{122} + \frac{3}{n^4} E_1{}^3 E_2{}^2 + \frac{1}{n^2} (2E_1{}^2 E_{22} + 4E_1 E_2 E_{12})$$

$$K_{23} = E_{123} + \frac{3}{n^4} E_1{}^2 E_2{}^3 + \frac{1}{n^2} (E_1{}^2 E_{23} + 2E_1 E_2 (E_{13} + E_{22}) + E_2{}^2 E_{12})$$

$$K_{33} = E_{133} + \frac{3}{n^4} E_1 E_2{}^4 + \frac{1}{n^2} (4E_1 E_2 E_{23} + 2E_2{}^2 E_{13})$$

$$\Lambda_{11} = E_{112} + \frac{3}{n^4} E_1{}^4 E_2 + \frac{1}{n^2} (2E_1{}^2 E_{12} + 4E_1 E_2 E_{11})$$

$$\Lambda_{12} = E_{122} + \frac{3}{n^4} E_1{}^3 E_2{}^2 + \frac{1}{n^2} (E_1{}^2 E_{22} + 4E_1 E_2 E_{12} + E_2{}^2 E_{11})$$

$$\Lambda_{13} = E_{123} + \frac{3}{n^4} E_1{}^2 E_2{}^3 + \frac{1}{n^2} (E_1{}^2 E_{23} + 2E_1 E_2 E_{13} + 3E_2{}^2 E_{12})$$

$$\Lambda_{22} = E_{222} + \frac{3}{n^4} E_1{}^2 E_2{}^3 + \frac{1}{n^2} (4E_1 E_2 E_{22} + 2E_2{}^2 E_{12})$$

$$\Lambda_{23} = E_{223} + \frac{3}{n^4} E_1 E_2{}^4 + \frac{1}{n^2} [2E_1 E_2 E_{23} + E_2{}^2 (3E_{22} + E_{13})]$$

$$\Lambda_{33} = E_{233} + \frac{3}{n^4} E_2{}^5 + \frac{1}{n^2} (6E_2{}^2 E_{23}). \qquad (29.4)$$

From Equations (29.3) and (29.4) we find the interrelations

$$\begin{aligned} \Lambda_1 - K_2 &= 0 \\ \Lambda_{11} - K_{12} &= (2/n^2)\, E_1 (E_2 E_{11} - E_1 E_{12}) \\ \Lambda_{12} - K_{22} &= (1/n^2)\, (E_2{}^2 E_{11} - E_1{}^2 E_{22}) \\ \Lambda_{13} - K_{23} &= (2/n^2)\, (E_2{}^2 E_{12} - E_1 E_2 E_{22}). \end{aligned} \qquad (29.5)$$

Comparison with Equations (27.55) and (27.56) permits us to consider the K_i and Λ_i as the image-error functions for an object situated at the exit pupil and projected backwards through the system into the object space. Some of the K_i and Λ_i can be computed from the M_i and N_i. If we introduce as abbreviations

$$\mu_1 = \frac{1}{n'^2} M_o^3 - \frac{1}{n^2} K_o^2 M_o \qquad \sigma_1 = 3\left(\frac{M_o^5}{n'^4} - \frac{K_o^4 M_o}{n^4}\right)$$

$$\mu_2 = \frac{1}{n'^2} M_o^2 N_o - \frac{1}{n^2} K_o M_o^2 \qquad \sigma_2 = 3\left(\frac{M_o^4 N_o}{n'^4} - \frac{K_o^3 M_o^2}{n^4}\right)$$

$$\mu_3 = \frac{1}{n'^2} M_o N_o^2 - \frac{1}{n^2} M_o^3 \qquad \sigma_3 = 3\left(\frac{M_o^3 N_o^2}{n'^4} - \frac{K_o^2 M_o^3}{n^4}\right)$$

$$\sigma_4 = 3\left(\frac{M_o^2 N_o^3}{n'^4} - \frac{K_o M_o^4}{n^4}\right)$$

$$\sigma_5 = 3\left(\frac{M_o N_o^4}{n'^4} - \frac{M_o^5}{n^4}\right), \qquad (29.6)$$

we find [by comparing Equations (29.3) and (29.4) with (27.55) and (27.56)]

$$\begin{aligned} K_2 &= M_1 - \mu_1 = \Lambda_1 \\ K_3 &= N_1 - \mu_2, \quad \Lambda_2 = M_2 - \mu_2 \\ &\qquad\qquad \Lambda_3 = M_3 - \mu_3 = N_2 - \mu_3 \end{aligned} \qquad (29.7)$$

and

$$K_{12} = M_{11} + \sigma_1 + \frac{1}{n^2}[4K_o^2 K_2 + 2K_o\Lambda_o K_1] - \frac{6}{n'^2} M_o^2 M_1$$

$$K_{13} = N_{11} + \sigma_2 + \frac{1}{n^2}[3K_o^2 K_3 + 2K_o\Lambda_o K_2 + M_o^2 K_1] - \frac{1}{n'^2}[2M_o^2 N_1 + 4M_o N_o M_1]$$

$$K_{22} = M_{12} + \sigma_2 + \frac{1}{n^2}[2K_o^2\Lambda_2 + 4K_o\Lambda_o K_2] - \frac{1}{n'^2}[M_o^2(N_1 + 3M_2) + 2M_o N_o M_1]$$

$$K_{23} = M_{13} + \sigma_3 + \frac{1}{n^2}[K_o^2\Lambda_3 + 2K_o\Lambda_o(K_3 + \Lambda_2) + \Lambda_o^2 K_2] - \frac{1}{n'^2}[3M_o^2 M_3 + 2M_o N_o N_1 + N_o^2 M_1]$$

$$K_{33} = N_{13} + \sigma_4 + \frac{2}{n^2} [2K_o \Lambda_o \Lambda_3 + \Lambda_o{}^2 K_3]$$

$$- \frac{1}{n'^2} [M_o{}^2 N_3 + 2M_o N_o N_2 + 3 N_o{}^2 N_1] \qquad (29.8)$$

$$\Lambda_{11} = M_{11} + \sigma_1 + \frac{1}{n^2} [2K_o{}^2 K_2 + 4K_o \Lambda_o K_1] - \frac{6}{n'^2} M_o{}^2 M_1$$

$$\Lambda_{12} = M_{12} + \sigma_2 + \frac{1}{n^2} [\Lambda_o{}^2 K_1 + 4K_o \Lambda_o K_2 + K_o{}^2 \Lambda_2]$$

$$- \frac{1}{n'^2} [M_o{}^2 (N_1 + 3M_2) + 2M_o N_o M_1]$$

$$\Lambda_{13} = M_{13} + \sigma_3 + \frac{1}{n^2} [3\Lambda_o{}^2 K_2 + 2K_o \Lambda_o K_3 + K_o{}^2 \Lambda_3]$$

$$- \frac{1}{n'^2} [3M_o{}^2 M_3 + 2M_o N_o N_1 + N_o{}^2 M_1]$$

$$\Lambda_{22} = M_{22} + \sigma_3 + \frac{2}{n^2} [\Lambda_o{}^2 K_2 + 2K_o \Lambda_o \Lambda_2]$$

$$- \frac{2}{n'^2} [M_o{}^2 M_3 + 2M_o N_o M_2]$$

$$\Lambda_{23} = M_{23} + \sigma_4 + \frac{1}{n^2} [\Lambda_o{}^2 (K_3 + 3\Lambda_2) + 2K_o \Lambda_o \Lambda_3]$$

$$- \frac{1}{n'^2} [M_o{}^2 N_3 + 4M_o N_o M_3 + N_o{}^2 M_2]$$

$$\Lambda_{33} = M_{33} + \sigma_5 + \frac{6}{n^2} \Lambda_o{}^2 \Lambda_3 - \frac{1}{n'^2} (4M_o N_o N_3 + 2N_o{}^2 M_3),$$

showing the connection between the development coefficients of the functions K, Λ, M, and N.

In the last chapter we investigated the changes arising in the image-error coefficients when the image origin (the stop) is shifted. The equations obtained there will now be rewritten with the use of matrix algebra. We find, instead of (28.10), the two matrix equations

$$\begin{pmatrix} \frac{1}{\alpha^2}\tilde{N}_1 \\ \frac{1}{\alpha^3}\tilde{N}_2 \\ \frac{1}{\alpha^4}\tilde{N}_3 \end{pmatrix} = \begin{pmatrix} 1 & -2\beta & \beta^2 \\ 0 & 1 & -\beta \\ 0 & 0 & 1 \end{pmatrix} \begin{pmatrix} N_1 \\ N_2 \\ N_3 \end{pmatrix}, \begin{pmatrix} \frac{1}{\alpha}\tilde{M}_1 \\ \frac{1}{\alpha^2}\tilde{M}_2 \\ \frac{1}{\alpha^3}\tilde{M}_3 \end{pmatrix} = \begin{pmatrix} 1 & -2\beta & \beta^2 \\ 0 & 1 & -\beta \\ 0 & 0 & 1 \end{pmatrix} \begin{pmatrix} M_1 - \beta N_1 \\ M_2 - \beta N_2 \\ M_3 - \beta N_3 \end{pmatrix}$$

with $\tilde{N}_o = \alpha N_o$, $\tilde{M}_o = \alpha M_o$, (29.9)

and analogously for Equations (28.11) and (28.12)

$$\begin{pmatrix} \frac{1}{\alpha^2}\left[\tilde{N}_{11} + \frac{2k'}{n'\alpha}(\tilde{N}_1{}^2 + 2\tilde{M}_1\tilde{N}_2)\right] \\ \frac{1}{\alpha^3}\left[\tilde{N}_{12} + \frac{k'}{n'\alpha}(2\tilde{N}_1\tilde{N}_2 + (2\tilde{M}_2 + \tilde{N}_1)\tilde{N}_2 + \tilde{M}_1\tilde{N}_3)\right] \\ \frac{1}{\alpha^4}\left[\tilde{N}_{13} + \frac{2k'}{n'\alpha}(\tilde{N}_1\tilde{N}_3 + \tilde{N}_1\tilde{N}_3 + \tilde{M}_3\tilde{N}_2)\right] \\ \frac{1}{\alpha^4}\left[\tilde{N}_{22} + \frac{2k'}{n'\alpha}(\tilde{N}_2{}^2 + \tilde{N}_2{}^2 + \tilde{M}_2\tilde{N}_3)\right] \\ \frac{1}{\alpha^5}\left[\tilde{N}_{23} + \frac{k'}{n'\alpha}(2\tilde{N}_2\tilde{N}_3 + \tilde{N}_3\tilde{N}_2 + (2\tilde{N}_2 + \tilde{M}_3)\tilde{N}_3)\right] \\ \frac{1}{\alpha^6}\left[\tilde{N}_{33} + \frac{2k'}{n'\alpha}(\tilde{N}_3{}^2 + 2\tilde{N}_3{}^2)\right] \end{pmatrix} = B_5 \begin{pmatrix} N_{11} \\ N_{12} \\ N_{13} \\ N_{22} \\ N_{23} \\ N_{33} \end{pmatrix}$$

(29.10)

$$\begin{pmatrix} \left[\tilde{M}_{11} + 2\dfrac{k'}{n'\alpha}(\tilde{N}_1\tilde{M}_1 + 2\tilde{M}_1\tilde{M}_2)\right] \\ \left[\tilde{M}_{12} + \dfrac{k'}{n'\alpha}(\tilde{M}_1\tilde{N}_2 + \tilde{N}_1\tilde{M}_2 + (2\tilde{M}_2 + \tilde{N}_1)\tilde{M}_2 + \tilde{M}_1\tilde{M}_3)\right] \\ \left[\tilde{M}_{13} + \dfrac{k'}{n'\alpha}(\tilde{M}_1\tilde{N}_3 + \tilde{M}_3\tilde{N}_1 + 2\tilde{N}_1\tilde{M}_3 + 2\tilde{M}_3\tilde{M}_2)\right] \\ \left[\tilde{M}_{22} + 2\dfrac{k'}{n'\alpha}(\tilde{N}_2\tilde{M}_2 + \tilde{N}_2\tilde{M}_2 + \tilde{M}_2\tilde{M}_3)\right] \\ \left[\tilde{M}_{23} + \dfrac{k'}{n'\alpha}(\tilde{M}_2\tilde{N}_3 + \tilde{M}_3\tilde{N}_2 + \tilde{N}_3\tilde{M}_2 + (2\tilde{N}_2 + \tilde{M}_3)\tilde{M}_3)\right] \\ \left[\tilde{M}_{33} + 2\dfrac{k'}{n'\alpha}(\tilde{N}_3\tilde{M}_3 + 2\tilde{N}_3\tilde{M}_3)\right] \end{pmatrix} = B_5 \begin{pmatrix} M_{11} - \beta N_{11} \\ M_{12} - \beta N_{12} \\ M_{13} - \beta N_{13} \\ M_{22} - \beta N_{22} \\ M_{23} - \beta N_{23} \\ M_{33} - \beta N_{33} \end{pmatrix}$$

(the left-hand sides have been arranged to show their structure as compared to the later equations of this chapter),

where

$$B_5 = \begin{pmatrix} 1 & -4\beta & 2\beta^2 & 4\beta^2 & -4\beta^3 & \beta^4 \\ 0 & 1 & -\beta & -2\beta & 3\beta^2 & -\beta^3 \\ 0 & 0 & 1 & 0 & -2\beta & \beta^2 \\ 0 & 0 & 0 & 1 & -2\beta & \beta^2 \\ 0 & 0 & 0 & 0 & 1 & -\beta \\ 0 & 0 & 0 & 0 & 0 & 1 \end{pmatrix}, \qquad (29.11)$$

and where k' is the shift of the exit pupil and α and β are abbreviations defined by

$$\alpha = \frac{1}{1 + (k'/n')N_o}, \quad \beta = \frac{(k'/n')\,M_o}{1 + (k'/n')\,N_o}. \qquad (29.12)$$

Investigating the changes of K and Λ with a shift of the exit pupil, we obtain from

$$-n\,\Xi = -n\xi/\zeta = Kx + \Lambda x_P{}' = \tilde{K}x + \tilde{\Lambda}\tilde{x}_P{}'$$
$$-n\,\mathrm{H} = -n\eta/\zeta = Ky + \Lambda y_P{}' = \tilde{K}y + \tilde{\Lambda}y_P{}'$$

with [*cf.* (28.3)]

$$\tilde{x}_P{}' = x_P{}' + k'\,\Xi' = x_P{}'\left(1 + \frac{k'}{n'}N\right) + \frac{k'}{n'}Mx$$

$$\tilde{y}_P{}' = y_P{}' + k'\,\mathrm{H}' = y_P{}'\left(1 + \frac{k'}{n'}N\right) + \frac{k'}{n'}My \qquad (29.13)$$

the identities

$$\tilde{K} = K - \frac{\Lambda\,(k'/n')\,M}{1 + (k'/n')\,N}, \quad \tilde{\Lambda} = \frac{\Lambda}{1 + (k'/n')\,N}. \qquad (29.14)$$

Carrying out the calculation in detail gives for the first- and third-order coefficients

$$\tilde{K}_o = K_o - \beta M_o, \quad \tilde{\Lambda}_o = \alpha M_o$$

$$\begin{bmatrix} \tilde{K}_1 \\ \frac{1}{\alpha}\tilde{K}_2 \\ \frac{1}{\alpha^2}\tilde{K}_3 \end{bmatrix} = \begin{bmatrix} 1 & -2\beta & \beta^2 \\ 0 & 1 & -\beta \\ 0 & 0 & 1 \end{bmatrix} \begin{bmatrix} K_1 - \beta(\Lambda_1 + M_1) + \beta^2 N_1 \\ K_2 - \beta(\Lambda_2 + M_2) + \beta^2 N_2 \\ K_3 - \beta(\Lambda_3 + M_3) + \beta^2 N_3 \end{bmatrix}$$

$$\begin{bmatrix} \frac{1}{\alpha}\tilde{\Lambda}_1 \\ \frac{1}{\alpha^2}\tilde{\Lambda}_2 \\ \frac{1}{\alpha^3}\tilde{\Lambda}_3 \end{bmatrix} = \begin{bmatrix} 1 & -2\beta & \beta^2 \\ 0 & 1 & -\beta \\ 0 & 0 & 1 \end{bmatrix} \begin{bmatrix} \Lambda_1 - \beta N_1 \\ \Lambda_2 - \beta N_2 \\ \Lambda_3 - \beta N_3 \end{bmatrix}, \qquad (29.15)$$

and for the fifth-order coefficients,

$$\left\{\begin{matrix} \left[\tilde{K}_{11} + \frac{2k'}{n'\alpha}(\tilde{M}_1\tilde{A}_1 + 2\tilde{M}_1\tilde{K}_2)\right] \\ \frac{1}{\alpha}\left[\tilde{K}_{12} + \frac{k'}{n'\alpha}(\tilde{M}_1\tilde{A}_2 + \tilde{M}_2\tilde{A}_1 + (2\tilde{M}_2 + \tilde{N}_1)\tilde{K}_2 + \tilde{M}_1\tilde{K}_3)\right] \\ \frac{1}{\alpha^2}\left[\tilde{K}_{13} + \frac{k'}{n'\alpha}(\tilde{M}_1\tilde{A}_3 + \tilde{M}_3\tilde{A}_1 + 2\tilde{N}_1\tilde{K}_3 + 2\tilde{M}_3\tilde{K}_2)\right] \\ \frac{1}{\alpha^2}\left[\tilde{K}_{22} + \frac{2k'}{n'\alpha}(\tilde{M}_2\tilde{A}_2 + \tilde{N}_2\tilde{K}_2 + \tilde{M}_2\tilde{K}_3)\right] \\ \frac{1}{\alpha^3}\left[\tilde{K}_{23} + \frac{k'}{n'\alpha}[\tilde{M}_2\tilde{A}_3 + \tilde{M}_3\tilde{A}_2 + \tilde{N}_3\tilde{K}_2 + (2\tilde{N}_2 + \tilde{M}_3)\tilde{K}_3]\right] \\ \frac{1}{\alpha^4}\left[\tilde{K}_{33} + \frac{2k'}{n'\alpha}(\tilde{M}_3\tilde{A}_3 + 2\tilde{N}_3\tilde{K}_3)\right] \end{matrix}\right\}$$

$$= B_5 \left\{\begin{matrix} K_{11} - \beta(A_{11} + M_{11}) + \beta^2 N_{11} \\ K_{12} - \beta(A_{12} + M_{12}) + \beta^2 N_{12} \\ K_{13} - \beta(A_{13} + M_{13}) + \beta^2 N_{13} \\ K_{22} - \beta(A_{22} + M_{22}) + \beta^2 N_{22} \\ K_{23} - \beta(A_{23} + M_{23}) + \beta^2 N_{23} \\ K_{33} - \beta(A_{33} + M_{33}) + \beta^2 N_{33} \end{matrix}\right\} \qquad (29.16)$$

$$\begin{bmatrix} \frac{1}{\alpha}\left[\tilde{A}_{11}+2\frac{k'}{n'\alpha}(\tilde{N}_1\tilde{A}_1+2\tilde{M}_1\tilde{A}_2)\right] \\ \frac{1}{\alpha^2}\left[\tilde{A}_{12}+\frac{k'}{n'\alpha}[\tilde{N}_1\tilde{A}_2+\tilde{N}_2\tilde{A}_1+(2\tilde{M}_2+\tilde{N}_1)\tilde{A}_2+\tilde{M}_1\tilde{A}_3]\right] \\ \frac{1}{\alpha^3}\left[\tilde{A}_{13}+\frac{k'}{n'\alpha}(\tilde{A}_1\tilde{N}_3+\tilde{A}_3\tilde{N}_1+2\tilde{N}_1\tilde{A}_3+2\tilde{M}_3\tilde{A}_2)\right] \\ \frac{1}{\alpha^3}\left[\tilde{A}_{22}+\frac{2k'}{n'\alpha}(\tilde{A}_2\tilde{N}_2+\tilde{N}_2\tilde{A}_2+\tilde{M}_2\tilde{A}_3)\right] \\ \frac{1}{\alpha^4}\left[\tilde{A}_{23}+\frac{k'}{n'\alpha}[\tilde{A}_2\tilde{N}_3+\tilde{A}_3\tilde{N}_2+\tilde{N}_3\tilde{A}_2+(2\tilde{N}_2+\tilde{M}_3)\tilde{A}_3]\right] \\ \frac{1}{\alpha^5}\left[\tilde{A}_{33}+\frac{2k'}{n'\alpha}(\tilde{A}_3\tilde{N}_3+2\tilde{A}_3\tilde{N}_3)\right] \end{bmatrix}$$

$$= B_5 \begin{bmatrix} A_{11}-\beta N_{11} \\ A_{12}-\beta N_{12} \\ A_{13}-\beta N_{13} \\ A_{22}-\beta N_{22} \\ A_{23}-\beta N_{23} \\ A_{33}-\beta N_{33} \end{bmatrix},$$

where B_5 is the transformation matrix given in (29.11), that is,

$$B_5 = \begin{bmatrix} 1 & -4\beta & 2\beta^2 & 4\beta^2 & -4\beta^3 & \beta^4 \\ 0 & 1 & -\beta & -2\beta & 3\beta^2 & -\beta^3 \\ 0 & 0 & 1 & 0 & -2\beta & \beta^2 \\ 0 & 0 & 0 & 1 & -2\beta & \beta^2 \\ 0 & 0 & 0 & 0 & 1 & -\beta \\ 0 & 0 & 0 & 0 & 0 & 1 \end{bmatrix}. \qquad (29.16a)$$

In a similar manner we can now treat the change of image errors if the object is shifted. The formulae can be obtained by inspection by interchanging the indices one and three and by interchanging K and N, Λ and M, n and n', and k and $-k'$. Using instead of α and β the abbreviations λ and δ given by

$$\lambda = \frac{1}{1-(k/n)\,K_o}, \quad \delta = \frac{-(k/n)\,\Lambda_o}{1-(k/n)\,K_o}, \tag{29.17}$$

where k is the shift of the object point, we find in first order

$$\begin{aligned} \bar{K}_o &= K_o\gamma \\ \bar{\Lambda}_o = \bar{M}_o &= \Lambda_o\gamma = M_o - K_o\delta \\ \bar{N}_o &= \qquad\qquad N_o - M_o\delta, \end{aligned} \tag{29.18}$$

for the third-order terms:

$$\begin{bmatrix} \frac{1}{\gamma^4}\bar{K}_1 \\ \frac{1}{\gamma_3}\bar{K}_2 \\ \frac{1}{\gamma^2}\bar{K}_3 \end{bmatrix} = D_3 \begin{bmatrix} K_1 \\ K_2 \\ K_3 \end{bmatrix}, \quad \begin{bmatrix} \frac{1}{\gamma_3}\bar{\Lambda}_1 \\ \frac{1}{\gamma^2}\bar{\Lambda}_2 \\ \frac{1}{\gamma}\bar{\Lambda}_3 \end{bmatrix} = D_3 \begin{bmatrix} \Lambda_1-\delta K_1 \\ \Lambda_2-\delta K_2 \\ \Lambda_3-\delta K_3 \end{bmatrix} \tag{29.19}$$

$$\begin{bmatrix} \frac{1}{\gamma_3}\bar{M}_1 \\ \frac{1}{\gamma^2}\bar{M}_2 \\ \frac{1}{\gamma}\bar{M}_3 \end{bmatrix} = D_3 \begin{bmatrix} M_1-\delta K_1 \\ M_2-\delta K_2 \\ M_3-\delta K_3 \end{bmatrix}, \quad \begin{bmatrix} \frac{1}{\gamma^2}\bar{N}_1 \\ \frac{1}{\gamma}\bar{N}_2 \\ \bar{N}_3 \end{bmatrix} = D_3 \begin{bmatrix} N_1-\delta(\Lambda_1+M_1)+\delta^2 K_1 \\ N_2-\delta(\Lambda_2+M_2)+\delta^2 K_2 \\ N_3-\delta(\Lambda_3+M_3)+\delta^2 K_3 \end{bmatrix},$$

with

$$D_3 = \begin{bmatrix} 1 & 0 & 0 \\ -\delta & 1 & 0 \\ \delta^2 & -2\delta & 1 \end{bmatrix}, \tag{29.19a}$$

and for the fifth order

$$\begin{Bmatrix} \frac{1}{\gamma^6}\left[\bar{K}_{11} - \frac{2k}{n\gamma}(\bar{K}_1{}^2 + 2\bar{K}_1{}^2)\right] \\ \frac{1}{\gamma^5}\left[\bar{K}_{12} - \frac{k}{n\gamma}[2\,\bar{K}_1\bar{K}_2 + \bar{K}_1\bar{K}_2 + (2\,\bar{K}_2 + \bar{\Lambda}_1)\,\bar{K}_1]\right] \\ \frac{1}{\gamma^4}\left[\bar{K}_{13} - \frac{k}{n\gamma}(2\,\bar{K}_1\bar{K}_3 + 2\,\bar{K}_1\bar{K}_3 + 2\,\bar{\Lambda}_1\bar{K}_2)\right] \\ \frac{1}{\gamma^4}\left[\bar{K}_{22} - \frac{2k}{n\gamma}(\bar{K}_2{}^2 + \bar{K}_2{}^2 + \bar{\Lambda}_2\bar{K}_1)\right] \\ \frac{1}{\gamma^3}\left[\bar{K}_{23} - \frac{k}{n\gamma}[2\,\bar{K}_3\bar{K}_2 + (2\,\bar{\Lambda}_2 + \bar{K}_3)\bar{K}_2 + \bar{\Lambda}_3\bar{K}_1]\right] \\ \frac{1}{\gamma^2}\left[\bar{K}_{33} - \frac{2k}{n\gamma}(\bar{K}_3{}^2 + 2\,\bar{\Lambda}_3\bar{K}_2)\right] \end{Bmatrix} = D_5 \begin{Bmatrix} K_{11} \\ K_{12} \\ K_{13} \\ K_{22} \\ K_{23} \\ K_{33} \end{Bmatrix} \tag{29.20}$$

$$\begin{Bmatrix} \frac{1}{\gamma^5}\left[\bar{\Lambda}_{11} - \frac{2k}{n\gamma}(\bar{\Lambda}_1\bar{K}_1 + 2\,\bar{\Lambda}_1\bar{K}_1)\right] \\ \frac{1}{\gamma^4}\left[\bar{\Lambda}_{12} - \frac{k}{n\gamma}[\bar{\Lambda}_2\bar{K}_1 + \bar{\Lambda}_1\bar{K}_2 + \bar{\Lambda}_2\bar{K}_1 + (2\bar{K}_2 + \bar{\Lambda}_1)\bar{\Lambda}_1]\right] \\ \frac{1}{\gamma^3}\left[\bar{\Lambda}_{13} - \frac{k}{n\gamma}(\bar{\Lambda}_1\bar{K}_3 + \bar{\Lambda}_3\bar{K}_1 + 2\,\bar{\Lambda}_1\bar{K}_3 + 2\,\bar{\Lambda}_1\bar{\Lambda}_2)\right] \\ \frac{1}{\gamma^3}\left[\bar{\Lambda}_{22} - \frac{2k}{n\gamma}(\bar{\Lambda}_2\bar{K}_2 + \hat{\Lambda}_2\bar{K}_2 + \bar{\Lambda}_2\bar{\Lambda}_1)\right] \\ \frac{1}{\gamma^2}\left[\bar{\Lambda}_{23} - \frac{k}{n\gamma}[\bar{\Lambda}_3\bar{K}_2 + \bar{\Lambda}_2\bar{K}_3 + (2\,\bar{\Lambda}_2 + \bar{K}_3)\,\bar{\Lambda}_2 + \bar{\Lambda}_1\bar{\Lambda}_3]\right] \\ \frac{1}{\gamma}\left[\Lambda_{33} - \frac{2k}{n\gamma}(\bar{\Lambda}_3\bar{K}_3 + 2\,\bar{\Lambda}_2\bar{\Lambda}_3)\right] \end{Bmatrix} = D_5 \begin{Bmatrix} \Lambda_{11} - \delta K_{11} \\ \Lambda_{12} - \delta K_{12} \\ \Lambda_{13} - \delta K_{13} \\ \Lambda_{22} - \delta K_{22} \\ \Lambda_{23} - \delta K_{23} \\ \Lambda_{33} - \delta K_{33} \end{Bmatrix}$$

and

$$\begin{pmatrix} \frac{1}{\gamma^5}\left[\bar{M}_{11} - \frac{2k}{n\gamma}(\bar{K}_1\bar{M}_1 + 2\bar{K}_1\bar{M}_1)\right] \\ \frac{1}{\gamma^4}\left[\bar{M}_{12} - \frac{k}{n\gamma}[\bar{K}_1\bar{M}_2 + \bar{K}_2\bar{M}_1 + \bar{K}_1\bar{M}_2 + (2\bar{K}_2 + \bar{\Lambda}_1)\bar{M}_1]\right] \\ \frac{1}{\gamma^3}\left[\bar{M}_{13} - \frac{k}{n\gamma}(\bar{K}_1\bar{M}_3 + \bar{K}_3\bar{M}_1 + 2\bar{K}_3\bar{M}_1 + 2\,\bar{\Lambda}_1\bar{M}_2)\right] \\ \frac{1}{\gamma^3}\left[\bar{M}_{22} - \frac{2k}{n\gamma}(\bar{K}_2\bar{M}_2 + \bar{K}_2\bar{M}_2 + \bar{\Lambda}_2\bar{M}_1)\right] \\ \frac{1}{\gamma^2}\left[\bar{M}_{23} - \frac{k}{n\gamma}[\bar{K}_3\bar{M}_2 + \bar{K}_2\bar{M}_3 + (2\,\bar{\Lambda}_2 + \bar{K}_3)\bar{M}_2 + \bar{\Lambda}_3\bar{M}_1]\right] \\ \frac{1}{\gamma}\left[\bar{M}_{33} - \frac{2k}{n\gamma}(\bar{K}_3\bar{M}_3 + 2\,\bar{\Lambda}_3\bar{M}_2)\right] \end{pmatrix}$$

$$= D_5 \begin{pmatrix} M_{11} - \delta K_{11} \\ M_{12} - \delta K_{12} \\ M_{13} - \delta K_{13} \\ M_{22} - \delta K_{22} \\ M_{23} - \delta K_{23} \\ M_{33} - \delta K_{33} \end{pmatrix} \qquad (29.21)$$

$$\begin{pmatrix} \frac{1}{\gamma^4}\left[\bar{N}_{11} - \frac{2k}{n\gamma}(\bar{M}_1\bar{\Lambda}_1 + 2\,\bar{K}_1\bar{N}_1)\right] \\ \frac{1}{\gamma^3}\left[\bar{N}_{12} - \frac{k}{n\gamma}[\bar{M}_2\bar{\Lambda}_1 + \bar{M}_1\bar{\Lambda}_2 + \bar{K}_1\bar{N}_2 + (2\,\bar{K}_2 + \bar{\Lambda}_1)\bar{N}_1]\right] \\ \frac{1}{\gamma^2}\left[\bar{N}_{13} - \frac{k}{n\gamma}(\bar{M}_1\bar{\Lambda}_3 + \bar{M}_3\bar{\Lambda}_1 + 2\,\bar{K}_3\bar{N}_1 + 2\,\bar{\Lambda}_1\bar{N}_2)\right] \\ \frac{1}{\gamma^2}\left[\bar{N}_{22} - \frac{2k}{n\gamma}(\bar{M}_2\bar{\Lambda}_2 + \bar{K}_2\bar{N}_2 + \bar{\Lambda}_2\bar{N}_1)\right] \\ \frac{1}{\gamma}\left[\bar{N}_{23} - \frac{k}{n\gamma}[\bar{M}_3\bar{\Lambda}_2 + \bar{M}_2\bar{\Lambda}_3 + (2\,\bar{\Lambda}_2 + \bar{K}_3)\bar{N}_2 + \bar{\Lambda}_3\bar{N}_1]\right] \\ \left[\bar{N}_{33} - \frac{2k}{n\gamma}(\bar{M}_3\bar{\Lambda}_3 + 2\,\bar{\Lambda}_3\bar{N}_2)\right] \end{pmatrix}$$

$$= D_5 \begin{pmatrix} N_{11} - \delta(\Lambda_{11} + M_{11}) + \delta^2 K_{11} \\ N_{12} - \delta(\Lambda_{12} + M_{12}) + \delta^2 K_{12} \\ N_{13} - \delta(\Lambda_{13} + M_{13}) + \delta^2 K_{13} \\ N_{22} - \delta(\Lambda_{22} + M_{22}) + \delta^2 K_{22} \\ N_{23} - \delta(\Lambda_{23} + M_{23}) + \delta^2 K_{23} \\ N_{33} - \delta({}_{33}\Lambda + M_{33}) + \delta^2 K_{33} \end{pmatrix},$$

with

$$D_5 = \begin{pmatrix} 1 & 0 & 0 & 0 & 0 & 0 \\ -\delta & 1 & 0 & 0 & 0 & 0 \\ \delta^2 & -2\delta & 1 & 0 & 0 & 0 \\ \delta^2 & -2\delta & 0 & 1 & 0 & 0 \\ -\delta^3 & 3\delta^2 & -\delta & -2\delta & 1 & 0 \\ \delta^4 & 4\,\delta^3 & 2\delta^2 & 4\delta^2 & -4\delta & 1 \end{pmatrix}, \qquad (29.22)$$

Imaging a Curved Object

Let us investigate the image of a curved object by a rotation-symmetric optical system. Let

$$\bar{z}/n = A_1\bar{e}_1 + \tfrac{1}{2}A_{11}\bar{e}_1{}^2 \tag{29.23}$$

with

$$2\bar{e}_1 = \bar{x}^2 + \bar{y}^2,$$

where $\bar{x}$, $\bar{y}$, $\bar{z}$ are the coordinates of the curved object. We find from Equations (28.1) and (29.1) that

$$\begin{aligned} -n\ \Xi &= Kx + \Lambda x_P{}' = \bar{K}\bar{x} + \bar{\Lambda} x_P{}' \\ n'\ \Xi' &= Mx + Nx_P{}' = \bar{M}\bar{x} + \bar{N}x_P{}' \end{aligned} \tag{29.24}$$

and

$$\begin{aligned} \bar{x} &= x + \left(\frac{\bar{z}}{n}\right) n\ \Xi = x\left(1 - \frac{\bar{z}}{n}K\right) - x_P{}'\frac{\bar{z}}{n}\Lambda \\ \bar{y} &= y + \left(\frac{\bar{z}}{n}\right) n\ H = y\left(1 - \frac{\bar{z}}{n}K\right) - y_P{}'\frac{\bar{z}}{n}\Lambda. \end{aligned} \tag{29.25}$$

From this it follows that

$$\begin{aligned} \bar{K} &= \frac{K}{1-(\bar{z}/n)\,K} & \bar{\Lambda} &= \frac{\Lambda}{1-(\bar{z}/n)\,K} \\ \bar{M} &= \frac{M}{1-(\bar{z}/n)\,K} & \bar{N} &= N + \frac{\Lambda M\bar{z}/n}{1-K\bar{z}/n,}, \end{aligned} \tag{29.26}$$

where we have to keep in mind that in Equations (29.26) $\bar{z}$ is known as a function of $\bar{e}_1$, whereas K, Λ, M, and N are given as functions of the coordinates x, y on the plane. Moreover, we want $\bar{K}$, $\bar{\Lambda}$, $\bar{M}$ and $\bar{N}$ as functions of the $\bar{e}_i$, that is, the coordinates of the curved object surface. Equations (29.25) lead to

$$\begin{aligned} \bar{e}_1 &= e_1\left(1-\frac{\bar{z}}{n}K\right)^2 - e_2\frac{\bar{z}}{n}\Lambda\left(1-\frac{\bar{z}}{n}K\right) + e_3\left(\frac{\bar{z}}{n}\Lambda\right)^2 \\ \bar{e}_2 &= e_2\left(1-\frac{\bar{z}}{n}K\right) - 2e_3\frac{\bar{z}}{n}\Lambda \\ \bar{e}_3 &= e_3. \end{aligned} \tag{29.27}$$

From Equations (29.27) and (29.23) we can calculate $\bar{z}$ as a function of the plane coordinates e_i. Let us assume

$$\bar{z}/n = z_1e_1 + z_2e_2 + z_3e_3 + \tfrac{1}{2}(z_{11}e_1^2 + 2z_{12}e_1e_2 + 2z_{13}e_1e_3 + z_{22}e_2^2 + 2z_{23}e_2e_3 + z_{33}e_3^2). \qquad (29.28)$$

Insert this into Equations (29.27) and insert $\bar{e}_1$ and $\bar{z}/n$ into (29.23). A comparison of coefficients after carrying out this calculation gives

$$\begin{aligned} &z_1 = A_1 && z_{11} = A_{11} - 4K_oA_1^2 \\ &z_2 = z_3 = 0 && z_{12} = -M_oA_1^2 \\ & && z_{13} = z_{22} = z_{23} = z_{33} = 0, \end{aligned} \qquad (29.29)$$

which lead to

$$\begin{aligned} \bar{e}_1 &= e_1 - \tfrac{1}{2}e_1^2(4A_1K_o) - e_1e_2A_1M_o \\ \bar{e}_2 &= e_2 - e_1e_2A_1K_o - 2e_1e_3A_1M_o \\ \bar{e}_3 &= e_3. \end{aligned} \qquad (29.30)$$

Developing $\bar{K}$, $\bar{\Lambda}$, $\bar{M}$, and $\bar{N}$ as functions of the $\bar{e}_i$, that is,

$$\bar{K} = K_o + \sum_i \bar{K}_i\bar{e}_i + \tfrac{1}{2}\sum_{i\varkappa} \bar{K}_{i\varkappa}\bar{e}_i\bar{e}_\varkappa, \text{ etc.} \qquad (29.31)$$

expressing on both sides of (29.26) the $\bar{e}_i$ as functions of the e_i, and comparing coefficients gives the values of the image-error coefficients for a curved surface in terms of those of a flat surface. The results for the first- and third-order terms are

$$\begin{aligned} &\bar{K}_o = K_o && \bar{\Lambda}_o = M_o \\ &\bar{K}_1 = K_1 + A_1K_o^2 && \bar{\Lambda}_1 = \Lambda_1 + A_1M_oK_o \\ &\bar{K}_2 = K_2 && \bar{\Lambda}_2 = \Lambda_2 \\ &\bar{K}_3 = K_3 && \bar{\Lambda}_3 = \Lambda_3 \\ &\bar{M}_o = M_o && \bar{N}_o = N_o \\ &\bar{M}_1 = M_1 + A_1M_oK_o && \bar{N}_1 = N_1 + A_1M_o^2 \\ &\bar{M}_2 = M_2 && \bar{N}_2 = N_2 \\ &\bar{M}_3 = M_3 && \bar{N}_3 = N_3 \end{aligned} \qquad (29.32)$$

and for the fifth-order terms,

$$\begin{aligned}
\bar{K}_{11} &= K_{11} + A_{11}K_o^2 + 2A_1^2K_o^3 + 8A_1K_oK_1 \\
\bar{K}_{12} &= K_{12} + A_1(M_oK_1 + 3K_oK_2) \\
\bar{K}_{13} &= K_{13} + 2A_1(M_oK_2 + K_oK_3) \\
\bar{\Lambda}_{11} &= \Lambda_{11} + A_{11}M_oK_o + 2M_oK_o^2A_1^2 + 2A_1(M_oK_1 + 3K_o\Lambda_1) \\
\bar{\Lambda}_{12} &= \Lambda_{12} + A_1(M_oK_2 + M_o\Lambda_1 + 2K_o\Lambda_2) \\
\bar{\Lambda}_{13} &= \Lambda_{13} + A_1(K_o\Lambda_3 + M_oK_3 + 2M_o\Lambda_2) \\
\bar{M}_{11} &= M_{11} + M_o\mathrm{K}_oA_{11} + 2M_oK_o^2A_1^2 + 6A_1K_oM_1 + 2A_1M_oK_1 \\
\bar{M}_{12} &= M_{12} + A_1(M_oM_1 + M_oK_2 + 2K_oM_2) \\
\bar{M}_{13} &= M_{13} + A_1(2M_oM_2 + M_oK_3 + K_oM_3) \\
\bar{N}_{11} &= N_{11} + M_o^2A_{11} + 2M_o^2K_oA_1^2 \\
&\qquad + 2A_1(M_oM_1 + M_o\Lambda_1 + 2K_oN_1) \\
\bar{N}_{12} &= N_{12} + A_1(M_oN_1 + M_oM_2 + M_o\Lambda_2 + K_oN_2) \\
\bar{N}_{13} &= N_{13} + A_1M_o(2N_2 + \Lambda_3 + M_3),
\end{aligned} \tag{29.33}$$

the other coefficients being unchanged.

The diapoints of a curved surface can be computed by using Equations (29.24). An arbitrary point on the image ray is given by

$$\begin{aligned}
x' &= x_P' + \bar{z}'\,\Xi' = \bar{M}\,\frac{\bar{z}'}{n'}\,\bar{x} + x_P'\left(1 + \frac{\bar{z}'}{n'}\,\bar{N}\right) \\
y' &= y_P' + \bar{z}'\,H' = \bar{M}\,\frac{\bar{z}'}{n'}\,\bar{y} + y_P'\left(1 + \frac{\bar{z}'}{n'}\,\bar{N}\right),
\end{aligned} \tag{29.34}$$

which lead to the diapoint formulae

$$\begin{aligned}
\bar{x}_D' &= -(\bar{M}/\bar{N})\,\bar{x} \\
\bar{y}_D' &= -(\bar{M}/\bar{N})\,\bar{y} \\
\bar{z}_D'/n' &= -(1/\bar{N}).
\end{aligned} \tag{29.35}$$

We shall assume that the object surface is imaged sharply without distortion. Thus the value of $\bar{z}_D'$ in Equations (29.35) must be dependent only on the object point and not on the ray chosen, so that $\bar{N}$ is independent of $\bar{e}_2$ and $\bar{e}_3$. Furthermore, the diamagnification $-\bar{M}/\bar{N}$ must be constant $= -M_o/N_o$ (noting from (29.32) that $\bar{M}_o = M_o, \bar{N}_o = N_o$). Since $\bar{N}$ is independent of $\bar{e}_2$ and $\bar{e}_3$ and the ratio $\bar{M}/\bar{N}$ is constant, it follows that $\bar{M}$ is independent of $\bar{e}_2$ and $\bar{e}_3$.

These considerations lead to the relations

$$\begin{aligned} &\bar{N}_2 = \bar{N}_3 = 0, \quad \bar{N}_{12} = \bar{N}_{13} = \bar{N}_{22} = \bar{N}_{23} = \bar{N}_{33} = 0 \\ &\bar{M}_2 = \bar{M}_3 = 0, \quad \bar{M}_{12} = \bar{M}_{13} = \bar{M}_{22} = \bar{M}_{23} = \bar{M}_{33} = 0 \\ &\bar{M}_1 N_o - \bar{N}_1 M_o = 0, \quad \bar{M}_{11} N_o - \bar{N}_{11} M_o = 0, \end{aligned} \tag{29.36}$$

the last two equations being obtained by expanding $\bar{M}/\bar{N}$ in terms of $\bar{e}_1$ and equating the nonconstant terms to zero.

Insertion of these relations into Equations (29.32) and (29.33) leads to

$$\begin{aligned} &\bar{M}_1 = M_1 + A_1 M_o K_o,\ M_2 = M_3 = 0 \\ &\bar{M}_{11} = M_{11} + M_o K_o A_{11} + 2A_1 (M_o K_o^2 A_1 + 3K_o M_1 + M_o K_1) \\ &M_{12} = -A_1 (M_o M_1 + M_o K_2) \\ &M_{13} = -A_1 M_o K_3 \\ &M_{22} = M_{23} = M_{33} = 0 \\ &\bar{N}_1 = N_1 + A_1 M_o^2,\ N_2 = N_3 = 0 \\ &\bar{N}_{11} = N_{11} + M_o^2 A_{11} \\ &\qquad + 2A_1 (M_o^2 K_o A_1 + M_o M_1 + M_o A_1 + 2\,K_o N_1) \\ &N_{12} = -A_1 (M_o N_1 + M_o A_2) \\ &N_{13} = -A_1 M_o A_3 \\ &N_{22} = N_{23} = N_{33} = 0, \end{aligned} \tag{29.37}$$

and from the last equations of (29.36)

$$\begin{aligned} &0 = \bar{M}_1 N_o - \bar{N}_1 M_o = M_1 N_o - N_1 M_o + A_1 M_o (K_o N_o - M_o^2) \\ &0 = \bar{M}_{11} N_o - \bar{N}_{11} M_o = \\ &\quad M_{11} N_o - N_{11} M_o + A_{11} M_o (K_o N_o - M_o^2) \\ &\quad + 2A_1 [M_o K_o A_1 (K_o N_o - M_o^2) + M_1 (K_o N_o - M_o^2) \\ &\quad + 2K_o (M_1 N_o - N_1 M_o) + M_o (K_1 N_o - A_1 M_o)]. \end{aligned} \tag{29.38}$$

Combining these results with (29.37) and taking note of (29.7) one obtains

$$M_1 = \frac{M_o}{N_o}[N_1 + A_1(M_o^2 - K_oN_o)], \quad N_1 = N_1$$

$$M_2 = 0 \qquad N_2 = 0$$

$$M_3 = 0 \qquad N_3 = 0$$

$$M_{11} = \frac{M_o}{N_o}[N_{11} + (A_{11} - 2A_1^2K_o)(M_o^2 - K_oN_o)] \tag{29.39}$$

$$+ \frac{2A_1}{N_o}[M_o^2(M_1 - \mu_1) + (M_o^2 - K_oN_o)M_1 - M_oN_oK_1], \; N_{11} = N_{11}$$

$$M_{12} = M_oA_1(\mu_1 - 2M_1) \qquad N_{12} = M_oA_1(\mu_2 - N_1)$$

$$M_{13} = M_oA_1(\mu_2 - N_1) \qquad N_{13} = M_oA_1\mu_3$$

$$M_{22} = M_{23} = M_{33} = 0 \qquad N_{22} = N_{23} = N_{33} = 0,$$

the quantities μ_i being given in Equations (29.6).

It is evident from the third equation of (29.35) that n'/N_o gives the distance of the exit pupil from the Gaussian plane. Thus the value of N_o is known once the position of the exit pupil has been given.

Equations (29.39) show that, if N_o, M_o, K_o, N_1, K_1, and N_{11} are given for an optical system, then the other image-error coefficients M_i, N_i are determined. If K_{11} is also given, then all of the coefficients K_i, A_i can also be obtained by using Equations (29.6), (29.7), and (29.8).

The equation of the image surface can be found from Equations (29.35). We need merely set $\bar{x} = 0$, $\bar{y}^2 = 2\,\bar{e}_1$ and eliminate $\bar{e}_1$ to obtain the equation of the diapoint curve, which gives the cross-section shape of the image surface. We find first

$$\bar{y}_D'^2 = 2\bar{e}_1M_o^2/N_o^2$$

$$-\frac{\bar{z}_D'}{n'} = \frac{1}{N_o} - \frac{\bar{N}_1}{N_o^2}\bar{e}_1 + \frac{\frac{1}{2}\bar{e}_1^2}{N_o^3}(2\bar{N}_1^2 - N_o\bar{N}_{11}) \tag{29.40}$$

with $\bar{N}_1$ and $\bar{N}_{11}$ given by (29.37). With the variables written merely as y' and z' this yields

$$\frac{z'}{n'} + \frac{1}{N_o} = \frac{y'^2}{2M_o^2}\left[\bar{N}_1 + \frac{y'^2N_o}{4M_o^2}(N_o\bar{N}_{11} - 2\bar{N}_1^2)\right] \tag{29.41}$$

for the equation of the cross-section curve. The vertex curvature is evidently equal to $n'\bar{N}_1/M_o^2$.

Since the vertex curvature c of the object surface is equal to nA_1, by using Equations (29.37) to evaluate $\bar{N}_1$, we obtain the relation

$$\frac{c'}{n'} = \frac{c}{n} + \frac{N_1}{M_o^2} \qquad (29.42)$$

between the curvatures. This is the so-called Petzval condition. Equation (29.41) gives also the equation for the zonal value of the curvature.

CHAPTER THIRTY

Computation of Third- and Fifth-Order Coefficients for a Single Surface

The computation of the image-error functions K, Λ, M, N or, what is equivalent, of one of the characteristic functions, for instance, the point characteristic E up to the fifth order is the subject of discussion in this chapter and the next. In this chapter we compute the image functions for a single refracting surface. In Chapter 31 it will be shown how to compute the functions for a system composed of two parts if the respective functions for each part are known. Once both problems have been solved, the numerical calculation of the coefficients up to the fifth order and further can be achieved for a given optical system.

Image-Error Functions for a Single Surface

Let us choose the object origin at the vertex of the refracting (or reflecting) surface. The image-side origin shall at the beginning be arbitrary; later we may place it at the center of curvature of the surface if the surface has a finite curvature. Let the surface be given by

$$\bar{z}/n = A_1\bar{e}_1 + \tfrac{1}{2}A_{11}\bar{e}_1^2 + \tfrac{1}{6}A_{111}\bar{e}_1^3 \tag{30.1}$$

with

$$2\bar{e}_1 = \bar{x}^2 + \bar{y}^2,$$

$\bar{x}$, $\bar{y}$, $\bar{z}$ being the coordinates of the point of intersection of the ray with the surface. Let d be the distance of the exit pupil from the vertex. Since the surface is imaged upon itself with a magnification equal to unity, we have from (29.35)

$$\bar{M} = -\bar{N}. \tag{30.2}$$

Furthermore we find (since the diapoint coincides with the object point)

$$\bar{z} - z_D' = d \quad \text{or} \quad \frac{z_D'}{n'} = -\frac{1}{\bar{N}} = -\frac{d}{n'} + \frac{n}{n'}(A_1\bar{e}_1 + \tfrac{1}{2}A_{11}\bar{e}_1^2), \tag{30.3}$$

which shows that $\bar{N}$ and therefore also $\bar{M}$, as functions of the curvilinear coordinates $\bar{e}_1$, $\bar{e}_2$, $\bar{e}_3$, are functions of $\bar{e}_1$ alone. The knowledge of $\bar{M}$ and $\bar{N}$ alone is not sufficient to compute K, Λ, M, N, but we must add to this the calculation of $\bar{K}$ for the principal rays ($\bar{e}_2 = \bar{e}_3 = x' = y' = 0$) as a function of $\bar{e}_1$ alone. To do this we must use the refraction law.

The refraction law states that the vector $\vec{s}' - \vec{s}$ has the direction of the normal vector. Because of Equation (30.1) the normal vector at the point $\bar{x}$, $\bar{y}$ is, proportional to

$$-(A_1 + A_{11}\bar{e}_1 + \tfrac{1}{2}A_{111}\bar{e}_1^2)\,\bar{x} : -(A_1 + A_{11}\bar{e}_1 + \tfrac{1}{2}A_{111}\bar{e}_1^2)\,\bar{y} : 1/n$$
$$= (\xi' - \xi) : (\eta' - \eta) : (\zeta' - \zeta). \tag{30.4}$$

Equation (29.24) shows that, for $x_P' = y_P' = 0$,

$$\bar{K} = -n\,\Xi/\bar{x} = -n\,H/\bar{y}$$
$$\bar{N} = -\bar{M} = -n'\,\Xi'/\bar{x} = -n'\,H'/\bar{y} \tag{30.5}$$

with

$$\Xi = \xi/\zeta, \quad H = \eta/\zeta.$$

Setting as abbreviations

$$\xi/\bar{x} = \eta/\bar{y} = \tau$$
$$\xi'/\bar{x} = \eta'/\bar{y} = \tau', \tag{30.6}$$

we find instead of (30.4) the single equation

$$\tau' - \tau + n(\zeta' - \zeta)(A_1 + A_{11}\bar{e}_1 + \tfrac{1}{2}A_{111}\bar{e}_1^2) = 0. \tag{30.7}$$

Equations (30.6) give

$$\zeta^2 = n^2 - \xi^2 - \eta^2 = n^2 - 2\bar{e}_1\tau^2$$
$$\zeta'^2 = n'^2 - \xi'^2 - \eta'^2 = n'^2 - 2\bar{e}_1\tau'^2. \tag{30.8}$$

From (30.5) we derive

$$\bar{K}\zeta + n\tau = 0$$
$$\bar{N}\zeta' + n'\tau' = 0, \tag{30.9}$$

where here the expansions of $\bar{K}$, $\bar{N}$ are to be written omitting the terms in $\bar{e}_2$ and $\bar{e}_3$. Developing τ and τ' in series

$$\begin{aligned}\tau &= \tau_o + \tau_1\bar{e}_1 + \tfrac{1}{2}\tau_{11}\bar{e}_1^2\\ \tau' &= \tau_o' + \tau_1'\bar{e}_1 + \tfrac{1}{2}\tau_{11}'\bar{e}_1^2\end{aligned} \qquad (30.10)$$

we find [since $\bar{K}_o = K_o$, $\bar{N}_0 = N_0$, *cf.* (29.32)]

$$\tau_o = -K_o, \quad \tau_o' = -N_0.$$

In order to develop ζ and ζ' we can assume

$$\begin{aligned}\zeta &= n + \zeta_1\bar{e}_1 + \tfrac{1}{2}\zeta_{11}\bar{e}_1^2\\ \zeta' &= n' + \zeta_1'\bar{e}_1 + \tfrac{1}{2}\zeta_{11}'\bar{e}_1^2.\end{aligned} \qquad (30.11)$$

Inserting this development into Equations (30.8) we find

$$\begin{aligned}\zeta_1 &= -K_o^2/n & \zeta_1' &= -N_0^2/n'\\ \zeta_{11} &= 4K_o\tau_1/n - K_o^4/n^3 & \zeta_{11}' &= 4N_0\tau_1'/n' - N_0^4/n'^3.\end{aligned} \qquad (30.12)$$

Substitution of these values into the Equations (30.9) leads finally to

$$\begin{aligned}-\tau &= K_o + (\bar{K}_1 - K_o^3/n^2)\,\bar{e}_1\\ &\quad + \tfrac{1}{2}(\bar{K}_{11} - 6K_o^2\bar{K}_1/n^2 + 3K_o^5/n^4)\bar{e}_1^2\\ -\tau' &= N_0 + (\bar{N}_1 - N_0^3/n'^2)\,\bar{e}_1\\ &\quad + \tfrac{1}{2}(\bar{N}_{11} - 6N_0^2\bar{N}_1/n'^2 + 3N_0^5/n'^4)\,\bar{e}_1^2\\ \zeta &= n - \frac{K_o^2}{n}\bar{e}_1 + \tfrac{1}{2}\bar{e}_1^2\frac{1}{n}\left(3\frac{K_o^4}{n^2} - 4K_o\bar{K}_1\right)\\ \zeta' &= n' - \frac{N_0^2}{n'}\bar{e}_1 + \tfrac{1}{2}\bar{e}_1^2\frac{1}{n'}\left(3\frac{N_0^4}{n'^2} - 4N_0\bar{N}_1\right).\end{aligned} \qquad (30.13)$$

Inserting these values into Equation (30.7) gives (up to the fifth order)

$$K_o - N_0 = nA_1(n - n')$$

$$\bar{K}_1 - \bar{N}_1 = nA_{11}(n - n') - nA_1\left(\frac{K_o^2}{n} - \frac{N_0^2}{n'}\right) + \frac{K_o^3}{n^2} - \frac{N_0^3}{n'^2}$$

$$\bar{K}_{11} - \bar{N}_{11} = nA_{111}(n - n') - 2nA_{11}\left(\frac{K_o^2}{n} - \frac{N_o^2}{n'}\right)$$

$$+ 6\left(\frac{K_o^2\bar{K}_1}{n^2} - \frac{N_o^2\bar{N}_1}{n'^2}\right) - 4nA_1\left(\frac{K_o\bar{K}_1}{n} - \frac{N_o\bar{N}_1}{n'}\right)$$

$$+ 3\,nA_1\left(\frac{K_o^4}{n^3} - \frac{N_o^4}{n'^3}\right) - 3\left(\frac{K_o^5}{n^4} - \frac{N_o^5}{n'^4}\right). \qquad (30.14)$$

For a surface, which is given by (30.1), Equation (30.3) gives

$$\begin{aligned} N_o &= n'/d \\ \bar{N}_1 &= (n'/d)^2\,(n/n')\,A_1 \\ \bar{N}_{11} &= (n'/d)^2\,(1/n')\,[nA_{11} + 2\,(nA_1)^2/d]. \end{aligned} \qquad (30.15)$$

Equations (30.14) then permit us to compute K_o, $\bar{K}_1$, and $\bar{K}_{11}$. Because of (30.2) ($\bar{M} = -\bar{N}$), both are functions of $\bar{e}_1$ alone. Hence these data in connection with Equations (29.32) and (29.33) are sufficient to compute K, Λ, M, N, that is, their development coefficients, relative to an object plane at the vertex up to the fifth order.

However, the following procedure seems more practical. Assuming $A_1 \neq 0$, we assume the exit pupil to lie at the center of curvature of the refracting surface and calculate K, Λ, M, N for this special pupil position. Using the formulae of the last chapter we can shift the pupil to any desired position, for instance, to the vertex of the next surface. The formulae thus obtained give the desired values except for the case $A_1 = 0$, which, however, can be obtained as a limiting value.

It will be convenient to introduce the following abbreviations:

$$\begin{aligned} R_1 &= nA_1 \\ R_{11} &= nA_{11} - (nA_1)^3 \\ R_{111} &= nA_{111} - 9\,(nA_{11})\,(nA_1)^2 + 6\,(nA_1)^5, \end{aligned} \qquad (30.16)$$

R_1 denoting the curvature of the surface, R_{11} and R_{111} being zero if the refracting surface is a sphere.

Image Functions with Image Origin at Center and Object Origin at Vertex

If $d = r = 1/R_1$, we obtain from Equations (30.14) and (30.15)

$$N_o = n'R_1, \quad M_o = -n'R_1 = \Lambda_o, \quad K_o = nR_1 \qquad (30.17)$$

for the first-order coefficients, which are the same for plane and curved coordinates [*cf.* (29.32)]. From Equations (30.14), and (30.15) we find for the third-order terms

$$\bar{N}_1 = n'R_1^3, \quad \bar{K}_1 = n'R_1^3 + (n - n')(R_{11} + R_1^3), \quad (30.18)$$

leading, because of (29.32), to

$$N_1 = n'^2\left(\frac{1}{n'} - \frac{1}{n}\right)R_1^3, \quad N_2 = N_3 = 0$$

$$K_1 = (n - n')\,R_{11}$$

$$M_1 = 0, M_2 = M_3 = 0. \qquad (30.19)$$

The other third-order values we find from Equations (29.7), considering that (29.6) give

$$\mu_1 = 0$$

$$\mu_2 = n'^2R_1^3\left(\frac{1}{n'} - \frac{1}{n}\right) = N_1$$

$$\mu_3 = -n'^3R_1^3\left(\frac{1}{n'^2} - \frac{1}{n^2}\right), \qquad (30.20)$$

leading to

$$\Lambda_1 = \mathrm{K}_2 = 0 \qquad \Lambda_2 = -N_1 \qquad (30.21)$$

$$K_3 = 0 \qquad \Lambda_3 = -\mu_3 = n'^3R_1^3\left(\frac{1}{n'^2} - \frac{1}{n^2}\right).$$

Collecting the third-order terms, we find

$$K_1 = (n - n')R_{11} \quad \Lambda_1 = 0 \quad M_1 = 0 \quad N_1 = n'^2\left(\frac{1}{n'} - \frac{1}{n}\right)R_1^3$$

$$K_2 = 0 \quad \Lambda_2 = -N_1 \quad M_2 = 0 \quad N_2 = 0$$

$$K_3 = 0 \quad \Lambda_3 = N_1\left(1 + \frac{n'}{n}\right) \quad M_3 = 0 \quad N_3 = 0. \qquad (30.22)$$

Let us now compute the fifth-order terms, Equations (30.15) give

$$\begin{aligned}
&\bar{N}_{11} = -\bar{M}_{11} = n'R_1^2(R_{11} + 3R_1^3) && \bar{N}_{22} = -\bar{M}_{22} = 0 \\
&\bar{N}_{12} = -\bar{M}_{12} = 0 && \bar{N}_{23} = -\bar{M}_{23} = 0 \\
&\bar{N}_{13} = -\bar{M}_{13} = 0 && \bar{N}_{33} = -\bar{M}_{33} = 0.
\end{aligned} \tag{30.23}$$

Equations (29.33) then lead to

$$\begin{aligned}
&N_{11}=n'^2R_1^2(R_{11}-R_1^3)\left(\frac{1}{n'}-\frac{1}{n}\right)=R_1^2\left(\frac{n'}{n}K_1-N_1\right) && M_{11}=2\frac{n'}{n}R_1^2K_1 \\
&N_{12}=0 && M_{12}=0 \\
&N_{13}=\frac{n'}{n}R_1^2\Lambda_3=\frac{n'}{n}R_1^2N_1\left(1+\frac{n'}{n}\right) && M_{13}=0 \\
&N_{22}=N_{23}=N_{33}=0 && M_{22}=M_{23}=M_{33}=0.
\end{aligned} \tag{30.24}$$

The third of Equations (30.14) and the first of (29.33) give

$$\bar{K}_{11}=(n-n')[R_{111}+9R_1^2R_{11}+3R_1^5]+n'R_1^2(R_{11}+3R_1^3) \tag{30.25}$$

and

$$K_{11}=(n-n')R_{111}.$$

From (29.8), taking note of Equations (29.6), we obtain the remaining K's and Λ's. This gives the following values:

$$\begin{aligned}
&K_{11} = (n-n')R_{111} && \Lambda_{11} = -2\frac{n'}{n}R_1^2K_1 \\
&K_{12} = 0 && \Lambda_{12} = \frac{n'^2}{n^2}R_1^2K_1 + R_1^2N_1 \\
&K_{13} = \frac{n'}{n}\left(1+\frac{n'}{n}\right)K_1R_1^2 && \Lambda_{13} = -2\frac{n'}{n}R_1^2N_1 \\
&K_{22} = 0 && \Lambda_{22} = \left(\frac{n'}{n}-3\right)R_1^2N_1 \\
&K_{23} = 0 && \Lambda_{23} = \left(1+\frac{n'}{n}\right)\left(3-2\frac{n'}{n}\right)R_1^2N_1 \\
&K_{33} = 0 && \Lambda_{33} = -3\left(1+\frac{n'}{n}\right)^2\left(1-\frac{n'}{n}\right)R_1^2N_1.
\end{aligned} \tag{30.26}$$

For the sphere we have $R_{11} = R_{111} = 0$, or

$$K_o = nR_1 \quad \Lambda_o = M_o = -n'R_1 \qquad N_o = n'R_1$$

$$K_1 = 0 \quad \Lambda_1 = 0, \qquad M_1 = 0 \quad N_1 = n'R_1^3\left(1 - \frac{n'}{n}\right)$$

$$K_2 = 0 \quad \Lambda_2 = -N_1, \qquad M_2 = 0 \quad N_2 = 0$$

$$K_3 = 0 \quad \Lambda_3 = N_1\left(1 + \frac{n'}{n}\right), \qquad M_3 = 0 \quad N_3 = 0, \qquad (30.27)$$

and

$$K_{11} = 0 \quad \Lambda_{11} = 0$$

$$K_{12} = 0 \quad \Lambda_{12} = n'R_1^5\left(1 - \frac{n'}{n}\right)$$

$$K_{13} = 0 \quad \Lambda_{13} = -2\frac{n'^2}{n}R_1^5\left(1 - \frac{n'}{n}\right)$$

$$K_{22} = 0 \quad \Lambda_{22} = \left(\frac{n'}{n} - 3\right)R_1^5 n'\left(1 - \frac{n'}{n}\right)$$

$$K_{23} = 0 \quad \Lambda_{23} = n'\left(1 - \frac{n'^2}{n^2}\right)\left(3 - \frac{2n'}{n}\right)R_1^5$$

$$K_{33} = 0 \quad \Lambda_{33} = -3n'\left(1 - \frac{n'^2}{n^2}\right)^2 R_1^5$$

$$M_{11} = 0 \quad N_{11} = -n'R_1^5\left(1 - \frac{n'}{n}\right)$$

$$M_{12} = 0 \quad N_{12} = 0 \qquad (30.28)$$

$$M_{13} = 0 \quad N_{13} = \frac{n'^2}{n}\left(1 - \frac{n'^2}{n^2}\right)R_1^5$$

$$M_{22} = 0 \quad N_{22} = 0$$

$$M_{23} = 0 \quad N_{23} = 0$$

$$M_{33} = 0 \quad N_{33} = 0.$$

Image Functions for Exit Pupil at a Distance d from the Vertex

Shifting the exit pupil the distance $k' = d - r$ from the center, we can use Formulae (29.9) to (29.16), where (29.12) and the relation $n'/N_o = r$ lead to

$$\alpha = r/d, \quad \beta = \alpha - 1, \quad k' = -r\beta/\alpha. \tag{30.29}$$

We then find, using (30.22) to (30.26) to evaluate the coefficients of K, Λ, M, N on the right-hand sides,

$$\begin{bmatrix} \frac{1}{\alpha^2}\tilde{N}_1 \\ \frac{1}{\alpha^3}\tilde{N}_2 \\ \frac{1}{\alpha^4}\tilde{N}_3 \end{bmatrix} = B_3 \begin{bmatrix} N_1 \\ 0 \\ 0 \end{bmatrix}, \quad \begin{bmatrix} \frac{1}{\alpha}\tilde{M}_1 \\ \frac{1}{\alpha^2}\tilde{M}_2 \\ \frac{1}{\alpha^3}\tilde{M}_3 \end{bmatrix} = B_3 \begin{bmatrix} -\beta N_1 \\ 0 \\ 0 \end{bmatrix} \tag{30.30}$$

$$\begin{bmatrix} \frac{1}{\alpha}\tilde{\Lambda}_1 \\ \frac{1}{\alpha^2}\tilde{\Lambda}_2 \\ \frac{1}{\alpha^3}\tilde{\Lambda}_3 \end{bmatrix} = B_3 \begin{bmatrix} -\beta N_1 \\ -N_1 \\ N_1\left(1+\frac{n'}{n}\right) \end{bmatrix}, \quad \begin{bmatrix} \tilde{K}_1 \\ \frac{1}{\alpha}\tilde{K}_2 \\ \frac{1}{\alpha^2}\tilde{K}_3 \end{bmatrix} = B_3 \begin{bmatrix} K_1 + \beta^2 N_1 \\ \beta N_1 \\ -\beta N_1\left(1+\frac{n'}{n}\right) \end{bmatrix},$$

with

$$B_3 = \begin{bmatrix} 1 & -2\beta & \beta^2 \\ 0 & 1 & -\beta \\ 0 & 0 & 1 \end{bmatrix}, \tag{30.31}$$

leading to

$$\tilde{M}_o = \alpha M_o \quad \tilde{N}_o = \alpha N_o \qquad \tilde{\Lambda}_o = \alpha M_o$$

$$\tilde{N}_1 = \alpha^2 N_1, \quad \tilde{M}_1 = -\,\alpha\beta N_1, \quad \tilde{\Lambda}_1 = \alpha\beta N_1 \left(\alpha + \beta \frac{n'}{n}\right),$$

$$\tilde{N}_2 = 0, \qquad \tilde{M}_2 = 0, \qquad \tilde{\Lambda}_2 = -\,\alpha^2 N_1 \left(\alpha + \beta \frac{n'}{n}\right),$$

$$\tilde{N}_3 = 0, \qquad \tilde{M}_3 = 0 \qquad \tilde{\Lambda}_3 = \alpha^3 N_1 \left(1 + \frac{n'}{n}\right),$$

$$\tilde{K}_o = K_o - \beta M_o$$

$$\tilde{K}_1 = K_1 - \beta^2 N_1 \left(\alpha + \beta \frac{n'}{n}\right)$$

$$\tilde{K}_2 = \alpha\beta N_1 \left(\alpha + \beta \frac{n'}{n}\right)$$

$$\tilde{K}_3 = -\,\alpha^2 \beta N_1 \left(1 + \frac{n'}{n}\right), \tag{30.32}$$

and, in fifth order,

$$\tilde{N}_{11} = \frac{2r}{n'}\frac{\beta}{\alpha^2}\tilde{N}_1{}^2 + \alpha^2 (N_{11} + 2\beta^2 N_{13}), \qquad \tilde{N}_{22} = 0$$

$$\tilde{N}_{12} = -\,\alpha^3 \beta N_{13} \qquad \tilde{N}_{23} = 0$$

$$\tilde{N}_{13} = \alpha^4 N_{13} \qquad \tilde{N}_{33} = 0$$

$$\tilde{M}_{11} = \frac{2r}{n'}\frac{\beta}{\alpha^2}\tilde{M}_1 \tilde{N}_1 + \alpha (M_{11} - \beta N_{11} - 2\beta^3 N_{13}), \quad \tilde{M}_{22} = 0$$

$$\tilde{M}_{12} = \alpha^2 \beta^2 N_{13} \qquad \tilde{M}_{23} = 0$$

$$\tilde{M}_{13} = -\,\alpha^3 \beta N_{13} \qquad \tilde{M}_{33} = 0$$

$$\tilde{\Lambda}_{11} = \frac{2r}{n'}\frac{\beta}{\alpha^2}(\tilde{\Lambda}_1 \tilde{N}_1 + 2\tilde{\Lambda}_2 \tilde{M}_1) + \alpha [\Lambda_{11} - \beta (N_{11} + 4\Lambda_{12}) + 2\beta^2 (\Lambda_{13} + 2\Lambda_{22}) - 2\beta^3 (N_{13} + 2\Lambda_{23}) + \beta^4 \Lambda_{33}]$$

$$\tilde{\Lambda}_{12} = \frac{r}{n'} \frac{\beta}{a^2} (2\tilde{\Lambda}_2 \tilde{N}_1 + \tilde{\Lambda}_3 \tilde{M}_1)$$

$$+ a^2 [\Lambda_{12} - \beta (\Lambda_{13} + 2\Lambda_{22}) + \beta^2 (N_{13} + 3\Lambda_{23}) - \beta^3 \Lambda_{33}]$$

$$\tilde{\Lambda}_{13} = \frac{r}{n'} \frac{\beta}{a^2} 3\tilde{\Lambda}_3 \tilde{N}_1 + a^3 [\Lambda_{13} - \beta (N_{13} + 2\Lambda_{23}) + \beta^2 \Lambda_{33}]$$

$$\tilde{\Lambda}_{22} = a^3 [\Lambda_{22} - 2\beta \Lambda_{23} + \beta^2 \Lambda_{33}]$$

$$\tilde{\Lambda}_{23} = a^4 [\Lambda_{23} - \beta \Lambda_{33}]$$

$$\tilde{\Lambda}_{33} = a^5 \Lambda_{33}$$

$$\tilde{K}_{11} = \frac{6r}{n} \frac{\beta}{a^2} \tilde{M}_1 \tilde{\Lambda}_1 + [K_{11} - \beta (\Lambda_{11} + M_{11})$$

$$+ \beta^2 (N_{11} + 4\Lambda_{12} + 2K_{13}) - 2\beta^3 (\Lambda_{13} + 2\Lambda_{22})$$

$$+ 2\beta^4 (N_{13} + 2\Lambda_{23}) - \beta^5 \Lambda_{33}]$$

$$\tilde{K}_{12} = \frac{r}{n'} \frac{\beta}{a^2} (\tilde{\Lambda}_2 \tilde{M}_1 + \tilde{K}_2 \tilde{N}_1 + \tilde{K}_3 \tilde{M}_1) - a\beta [(\Lambda_{12} + K_{13})$$

$$- \beta (\Lambda_{13} + 2\Lambda_{22}) + \beta^2 (N_{13} + 3\Lambda_{23}) - \beta^3 \Lambda_{33}]$$

$$\tilde{K}_{13} = \frac{r}{n'} \frac{\beta}{a^2} (\tilde{M}_1 \tilde{\Lambda}_3 + 2\tilde{N}_1 \tilde{K}_3)$$

$$+ a^2 [K_{13} - \beta \Lambda_{13} + \beta^2 (N_{13} + 2\Lambda_{23}) - \beta^3 \Lambda_{33}]$$

$$\tilde{K}_{22} = - a^2 \beta [\Lambda_{22} - 2\beta \Lambda_{23} + \beta^2 \Lambda_{33}]$$

$$\tilde{K}_{23} = - a^3 \beta [\Lambda_{23} - \beta \Lambda_{33}]$$

$$\tilde{K}_{33} = - a^4 \beta \Lambda_{33}. \tag{30.33}$$

The derivation of Equations (30.32) and (30.33) was carried out by shifting the exit pupil from the center of curvature. However, the formulae remain correct if we go to the limit as $R_1 \to 0$, in which case we have from (30.29)

$$aR_1 \to 1/d, \quad \beta R_1 \to 1/d, \tag{30.34}$$

giving finite values. For a general surface having zero curvature,

$$R_{11} = nA_{11}, \quad R_{111} = nA_{111} \tag{30.35}$$

need not be zero. We find in this case

$$\tilde{N}_1=\tilde{N}_2=\tilde{N}_3=0 \quad \tilde{\Lambda}_1=\frac{n'}{d^3}\left(1-\frac{n'^2}{n^2}\right) \qquad \tilde{\Lambda}_2=-\tilde{\Lambda}_1 \quad \tilde{\Lambda}_3=\tilde{\Lambda}_1$$

$$\tilde{M}_1=\tilde{M}_2=\tilde{M}_3=0 \quad \tilde{K}_1=(n-n')R_{11}-\tilde{\Lambda}_1 \qquad \tilde{K}_2=\tilde{\Lambda}_1 \qquad \tilde{K}_3=-\tilde{\Lambda}_1$$

$$\tilde{N}_{11}=n'\left(1-\frac{n'}{n}\right)\frac{R_{11}}{d^2}, \quad \tilde{M}_{11}=-\tilde{N}_{11}, \quad \tilde{\Lambda}_{11}=-\tilde{N}_{11}\left(1+\frac{4n'}{n}\right)+\tilde{\Lambda}_{33}$$

$$\tilde{N}_{12}=0 \qquad \tilde{M}_{12}=0 \qquad \tilde{\Lambda}_{12}=\frac{n'}{n}\tilde{N}_{11}-\tilde{\Lambda}_{33}$$

$$\tilde{N}_{13}=0 \qquad \tilde{M}_{13}=0 \qquad \tilde{\Lambda}_{13}=\tilde{\Lambda}_{33}$$

$$\tilde{N}_{22}=0 \qquad \tilde{M}_{22}=0 \qquad \tilde{\Lambda}_{22}=\tilde{\Lambda}_{33}$$

$$\tilde{N}_{23}=0 \qquad \tilde{M}_{23}=0 \qquad \tilde{\Lambda}_{23}=-\tilde{\Lambda}_{33}$$

$$\tilde{N}_{33}=0 \qquad \tilde{M}_{33}=0 \qquad \tilde{\Lambda}_{33}=-\frac{3n'}{d^5}\left(1-\frac{n'^2}{n^2}\right)^2$$

$$\tilde{K}_{11}=n\left(1-\frac{n'}{n}\right)R_{111}+3\left(1+\frac{2n'}{n}\right)\tilde{N}_{11}-\tilde{\Lambda}_{33}$$

$$\tilde{K}_{12}=-\left(1+\frac{2n'}{n}\right)\tilde{N}_{11}+\tilde{\Lambda}_{33}$$

$$\tilde{K}_{13}=\left(1+\frac{n'}{n}\right)\tilde{N}_{11}-\tilde{\Lambda}_{33}$$

$$\tilde{K}_{22}=-\tilde{\Lambda}_{33}$$

$$\tilde{K}_{23}=\tilde{\Lambda}_{33}$$

$$\tilde{K}_{33}=-\tilde{\Lambda}_{33}. \tag{30.36}$$

Knowing the K, Λ, M, N we can compute the coefficients of the characteristic function from (27.55), (27.56), (29.3), and (29.4). They are equivalent to

$$E_1=K_o \qquad E_2=\Lambda_o=M_o \qquad E_3=N_o$$

$$E_{11}=K_1-\frac{1}{n^2}K_o{}^3 \qquad E_{22}=M_2-\frac{1}{n'^2}M_o{}^2N_o$$

$$E_{12} = M_1 - \frac{1}{n'^2} M_o^3 \qquad E_{23} = M_3 - \frac{1}{n'^2} M_o N_o^2$$

$$E_{13} = N_1 - \frac{1}{n'^2} M_o^2 N_o \quad E_{33} = N_3 - \frac{1}{n'^2} N_o^3 \qquad (30.37)$$

and

$$E_{111} = K_{11} - \frac{6}{n^2} K_o^2 K_1 + \frac{3}{n^4} K_o^5$$

$$E_{112} = M_{11} - \frac{6}{n'^2} M_o^2 M_1 + \frac{3}{n'^4} M_o^5$$

$$E_{113} = N_{11} - \frac{2}{n'^2} M_o (M_o N_1 + 2N_o M_1) + \frac{3}{n'^4} M_o^4 N_o$$

$$E_{122} = M_{12} - \frac{1}{n'^2} M_o [M_o (N_1 + 3M_2) + 2N_o M_1] + \frac{3}{n'^4} M_o^4 N_o$$

$$E_{123} = M_{13} - \frac{1}{n'^2} [3M_o^2 M_3 + 2M_o N_o N_1 + N_o^2 M_1]$$

$$+ \frac{3}{n'^4} M_o^3 N_o^2$$

$$E_{222} = M_{22} - \frac{2}{n'^2} [M_o^2 M_3 + 2M_o N_o M_2] + \frac{3}{n'^4} M_o^3 N_o^2$$

$$E_{133} = N_{13} - \frac{1}{n'^2} [M_o^2 N_3 + 2M_o N_o N_2 + 3N_o^2 N_1] + \frac{3}{n'^4} M_o^2 N_o^3$$

$$E_{223} = M_{23} - \frac{1}{n'^2} [M_o^2 N_3 + 4M_o N_o M_3 + N_o^2 M_2] + \frac{3}{n'^4} M_o^2 N_o^3$$

$$E_{233} = M_{33} - \frac{2}{n'^2} [2M_o N_o N_3 + N_o^2 M_3] + \frac{3}{n'^4} M_o N_o^4$$

$$E_{333} = N_{33} - \frac{6}{n'^2} N_o^2 N_3 + \frac{3}{n'^4} N_0^5. \qquad (30.38)$$

Specializing for refraction at a single surface with object origin at the vertex and exit pupil at the center, we find [*cf.* (30.37) etc.]

$$E_1 = nR_1 \qquad E_2 = -n'R_1 \qquad E_3 = n'R_1$$

$$E_{11} = K_1 - \frac{n}{n'} N_1 - n'R_1^3 \qquad E_{22} = -n'R_1^3$$

$$E_{12} = n'R_1^3 \qquad E_{23} = n'R_1^3$$

$$E_{13} = N_1 - n'R_1^3 \qquad E_{33} = -n'R_1^3 \qquad (30.39)$$

and

$$E_{111} = K_{11} - 6R_1^2K_1 + 3\frac{n}{n'}R_1^2N_1 + 3n'R_1^5$$

$$E_{112} = 2\frac{n'}{n}R_1^2K_1 - 3n'R_1^5$$

$$E_{113} = \frac{n'}{n}R_1^2K_1 - 3R_1^2N_1 + 3n'R_1^5$$

$$E_{122} = -R_1^2N_1 + 3n'R_1^5$$

$$E_{123} = 2R_1^2N_1 - 3n'R_1^5$$

$$E_{222} = -3n'R_1^5$$

$$E_{133} = -N_1R_1^2\left[3 - \frac{n'}{n} - \frac{n'^2}{n^2}\right] + 3n'R_1^5$$

$$E_{223} = 3n'R_1^5$$

$$E_{233} = -3n'R_1^5$$

$$E_{333} = 3n'R_1^5, \qquad (30.40)$$

where

$$K_1 = \left(1 - \frac{n'}{n}\right) nR_{11}, \quad K_{11} = \left(1 - \frac{n'}{n}\right) nR_{11}, \quad N_1 = \left(1 - \frac{n'}{n}\right) n'R_1^3.$$

For refraction at a surface of zero curvature with the exit pupil at the distance d from the vertex, we find from (30.36)

$$E_1 = n'/d \qquad E_2 = -n'/d \qquad E_3 = n'/d$$

$$\begin{aligned} E_{11} &= K_1 - n'/d^3 & E_{22} &= -\,n'/d^3 \\ E_{12} &= n'/d^3 & E_{23} &= n'/d^3 \\ E_{13} &= -\,n'/d^3 & E_{33} &= -\,n'/d^3 \end{aligned} \tag{30.41}$$

and

$$E_{111} = K_{11} + 3\frac{n'}{n}K_1/d^2 + 3n'/d^5$$

$$E_{112} = -\frac{n'}{n}K_1/d^2 - 3n'/d^5$$

$$E_{113} = \frac{n'}{n}K_1/d^2 + 3n'/d^5$$

$$E_{122} = 3n'/d^5$$

$$\begin{aligned} E_{123} &= -\,3n'/d^5 & E_{222} &= -\,3n'/d^5 \\ E_{133} &= 3n'/d^5 & E_{223} &= 3n'/d^5 \\ E_{233} &= -\,3n'/d^5 & E_{333} &= 3n'/d^5. \end{aligned} \tag{30.42}$$

Finally, for the coefficients of E for a general refracting surface with the object plane at the vertex and the exit pupil at the distance d, we find from (30.32) and (30.33), if we abbreviate with

$$\alpha = 1/dR_1, \quad \beta = \alpha - 1, \tag{30.43}$$

the values

$$\begin{aligned} &E_1 = nR_1\left(1 + \beta\frac{n'}{n}\right), \quad E_2 = -\,\alpha n'R_1, \quad E_3 = \alpha n'R_1 \\ &E_{11} = K_1 + N_1\left(2\beta^2 - \frac{n}{n'}\right) - \alpha^3 n'R_1^3 \qquad E_{22} = -\,\alpha^3 n'R_1^3 \\ &E_{12} = -\,\alpha\beta N_1 + \alpha^3 n'R_1^3 \qquad E_{23} = \alpha^3 n'R_1^3 \\ &E_{13} = \alpha^2 N_1 - \alpha^3 n'R_1^3 \qquad E_{33} = -\,\alpha^3 n'R_1^3 \end{aligned} \tag{30.44}$$

and for the fifth-order coefficients, abbreviating with

$$\varkappa = 3 - \frac{n'}{n} - \frac{n'^2}{n^2}, \tag{30.45}$$

we find

$$E_{111} = K_{11} - 3R_1^2 K_1 \left(2 + 4\frac{n'}{n}\beta - \frac{n'}{n}\beta^2\right) + 3n'\alpha^5 R_1^5$$
$$+ 3N_1 R_1^2 \left[\frac{n}{n'} - 7\beta^2 - 2\beta^3\left(2 + 3\frac{n'}{n} - \frac{n'^2}{n^2}\right)\right.$$
$$\left. - \beta^4\left(1 + \frac{n'}{n} + \frac{n'^2}{n^2} - 2\frac{n'^3}{n^3}\right)\right]$$

$$E_{112} = \alpha K_1 R_1^2 \frac{n'}{n}(2 - \beta)$$
$$+ \alpha\beta N_1 R_1^2 \left[7 + 2\beta\left(5 + \frac{n'}{n}\right) + 2\beta^2\varkappa\right] - 3n'\alpha^5 R_1^5$$

$$E_{113} = \alpha^2 K_1 R_1^2 \frac{n'}{n} - \alpha^2 N_1 R_1^2 \left[3 + 2\beta\left(3 + \frac{n'}{n}\right) + 2\beta^2\varkappa\right]$$
$$+ 3n'\alpha^5 R_1^5$$

$$E_{122} = -\alpha^2 N_1 R_1^2 (1 + 4\beta + \beta^2\varkappa) + 3n'\alpha^5 R_1^5 \tag{30.46}$$

$$E_{123} = \alpha^3 N_1 R_1^2 (2 + \beta\varkappa) - 3n'\alpha^5 R_1^5$$

$$E_{222} = -3n'\alpha^5 R_1^5$$

$$E_{133} = -\alpha^4 N_1 R_1^2 \varkappa + 3n'\alpha^5 R_1^5$$

$$E_{223} = 3n'\alpha^5 R_1^5$$

$$E_{233} = -3n'\alpha^5 R_1^5$$

$$E_{333} = 3n'\alpha^5 R_1^5,$$

where

$$K_1 = \left(1 - \frac{n'}{n}\right) nR_{11}, \quad N_1 = \left(1 - \frac{n'}{n}\right) n'R_1^3$$

$$K_{11} = \left(1 - \frac{n'}{n}\right) nR_{111}. \tag{30.47}$$

These general formulae reduce to the formulae for the sphere if we set $K_1 = K_{11} = 0$. They reduce to the formulae for a system with zero curvature if we replace αR_1 by $1/d$ and let $R_1 \rightarrow 0$, which leads to $\beta R_1 = 1/d$ also. They give the formulae for the center of curvature as exit pupil, if we set $\alpha = 1$, $\beta = 0$.

CHAPTER THIRTY-ONE

Calculation of the Characteristic Function for a Combined System If the Characteristic Functions Are Given for the Parts

Let us choose three coordinate origins on the common axis of the system. Let one be in the object space, one in the intermediate space, which is the image space for the first system and the object space for the second, and one in the image space with the z, z', z'' axes coinciding with the common axis of rotation (optical axis), the y, y', y'' axes perpendicular to the optical axis and lying in the meridional plane, and the x, x', x'' axes normal to the meridional plane, that is, having a direction which we may call the *sagittal direction.*

A ray is assumed to have the direction cosines ξ, η, ζ; ξ', η', ζ'; ξ'', η'', ξ'' in the object, intermediate, and image spaces, respectively, and to intersect the planes $z = 0$, $z' = 0$, $z'' = 0$ in the points whose coordinates are x, y; x', y'; x'', y'', respectively, Let $\bar{E}$ be the light path along the ray from the plane $z = 0$ to the plane $z' = 0$, $\bar{\bar{E}}$ the light path from the plane $z' = 0$ to $z'' = 0$, and $E = \bar{E} + \bar{\bar{E}}$ the light path from $z = 0$ to $z'' = 0$.

The function $\bar{E}$ can then be considered as a function of the coordinates $\bar{e}_1$, $\bar{e}_2$, $\bar{e}_3$ with

$$2\bar{e}_1 = x^2 + y^2, \quad \bar{e}_2 = xx' + yy', \quad 2\bar{e}_3 = x'^2 + y'^2, \tag{31.1}$$

$\bar{\bar{E}}$ as a function of $\bar{\bar{e}}_1$, $\bar{\bar{e}}_2$, $\bar{\bar{e}}_3$ with

$$2\bar{\bar{e}}_1 = x'^2 + y'^2, \quad \bar{\bar{e}}_2 = x'x'' + y'y'', \quad 2\bar{\bar{e}}_3 = x''^2 + y''^2, \tag{31.2}$$

and E as a function of e_1, e_2, e_3 with

$$2e_1 = x^2 + y^2, \quad e_2 = xx'' + yy'', \quad 2e_3 = x''^2 + y''^2. \tag{31.3}$$

The theorem of Bruns-Hamilton (20.5) tells us that the direction cosines of the object ray, intermediate ray, and image ray are found from

$$
\begin{aligned}
-\xi &= \tilde{\bar{E}}_1 x + \tilde{\bar{E}}_2 x' = \tilde{E}_1 x + \tilde{E}_2 x'' \\
\xi' &= \tilde{\bar{E}}_2 x + \tilde{\bar{E}}_3 x' = -(\tilde{\bar{\bar{E}}}_1 x' + \tilde{\bar{\bar{E}}}_2 x'') \qquad (31.4)^* \\
\xi'' &= \tilde{\bar{\bar{E}}}_2 x' + \tilde{\bar{\bar{E}}}_3 x'' = \tilde{E}_2 x + \tilde{E}_3 x'',
\end{aligned}
$$

and analogously for η, η', η''.

Solving for x' in (31.4) we find

$$(\tilde{\bar{E}}_3 + \tilde{\bar{\bar{E}}}_1)\, x' = -\tilde{\bar{E}}_2 x - \tilde{\bar{\bar{E}}}_2 x'', \qquad (31.5)$$

and then inserting this into the other formulae of (31.4), we obtain the identities

$$
\begin{aligned}
\tilde{E}_1 &= \tilde{\bar{E}}_1 - \frac{\tilde{\bar{E}}_2{}^2}{\tilde{\bar{E}}_3 + \tilde{\bar{\bar{E}}}_1} \\
\tilde{E}_2 &= -\frac{\tilde{\bar{E}}_2 \tilde{\bar{\bar{E}}}_2}{\tilde{\bar{E}}_3 + \tilde{\bar{\bar{E}}}_1} \qquad (31.6) \\
\tilde{E}_3 &= \tilde{\bar{\bar{E}}}_3 - \frac{\tilde{\bar{\bar{E}}}_2{}^2}{\tilde{\bar{E}}_3 + \tilde{\bar{\bar{E}}}_1}.
\end{aligned}
$$

However, the left-hand side is a function of e_1, e_2, e_3, whereas the right-hand side is a function of the coordinates of the first and second systems.

We find from (31.1), (32.2), (31.3), and (31.5), writing the latter also for y',

$$
\begin{aligned}
&\bar{e}_1 = e_1 \\
&\bar{e}_2\, (\tilde{\bar{E}}_3 + \tilde{\bar{\bar{E}}}_1) + 2\tilde{\bar{E}}_1 e_1 + \tilde{\bar{\bar{E}}}_2 e_2 = 0 \\
&\bar{e}_3\, (\tilde{\bar{E}}_3 + \tilde{\bar{\bar{E}}}_1)^2 = \tilde{\bar{E}}_2{}^2 e_1 + \tilde{\bar{E}}_2 \tilde{\bar{\bar{E}}}_3 e_2 + \tilde{\bar{\bar{E}}}_2{}^2 e_3 = \bar{\bar{e}}_1\, (\tilde{\bar{E}}_3 + \tilde{\bar{\bar{E}}}_1)^2 \qquad (31.7) \\
&\bar{\bar{e}}_2\, (\tilde{\bar{E}}_3 + \tilde{\bar{\bar{E}}}_1) + \tilde{\bar{E}}_2 e_2 + 2\tilde{\bar{\bar{E}}}_2 e_3 = 0 \\
&\bar{\bar{e}}_3 = e_3.
\end{aligned}
$$

* The notation $\widetilde{E}_i$ signifies here that the function is meant and not the coefficient of the series development.

In these formulae, the $\tilde{E}_i$, $\tilde{\bar{E}}_i$, $\tilde{\bar{\bar{E}}}_i$ are still functions of their respective variables. However, Equations (31.7) suffice to express the $\bar{e}_i$, $\bar{\bar{e}}_i$ as functions of the e_i. Let us assume first

$$
\begin{aligned}
\bar{e}_1 &= e_1 \\
\bar{e}_2 &= \sum_i \delta_i e_i + \tfrac{1}{2} \sum_{i\varkappa} \delta_{i\varkappa} e_i e_\varkappa \\
\bar{e}_3 &= \sum_i \varkappa_i e_i + \tfrac{1}{2} \sum_{i\varkappa} \varkappa_{i\varkappa} e_i e_\varkappa = \bar{\bar{e}}_1 \\
\bar{\bar{e}}_2 &= \sum_i \beta_i e_i + \tfrac{1}{2} \Sigma \beta_{i\varkappa} e_i e_\varkappa \\
\bar{\bar{e}}_3 &= e_3
\end{aligned}
\qquad (31.8)
$$

with unknown coefficients. Abbreviating with

$$
\begin{aligned}
-(\bar{E}_3 + \bar{\bar{E}}_1) &= \varkappa \\
\bar{E}_2 &= \beta\varkappa \\
\bar{\bar{E}}_2 &= \delta\varkappa,
\end{aligned}
\qquad (31.9)
$$

where we mean this time by $\bar{E}_i$, $\bar{\bar{E}}_i$ the coefficients of the Taylor development, that is, the values of $\tilde{\bar{E}}_i$, $\tilde{\bar{\bar{E}}}_i$ for $e_i = 0$, we find from Equations (31.7)

$$
\begin{array}{lll}
\delta_1 = 2\beta & \varkappa_1 = \beta^2 & \beta_1 = 0 \\
\delta_2 = \delta & \varkappa_2 = \beta\delta & \beta_2 = \beta \\
\delta_3 = 0 & \varkappa_3 = \delta^2 & \beta_3 = 2\delta.
\end{array}
\qquad (31.10)
$$

Inserting the first-order terms into the developments of $\tilde{\bar{E}}_i$ and $\tilde{\bar{\bar{E}}}_i$, we obtain for the first-order coefficients of $\tilde{\bar{E}}_i$, $\tilde{\bar{\bar{E}}}_i$ as functions of the e_i:

$$
\begin{array}{ll}
\bar{E}_{i1} + 2\beta E_{i2} + \beta^2 E_{i3} & \beta^2 \bar{\bar{E}}_{i1} \\
\delta\,(\bar{E}_{i2} + \beta \bar{E}_{i3}) & \beta\,(\bar{\bar{E}}_{i1}\delta + \bar{\bar{E}}_{i2}) \\
\delta^2 \bar{E}_{i3} & \delta^2 \bar{\bar{E}}_{i1} + 2\delta \bar{\bar{E}}_{i2} + \bar{\bar{E}}_{i3}.
\end{array}
\qquad (31.11)
$$

By inserting this development into (31.7) we can compute the $\delta_{i\varkappa}$, $\varkappa_{i\varkappa}$, $\beta_{i\varkappa}$. Before doing so, we introduce the abbreviations $\bar{P}_{i\varkappa}$, $\bar{\bar{P}}_{i\varkappa}$ defined by

$$\begin{Bmatrix} \overline{P}_{11} \\ \overline{P}_{12} \\ \overline{P}_{13} \\ \overline{P}_{22} \\ \overline{P}_{23} \\ \overline{P}_{33} \end{Bmatrix} = \begin{Bmatrix} 1 & 4\beta & 2\beta^2 & 4\beta^2 & 4\beta^3 & \beta^4 \\ 0 & 1 & \beta & 2\beta & 3\beta^2 & \beta^3 \\ 0 & 0 & 1 & 0 & 2\beta & \beta^2 \\ 0 & 0 & 0 & 1 & 2\beta & \beta^2 \\ 0 & 0 & 0 & 0 & 1 & \beta \\ 0 & 0 & 0 & 0 & 0 & 1 \end{Bmatrix} \begin{Bmatrix} \bar{E}_{11} \\ \bar{E}_{12} \\ \bar{E}_{13} \\ \bar{E}_{22} \\ \bar{E}_{23} \\ \bar{E}_{33} \end{Bmatrix}$$

$$\begin{Bmatrix} \overline{\overline{P}}_{11} \\ \overline{\overline{P}}_{12} \\ \overline{\overline{P}}_{13} \\ \overline{\overline{P}}_{22} \\ \overline{\overline{P}}_{23} \\ \overline{\overline{P}}_{33} \end{Bmatrix} = \begin{Bmatrix} 1 & 0 & 0 & 0 & 0 & 0 \\ \delta & 1 & 0 & 0 & 0 & 0 \\ \delta^2 & 2\delta & 1 & 0 & 0 & 0 \\ \delta^2 & 2\delta & 0 & 1 & 0 & 0 \\ \delta^3 & 3\delta^2 & \delta & 2\delta & 1 & 0 \\ \delta^4 & 4\delta^3 & 2\delta^2 & 4\delta^2 & 4\delta & 1 \end{Bmatrix} \begin{Bmatrix} \overline{\overline{E}}_{11} \\ \overline{\overline{E}}_{12} \\ \overline{\overline{E}}_{13} \\ \overline{\overline{E}}_{22} \\ \overline{\overline{E}}_{23} \\ \overline{\overline{E}}_{33} \end{Bmatrix}. \tag{31.12}$$

Comparison with the shifting formulae for the $E_{i\varkappa}$ shows that, aside from a factor, the $\overline{P}_{i\varkappa}$ and $\overline{\overline{P}}_{i\varkappa}$ can be considered as image errors for the first system taken on a plane conjugate to the image-side origin, and as image errors for the second system for an object plane at the image of the object origin through the first system.

As functions of the $\overline{P}_{i\varkappa}$, $\overline{\overline{P}}_{i\varkappa}$ we find

$$\begin{aligned}
\varkappa\beta_{11} &= 4(\beta^3\overline{\overline{P}}_{11} + \overline{P}_{12}) \\
\varkappa\beta_{12} &= [3\beta^2\overline{\overline{P}}_{12} + \delta\,(\overline{P}_{13} + 2\overline{P}_{22})] \\
\varkappa\beta_{13} &= 2\,(\beta\overline{\overline{P}}_{13} + \delta^2\overline{P}_{23}) \\
\varkappa\beta_{22} &= 2\,(\beta\overline{\overline{P}}_{22} + \delta^2\overline{P}_{23}) \\
\varkappa\beta_{23} &= (\overline{\overline{P}}_{23} + \delta^3\overline{P}_{33}) \\
\varkappa\beta_{33} &= 0 \\
\varkappa\varkappa_{11} &= 4\beta\,(\beta^3\overline{\overline{P}}_{11} + \overline{P}_{12}) \\
\varkappa\varkappa_{12} &= \beta^3\,(3\overline{\overline{P}}_{12} + \delta\overline{\overline{P}}_{11}) + \delta\,[\overline{P}_{12} + \beta\,(\overline{P}_{13} + 2\overline{P}_{22})] \\
\varkappa\varkappa_{13} &= 2\,[\beta^2\,(\overline{\overline{P}}_{13} + \delta\overline{\overline{P}}_{12}) + \delta^2\,(\overline{P}_{13} + \beta\overline{P}_{23})] \\
\varkappa\varkappa_{22} &= 2\,[\beta^2\,(\overline{\overline{P}}_{22} + \delta\overline{\overline{P}}_{12}) + \delta^2\,(\overline{P}_{22} + \beta\overline{P}_{23})] \\
\varkappa\varkappa_{23} &= \beta\,[\overline{\overline{P}}_{23} + \delta\,(\overline{\overline{P}}_{13} + 2\overline{\overline{P}}_{22})] + \delta^3\,(3\overline{P}_{23} + \beta\overline{P}_{33})
\end{aligned}$$

$$\begin{aligned}
\varkappa\varkappa_{33} &= 4\delta\,(\bar{\bar{P}}_{23} + \delta^3\bar{P}_{33}) \\
\varkappa\delta_{11} &= 0 \\
\varkappa\delta_{12} &= \bar{P}_{12} + \beta^3\bar{\bar{P}}_{11} \\
\varkappa\delta_{13} &= 2\,(\delta\bar{P}_{13} + \beta^2\bar{\bar{P}}_{12}) \\
\varkappa\delta_{22} &= 2\,(\delta\bar{P}_{22} + \beta^2\bar{\bar{P}}_{11}) \\
\varkappa\delta_{23} &= 3\delta^2\bar{P}_{23} + \beta\,(\bar{\bar{P}}_{13} + 2\bar{\bar{P}}_{22}) \\
\varkappa\delta_{33} &= 4\,(\delta^3\bar{P}_{33} + \bar{\bar{P}}_{23}).
\end{aligned} \tag{31.13}$$

Inserting these values into (31.8) we calculate $\tilde{\bar{E}}_i$ and $\tilde{\bar{\bar{E}}}_i$ as functions of the e_i, after which Equations (31.6) give finally the E_i, $E_{i\varkappa}$, $E_{i\varkappa\lambda}$ as functions of the corresponding coefficients of the two individual systems. With the help of the $\bar{P}_{i\varkappa}$ and $\bar{\bar{P}}_{i\varkappa}$ the final results are written

$$\begin{aligned}
E_1 &= \bar{E}_1 + \bar{E}_2\beta \\
E_2 &= \bar{E}_2\delta = \bar{\bar{E}}_2\beta \\
E_3 &= \bar{\bar{E}}_3 + \bar{\bar{E}}_2\delta
\end{aligned} \tag{31.14}$$

for the first-order terms, and

$$\begin{aligned}
E_{11} &= \bar{P}_{11} + \beta^4\bar{\bar{P}}_{11} & E_{22} &= \delta^2\bar{P}_{22} + \beta^2\bar{\bar{P}}_{22} \\
E_{12} &= \delta\bar{P}_{12} + \beta^3\bar{\bar{P}}_{12} & E_{23} &= \delta^3\bar{P}_{23} + \beta\bar{\bar{P}}_{23} \\
E_{13} &= \delta^2\bar{P}_{13} + \beta^2\bar{\bar{P}}_{13} & E_{33} &= \delta^4\bar{P}_{33} + \bar{\bar{P}}_{33}
\end{aligned} \tag{31.15}$$

for the third-order terms. For the fifth-order terms, we abbreviate with $\bar{P}_{i\varkappa\lambda}$ and $\bar{\bar{P}}_{i\varkappa\lambda}$ defined by

$$\begin{pmatrix} \bar{P}_{111} \\ \bar{P}_{112} \\ \bar{P}_{113} \\ \bar{P}_{122} \\ \bar{P}_{123} \\ \bar{P}_{222} \\ \bar{P}_{133} \\ \bar{P}_{223} \\ \bar{P}_{233} \\ \bar{P}_{333} \end{pmatrix} = \begin{pmatrix}
1 & 6\beta & 3\beta^2 & 12\beta^2 & 12\beta^3 & 8\beta^3 & 3\beta^4 & 12\beta^4 & 6\beta^5 & \beta^6 \\
0 & 1 & \beta & 4\beta & 6\beta^2 & 4\beta^2 & 2\beta^3 & 8\beta^3 & 5\beta^4 & \beta^5 \\
0 & 0 & 1 & 0 & 4\beta & 0 & 2\beta^2 & 4\beta^2 & 4\beta^3 & \beta^4 \\
0 & 0 & 0 & 1 & 2\beta & 2\beta & \beta^2 & 5\beta^2 & 4\beta^3 & \beta^4 \\
0 & 0 & 0 & 0 & 1 & 0 & \beta & 2\beta & 3\beta^2 & \beta^3 \\
0 & 0 & 0 & 0 & 0 & 1 & 0 & 3\beta & 3\beta^2 & \beta^3 \\
0 & 0 & 0 & 0 & 0 & 0 & 1 & 0 & 2\beta & \beta^2 \\
0 & 0 & 0 & 0 & 0 & 0 & 0 & 1 & 2\beta & \beta^2 \\
0 & 0 & 0 & 0 & 0 & 0 & 0 & 0 & 1 & \beta \\
0 & 0 & 0 & 0 & 0 & 0 & 0 & 0 & 0 & 1
\end{pmatrix} \begin{pmatrix} \bar{E}_{111} \\ \bar{E}_{112} \\ \bar{E}_{113} \\ \bar{E}_{122} \\ \bar{E}_{123} \\ \bar{E}_{222} \\ \bar{E}_{133} \\ \bar{E}_{223} \\ \bar{E}_{233} \\ \bar{E}_{333} \end{pmatrix} \tag{31.16}$$

and

$$\begin{bmatrix} \bar{\bar{\bar{P}}}_{111} \\ \bar{\bar{\bar{P}}}_{112} \\ \bar{\bar{\bar{P}}}_{113} \\ \bar{\bar{\bar{P}}}_{122} \\ \bar{\bar{\bar{P}}}_{123} \\ \bar{\bar{\bar{P}}}_{222} \\ \bar{\bar{\bar{P}}}_{133} \\ \bar{\bar{\bar{P}}}_{223} \\ \bar{\bar{\bar{P}}}_{233} \\ \bar{\bar{\bar{P}}}_{333} \end{bmatrix} = \begin{bmatrix} 1 & 0 & 0 & 0 & 0 & 0 & 0 & 0 & 0 & 0 \\ \delta & 1 & 0 & 0 & 0 & 0 & 0 & 0 & 0 & 0 \\ \delta^2 & 2\delta & 1 & 0 & 0 & 0 & 0 & 0 & 0 & 0 \\ \delta^2 & 2\delta & 0 & 1 & 0 & 0 & 0 & 0 & 0 & 0 \\ \delta^3 & 3\delta^2 & \delta & 2\delta & 1 & 0 & 0 & 0 & 0 & 0 \\ \delta^3 & 3\delta^2 & 0 & 3\delta & 0 & 1 & 0 & 0 & 0 & 0 \\ \delta^4 & 4\delta^3 & 2\delta^2 & 4\delta^2 & 4\delta & 0 & 1 & 0 & 0 & 0 \\ \delta^4 & 4\delta^3 & \delta^2 & 5\delta^2 & 2\delta & 2\delta & 0 & 1 & 0 & 0 \\ \delta^5 & 5\delta^4 & 2\delta^3 & 8\delta^3 & 6\delta^2 & 4\delta^2 & \delta & 4\delta & 1 & 0 \\ \delta^6 & 6\delta^5 & 3\delta^4 & 12\delta^4 & 12\delta^3 & 8\delta^3 & 3\delta^2 & 12\delta^2 & 6\delta & 1 \end{bmatrix} \begin{bmatrix} \bar{\bar{\bar{E}}}_{111} \\ \bar{\bar{\bar{E}}}_{112} \\ \bar{\bar{\bar{E}}}_{113} \\ \bar{\bar{\bar{E}}}_{122} \\ \bar{\bar{\bar{E}}}_{123} \\ \bar{\bar{\bar{E}}}_{222} \\ \bar{\bar{\bar{E}}}_{133} \\ \bar{\bar{\bar{E}}}_{223} \\ \bar{\bar{\bar{E}}}_{233} \\ \bar{\bar{\bar{E}}}_{333} \end{bmatrix}. \tag{31.17}$$

Using these abbreviations we find, for the fifth-order coefficients,

$$E_{111} = \bar{P}_{111} + \beta^6 \bar{\bar{P}}_{111} + \frac{6}{\varkappa} (\bar{P}_{12} + \beta^3 \bar{\bar{P}}_{11})^2$$

$$E_{112} = \delta \bar{P}_{112} + \beta^5 \bar{\bar{P}}_{112}$$
$$+ \frac{2}{\varkappa} [\bar{P}_{12} + \beta^3 \bar{\bar{P}}_{11}] [\delta (\bar{P}_{13} + 2\bar{P}_{22}) + 3\beta^2 \bar{\bar{P}}_{12}]$$

$$E_{113} = \delta^2 \bar{P}_{113} + \beta^4 \bar{\bar{P}}_{113}$$
$$+ \frac{2}{\varkappa} [2 (\bar{P}_{12} + \beta^3 \bar{\bar{P}}_{11}) (\delta^2 \bar{P}_{23} + \beta \bar{\bar{P}}_{13}) + (\delta \bar{P}_{13} + \beta^2 \bar{\bar{P}}_{12})^2]$$

$$E_{122} = \delta^2 \bar{P}_{122} + \beta^4 \bar{\bar{P}}_{122} + \frac{2}{\varkappa} \{(\bar{P}_{12} + \beta^3 \bar{\bar{P}}_{11}) (\delta^2 \bar{P}_{23} + \beta \bar{\bar{P}}_{22})$$
$$+ (\delta \bar{P}_{22} + \beta^2 \bar{\bar{P}}_{12}) [\delta(\bar{P}_{13} + \bar{P}_{22}) + 2\beta^2 \bar{\bar{P}}_{12}]\}$$

$$E_{123} = \delta^3 \bar{P}_{123} + \beta^3 \bar{\bar{P}}_{123} + \frac{1}{\varkappa} \{(\bar{P}_{12} + \beta^3 \bar{\bar{P}}_{11}) (\delta^3 \bar{P}_{33} + \bar{\bar{P}}_{23})$$
$$+ (\delta^2 \bar{P}_{23} + \beta \bar{\bar{P}}_{13}) [\delta(\bar{P}_{13} + 2\bar{P}_{22}) + 3\beta^2 \bar{\bar{P}}_{12}]$$
$$+ 2 (\delta \bar{P}_{13} + \beta^2 \bar{\bar{P}}_{12}) (\delta^2 \bar{P}_{23} + \beta \bar{\bar{P}}_{22})\}$$

$$E_{222} = \delta^3 \bar{P}_{222} + \beta^3 \bar{\bar{P}}_{222} + \frac{6}{\varkappa} (\delta \bar{P}_{22} + \beta^2 \bar{\bar{P}}_{12}) (\delta^2 \bar{P}_{23} + \beta \bar{\bar{P}}_{22})$$

$$E_{133} = \delta^4 \overline{P}_{133} + \beta^2 \overline{\overline{P}}_{133}$$

$$+ \frac{2}{\varkappa} [2 (\delta \overline{P}_{13} + \beta^2 \overline{\overline{P}}_{12}) (\delta^3 \overline{P}_{33} + \overline{\overline{P}}_{23}) + (\delta^2 \overline{P}_{23} + \beta \overline{\overline{P}}_{13})^2]$$

$$E_{223} = \delta^4 \overline{P}_{223} + \beta^2 \overline{\overline{P}}_{223} + \frac{2}{\varkappa} \{(\delta^3 \overline{P}_{33} + \overline{\overline{P}}_{23}) (\delta \overline{P}_{22} + \beta^2 \overline{\overline{P}}_{12})$$
$$+ (\delta^2 \overline{P}_{23} + \beta \overline{\overline{P}}_{22}) [2\delta^2 \overline{P}_{23} + \beta (\overline{\overline{P}}_{13} + \overline{\overline{P}}_{22})]\}$$

$$E_{233} = \delta^5 \overline{P}_{233} + \beta \overline{\overline{P}}_{233}$$

$$+ \frac{2}{\varkappa} [\delta^3 \overline{P}_{33} + \overline{\overline{P}}_{23}] [3\delta^2 \overline{P}_{23} + \beta (\overline{\overline{P}}_{13} + 2\overline{\overline{P}}_{22})]$$

$$E_{333} = \delta^6 \overline{P}_{333} + \overline{\overline{P}}_{333} + \frac{6}{\varkappa} [\delta^3 \overline{P}_{33} + \overline{\overline{P}}_{23}]^2. \tag{31.18}$$

These formulae, together with those in the last chapter, permit us to compute the coefficients of the characteristic function for an optical system with a finite number of surfaces.

PART VIII. INTERPOLATION THEORY OF THE OPTICAL IMAGE

CHAPTER THIRTY-TWO

Calculation of Spot Diagrams by an Interpolation Method

In Part I it was seen how to trace rays through an optical system; in Parts III and V it was found that the image formation in an optical system is given by a characteristic function E, which can be taken as the light path between the object point and a terminal point (which we shall here assume to lie in the plane of the exit pupil). In optical systems having rotational symmetry, E is a function of three variables. If x and y are the coordinates of the object point and x' and y', of the terminal point, E is a function of e_1, e_2, e_3 with

$$\begin{aligned} e_1 &= \tfrac{1}{2}(x^2 + y^2) \\ e_2 &= xx' + yy' \\ e_3 &= \tfrac{1}{2}(x'^2 + y'^2). \end{aligned} \tag{32.1}$$

In this case the optical direction cosines [*cf.* (20.5)] are given by

$$\begin{aligned} -\xi &= \bar{E}_1 x + \bar{E}_2 x' \qquad & \xi' &= \bar{E}_2 x + \bar{E}_3 x' \\ -\eta &= \bar{E}_1 y + \bar{E}_2 y' \qquad & \eta' &= \bar{E}_2 y + \bar{E}_3 y', \end{aligned} \tag{32.2}$$

where $\bar{E}_1$, $\bar{E}_2$, and $\bar{E}_3$ are abbreviations for $\partial E/\partial e_1$, $\partial E/\partial e_2$, and $\partial E/\partial e_3$, respectively.

Equations (32.2) now enable us to compute the intersection points of the rays with an arbitrary plane at a distance k' from the exit pupil as

$$\begin{aligned} x'k' &= k'(\bar{E}_2/\zeta')\,x + (1 + k'\bar{E}_3/\zeta')\,x' \\ y'k' &= k'(\bar{E}_2/\zeta')\,y + (1 + k'\bar{E}_3/\zeta')\,y', \end{aligned} \tag{32.3}$$

with

$$\zeta' = \sqrt{n'^2 - \xi'^2 - \eta'^2}$$
$$= \sqrt{n'^2 - 2\,(\bar{E}_2{}^2 e_1 + \bar{E}_2 \bar{E}_3 e_2 + \bar{E}_3{}^2 e_3)}.$$

If the abbreviations

$$M = n'\bar{E}_2/\zeta', \quad N = n'\bar{E}_3/\zeta' \tag{32.4}$$

are used (as in Chapter 27), Equations (32.3) give, for the intersection points of the rays with the plane at the distance k' from the exit pupil,

$$x'_{k'} = \frac{k'}{n'} Mx + \left(1 + \frac{k'}{n'} N\right) x'$$
$$y'_{k'} = \frac{k'}{n'} My + \left(1 + \frac{k'}{n'} N\right) y'. \tag{32.5}$$

The diapoint (the point where the ray intersects the meridional plane) is given as in (27.54) by

$$x_D' = -\,(M/N)\,x, \quad y_D' = -\,(M/N)\,y, \quad z_D' = -\,n'/N. \tag{32.6}$$

In Part VII, E was developed into a series, and the coefficients of its Taylor development were given as functions of the data of the optical system up to what we called the "fifth order." This corresponds to the coefficients of E up to the third order as functions of e_1, e_2, e_3:

$$E = E_o + \sum_{i=1}^{3} E_i e_i + \tfrac{1}{2}\sum_{i,\varkappa=1}^{3} E_{i\varkappa} e_i e_\varkappa + \tfrac{1}{6}\sum_{i,\varkappa,\lambda=1}^{3} E_{i\varkappa\lambda} e_i e_\varkappa e_\lambda. \tag{32.7}$$

From this development we can calculate M and N to the second order, and, by inserting this development into Equations (32.5) and (32.6), compute approximately the coordinates of the diapoints as well as the coordinates of the intersection points of the ray with a plane at the distance k' from the exit pupil.

These data, however, can also be computed for each individual ray from the ray-tracing formulae given in Part I. Unfortunately, for systems with sizable aperture and field, the results of the two methods do not agree very well, owing simply to the fact that the Taylor series given by Equation (32.7) does not converge rapidly. Since the development in (32.7) contains three linear, six quadratic, and ten cubic coefficients, we see that a further extension of the number of coefficients used would cause difficulties both in computation and in geometrical interpretations. A different approach has therefore been suggested by the writer.

By tracing rays we can calculate the coordinates x_D', y_D', z_D' of the diapoints for a small but sufficient number of rays coming from a fixed object point, $x = x_o$, $y = y_o$, $e_1 = \frac{1}{2}(x_o^2 + y_o^2)$. There is no loss of generality, because of the rotational symmetry, to assume one of the coordinates to be zero, for instance, $x_o = 0$. From (32.5), values of M and N are calculated for the small number of rays selected, that is,

$$M = (y_D'/y)\,(n'/z_D'), \qquad N = -\,n'/z_D'. \tag{32.8}$$

We then try to fit the numerical values indicated by (32.8) by second-order developments in e_2 and e_3:

$$\begin{aligned} M &= \bar{M}_o + \bar{M}_2 e_2 + \bar{M}_3 e_3 + \tfrac{1}{2}(\bar{M}_{22} e_2^3 + 2\bar{M}_{23} e_2 e_3 + \bar{M}_{33} e_3^2) \\ N &= \bar{N}_o + \bar{N}_2 e_2 + \bar{N}_3 e_3 + \tfrac{1}{2}(\bar{N}_{22} e_2^2 + 2\bar{N}_{23} e_2 e_3 + \bar{N}_{33} e_3^2), \end{aligned} \tag{32.9}^*$$

determining the coefficients by the least-square method (see the Appendix for a description of this method). Having found M and N as functions of e_2 and e_3, that is, as functions of x', y' (the coordinates of the intersection points of the rays with the exit pupil), we can then compute M and N for a large number of rays, which we may choose to give an even distribution over the exit pupil, Equations (32.9) serving as interpolation formulae. It is not certain in advance that this interpolation procedure will work, but the writer has tested a large number of systems, comparing the results of the interpolation method with the actual ray-tracing results (obtained by means of I.B.M. computing machines), and has found the agreement completely satisfactory for optical systems whose apertures were smaller than $f/1.8$.†

* The notation $\bar{M}_i$, $\bar{N}_i$ is adopted here to emphasize that the expansions here written apply to a fixed object point. The values of the $\bar{M}_i$, $\bar{N}_i$ depend on the object point.

† The "f-number" means the ratio of the focal length of the lens to the diameter of its entrance pupil.

It will always be advisable to trace more than six rays through the system (in practice ten seems to be sufficient) in order to compute the six coefficients of M and the six coefficients of N. If the rays (and their intersection points with the entrance or exit pupil) are suitably chosen, the spread of the residuals will indicate whether or not the approximation is satisfactory.

Another good test of the quality of the approximation is obtained by investigating the rays from an axis point. In this case the diapoints lie on the axis. We have $e_1 = e_2 = 0$ in Equations (32.1), that is, M and N become functions of e_3 alone:

$$\begin{aligned} \bar{M} &= \bar{M}_o + \bar{M}_3 e_3 + \tfrac{1}{2} \bar{M}_{33} e_3^2 \\ \bar{N} &= \bar{N}_o + \bar{N}_3 e_3 + \tfrac{1}{2} \bar{N}_{33} e_3^2. \end{aligned} \qquad (32.10)$$

Whereas the $\bar{N}$ can be calculated for the axis point in the same way as usual ($\bar{N}$ is now what is generally called "spherical aberration") the vanishing of y and y_D' makes it difficult to compute $\bar{M}$ for the axis point from Equations (32.8).

However, Equations (32.4) show that

$$\bar{M}/\bar{N} = \bar{E}_2/\bar{E}_3, \qquad (32.11)$$

and from (32.3) applied to an axis point ($x = y = 0$) we have

$$\xi'/\xi = \eta'/\eta = -\bar{E}_3/\bar{E}_2 = -\bar{N}/\bar{M}. \qquad (32.12)$$

Since the ray-tracing computation gives ξ, η, ξ', η', while $\bar{N}$ has been already found, we can then find the function $\bar{M}$ for an axis point:

$$\bar{M} = -\bar{N}(\xi/\xi') = -\bar{N}(\eta/\eta'). \qquad (32.13)$$

Equation (32.12) is known in optics as the *generalized sine condition,* since the ratio of the direction cosines is proportional to the ratio of the sines of the angles σ and σ' which the object and image rays from an axis point form with the axis.

To return to the question of accuracy, it seems safe to say that, if the spherical aberration and the generalized sine condition, that is the functions $\bar{M}$ and $\bar{N}$ for the axis point, can be safely fitted by curves of the form of Equations (32.10), then it can be expected that the off-axis points are fitted by polynomials of the order used in Equations (32.9). This can be tested by tracing four or more rays from the axis point through the system, in order to determine the coefficients of (32.10). If the approximation is unsatisfactory, one has to trace more rays from each object point and determine the four coefficients of the third order in the developments of M and N, that is,

$$M = \bar{M}_o + \bar{M}_2 e_2 + \bar{M}_3 e_3 + \tfrac{1}{2}\,(\bar{M}_{22} e_2{}^2 + 2\bar{M}_{23} e_2 e_3 + \bar{M}_{33} e_3{}^2) \\ + \tfrac{1}{6}\,(\bar{M}_{222} e_2{}^3 + 3\bar{M}_{223} e_2{}^2 e_3 + 3\bar{M}_{233} e_2 e_3{}^2 + \bar{M}_{333} e_3{}^3) \quad (32.14)$$

and analogously for N. For the rest of the book, we shall restrict ourselves to the consideration of the case of most practical importance, those for which Equations (32.9) are valid. The generalization is left to the reader.

We assume, therefore, that we have calculated the functions $\bar{M}$ and $\bar{N}$ for a given optical system for a number of object points. In general one should calculate the functions for at least three object points, namely, the axis point, the extreme point in the field for which we want to correct the optical system, and an intermediate point. For a more thorough study, two more object points are recommended.

In Chapter 11 it was shown how to construct the vignetting diagram in a practical optical system. We use this method to construct the vignetting diagram in the exit pupil for each object point. We then choose in the exit pupil a large number of points with coordinates x', y' evenly distributed over the vignetted exit pupil. A triangular arrangement would be theoretically most suitable, but a square pattern is generally more convenient. With the interpolation formula (32.9), we calculate the function values M and N for the rays coming from the object point in question and passing through the discrete points in the exit pupil. Equations (32.5) can then be used to calculate the intersection points of all the rays in one or more planes (using one or more values of k', the distances of the various image planes from the exit pupil).

The coordinate points thus obtained are plotted in a set of spot diagrams. If we can assume, as will be the case in most well-designed optical instruments, that the exit pupil is evenly filled with light, we can conclude that the density distribution of the

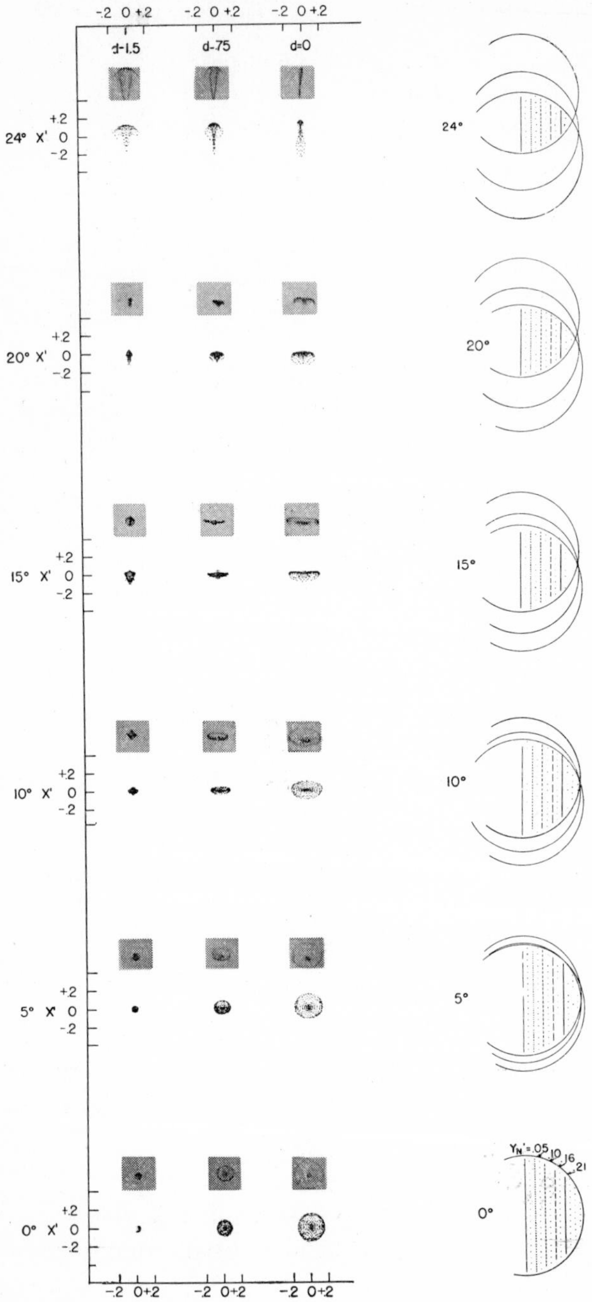

Fig. 32.1. Comparison of spot diagrams with photographs taken of various object points using actual manufactured lens.

points is proportional to the intensity distribution of the light in the image plane being considered.

The spot diagrams for three image planes and five object points (specified by their angular distances from the axis) are shown for a certain optical system in Figure 32.1. Photomicrographs of the corresponding images formed by an actual lens manufactured from the same data are also shown. The agreement is remarkable if one considers that no optical system is perfectly made, and that geometrical optics alone does not take into account diffraction effects.

The next chapters will be devoted to analyzing the spot diagrams obtained by the methods here described. We shall later investigate also what information can be obtained from the spot diagrams, particularly with respect to their use in designing optical systems.

CHAPTER THIRTY-THREE

Analysis of the Spot Diagrams

It is not always easy to follow the variations in the spot diagrams of a complicated optical system when these vary as functions of the system data. This very important problem can be facilitated if we analyze the spot diagrams in the following way. In Equations (32.5), $x'_{k'}$ and $y'_{k'}$ are fifth-degree polynomials in x', y'. We split each of these two polynomials into the sum of five polynomials of degrees one to five and investigate separately the spot diagrams that are given by the members of each order taken alone. Now

$$x'_{k'} - (k'/n')\,\overline{M}_o x = x_{\rm I}' + x_{\rm II}' + x_{\rm III}' + x_{\rm I}'{}_{\rm V}' + x_{\rm V}'$$
$$y'_{k'} - (k'/n')\,\overline{M}_o y = y_{\rm I}' + y_{\rm II}' + y_{\rm III}' + y_{\rm IV}' + y_{\rm V}' \qquad (33.1)$$

or in vector form,

$$\vec{a}'_{k'} - (k'/n')\,\overline{M}_o\vec{a} = \vec{a}_{\rm I}' + \vec{a}_{\rm I}' + \vec{a}_{\rm III}' + \vec{a}_{\rm IV}' + \vec{a}_{\rm V}', \qquad (33.2)$$

so that a spot diagram, regarded as a vector diagram, can be considered as the vectorial sum of five separate vector diagrams, which we can investigate separately. Comparing Equations (32.5) and (33.1) and considering the expansions of M and N indicated in (32.9), we find for the first-order terms

$$x_{\rm I}' = [1 + (k'/n')\,\overline{N}_o]\,x' + (k'/n')\,\overline{M}_2 e_2 x$$
$$y_{\rm I}' = [1 + (k'/n')\,\overline{N}_o]\,y' + (k'/n')\,\overline{M}_2 e_2 y \qquad (33.3)$$

and for the second-order terms:

$$x_{\rm II}' = (k'/n')\,\overline{N}_2 e_2 x' + (k'/n')\,(\overline{M}_3 e_3 + \tfrac{1}{2}\,\overline{M}_{22} e_2^2)\,x$$
$$y_{\rm II}' = (k'/n')\,\overline{N}_2 e_2 y' + (k'/n')\,(\overline{M}_3 e_3 + \tfrac{1}{2}\,\overline{M}_{22} e_2^2)\,y. \qquad (33.4)$$

For the third-order terms we find

$$x_{\mathrm{III}}' = \frac{k'}{n'}(\bar{N}_3 e_3 + \tfrac{1}{2}\bar{N}_{22}e_2^2)\,x' + \frac{k'}{n'}\bar{M}_{23}e_2e_3x$$

$$y_{\mathrm{III}}' = \frac{k'}{n'}(\bar{N}_3 e_3 + \tfrac{1}{2}\bar{N}_{22}e_2^2)\,y' + \frac{k'}{n'}\bar{M}_{23}e_2e_3y, \tag{33.5}$$

for the fourth-order terms,

$$x_{\mathrm{IV}}' = \frac{k'}{n'}\bar{N}_{23}e_2e_3x' + \tfrac{1}{2}\frac{k'}{n'}\bar{M}_{33}e_3^2x$$

$$y_{\mathrm{IV}}' = \frac{k'}{n'}\bar{N}_{23}e_2e_3y' + \tfrac{1}{2}\frac{k'}{n'}\bar{M}_{33}e_3^2y, \tag{33.6}$$

and finally, for the fifth-order terms,

$$x_{\mathrm{V}}' = \tfrac{1}{2}\frac{k'}{n'}\bar{N}_{33}e_3^2x'$$

$$y_{\mathrm{V}}' = \tfrac{1}{2}\frac{k'}{n'}\bar{N}_{33}e_3^2y'. \tag{33.7}$$

Besides these equations we have

$$x_o' = (k'/n')\,\bar{M}_ox \tag{33.8}$$
$$y_o' = (k'/n')\,\bar{M}_oy,$$

giving the point where the principal ray of the bundle intersects the image plane at the distance k' from the exit pupil.

In the case of an axis point, we have $e_2 = x = y = 0$, and the equations simplify to

$$x_o' = x_{\mathrm{II}}' = x_{\mathrm{IV}}' = 0$$
$$y_o' = y_{\mathrm{II}}' = y_{\mathrm{IV}}' = 0 \tag{33.9}$$

$$x_{\mathrm{I}}' = \left(1 + \frac{k'}{n'}\bar{N}_o\right)x', \quad x_{\mathrm{III}}' = \frac{k'}{n'}\bar{N}_3e_3x', \quad x_{\mathrm{V}}' = \tfrac{1}{2}\frac{k'}{n'}\bar{N}_{33}e_3^2x'$$

$$y_{\mathrm{I}}' = \left(1 + \frac{k'}{n'}\bar{N}_o\right)y', \quad y_{\mathrm{III}}' = \frac{k'}{n'}\bar{N}_3e_3y', \quad y_{\mathrm{V}}' = \tfrac{1}{2}\frac{k'}{n'}\bar{N}_{33}e_3^2y'. \tag{33.10}$$

Returning to the general case, let us now introduce polar coordinates in the object plane and in the exit pupil and assume $x = 0$ (without loss of generality because of the rotational symmetry). We can calculate the spot diagrams of a point as functions of r' (the radius of the intersection point in the exit pupil, also called "aperture") and χ (azimuth angle). Setting

$$\begin{gathered} x = 0 \qquad y = r \\ x' = r' \sin \chi, \quad y' = r' \cos \chi \\ 2e_1 = r^2, \quad e_2 = rr' \cos \chi, \quad 2e_3 = r'^2, \end{gathered} \tag{33.11}$$

we find

$$\begin{aligned} x_o' &= 0 \qquad & x_{\mathrm{I}}' &= \left(1 + \frac{k'}{n'} \bar{N}_o\right) r' \sin \chi \\ y_o' &= \frac{k'}{n'} \bar{M}_o r \qquad & y_{\mathrm{I}}' &= \left(1 + \frac{k'}{n'} (\bar{N}_o + r^2 \bar{M}_2)\right) r' \cos \chi \end{aligned}$$

$$\begin{aligned} x_{\mathrm{II}}' &= \frac{k'}{n'} r'^2 r \bar{N}_2 \cos \chi \sin \chi \\ y_{\mathrm{II}}' &= \tfrac{1}{2} \frac{k'}{n'} r'^2 r \, [\bar{M}_3 + (\bar{M}_{22} r^2 + 2\bar{N}_2) \cos^2 \chi] \\ x_{\mathrm{III}}' &= \tfrac{1}{2} \frac{k'}{n'} r'^3 \, [\bar{N}_3 + \bar{N}_{22} r^2 \cos^2 \chi] \sin \chi \\ y_{\mathrm{III}}' &= \tfrac{1}{2} \frac{k'}{n'} r'^3 \, [\bar{N}_3 + (\bar{M}_{23} + \bar{N}_{22} \cos^2 \chi) \, r^2] \cos \chi \\ x_{\mathrm{IV}}' &= \tfrac{1}{2} \frac{k'}{n'} r'^4 r \, [\bar{N}_{23} \cos \chi \sin \chi] \\ y_{\mathrm{IV}}' &= \tfrac{1}{2} \frac{k'}{n'} r'^4 r \, [\tfrac{1}{4} \bar{M}_{33} + \bar{N}_{23} \cos^2 \chi] \\ x_{\mathrm{V}}' &= \tfrac{1}{8} \frac{k'}{n'} r'^5 \, \bar{N}_{33} \sin \chi \\ y_{\mathrm{V}}' &= \tfrac{1}{8} \frac{k'}{n'} r'^5 \bar{N}_{33} \cos \chi. \end{aligned} \tag{33.12}$$

This use of polar coordinates is very helpful because one can thereby easily investigate the rays coming from an object point and passing through a series of concentric circles in the exit pupil, thus obtaining a good idea of the form of the various images.

Let us now investigate each of the partial spot diagrams separately and examine their various forms corresponding to specific values of the $\bar{M}_i$ and $\bar{N}_i$. In doing this we must keep two facts in mind. First, all the coefficients $\bar{M}_i$, $\bar{N}_i$ of M and N will be considered as functions of the position of the object point, that is, as functions of e_1. Only in the case of a fixed object point can we consider the coefficients as constants.

Second, the coefficients $\bar{M}_i$, $\bar{N}_i$, as determined by our fifth-order interpolation method, deviate slightly from the corresponding fifth-order approximation coefficients. If we develop M and N as functions of e_1, e_2, e_3 and then order the terms with respect to e_2 and e_3, we obtain

$$\bar{M} = (M_o + M_1e_1 + \tfrac{1}{2}M_{11}e_1^2) + (M_2 + M_{12}e_1)\, e_2 + (M_3 + M_{13}e_1)\, e_3 + \tfrac{1}{2}\,(M_{22}e_2^2 + 2M_{23}e_2e_2 + \tfrac{1}{2}M_{33}e_3^2). \tag{33.13}$$

If the $\bar{M}_i$ were ordinary Taylor series coefficients, we should then have

$$\begin{aligned} \bar{M}_o &= M_o + M_1e_1 + \tfrac{1}{2}\, M_{11}e_1^2 & \bar{M}_{22} &= M_{22} \\ \bar{M}_2 &= M_2 + M_{12}e_1 & \bar{M}_{23} &= M_{23} \\ \bar{M}_3 &= M_3 + M_{13}e_1 & \bar{M}_{33} &= M_{33}, \end{aligned} \tag{33.14}$$

and correspondingly for the coefficients of $\bar{N}$. Thus it appears that $\bar{M}_2$ and $\bar{M}_3$ are linear functions of e_1, and $\bar{M}_{22}$, $\bar{M}_{23}$, $\bar{M}_{33}$ are constant. However, in the interpolation theory, these coefficients are computed from the ray trace by least-square methods independently for each object point and therefore do not necessarily satisfy Equations (33.14) when considered as functions of e_1. Nevertheless, in practice it has been found that they do.

What is more, in the approximation theory, the M_i and N_i were not independent but were related as functions derived from E. We had from (27.57)

$$M_3 = N_2$$

$$M_{31} = N_{21} - 2\frac{M_o}{n'^2}(M_2N_o - N_2M_o)$$

$$M_{32} = N_{22} - \frac{1}{n'^2}(N_o^2M_2 - N_oM_o(M_3 - N_2) - M_o^2N_3)$$

$$M_{33} = N_{23} - 2\frac{N_o}{n'^2}(N_oM_3 - M_oN_3). \tag{33.15}$$

In our computation of the coefficients by least squares we have not imposed this restriction on the coefficients. The deviations of the coefficients thus obtained from the relation in (33.15) is a sign that higher order terms of the characteristic function affect the least-square solution. It will be found that the better the least-square function fits, the more nearly are Equations (33.15) fulfilled, so that the deviations from these relations give a clue with respect to the accuracy of the approximation. This means that the geometrical conlusions drawn from the approximation theory (*cf.* Chapter 27) are similar to but also slightly different from those to be obtained from the following analysis of the spot diagrams.

After these preliminary remarks we shall start with the analysis of the partial spot diagrams, considering especially the case of an axis point ($r = 0$) and a near-axis point (where r^2 can be neglected).

The zero-degree terms give the image-plane intersection point ($r' = 0$) of the ray through the axis point of the exit pupil. We find from (33.12)

$$x_o' = 0$$

$$y_o' = \bar{M}_o(k'/n')\,r = \bar{M}_o(k'/n')\,y. \tag{33.16}$$

We can calculate $\bar{M}_o$ for various object points. If $\bar{M}_o$ changes as a function of the object point, the image is said to have *distortion*, and the variation of $\bar{M}_o$ as a function of $2e_1 = y^2 = r^2$ gives a measure for the distortion.

First-Degree Diagram

We have from (33.12)

$$x_{\mathrm{I}}' = \left(1 + \frac{k'}{n'}\,\bar{N}_o\right) r' \sin\chi$$

$$y_{\mathrm{I}}' = \left[1 + \frac{k'}{n'}\,(\bar{N}_o + r^2\bar{M}_2)\right] r' \cos\chi. \qquad (33.17)$$

Let us consider the rays going through a series of concentric circles in the exit pupil. Eliminating χ from Equations (33.17), we find

$$\frac{x_{\mathrm{I}}'^2}{[1 + (k'/n')\,\bar{N}_o]^2} + \frac{y_{\mathrm{I}}'^2}{(1 + (k'/n')\,(\bar{N}_o + r^2\bar{M}_2)]^2} = r'^2. \quad (33.18)$$

Equation (33.18) shows that the above-mentioned rays go through a set of concentric ellipses with semiaxes given by the numerical values of

$$r'\,[1 + (k'/n')\,\bar{N}_o], \quad r'\,[1 + (k'/n')\,(\bar{N}_o + r^2\bar{M}_2)]. \qquad (33.19)$$

Shifting the image plane, we find that, for

$$k' = -\,n'/\bar{N}_o, \qquad (33.20)$$

the ellipses reduce to meridional line elements, and that, for

$$k' = -\,n'/(\bar{N}_o + r^2\bar{M}_2), \qquad (33.21)$$

the ellipses reduce to a series of sagittal line elements.

For $\bar{M}_2 = 0$, all the ellipses become circles, and in the plane $k' = -\,n'/\bar{N}_o$, in this case, all the rays go through the axis point of the image plane.

The above case describes the first-order diagram for an axis point or a near-axis point, for which r^2 vanishes. We shall call $\bar{M}_2$ the *astigmatic contribution* to the image and analogously $\bar{N}_o$ and $(\bar{N}_o + r^2\bar{M}_2)$ the *sagittal and meridional astigmatic contributions*, respectively.

Second-Degree Diagram

If we examine all the equations of (33.12) except those of the first degree, we find that the coordinates are proportional to k', that is, the dimensions of the spot diagrams are proportional to the distance k' from the exit pupil to the image plane. Using the formulae

$$\begin{aligned} \sin 2\chi &= 2 \sin\chi \cos\chi \\ \cos 2\chi &= 2\cos^2\chi - 1, \end{aligned} \tag{33.22}$$

we may write the second-degree equations

$$\begin{aligned} x_{II}' &= \tfrac{1}{2}(k'/n')\, r'^2\, r\, \bar{N}_2 \sin 2\chi \\ y_{II}' &= \tfrac{1}{2}(k'/n')\, r'^2\, r\, [(\bar{M}_3 + \bar{N}_2 + \tfrac{1}{2}\bar{M}_{22}r^2) \\ &\quad + (\bar{N}_2 + \tfrac{1}{2}\bar{M}_{22}r^2)\cos 2\chi]. \end{aligned} \tag{33.23}$$

The rays through a series of concentric circles in the exit pupil pass through a series of eccentric ellipses in the image plane:

$$\frac{x_{II}'^2}{\bar{N}_2{}^2} + \frac{[y_{II}' - \frac{1}{2}(k'/n')\, r'^2 r\, (\bar{M}_3 + \bar{N}_2 + \frac{1}{2}\bar{M}_{22}r^2)]^2}{(\bar{N}_2 + \frac{1}{2}\bar{M}_{22}r^2)^2} = \left(\frac{1}{2}\,\frac{k'}{n'} r'^2 r\right)^2. \tag{33.24}$$

The centers of these ellipses are shifted in the meridional direction and have as envelopes, the straight lines

$$\bar{N}_2{}^2 y_{II}'^2 = x_{II}'^2 \bar{M}_3\, (\bar{M}_3 + 2\bar{N}_2 + \bar{M}_{22}r^2), \tag{33.25}$$

which are real if

$$\bar{M}_3\, (\bar{M}_3 + 2\bar{N}_2 + \bar{M}_{22}r^2) \geq 0. \tag{33.26}$$

The second-degree diagram will be called the *asymmetry diagram.* It is proportional in size to the object distance r and to the square of the aperture. In the neighborhood of the axis, that is, for small angles, we have, from (33.15), $\bar{M}_3 = \bar{N}_2$. The straight lines given by Equations (33.25) form, in this case, an angle of 30° with the y-axis. The ellipses become circles if $\bar{M}_{22} = 0$.

Third-Degree Diagram

The third-degree diagram is given by

$$x_{\mathrm{III}}' = \tfrac{1}{2}(k'/n')\, r'^3 [\bar{N}_3 + \bar{N}_{22} r^2 \cos^2 \chi) \sin \chi \qquad (33.27)$$
$$y_{\mathrm{III}}' = \tfrac{1}{2}(k'/n')\, r'^3 [\bar{N}_3 + \bar{M}_{23} r^2 + \bar{N}_{22} r^2 \cos^2 \chi] \cos \chi.$$

For an axis point, $r = 0$, these equations represent a series of concentric circles

$$x_{\mathrm{III}}'^2 + y_{\mathrm{III}}'^2 = \tfrac{1}{4}(k'^2/n'^2)\, r'^6 \bar{N}_3^2, \qquad (33.28)$$

the radii being proportional to $\bar{N}_3$ and to the third power of the aperture r'. In the general case, if $\bar{M}_{23}$, which we may call the *deformation coefficient*, is zero, the equation of the curves through a set of concentric apertures, $r' =$ const., in the exit pupil is given in polar-coordinate form by

$$r'_{k'} = \tfrac{1}{2}(k'/n')\, r'^3 [\bar{N}_3 + \bar{N}_{22} r^2 \cos^2 \chi) \qquad (33.29)$$

or in Cartesian coordinates by

$$x_{\mathrm{III}}'^2 + y_{\mathrm{III}}'^2 = (1/r')^4 [A x'^2 + (A + B)\, y'^2]^2, \qquad (33.30)$$

with

$$A = \tfrac{1}{2}(k'/n')\, r'^3 \bar{N}_3, \quad B = \tfrac{1}{2}(k'/n')\, r'^3 \bar{N}_{22} r^2.$$

In Figure 33.1 we give examples of various forms which these curves may take.

If $\bar{M}_{23}$ is not zero, the general equation of the curves is slightly more complex. Abbreviating with

$$A = \tfrac{1}{2}(k'/n')\, \bar{N}_3 r'^3 \qquad C = \tfrac{1}{2}(k'/n')\, \bar{M}_{23} r^2 r'^3. \qquad (33.31)$$
$$B = \tfrac{1}{2}(k'/n')\, \bar{N}_{22} r^2 r'^3,$$

we have the parametric equations

$$x_{\mathrm{III}}' = (A + B \cos^2\chi) \sin \chi \qquad (33.32)$$
$$y_{\mathrm{III}}' = (A + C + B \cos^2\chi) \cos \chi.$$

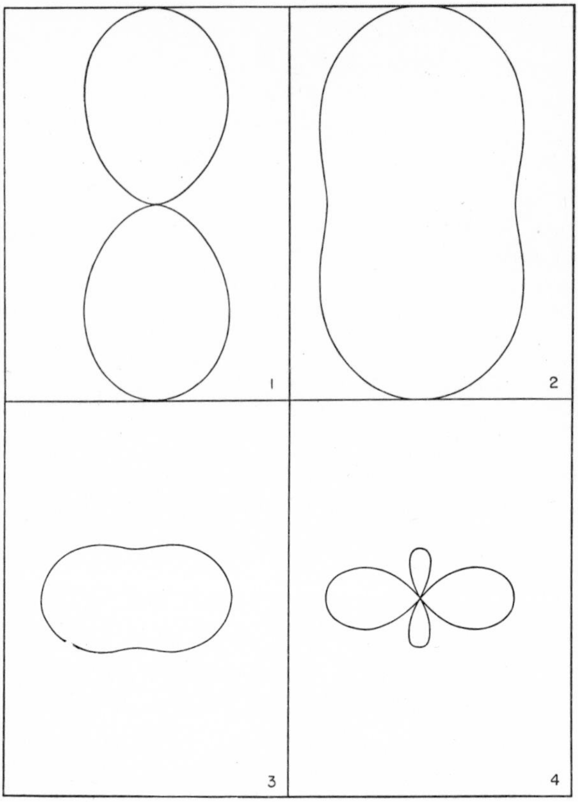

Fig. 33.1. Analysis of third-degree diagram (Gullstrand error) by concentric circles in the exit pupil. Typical curves obtained from Equations (33.30).

Eliminating χ leads again to a third-order relation between x_{III}' and y_{III}', which we write here simply as x', y', and this can be written in determinant form as

$$0=\begin{vmatrix} B^2 & 2B(A+C) & (A+C)^2 & -y'^2 & 0 & 0 \\ 0 & B^2+2BC & 2A(B+C)+C^2 & A^2-(x'^2+y'^2) & 0 & 0 \\ 0 & B^2 & 2B(A+C) & (A+C)^2 & -y'^2 & 0 \\ 0 & 0 & B^2+2BC & 2A(B+C)+C^2 & A^2-(x'^2+y'^2) & 0 \\ 0 & 0 & B^2 & 2B(A+C) & (A+C)^2 & -y'^2 \\ 0 & 0 & 0 & B^2+2BC & 2A(B+C)+C^2 & A^2-(x'^2+y'^2) \end{vmatrix} \tag{33.33}$$

We shall give some examples of the general curves in the next chapter.

Fourth-Degree Diagram

$$x_{IV}' = \tfrac{1}{2}\,(k'/n')\,r'^4 r\,[\bar{N}_{23} \cos\chi \sin\chi]$$
$$y_{IV}' = \tfrac{1}{2}\,(k'/n')\,r'^4 r\,[\tfrac{1}{4}\bar{M}_{33} + \bar{N}_{23} \cos^2\chi]. \qquad (33.34)$$

The curves corresponding to a set of concentric circles in the exit pupil, $r' = r_o'$, consist of a set of eccentric circles

$$\frac{x_{IV}'^2}{\left(\frac{1}{4}\frac{k'}{n'} r'^4 r \bar{N}_{23}\right)^2} + \frac{\left[y_{IV}' - \frac{1}{8}\frac{k'}{n'} r'^4 r\,(\bar{M}_{33} + 2\bar{N}_{23})\right]^2}{\left(\frac{1}{4}\frac{k'}{n'} r'^4 r\,\bar{N}_{23}\right)^2} = 1. \qquad (33.35)$$

These circles have an envelope given by the straight lines

$$\bar{N}_{23}^2 y_{IV}'^2 = \bar{M}_{33}\,(\tfrac{1}{4}\bar{M}_{33} + \bar{N}_{23})\,x_{IV}'^2. \qquad (33.36)$$

Fifth-Degree Diagram

The equations

$$x_V' = \tfrac{1}{8}\,(k'/n')\,r'^5 \bar{N}_{33} \sin\chi$$
$$y_V' = \tfrac{1}{8}\,(k'/n')\,r'^5 \bar{N}_{33} \cos\chi \qquad (33.37)$$

give, for the rays through a series of concentric circles in the exit pupil, a series of concentric circles in the image plane, with radii proportional to the fifth power of the aperture:

$$x_V'^2 + y_V'^2 = \left(\tfrac{1}{8}\frac{k'}{n'} r'^5 \bar{N}_{33}\right)^2. \qquad (33.38)$$

We have discussed the curves in which the rays through a series of concentric circles intersect the image planes, because this gives us a picture of the form of the nucleus of the image.

In appraising the image, we must, however, take into account the fact that, owing to vignetting (see Chapter 11), the exit pupil is in general not a circle, but the area common to three eccentric circular apertures. This is shown at the right side of Figure 32.1.

We shall give an example, in the next chapter, of how to use the spot-diagram analysis to ascertain the correction of an optical system.

In the investigation of a photographic objective, the object point is often assumed to be at infinity. The results contained in the last two chapters are only slightly changed by introducing into the formulae the direction cosines of the infinite point which we intend to image. This involves simply replacing r by $\tan \sigma$, where σ is the angle formed with the axis by the bundle of parallel rays coming from the infinite point.

CHAPTER THIRTY-FOUR

Analysis of the Spot Diagrams for a Sample System

To illustrate the meaning and the practical application of the results of the last chapter, a numerical example will be analyzed. Since the example is taken from the study of a photographic objective, we shall first transform the basic formulae to fit the case of an infinite object.

In this case the image functions M and N may be defined by

$$\Xi' = M\Xi + Nx' \qquad H' = MH + Ny', \tag{34.1}$$

where

$$\Xi = \frac{\xi}{\zeta}, \quad H = \frac{\eta}{\zeta}, \quad \Xi' = \frac{\xi'}{\zeta'}, \quad H' = \frac{\eta'}{\zeta'}, \tag{34.2}$$

where again ξ, η, ζ and ξ', η', ζ' are the optical direction cosines in the object and image spaces, respectively, and x', y' are the coordinates of the intersection points of the rays with the exit pupil. The coefficients M and N are functions of the symmetric functions of the (infinite) object-point coordinates (ξ, η) and exit-pupil coordinates (x', y'). In this case they are functions of v_1, v_2, v_3, where

$$2v_1 = \xi^2 + \eta^2, \quad v_2 = \xi x' + \eta y', \quad 2v_3 = x'^2 + y'^2. \tag{34.3}$$

The coordinates of the intersection point of a ray with a plane perpendicular to the axis at the distance k' from the exit pupil are then given by

$$x'_{k'} = x' + k'\,\Xi' = (1 + k'N)\,x' + k'M\,\Xi$$
$$y'_{k'} = y' + k'\,H' = (1 + k'N)\,y' + k'MH, \tag{34.4}$$

whereas the coordinates of the diapoint (the intersection with the meridional plane) are given by

$$\begin{aligned} x_D' &= -(M/N)\,\Xi \\ y_D' &= -(M/N)\,H \\ z_D' &= -(1/N). \end{aligned} \tag{34.5}$$

Because of the rotational symmetry of the system, no loss of generality results if we assume that $\xi = \Xi = 0$. In this case Formulae (34.1) to (34.5) reduce to

$$\begin{aligned} \Xi' &= Nx' & 2v_1 &= \eta^2 \\ H' &= Ny' + MH & v_2 &= \eta y' \\ & & 2v_3 &= x'^2 + y'^2 \end{aligned} \tag{34.6}$$

and

$$\begin{aligned} x'_{k'} &= (1 + k'N)\,x' & x_D' &= 0 \\ y'_{k'} &= (1 + k'N)\,y' + k'MH & y_D' &= -(M/N)\,H \\ z'_{k'} &= k' & z_D' &= -(1/N). \end{aligned}$$

The coordinates v_1, v_2, v_3 are connected with the first mixed characteristic $V\,(v_1, v_2, v_3)$, which can be related to M and N in the following way.

The Bruns-Hamilton equations for the first mixed characteristic function V analogous to the formulae in (20.7) are obtained from (16.4) in the form

$$\begin{aligned} \xi' &= V_2\xi + V_3x' & x &= V_1\xi + V_2x' \\ \eta' &= V_2\eta + V_3y' & y &= V_1\eta + V_2y', \quad (V_i = \partial V/\partial v_i). \end{aligned} \tag{34.7}$$

Comparison of Equations (34.7) and (34.1) gives

$$V_2 = M\zeta'/\zeta \qquad V_3 = N\zeta'. \tag{34.8}$$

However,

$$\begin{aligned} \xi^2 + \eta^2 + \zeta^2 &= n^2 \\ \xi'^2 + \eta'^2 + \zeta'^2 &= n'^2 \end{aligned} \tag{34.9}$$

or

$$n^2/\zeta^2 = \Xi^2 + H^2 + 1 = 1 + 2v_1/\zeta^2$$

$$\begin{aligned} n'^2/\zeta'^2 &= \Xi'^2 + H'^2 + 1 = 1 + M^2(\Xi^2 + H^2) \\ &\quad + 2MN(\Xi x' + Hy') + N^2(x'^2 + y'^2) \\ &= 1 + (2v_1/\zeta^2)M^2 + (2v_2/\zeta)MN + 2v_3N^2, \end{aligned} \tag{34.10}$$

which leads to

$$\begin{aligned} V_2 &= Mn'/\sqrt{\zeta^2(1 + 2N^2v_3) + 2MN\zeta v_2 + 2M^2v_1} \\ V_3 &= Nn'\zeta/\sqrt{\zeta^2(1 + 2N^2v_3) + 2MN\zeta v_2 + 2M^2v_1}, \end{aligned} \tag{34.11}$$

where

$$\zeta^2 = n^2 - 2v_1.$$

Equations (34.11) can serve to compute all the functional relationships between the development coefficients of M and N.

After this digression, let us return to Formulae (34.6). To illustrate the methods, we have selected an aerial lens of aperture $f/5.6$ with a field angle of 24 degrees.

Using the methods described in Chapter 11, we compute for each field angle (that is, for each infinite object point) the vignetted entrance and exit pupils and then trace a small number of rays suitably distributed over the vignetted entrance pupil through the optical system.

In general it will be sufficient to consider only two field angles and the axial bundle. In the practical example, however, we have investigated field angles of 0, 5, 10, 15, 20, and 24 degrees with the axis. For each angle the tracing of nine rays of the bundle is ordinarily sufficient, and for the axis the tracing of three rays suffices. (However, in the example, six axis rays were traced.)

By means of the tracing methods described in the first part of the book (see also the numerical example in the Appendix), the selected rays were traced through the system, and the coordinates of the diapoints as well as the coordinates x', y' of the intersection of the rays with the exit pupil were calculated. The left-hand side of Figure 34.1 shows the intersection points of the chosen rays in the vignetted exit pupil

Table VI gives the coordinates x', y' of the calculated rays in the exit pupil, the coordinates y_D', z_D' of the diapoints, and the corresponding values of M and N, the latter two being obtained by writing the last equations of (34.6) in the form*

$$M = y_D'/z_D'H = y_D'\zeta/z_D'\eta, \quad N = -1/z_D'. \tag{34.12}$$

For a given field angle, since the rays of the entering bundle are parallel, η, ζ, and v_1 are constant, and M and N become functions of v_2 and v_3. Assuming

$$\begin{aligned} M &= M_o + M_2v_2 + M_3v_3 + \tfrac{1}{2}(M_{22}v_2^2 + 2M_{23}v_2v_3 + M_{33}v_3^2) \\ N &= N_o + N_2v_2 + N_3v_3 + \tfrac{1}{2}(N_{22}v_2^2 + 2N_{23}v_2v_3 + N_{33}v_3^2), \end{aligned} \tag{34.13}$$

we can compute the coefficients M_i and N_i (Table VII) by fitting the calculated values in Equations (34.12) by least-square techniques. Having obtained these coefficients, we can compute M and N for a large number of rays, for instance, for the rays whose intersection points with the exit pupil are shown in the second column of Figure 34.1. The values of M and N for all these rays having been found, Formulae (34.6) give the intersection points with a plane at the (arbitrary) distance k' from the exit pupil, as well as the coordinates of their diapoints.

In choosing the above large number of rays to be investigated, it is important to select them so that their intersection points are evenly distributed over the vignetted exit pupil, as in Figure 34.1. Then we can say that each ray represents the same amount of light, and a plot of the intersection points of these rays with the image plane will give a fair idea of the illuminance distribution in this plane, areas having a high concentration of intersection points corresponding to areas of high illuminance in the image.

In Figure 34.2 we have plotted the intersection points of the rays passing through this lens with a set of three image planes and compared the resulting "spot diagrams" with a set of photomicrographs taken with point light sources by means of a manufactured optical system having the same constructional data as our mathematical example. Considering that no practical system can be perfectly built according to specifications, the

* For the axial rays the formula for M becomes indeterminate since $\eta = y_D' = 0$. Here we have $M = N\,x/\xi' = N\,y/\eta'$ [analogous to Eq. (32.13)], which follows from Eqs. (34.7) and (34.8) when $\xi = \eta = 0$. In the example in Table VI, the rays were chosen such that $y = \eta' = 0$, so the values for M had to be obtained from the formula $M = N\,x/\xi'$.

TABLE VI

Coordinates x' and y' of the Intersections of the Calculated Rays with the Exit Pupil, the Coordinates y_D' and z_D' of the Diapoints, and the Corresponding Values of M and N. (The tabulated values are to be multiplied by the factors at the heads of the respective columns.)

	x' $\times 10^2$	y' $\times 10^2$	y_D' $\times 10^2$	z_D' $\times 10^2$	M	N $\times 10^{-2}$
0°	+0.02576	0	0	+2.97370	−1.03041	−0.33628
	0.07729	0	0	2.97082	1.03050	0.33661
	0.12888	0	0	2.96571	1.03065	0.33719
	0.18055	0	0	2.95990	1.03083	0.33785
	0.23238	0	0	2.95624	1.03099	0.33827
	0.28445	0	0	2.96004	1.03102	0.33783
5°	+0.02563	+0.27347	+0.26692	+2.95740	−1.03164	−0.33814
	0.02565	+0.18533	0.26709	2.96038	1.03122	0.33779
	0.02578	−0.02178	0.26781	2.97089	1.03037	0.33660
	0.02594	−0.17215	0.26654	2.95682	1.03033	0.33820
	0.02603	−0.23319	0.26628	2.95419	1.03025	0.33850
	0.15404	+0.19995	0.26676	2.95613	1.03146	0.33828
	0.15477	−0.00718	0.26700	2.96089	1.03070	0.33774
	0.15597	−0.18792	0.26636	2.95466	1.03040	0.33845
	0.25852	−0.00778	0.26660	2.95577	1.03095	0.33832
10°	+0.02545	+0.25053	+0.53747	+2.95424	−1.03178	−0.33850
	0.02552	+0.19277	0.53801	2.95808	1.03147	0.33806
	0.02576	+0.01678	0.53912	2.96710	1.03046	0.33703
	0.02603	−0.13405	0.53677	2.95579	1.02989	0.33832
	0.02616	−0.19583	0.53596	2.95234	1.02955	0.33871
	0.12766	+0.19248	0.53741	2.95446	1.03159	0.33847
	0.12886	+0.01636	0.53790	2.95985	1.03065	0.33786
	0.13023	−0.13464	0.53623	2.95265	1.02996	0.33868
	0.23240	+0.01534	0.53669	2.95256	1.03088	0.33869
15°	+0.02533	+0.23054	+0.81598	+2.95232	−1.03149	−0.33872
	0.02543	+0.17338	0.81720	2.95724	1.03131	0.33815
	0.02574	+0.02737	0.81808	2.96264	1.03054	0.33754
	0.02604	−0.09382	0.81580	2.95650	1.02981	0.33824
	0.02621	−0.15549	0.81477	2.95442	1.02923	0.33848
	0.12757	+0.14398	0.81633	2.95412	1.03130	0.33851
	0.12883	+0.02668	0.81646	2.95639	1.03068	0.33825
	0.13034	−0.09429	0.81496	2.95342	1.02982	0.33859
	0.23238	+0.02498	0.81531	2.95205	1.03073	0.33875
20°	+0.02535	+0.18639	+1.10940	+2.95715	−1.03073	−0.33816
	0.02549	+0.12909	1.11128	2.96178	1.03087	0.33763
	0.02573	+0.04142	1.11214	2.96440	1.03076	0.33734
	0.02599	−0.04872	1.11147	2.96375	1.03036	0.33741
	0.02619	−0.11044	1.11133	2.96490	1.02984	0.33728
	0.12754	+0.12815	1.10950	2.95690	1.03092	0.33819
	0.12874	+0.04036	1.11041	2.95970	1.03079	0.33787
	0.13009	−0.04994	1.11053	2.96149	1.03028	0.33767
	0.23228	+0.03778	1.11023	2.95991	1.03055	0.33785
24°	+0.02529	+0.20115	+1.35800	+2.96379	−1.02913	−0.33741
	0.02543	+0.14422	1.36286	2.97119	1.03024	0.33657
	0.02568	+0.05720	1.36684	2.97715	1.03118	0.33589
	0.02596	−0.03222	1.36951	2.98162	1.03165	0.33539
	0.02607	−0.06263	1.37078	2.98421	1.03170	0.33510
	0.12730	+0.14294	1.36102	2.96743	1.03015	0.33699
	0.12856	+0.05575	1.36535	2.97417	1.03109	0.33623
	0.12999	−0.03388	1.36924	2.98170	1.03141	0.33538
	0.23203	+0.05221	1.36698	2.97946	1.03049	0.33563

TABLE VII

Coefficients of M_i and N_i Found by Fitting the Calculated Values of M and N. (The values in this table were obtained from the values of Table VI as tabulated without regard for the multiplying factor.)

	0°	5°	10°	15°	20°	24°
M_0	−1.03040	−1.03039	−1.03037	−1.03038	−1.03061	−1.03158
M_2		+0.02362	+0.02358	+0.02166	+0.01163	−0.01050
M_3	−0.03474	−0.03267	−0.02953	−0.02167	−0.00667	+0.01120
M_{22}		+0.34000	+0.39169	+0.39627	+0.38004	+0.45777
M_{23}		+0.23834	+0.25442	+0.24585	+0.26183	+0.35585
M_{33}	+0.95002	+0.92830	+1.04565	+1.18962	+1.23798	+1.68866
N_0	−0.33621	−0.33646	−0.33705	−0.33759	−0.33732	−0.33556
N_2		−0.03059	−0.02659	−0.01932	−0.00509	+0.01129
N_3	−0.14320	−0.13357	−0.11952	−0.10273	−0.07961	−0.04499
N_{22}		+0.18273	+0.26618	+0.33827	+0.43878	+0.44733
N_{23}		+0.82430	+0.89503	+1.09077	+1.30256	+1.58620
N_{33}	+5.07263	+4.65424	+4.31610	+4.55706	+5.31065	+5.72851

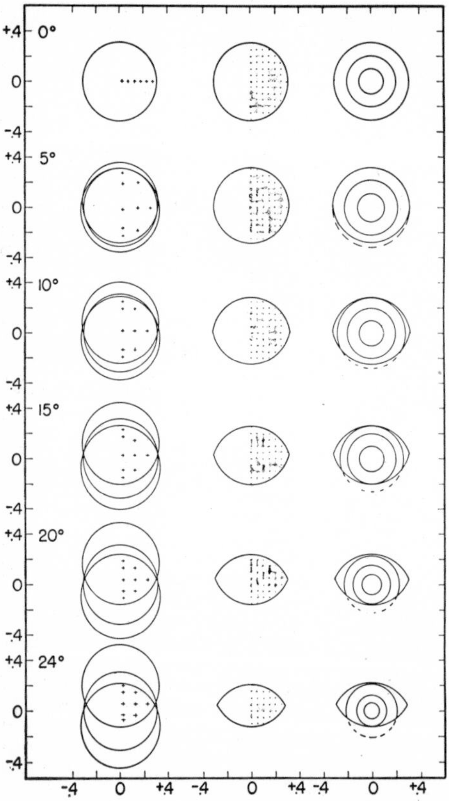

Fig. **34.1.** Diagram showing vignetting of lens used as example at the field angles shown. The intersecting circles in the left-hand column represent the mounts of the front and back components and the iris. The crosses represent the intersections of the exit pupil with the rays that were traced to give the coefficients in the interpolation formula, while the dots represent the intersections of the exit pupil with the rays used for plotting the spot diagrams. The three concentric circles in the right-hand column represent the zones in the exit pupil used to obtain the curves in the right-hand columns of Figures **34.4** and **34.5**. Scales are in millimeters.

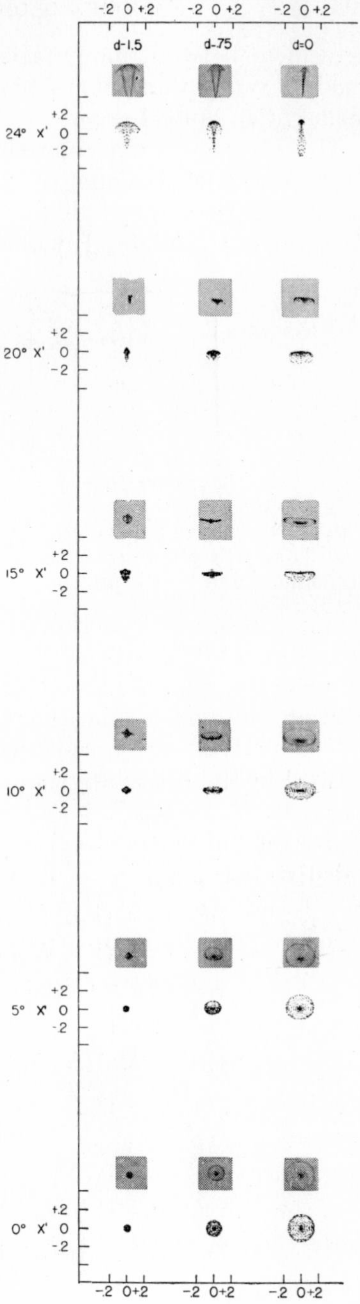

Fig. 34.2. Spot diagrams of lens used as example for six field angles and three image planes and photomicrographs of corresponding images of a point source obtained with the completed lens (*cf.* Fig. 32.1). Scales are in tenths of millimeters.

agreement between computation and performance is sufficiently good to verify that this method gives a valuable mathematical model of an optical system.

The accuracy of our approximation theory is shown by Figure 34.3. At the left is a spot diagram consisting of 218 points, each for a ray that was individually traced through the system. (Because of the bilateral symmetry, a single trace suffices for two

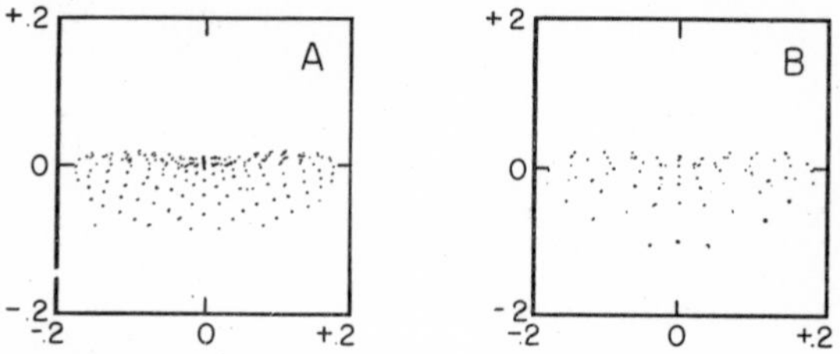

Fig. 34.3. Enlargements of 15° spot diagram in Figure 34.5. A, diagram containing 218 points each traced individually; B, diagram containing 86 points found by the interpolation formulae. Scales are in millimeters.

points except in the meridional plane.) At the right is a diagram consisting of 86 points obtained by interpolation from the traces of nine rays, using Equations (34.13). The slight difference in appearance arises from the difference in the number of points used.

The analysis of the spot diagrams, based on the method described in the preceding chapter, is shown in Figures 34.4 and 34.5.

For each of the five levels of errors we find a spot diagram, the calculation being done [*cf.* Eqs. (33.3) to (33.7)] by the equations

$$\begin{aligned}
x_{\mathrm{I}}' &= x'\,(1 + k'N_o) \\
y_{\mathrm{I}}' &= y'\,(1 + k'N_o) + k'M_2v_2H, \\
x_{\mathrm{II}}' &= k'x'\,[N_2v_2] \\
y_{\mathrm{II}}' &= k'\,[y'N_2v_2 + (M_3v_3 + \tfrac{1}{2}\,M_{22}v_2^2)\,H], \\
x_{\mathrm{III}}' &= k'x'\,[N_3v_3 + \tfrac{1}{2}\,N_{22}v_2^2] \qquad (34.14) \\
y_{\mathrm{III}}' &= k'\,[y'\,(N_3v_3 + \tfrac{1}{2}\,N_{22}v_2^2) + HM_{23}v_2v_3], \\
x_{\mathrm{IV}}' &= k'x'\,[N_{23}v_2v_3] \\
y_{\mathrm{IV}}' &= k'\,[y'N_{23}v_2v_3 + \tfrac{1}{2}\,M_{33}v_3^2H], \\
x_{\mathrm{V}}' &= k'x'\,\tfrac{1}{2}\,N_{33}v_3^2 \\
y_{\mathrm{V}}' &= k'y'\,\tfrac{1}{2}\,N_{33}v_3^2.
\end{aligned}$$

The understanding of the spot diagrams of every order can be facilitated if, as in the previous chapter, we investigate the rays through a series of concentric circles in the exit pupil, the centers of these circles being on the axis. In considering such a series of concentric circles, however, we must be conscious of the fact that, owing to vignetting, we cannot exhaust the vignetted aperture by a series of concentric circles around the axis point and that, as the radius exceeds a certain size, not all the circumference of the circle lies inside the vignetted pupil. This is made clear by the right-hand column of Figure 34.1, where the three concentric circles in each diagram represent the zones in the exit pupil through which the rays will be assumed to pass. The intersecting circles, as in the other columns, indicate the unobstructed aperture. The intercepts that the obstructed rays would make with the assumed image plane are shown in Figures 34.4 and 34.5 by points.

Referring to these figures, the rays through a set of concentric circles give, in the first-degree image, a set of concentric ellipses, in the second-degree image, a set of eccentric ellipses with their centers on the meridional line ($x' = 0$), and, for the third-degree errors, a set of concentric figures which may be lemniscates, ovals, ellipses, or circles. The fourth-degree figures consist of a set of eccentric circles, and the fifth-degree curves are concentric circles again. The sizes of the curves in the image plane are proportional to the first, second, third, fourth, and fifth powers, respectively, of the aperture radius. The equations of the respective curves can be written:

First Degree (Astigmatism)

$$\frac{x_{\mathrm{I}}'^2}{(A_1 r')^2} + \frac{y_{\mathrm{I}}'^2}{(B_1 r')^2} = 1, \qquad (34.15)$$

with

$$A_1 = 1 + k' N_o, \quad B_1 = 1 + k' (N_o + M_2 H \eta),$$

where r' is the radius of the circle in the exit pupil. This equation represents a set of concentric ellipses.

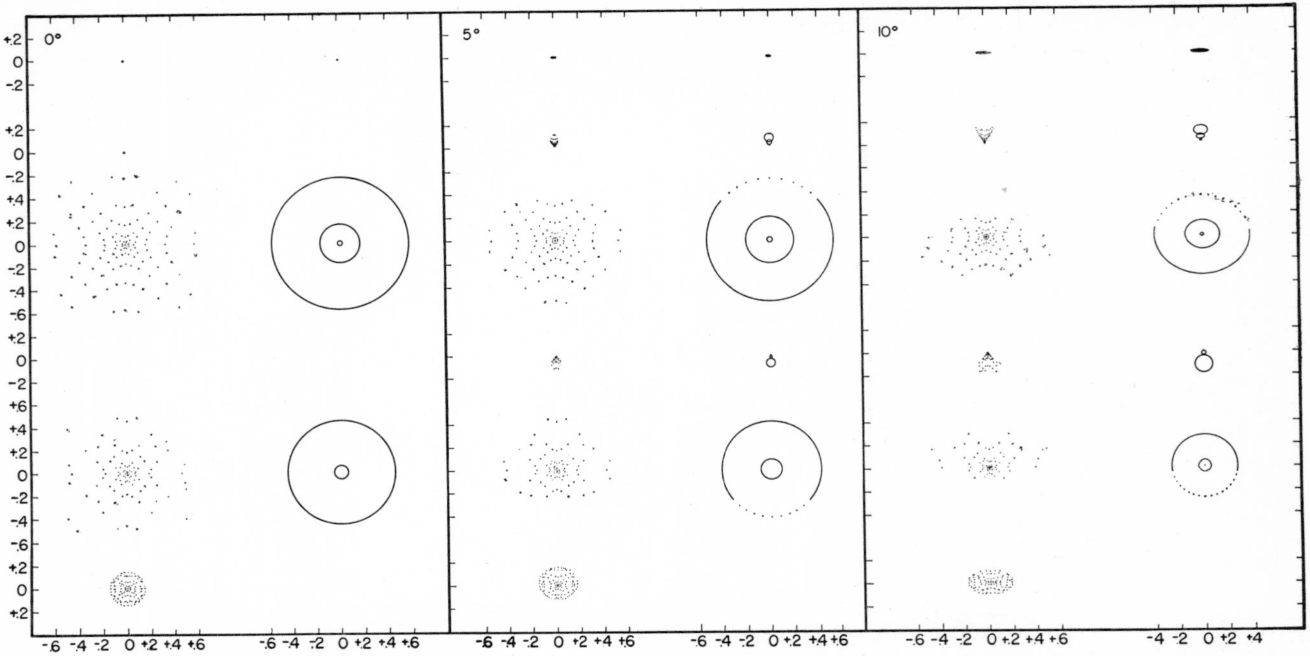

Fig. 34.4. Spot diagrams of lens used as example for three field angles. The first five rows represent the five sets of terms in the analysis and the last row, the actual image. The right-hand columns show for each field angle the curves produced on the assumed image plane by rays passing through the zones of the exit pupil indicated in Figure 34.1. The dotted parts of these curves are cut off by vignetting. Scales are in millimeters.

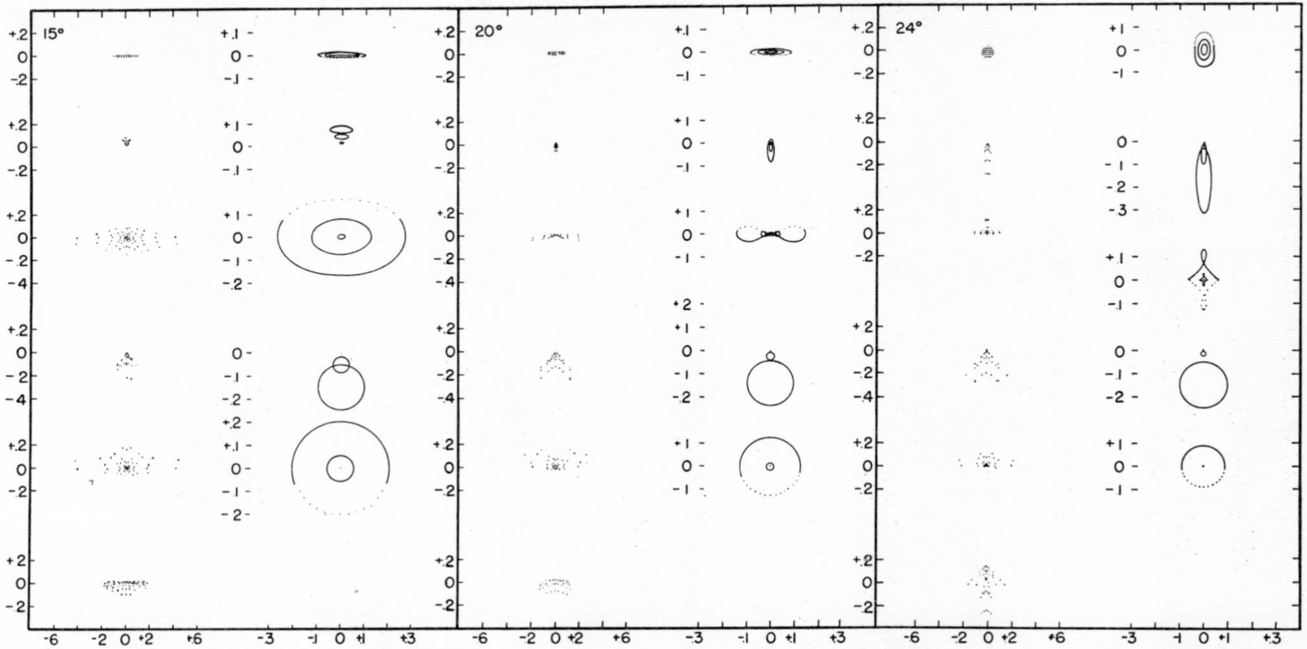

Fig. 34.5. Continuation of Figure 34.4 for larger field angles. The curves formed by the zonal rays are so small that they have been drawn to double scale, as indicated by the values on the axes. The curve representing the fifth-order aberration for the intermediate zone at 24° is a circle that is too small to show in the figure. Scales are in millimeters.

Second Degree (Asymmetry)

$$\frac{(y_{\text{II}}' - A_2 r'^2)^2}{(B_2 r'^2)^2} + \frac{x_{\text{II}}'^2}{(C_2 r'^2)^2} = 1, \tag{34.16}$$

with

$$\begin{aligned} A_2 &= \tfrac{1}{2}k'\,(M_3 H\, N_2 \eta + \tfrac{1}{2} M_{22}\eta^2 H) \\ B_2 &= \tfrac{1}{2}k'\,(N_2\eta + \tfrac{1}{2}M_{22}\eta^2 H) \\ C_2 &= \tfrac{1}{2}k'\,N_2\eta. \end{aligned}$$

These equations represent a set of eccentric ellipses. The shift of the center along the meridional direction is given by $A_2 r'^2$, while the lines given by

$$y_{\text{II}}'^2 (N_2\eta)^2 = x_{\text{II}}'^2 M_3 H\,(M_3 H + 2N_2\eta + M_{22}\eta^2 H) \tag{34.17}$$

form the common asymptotes.

Third Degree (Gullstrand Errors)

$$\begin{aligned} x_{\text{III}}' &= r'^3 \cos\phi\,[A_3 + B_3 \sin^2\phi] \\ y_{\text{III}}' &= r'^3 \sin\phi\,[C_3 + B_3 \sin^2\phi], \end{aligned} \tag{34.18}$$

with

$$\begin{aligned} A_3 &= \tfrac{1}{2}k'\,N_3 \\ B_3 &= \tfrac{1}{2}k'\,N_{22}\eta^2 \\ C_3 &= \tfrac{1}{2}k'\,(N_3 + M_{23}\eta H), \end{aligned} \tag{34.19}$$

giving a set of concentric ovals with double symmetry.

Fourth Degree

$$x_{\text{IV}}'^2 + (y_{\text{IV}}' - A_4 r'^4)^2 = (B_4 r'^4)^2, \tag{34.20}$$

with

$$\begin{aligned} A_4 &= \tfrac{1}{4}k'\,(N_{23}\eta + \tfrac{1}{2}\,M_{33}H) \\ B_4 &= \tfrac{1}{4}k'\,N_{23}\eta, \end{aligned}$$

giving a set of eccentric circles with the centers at $x' = 0$, $y' = A_4 r'^4$.

Fifth Degree

$$x_V'^2 + y_V'^2 = (A_5 r'^5)^2 \tag{34.21}$$

with

$$A_5 = \tfrac{1}{8} k' N_{33},$$

leading to a set of concentric circles with radii proportional to the fifth power of the aperture radius.

The coefficients A_i, B_i, and C_i in these equations for the lens used as an example are given in Table VIII. They are obviously functions of the field angle, but they do not change rapidly.

The first-, third-, and fifth-degree curves have double symmetry with respect to the x- and y-axes, whereas the second- and fourth-degree curves have symmetry only with respect to the meridional direction. It is obvious that, in a well-corrected optical system, each of these two groups of errors, the symmetric and the asymmetric, must balance within itself.

We shall now calculate the values of M and N for the axial point, that is, when $v_1 = v_2 = \eta = H = 0$, since the first equation of (34.12) does not determine M in this case.

Setting $M\ (v_1 = v_2 = 0) = \bar{M}$; $N\ (v_1 = v_2 = 0) = \bar{N}$, we have from Equations (34.7)

$$\begin{aligned} \eta' &= \bar{V}_3 y' \\ y &= \bar{V}_2 y' = (\bar{V}_2/\bar{V}_3)\,\eta', \end{aligned} \tag{34.22}$$

the notation $\bar{V}_i$ indicating that the functions V_i are specialized for the axial case. Hence we find from Equations (34.11)

$$\begin{aligned} \bar{V}_3 &= \bar{N} n'/\sqrt{1 + 2\bar{N}^2 v_3} = \eta'/y' \\ \bar{V}_2/\bar{V}_3 &= (1/n)\,\bar{M}/\bar{N} = y/\eta'. \end{aligned} \tag{34.23}$$

These formulae serve to compute

$$\begin{aligned} \bar{M} &= \bar{M}_o + \bar{M}_3 v_3 + \tfrac{1}{2}\,\bar{M}_{33} v_3^2 \\ \bar{N} &= \bar{N}_o + \bar{N}_3 v_3 + \tfrac{1}{2}\bar{N}_{33} v_3^2 \end{aligned} \tag{34.24}$$

from the ray trace. From Equations (34.12) we have also

$$-\,z_D' = \bar{N} = \bar{N}_o + \bar{N}_3 v_3 + \tfrac{1}{2}\bar{N}_{33} v_3^2,$$

TABLE VIII

Values of the Coefficients in Equations (34.15) to (34.21) for the Lens Used as an Example. (The tabulated values are to be multiplied by the factors at the heads of the respective columns.)

	First Order		*Second Order*			*Third Order*			*Fourth Order*		*Fifth Order*
Field Angle	A_1	B_1	A_2	B_2	C_2	A_3	B_3	C_3	A_4	B_4	A_5
	$+10^{-2}$	$\times 10^{-2}$	$\times 10^{-4}$	$\times 10^{-4}$	$\times 10^{-4}$	$\times 10^{-6}$	$\times 10^{-6}$	$\times 10^{-6}$	$\times 10^{-8}$	$\times 10^{-8}$	$\times 10^{-10}$
0°	+0.0078	+0.0078	0	0	0	−21.2946	0	−21.2946	0	0	+188.581
5°	−0.0666	−0.0127	+0.8047	+0.3797	+0.3965	−19.8625	+0.2064	−19.5923	− 8.3608	− 5.3415	+173.027
10°	−0.2420	−0.02731	+1.3061	+0.5318	+0.6866	−17.7732	+1.1935	−16.6148	−18.4097	−11.5559	+160.456
15°	−0.4026	+0.0441	+1.0781	+0.2147	+0.7435	−15.2765	+3.3697	−12.7410	−32.8402	−20.9905	+169.414
20°	−0.3223	+0.1083	−0.5831	−0.9441	+0.2589	−11.8384	+7.6330	− 6.9921	−49.8750	−33.1240	+197.430
24°	+0.2011	−0.3644	−3.9314	−3.1899	−0.6829	− 6.6902	+11.0057	+ 2.8923	−75.9206	−47.9700	+212.965

so that $\bar{N}$ is given by the sperical aberration of the axis beam, whereas $\bar{M}/\bar{N} = n\bar{V}_2/\bar{V}_3 = ny/\eta'$ is given by the so-called sine condition of the axis beam.

Equations (34.15) to (34.21) show that N_o, N_3, and N_{33} influence the symmetric or even aberrations, so that a correct balance of $\bar{N}_3$, $\bar{N}_{33}$, $\bar{M}_3$, and $\bar{M}_{33}$ will influence the off-axis image to a certain extent and counterbalance the other terms.

The way this procedure can be used to analyze and improve a lens is illustrated by Figure 34.6. Section I is for a certain lens

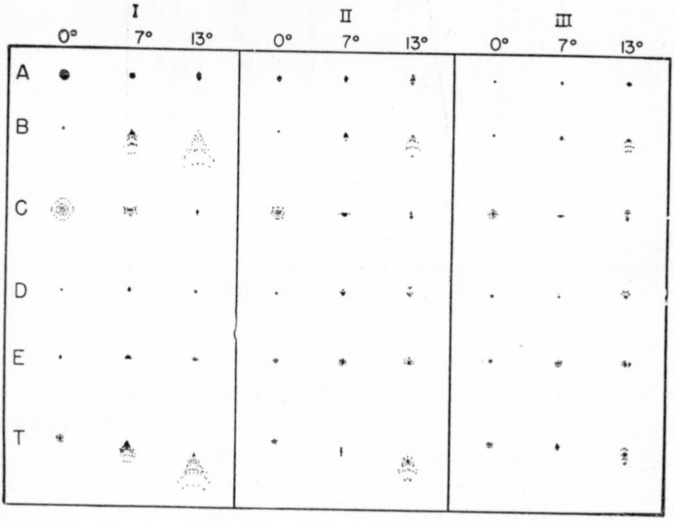

Fig. 34.6. Diagram showing how the performance of a certain lens was improved by analyzing the spot diagrams. Rows *A-E* in Section I represent the terms of the first to the fifth order at each of three field angles of the original lens; row *T* represents their sum, the actual image. Section II is for the lens when isoplanasie is corrected, and Section III shows the great over-all improvement that results when the isoplanasie is slightly undercorrected.

as originally designed, and the rows of spot diagrams lettered from *A* to *E* represent the five groups of terms from the first to the fifth order for the three field angles shown at the top. Row *T* represents the spot diagrams of the actual image. The principal rays in this row are displaced from the origin because the term of zero order, representing the distortion, has been included.

It is evident that the comet-like shape of the pattern at 13° arises from the second-degree or asymmetry error. Figure 34.7 shows at the left the curve of the Staeble-Lihotzky condition,

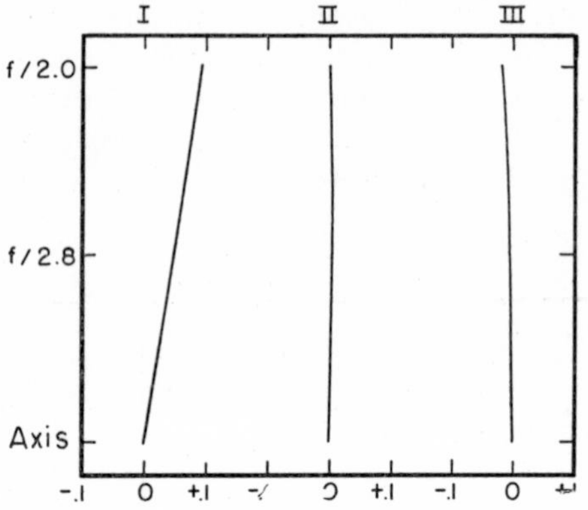

Fig. 34.7. Isoplanasie curves of the lens of Figure 34.6. The three sections of this figure correspond to the similarly numbered sections of Figure 34.6. Scales are in millimeters.

Equation (27.67), or *isoplanasie* curve for this lens, and it is clear that the isoplanasie is overcorrected. The design data were changed to accurately correct the isoplanasie, as shown by curve II, and the spot diagrams of Section II in Figure 34.6 resulted. The asymmetry error is still sizeable for the largest field angle. The isoplanasie was then slightly undercorrected, as shown by curve III in Figure 34.7, when the spot diagrams in Section III resulted. The second-degree errors now practically balance the fourth-degree errors and the system has a much better over-all image, although a further retouching might give a still better balance of the small symmetrical errors. For each of the three systems, the spot diagrams were made for the "best" focal position, which deviates slightly from the position of the axial focus.

It is the aim of the book to lead the reader to a simple mathematical model of an optical system, one which predicts the image formation for every object point with sufficient accuracy.

From the model thus obtained, it is possible to judge the image quality of the system. It is, moreover, possible from the spot diagrams to calculate the illuminance distribution in the image of an edge. Since the characteristic function E gives the light path from an object point to the exit pupil, and with it the phase distribution in the exit pupil, it is possible to adapt the methods here developed, to calculate the diffraction image approximately by replacing the diffraction integral with a sum. This, however, lies beyond the scope of this book.

PART IX. OPTICS IN GENERAL MEDIA

CHAPTER THIRTY-FIVE

Geometrical Optics in Inhomogeneous Media

Instead of starting with the laws of refraction and reflection, we could have developed the ideas in this book by starting from Fermat's principle. This principle states that light goes from an initial to a terminal point of its path along a curve C_o such that the curve integral

$$E = \int_{C_o} n ds \tag{35.1}$$

on the path taken by the light is such that, if $C(u)$ is a family of curves containing $C_o = C\ (u = 0)$ and connecting the initial and the terminal points, we have $(dE/du)_{u=o} = 0$ for any such family of curves.

The refractive index n will, in general, be a function of the position (x, y, z) and the direction $\dot{x}, \dot{y}, \dot{z}$, where the point means differentiation with respect to the curve parameter s. In order to have E independent of the curve parameter, we must assume n to be homogeneous of first order in the $\dot{x}, \dot{y}, \dot{z}$:

$$n\ (\lambda\dot{x}, \lambda\dot{y}, \lambda\dot{z}) = \lambda n\ (\dot{x}, \dot{y}, \dot{z}), \tag{35.2}$$

or, what is equivalent,

$$\frac{\partial n}{\partial \dot{x}}\dot{x} + \frac{\partial n}{\partial \dot{y}}\dot{y} + \frac{\partial n}{\partial \dot{z}}\dot{z} = n. \tag{35.3}$$

If Equation (35.2) is fulfilled and we change the curve parameter, we find from

$$s' = f(s), \quad ds'/ds = f' \tag{35.4}$$

that

$$\int_{C_o} n\left(\frac{dx}{ds'}, \frac{dy}{ds'}, \frac{dz}{ds'}\right) ds' = \int_{C_o} n\left(\frac{dx}{ds}, \frac{dy}{ds}, \frac{dz}{ds}\right) \frac{ds}{ds'}\, ds' \qquad (35.5)$$

$$= \int_{C_o} n\left(\frac{dx}{ds}, \frac{dy}{ds}, \frac{dz}{ds}\right) ds,$$

These equations show that E is independent of the curve parameter, which therefore can be selected arbitrarily. In general, we shall choose s to be the arc length along the curve C_o, that is, we postulate that

$$\dot{x}^2 + \dot{y}^2 + \dot{z}^2 = 1. \qquad (35.6)$$

The optical medium is called *isotropic* if the refractive index does not depend on direction. In this case, we fulfill the above postulate by formally setting [see (35.6)]

$$n = n_0\,(x,y,z)\,\sqrt{\dot{x}^2 + \dot{y}^2 + \dot{z}^2}, \qquad (35.7)$$

where n_0 is a function of x, y, z alone, not depending on the direction cosines. In most of this chapter, we shall restrict ourselves to considering the path of light in such a medium, which is *inhomogeneous* but *isotropic.*

In the general case, we can form two gradient vectors for each point and direction, the gradient vector $\vec{g}$ with coordinates $(\partial n/\partial x,\ \partial n/\partial y,\ \partial n/\partial z)$ and the gradient vector $\vec{m}$ with coordinates $(\partial n/\partial \dot{x},\ \partial n/\partial \dot{y},\ \partial n/\partial \dot{z})$.

According to the calculus of variations, the extremals of the variation problem (1) are given by the Euler differential equations, which are

$$\frac{d}{ds}\left(\frac{\partial n}{\partial \dot{x}}\right) = \frac{\partial n}{\partial x}, \quad \frac{d}{ds}\left(\frac{\partial n}{\partial \dot{y}}\right) = \frac{\partial n}{\partial y}, \quad \frac{d}{ds}\left(\frac{\partial n}{\partial \dot{z}}\right) = \frac{\partial n}{\partial z}, \qquad (35.8)$$

or in vector form

$$(d\vec{m}/ds) = \vec{g}. \qquad (35.9)$$

In the case of an isotropic space, we have from (35.8)

$$\begin{aligned} \partial n/\partial \dot{x} &= n_0\dot{x} \\ \partial n/\partial \dot{y} &= n_0\dot{y} \quad \text{or} \quad \vec{m} = n_0\vec{a}, \\ \partial n/\partial \dot{z} &= n_0\dot{z} \end{aligned} \qquad (35.10)$$

where $\vec{a}$ is the vector with coordinates x, y, z and $\dot{\vec{a}}$ the vector with coordinates $\dot{x}, \dot{y}, \dot{z}$. Equation (35.9) now reads

$$n_0\ddot{\vec{a}} + \dot{n}_0\dot{\vec{a}} = \vec{g}. \qquad (35.11)$$

We now introduce the vector

$$\vec{l} = \frac{1}{n_0}\vec{g} = \frac{1}{n_0}\,\text{grad}\, n_0 = \text{grad}\,(ln\; n_0) \qquad (35.12)$$

and call $\vec{l}$ the lead vector. Taking the arc length as parameter, so that

$$\dot{\vec{a}}^2 = 1, \quad \dot{n}_0/n_0 = \vec{l}\dot{\vec{a}} \qquad (35.13)$$

(the latter follows from the definition of the gradient), we obtain from Equation (35.11) the equation

$$\ddot{\vec{a}} = \vec{l} - (\dot{n}_0/n_0)\,\dot{\vec{a}} = \vec{l}\,(\dot{\vec{a}}^2) - (\vec{l}\dot{\vec{a}})\,\dot{\vec{a}} = (\dot{\vec{a}} \times \vec{l}) \times \dot{\vec{a}} \qquad (35.14)$$

as the differential equation for the light rays. This permits us to compute $\ddot{\vec{a}}$ if $\vec{a}$ and $\dot{\vec{a}}$ are known, that is, it gives in general a single ray in a given direction through a point.

From Equation (35.14) we derive

$$\ddot{\vec{a}} \times \dot{\vec{a}} = \vec{l} \times \dot{\vec{a}},\ [\dddot{\vec{a}}\,\ddot{\vec{a}}\,\dot{\vec{a}}] = [\dot{\vec{l}}\,\vec{l}\,\dot{\vec{a}}], \qquad (35.15)$$

which permits us to compute the curvature ϱ and torsion τ of a light ray as functions of $\vec{l}$ and $\dot{\vec{a}}$:

$$\varrho^2 = (\vec{l} \times \dot{\vec{a}})^2, \quad \tau = [\dot{\vec{l}}\,\vec{l}\,\dot{\vec{a}}]/(\vec{l} \times \dot{\vec{a}})^2. \qquad (35.16)$$

From (35.16) we show that all curves (for variable vector $\dot{\vec{a}}$) are straight lines if and only if $\vec{l} = 0$, that is, if

$$n = n_0 \qquad (35.17)$$

is constant, which means that the medium is homogeneous. All curves are plane if and only if

$$[\dot{\vec{l}}\,\vec{l}\,\dot{\vec{a}}] = 0. \qquad (35.18)$$

Equation (35.18) is equivalent to the existence of a function $\alpha\,(x, y, z)$ such that

$$\dot{\vec{l}} \times \dot{\vec{a}} = \alpha\,(\vec{l} \times \dot{\vec{a}}). \qquad (35.19)$$

This equation is, on the other hand, equivalent to the existence of a vector

$$\vec{p} = \varkappa (\vec{l} \times \vec{a}) \tag{35.20}$$

invariant along each extremal, that is, such that $\dot{\vec{p}} = 0$.

The relationship between a and $\varkappa$ can be found by differentiating (35.20), taking into account (35.14). We find

$$\begin{aligned} 0 = \dot{\vec{p}} &= \dot{\varkappa} (\vec{l} \times \vec{a}) + \varkappa (\dot{\vec{l}} \times \vec{a}) + \varkappa (\vec{l} \times \dot{\vec{a}}) \qquad (35.21) \\ &= \dot{\varkappa} (\vec{l} \times \vec{a}) + \varkappa (\dot{\vec{l}} \times \vec{a}) - \varkappa (\dot{n}_0/n_0) (\vec{l} \times \vec{a},) \end{aligned}$$

from which we derive

$$a = \frac{\dot{n}_0}{n_0} - \frac{\dot{\varkappa}}{\varkappa} = \frac{d}{ds} \ln \left(\frac{n_0}{\varkappa}\right) \tag{35.22}$$

or

$$\varkappa = C n_0 \, e^{-\int a \, ds}, \tag{35.23}$$

C being an arbitrary integration constant, whereas a and $\varkappa$ are in general functions of x, y, z.

All the light rays are circles if and only if, because of Equation (35.16), ϱ is constant along the curves. Then

$$\vec{p} = C (\vec{l} \times \vec{a}) \tag{35.24}$$

and we have

$$\varkappa = C, \ a = \frac{1}{n_0} \frac{dn_o}{ds} = \frac{\dot{n}_0}{n_0}. \tag{35.25}$$

In each case, $\vec{p}$ forms a first integral of the differential equations (35.14), so that we can obtain the analytical formulae for the curves by a quadrature.

Let us apply these results to the important practical cases in which we have a refractive medium with parallel or concentric layers.

Parallel Layers. We choose the coordinate system such that the z-axis is normal to the plane of constant refractive index. Then n is a function of z alone, and we have

$$\vec{l} = \frac{1}{n} \frac{dn}{dz} \vec{k} = \phi \vec{k}, \tag{35.26}$$

where $\vec{k}$ is the unit vector in the direction of the z-axis.

The differential equation of the light rays is

$$\ddot{\vec{a}} = (\dot{\vec{a}} \times \vec{l}) \times \dot{\vec{a}} = \phi\,(\dot{\vec{a}} \times \vec{k}) \times \dot{\vec{a}}. \tag{35.27}$$

Equation (35.26) gives

$$\vec{l} \times \ddot{\vec{a}} = \dot{\phi}\,(\vec{k} \times \ddot{\vec{a}}) = (\dot{\phi}/\phi)\,(\vec{l} \times \ddot{\vec{a}}), \tag{35.28}$$

which says that the light rays are plane curves.

From

$$\alpha = \dot{\phi}/\phi, \text{ we find } \varkappa = C\,(n/\phi), \tag{35.29}$$

which shows that the vector

$$\vec{p} = (n/\phi)\,(\vec{l} \times \dot{\vec{a}}) = n\,(\vec{k} \times \dot{\vec{a}}) \tag{35.30}$$

is invariant. This gives the theorem of *Bouguer*. The light rays in parallel-layer media form an angle i with the layer normal such that $n \sin i$ is constant along the rays.

If we ask for the condition that all the rays are circles, we find

$$n/\phi = C,$$

or, because of $\phi = (1/n)\,(dn/dz)$,

$$n = C/(C_1 - z), \tag{35.31}$$

a distribution of refractive indices which becomes infinite for the plane $z = C_1$.

Spherical Layers. Let us assume n to be a function of r, the length of the radius vector $\vec{a}$ measured from the origin, which we put at the center of the centrally symmetric layers. We then have

$$\vec{l} = \frac{1}{nr}\frac{dn}{dr}\vec{a} = \psi\vec{a} \tag{35.32}$$

$$\vec{l} \times \ddot{\vec{a}} = (\dot{\psi}/\psi)\,(\vec{l} \times \ddot{\vec{a}}).$$

This shows that we again have plane light rays. We find

$$\alpha = \dot{\psi}/\psi, \quad \varkappa = n/\psi. \tag{35.33}$$

The vector $\vec{p}$, invariant along the light rays, is given by

$$\vec{p} = (n/\psi)\,(\vec{l} \times \dot{\vec{a}}) = n\,(\vec{a} \times \dot{\vec{a}}). \tag{35.34}$$

Its length is $nr \sin i$, where i is the angle which the curve forms with the radius vector $\vec{a}$. The quantity $nr \sin i$ is invariant along the rays.

The light rays are all circles if

$$n = C\psi = \frac{C}{nr}\frac{dn}{dr}. \qquad (35.35)$$

Integration gives

$$n = \frac{2C}{C_1 - r^2}, \quad \psi = \frac{2}{C_1 - r^2}. \qquad (35.36)$$

If C_1 is positive, we again find that there exists a layer for which n is infinite. However, if C_1 is negative or $= -a^2$, we can choose our constants so that

$$n = \frac{n_0 a^2}{r^2 + a^2}, \quad \psi = -\frac{2}{r^2 + a^2}, \qquad (35.37)$$

n_0 being the index at the center. This index distribution represents Maxwell's fish eye. In this case, we find the curvature of the circles from

$$\varrho^2 = (\vec{l} \times \vec{a})^2 = (r\,\psi \sin i)^2 \qquad (35.38)$$

and the radius of curvature R is given by

$$R = 1/\varrho = +1/(r\psi \sin i). \qquad (35.39)$$

The distance m of the center of the circle from the center of symmetry is given by

$$\begin{aligned} m^2 &= R^2 + r^2 + 2rR \sin i = R^2 + r^2 - (r^2 + a^2) \qquad (35.40) \\ &= R^2 - a^2, \end{aligned}$$

which shows that all the circles have (in the language of geometry) a constant power a with respect to the system center.

PART X. APPENDIX

CHAPTER A

Vector Analysis

Given a fixed point O as origin of coordinates, we define vectors $\vec{a}$, $\vec{b}$, etc. as the directed line segments OA, OB, etc., where A, B, etc. are various points of space. If a set of perpendicular axes is chosen, the vectors $\vec{a}$, $\vec{b}$, etc. are uniquely determined by the ordinary rectangular coordinates of the points A, B, etc. It will be convenient, therefore, to use the sets of coordinates as representing the vectors themselves and write*

$$\vec{a} = (a_1, a_2, a_3), \quad \vec{b} = (b_1, b_2, b_3). \tag{A.1}$$

Two such vectors $\vec{a}$ and $\vec{b}$ are evidently equal ($OA = OB$) if and only if the corresponding coordinates are equal, which is to say that

$$a_1 = b_1, \qquad a_2 = b_2, \qquad a_3 = b_3. \tag{A.2}$$

The real numbers 0, 1, -2, 1/2, π, $\sqrt{2}$, etc. are called *scalars*, and the operation of multiplying a vector $\vec{a}$ by a scalar λ is defined by the formula

$$\lambda\vec{a} = \vec{a}\lambda = (\lambda a_1, \lambda a_2, \lambda a_3). \tag{A.3}$$

Geometrically this has the effect [*cf.* Fig. A.1] of giving a line segment OB in the same direction as OA but stretched in the ratio 1 to λ. If λ is negative, the new vector $\lambda\vec{a}$ is said to have a *sense of direction* opposite to that of $\vec{a}$.

The addition of two vectors is defined by the formula

$$\vec{a} + \vec{b} = (a_1 + b_1,\ a_2 + b_2,\ a_3 + b_3). \tag{A.4}$$

The geometrical meaning of $\vec{a} + \vec{b}$ proves to be simply the diagonal (from the origin) of the parallelogram constructed with

* Ordinary three-dimensional space is considered here. The definition of vectors in n-space is analogous.

OA and OB as two of its sides. A simpler construction for $\vec{a} + \vec{b}$ is obtained if one shifts the segment OB parallel to itself until its initial point coincides with A. Then the new position of B is the terminal point of $\vec{a} + \vec{b}$.

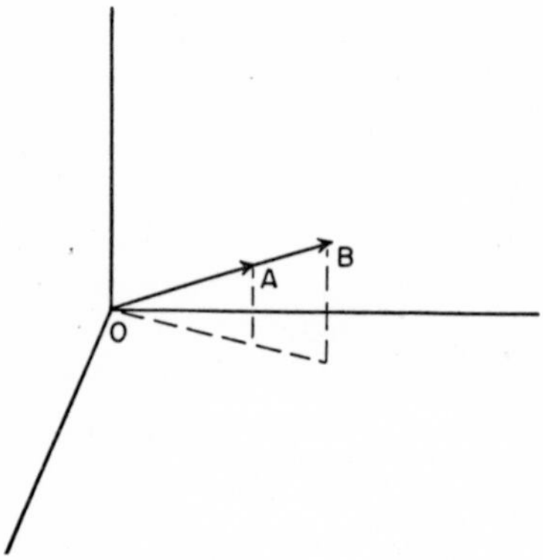

Fig. A.1. Multiplication by a scalar.

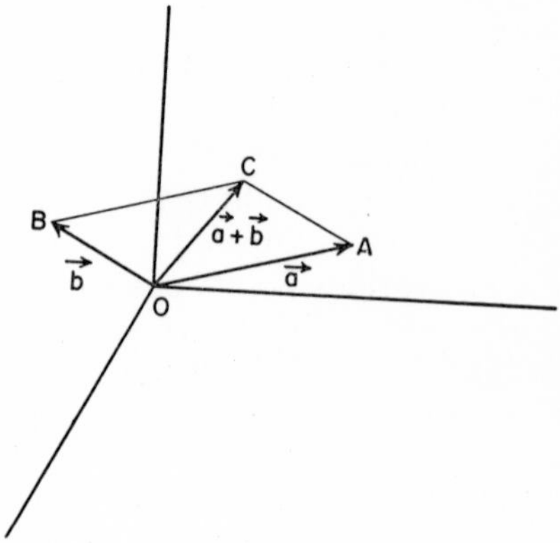

Fig. A.2. Addition of vectors.

From the above definitions it follows at once that for any scalars $\varkappa$, λ and any vectors $\vec{a}$, $\vec{b}$, $\vec{c}$:

$$\begin{aligned} &\varkappa\,(\lambda\vec{a}) = \lambda\,(\varkappa\vec{a}) = (\varkappa\lambda)\,\vec{a} \\ &(\varkappa + \lambda)\,\vec{a} = \varkappa\vec{a} + \lambda\vec{a} \\ &\varkappa\,(\vec{a} + \vec{b}) = \varkappa\vec{a} + \varkappa\vec{b} \\ &\vec{a} + \vec{b} = \vec{b} + \vec{a} \\ &(\vec{a} + \vec{b}) + \vec{c} = \vec{a} + (\vec{b} + \vec{c}). \end{aligned} \tag{A.5}$$

Thus many of the operations of ordinary algebra are possible with vector expressions. Subtraction of vectors is effected by the definition

$$\vec{a} + (-1)\,\vec{b} = \vec{a} - \vec{b}. \tag{A.6}$$

One can verify geometrically that $\vec{a} - \vec{b}$ has the length of and is parallel to the segment from the end point of $\vec{b}$ to the endpoint of $\vec{a}$.

An important concept connected with vectors is that of linear independence. A set of n vectors $\vec{a}_1, \vec{a}_2, \ldots \vec{a}_n$ is said to be *dependent* when there exists a linear relation between them or, more

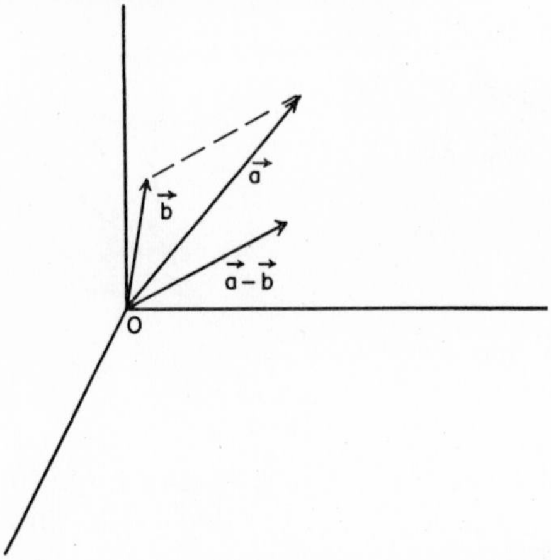

Fig. A.3. Subtraction of vectors.

precisely, if and only if there exist scalars, not all zero, such that

$$\varkappa_1\vec{a}_1 + \varkappa_2\vec{a}_2 + \ldots + \varkappa_n\vec{a}_n = 0, \tag{A.7}$$

where 0 indicates the zero vector (0, 0, 0). If the only possible scalars satisfying (A.7) are given by $\varkappa_1 = \varkappa_2 = \ldots = \varkappa_n = 0$, the vectors in question are said to be *independent*.

If two vectors $\vec{a}_1$ and $\vec{a}_2$ are dependent, then a relation of the form

$$\varkappa_1\vec{a}_1 + \varkappa_2\vec{a}_2 = 0 \tag{A.8}$$

with either $\varkappa_1$ or $\varkappa_2$ nonzero must hold. Thus at least one of the relations

$$\vec{a}_1 = -\,(k_2/k_1)\,\vec{a}_2,\ \vec{a}_2 = -\,(k_1/k_2)\,\vec{a}_1 \tag{A.9}$$

must hold, showing that the vectors have their end points in line with the origin. Conversely, such vectors are always dependent.

Consider now an equation of the form

$$\vec{x} = \vec{a} + \lambda\vec{b}. \tag{A.10}$$

If $\vec{a}$ and $\vec{b}$ (with $\vec{b} \neq 0$) are held fixed and the scalar λ is varied, the geometrical meaning of addition shows that the end point of x moves along a straight line through the end point of $\vec{a}$ and par-

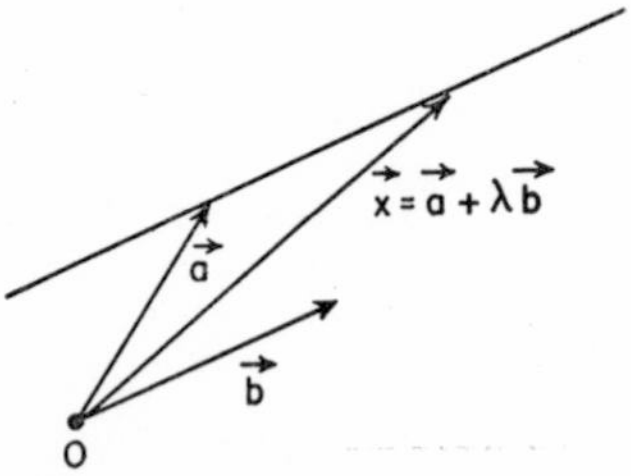

Fig. A.4. Vector equation of a straight line.

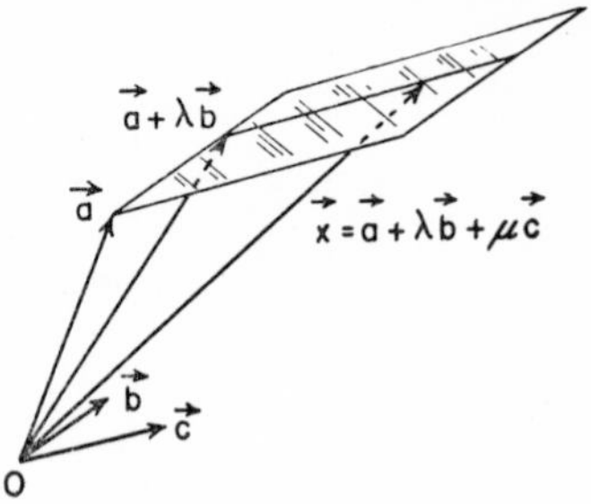

Fig. A.5. Vector equation of a plane.

allel* to the direction of $\vec{b}$. For this reason (A.10) is called the *vector equation of a straight line*. The line passes through the origin if and only if $\vec{a} = 0$.

Geometrical analysis of an equation of the form

$$\vec{x} = \vec{a} + \lambda\vec{b} + \mu\vec{c} \tag{A.11}$$

shows that it represents the equation of a plane provided $\vec{b}$ and $\vec{c}$ are independent. This plane passes through the end point of $\vec{a}$ and is parallel to the vectors $\vec{b}$ and $\vec{c}$. In fact, it contains the lines whose equations are

$$\vec{x} = \vec{a} + \lambda\vec{b}, \quad \vec{x} = \vec{a} + \mu\vec{c}. \tag{A.12}$$

The importance of the concept of the dependence of vectors is seen further in the following geometrical application. Three vectors $\vec{a}$, $\vec{b}$, and $\vec{c}$ are dependent if and only if they lie in the same plane through the origin. To see this, assume first that

$$\varkappa_1\vec{a} + \varkappa_2\vec{b} + \varkappa_3\vec{c} = 0, \tag{A.13}$$

* Vectors have been defined here as line segments with their initial points at the *origin*. In drawings it is sometimes helpful to picture a vector shifted parallel to itself. Here $\vec{b}$ can be drawn actually *along* the line in question.

with one of the scalars (say $\varkappa_1$) not zero. Then

$$\vec{a} = (-\varkappa_2/\varkappa_1)\,\vec{b} + (-\varkappa_3/\varkappa_1)\,\vec{c}, \tag{A.14}$$

and comparison with (A.11) shows that either $\vec{a}$ lies on the plane through the origin determined by vectors $\vec{b}$ and $\vec{c}$ or else $\vec{b}$ and $\vec{c}$ are proportional, in which case the three vectors surely lie in one plane. Conversely, if $\vec{a}$, $\vec{b}$, $\vec{c}$ are assumed to be three vectors lying in a plane, it is easily shown they are dependent. If one of the vectors is zero or any pair is dependent, the proof is trivial. If $\vec{b}$ and $\vec{c}$ are independent, $\vec{a}$ must satisfy the equation

$$\vec{x} = \lambda\vec{b} + \mu\vec{c} \tag{A.15}$$

of the plane through the origin determined by $\vec{b}$ and $\vec{c}$. This gives

$$(-1)\,\vec{a} + \lambda\vec{b} + \mu\vec{c} = 0, \tag{A.16}$$

with one of the coefficients nonzero.

An important algebraic application of the concept of dependence is the following. If a vector $\vec{x}$ is expressed as a linear combination of three independent vectors $\vec{a}$, $\vec{b}$, $\vec{c}$, that is, if

$$\vec{x} = \varkappa\vec{a} + \lambda\vec{b} + \mu\vec{c}, \tag{A.17}$$

then the coefficients of this expansion are unique. For, if another such expansion is possible, giving

$$\vec{x} = \varkappa'\vec{a} + \lambda'\vec{b} + \mu'\vec{c}, \tag{A.18}$$

then subtraction gives

$$0 = (\varkappa - \varkappa')\,\vec{a} + (\lambda - \lambda')\,\vec{b} + (\mu - \mu')\,\vec{c}. \tag{A.19}$$

But independent vectors can satisfy such a relation only if all three parentheses equal zero. Thus $\varkappa = \varkappa'$, $\lambda = \lambda'$, $\mu = \mu'$. The numbers $\varkappa$, λ, μ may be called the *coordinates* of $\vec{x}$ relative to the independent vectors $\vec{a}$, $\vec{b}$, $\vec{c}$.

Besides the product of a vector by a scalar, two other types of product are defined, both involving two vectors. If

$$\vec{a} = (a_1, a_2, a_3), \quad \vec{b} = (b_1, b_2, b_3) \tag{A.20}$$

are two vectors, their *scalar product* $\vec{a}\vec{b}$ (sometimes written $\vec{a}\cdot\vec{b}$) is defined by

$$\vec{a}\vec{b} = a_1b_1 + a_2b_2 + a_3b_3, \tag{A.21}$$

which is a single scalar number.

It is seen at once that this product satisfies the laws

$$\begin{aligned} \vec{a}\vec{b} &= \vec{b}\vec{a} \\ \vec{a}\,(\vec{b} + \vec{c}) &= \vec{a}\vec{b} + \vec{a}\vec{c} \\ (\lambda\vec{a})\,\vec{b} &= \lambda\,(\vec{a}\vec{b}) = \vec{a}\,(\lambda\vec{b}) \end{aligned} \tag{A.22}$$

and also that

$$\vec{a}^2 = \vec{a}\vec{a} = a_1^2 + a_2^2 + a_3^2 \tag{A.23}$$

gives the square of the length of the vector $\vec{a}$ (line segment OA). A vector whose length is unity is called a *unit vector.*

To see the geometrical meaning of the scalar product $\vec{a}\vec{b}$, compare the relation

$$(\vec{a}-\vec{b})^2 = \vec{a}^2 - 2\vec{a}\vec{b} + \vec{b}^2 \tag{A.24}$$

with the ordinary law of cosines applied to the triangle AOB:

$$\overline{AB}^2 = \overline{OA}^2 + \overline{OB}^2 - 2\overline{OA}\;\overline{OB}\cos\theta. \tag{A.25}$$

It is clear that $\vec{a}\vec{b}$ gives the cosine of the angle between the vectors $\vec{a}$ and $\vec{b}$ multiplied by the length (positive) of the vectors $\vec{a}$ and $\vec{b}$. Two nonzero vectors are *orthogonal* (perpendicular) if and only if $\vec{a}\vec{b} = 0$, that is if and only if $\cos\theta = 0$.

Consider now the three unit vectors along the coordinate axes:

$$\vec{\imath} = (1, 0, 0), \quad \vec{\jmath} = (0, 1, 0), \quad \vec{k} = (0, 0, 1). \tag{A.26}$$

Any vector $\vec{x} = (a_1, a_2, a_3)$ can be expressed as a linear combination of these, this being

$$\vec{x} = a_1\,\vec{\imath} + a_2\,\vec{\jmath} + a_3\vec{k}. \tag{A.27}$$

Furthermore the vectors $\vec{\imath}, \vec{\jmath}, \vec{k}$ are seen to be independent, so the expansion of any vector $\vec{x}$ in the form (A.27) is unique. The unit vectors defined by (A.26) satisfy the relations

$$\vec{\imath}^2 = \vec{\jmath}^2 = \vec{k}^2 = 1$$
$$\vec{\imath}\vec{\jmath} = \vec{\imath}\vec{k} = \vec{\jmath}\vec{k} = 0. \tag{A.28}$$

The representation of vectors in the form (A.27) is frequently useful.

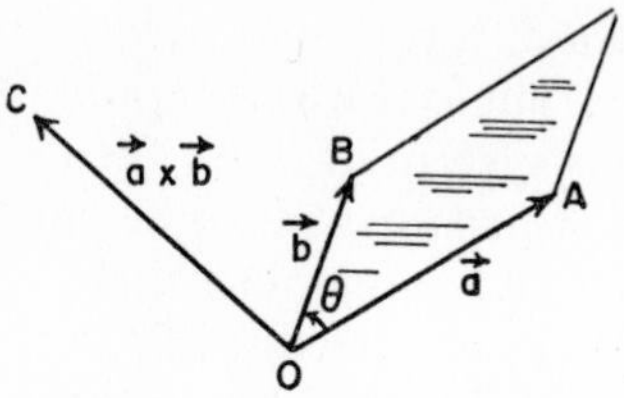

Fig. A.6. Vector product.

The other type of product involving two vectors is known as their *vector product*, $\vec{a} \times \vec{b}$. It is defined by the equation

$$\vec{a} \times \vec{b} = (a_2b_3 - a_3b_2)\,\vec{\imath} + (a_3b_1 - a_1b_3)\,\vec{\jmath} + (a_1b_2 - a_2b_1)\,\vec{k}, \tag{A.29}$$

where

$$\vec{a} = (a_1, a_2, a_3), \quad \vec{b} = (b_1, b_2, b_3).$$

This definition may be remembered easily by writing it as a third-order determinant* in the symbolic form

$$\vec{a} \times \vec{b} = \begin{vmatrix} \vec{\imath} & \vec{\jmath} & \vec{k} \\ a_1 & a_2 & a_3 \\ b_1 & b_2 & b_3 \end{vmatrix}, \tag{A.30}$$

* A second-order determinant may be defined by

$$\begin{vmatrix} a_1 & a_2 \\ b_1 & b_2 \end{vmatrix} = a_1b_2 - a_2b_1$$

and a third-order determinant by

$$\begin{vmatrix} a_1 & a_2 & a_3 \\ b_1 & b_2 & b_3 \\ c_1 & c_2 & c_3 \end{vmatrix} = a_1 \begin{vmatrix} b_2 & b_3 \\ c_2 & c_3 \end{vmatrix} - a_2 \begin{vmatrix} b_1 & b_3 \\ c_1 & c_3 \end{vmatrix} + a_3 \begin{vmatrix} b_1 & b_2 \\ c_1 & c_2 \end{vmatrix}.$$

where it is understood that this determinant is to be expanded by the first row giving (A.29).

The definition of $\vec{a} \times \vec{b}$ shows that it is a vector which is zero if $\vec{a} = 0$ or $\vec{b} = 0$. A simple calculation shows that

$$(\vec{a} \times \vec{b})\,\vec{a} = (\vec{a} \times \vec{b})\,\vec{b} = 0, \tag{A.31}$$

so that the vector $\vec{a} \times \vec{b}$ is perpendicular to $\vec{a}$ and to $\vec{b}$. One can verify that the vector $\vec{c}$ given by $\vec{c} = \vec{a} \times \vec{b}$ has its sense of direction so that the vector $\vec{a}, \vec{b}, \vec{c}$, in that order, have the same relative orientation as $\vec{i}, \vec{j}, \vec{k}$. Thus, if $\vec{i}, \vec{j}, \vec{k}$ represent the directions of a so-called *right-handed* system of axes, then every vector product $\vec{a} \times \vec{b}$ represents the third member of a right-handed system having $\vec{a}$ and $\vec{b}$ as its first two members. However, in this case all three vectors $\vec{a}, \vec{b}, \vec{c}$ are not necessarily mutually perpendicular.

The quantity $(\vec{a} \times \vec{b})^2$ is found by a routine calculation to be

$$\begin{aligned}(\vec{a} \times \vec{b})^2 &= \begin{vmatrix} a_2 & a_3 \\ b_2 & b_3 \end{vmatrix}^2 + \begin{vmatrix} a_3 & a_1 \\ b_3 & b_1 \end{vmatrix}^2 + \begin{vmatrix} a_1 & a_2 \\ b_1 & b_2 \end{vmatrix}^2 \\ &= (a_1^2 + a_2^2 + a_3^2)\,(b_1^2 + b_2^2 + b_3^2) \\ &\quad - (a_1b_1 + a_2b_2 + a_3b_3)^2 \\ &= \vec{a}^2\vec{b}^2\,(1 - \cos^2\theta) = \vec{a}^2\vec{b}^2\,\sin^2\theta.\end{aligned} \tag{A.32}$$

It follows that the length of $\vec{a} \times \vec{b}$ is equal to the area of the

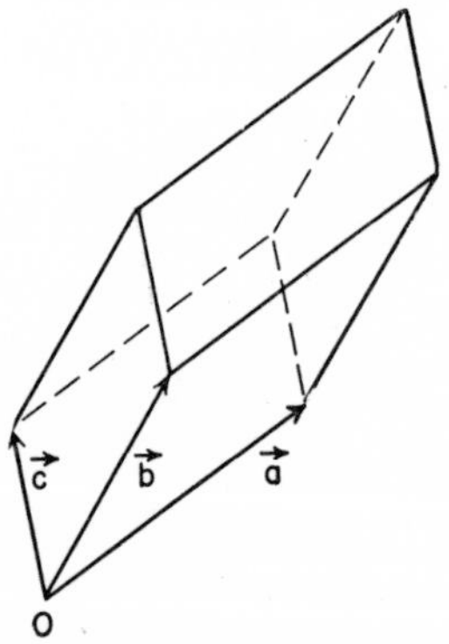

Fig. A.7. Triple product [$a\ b\ c$].

parallelogram having $\vec{a}$ and $\vec{b}$ as two of its sides. The calculation in (A.32) also gives the important formula

$$(\vec{a} \times \vec{b})^2 = \vec{a}^2\vec{b}^2 - (\vec{a}\vec{b})^2. \qquad \text{(A.33)}$$

From (A.30) one sees at once that the vector product obeys the laws

$$\begin{aligned} &\vec{a} \times (\vec{b} + \vec{c}) = \vec{a} \times \vec{b} + \vec{a} \times \vec{c} \\ &\vec{a} \times \vec{b} = -(\vec{b} \times \vec{a}) \\ &\lambda(\vec{a} \times \vec{b}) = (\lambda\vec{a}) \times \vec{b} = \vec{a} \times (\lambda\vec{b}). \end{aligned} \qquad \text{(A.34)}$$

Furthermore, $\vec{a} \times \vec{b} = 0$ if and only if $\vec{a}$ and $\vec{b}$ are dependent. This is because, when $\vec{a}$ and $\vec{b}$ are nonzero, the area of the parallelogram giving the length of $\vec{a} \times \vec{b}$ is zero if and only if $\vec{a}$ and $\vec{b}$ are dependent. The unit vectors $\vec{\imath}$, $\vec{\jmath}$, $\vec{k}$ are seen to satisfy the relations

$$\vec{\imath} \times \vec{\jmath} = \vec{k}, \quad \vec{\jmath} \times \vec{k} = \vec{\imath}, \quad \vec{k} \times \vec{\imath} = \vec{\jmath}, \qquad \text{(A.35)}$$

as the reader can quickly verify.

A so-called *triple product* of any three vectors $\vec{a}$, $\vec{b}$, $\vec{c}$ is defined by forming the scalar product $(\vec{a} \times \vec{b})\,\vec{c}$. If $\vec{a}$, $\vec{b}$, or $\vec{c}$ equals zero this product also equals zero. If none of the three vectors is zero, the value of the product gives the area of the parallelogram

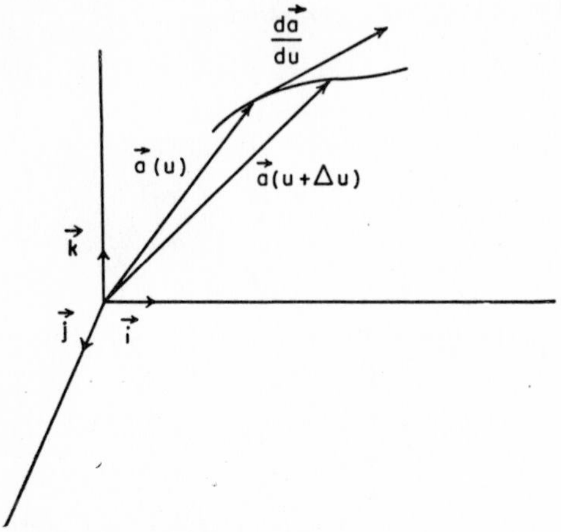

Fig. A.8. Derivative of a vector function.

formed with $\vec{a}$ and $\vec{b}$ as two sides multiplied by the length of the projection of $\vec{c}$ perpendicular to the plane of $\vec{a}$ and $\vec{b}$. Thus the triple product gives the volume of the parallelepiped constructed with $\vec{a}$, $\vec{b}$, and $\vec{c}$ as three of its edges, or the negative of this volume.

Using (A.30) one finds that

$$(\vec{a} \times \vec{b})\,\vec{c} = \begin{vmatrix} a_1 & a_2 & a_3 \\ b_1 & b_2 & b_3 \\ c_1 & c_2 & c_3 \end{vmatrix}, \tag{A.36}$$

giving the triple product in terms of the coordinates of the three vectors. It follows from this (and also from the geometrical discussion above) that the value of the triple product is unchanged if the vectors are permuted in cyclic order. Introducing the symbol $[\vec{a}\,\vec{b}\,\vec{c}]$ for the triple product, we thus have

$$[\vec{a}\,\vec{b}\,\vec{c}] = (\vec{a} \times \vec{b})\,\vec{c} = (\vec{b} \times \vec{c})\,\vec{a} = (\vec{c} \times \vec{a})\,\vec{b}. \tag{A.37}$$

Since the volume of the parallelepiped mentioned above is zero if and only if the three vectors lie in the same plane, it is clear that $[\vec{a}\,\vec{b}\,\vec{c}] = 0$ if and only if the vectors $\vec{a}$, $\vec{b}$, $\vec{c}$ are dependent.

From (A.36) one finds the following linearity property. For any scalars λ, λ' and any vectors $\vec{a}$, $\vec{a}'$, $\vec{b}$, $\vec{c}$,

$$[\lambda\vec{a} + \lambda'\vec{a}', \vec{b}, \vec{c}] = \lambda\,[\vec{a}\,b\,\vec{c}] + \lambda'\,[\vec{a}'\,b\,\vec{c}]. \tag{A.38}$$

Using (A.37) leads to similar formulae relative to the second and third vectors in the triple product.

In connection with a linear transformation of the form

$$\begin{aligned} \vec{a} &= \alpha_{11}\vec{a}' + \alpha_{12}\vec{b}' + \alpha_{13}\vec{c}' \\ \vec{b} &= \alpha_{21}\vec{a}' + \alpha_{22}\vec{b}' + \alpha_{23}\vec{c}' \\ \vec{c} &= \alpha_{31}\vec{a}' + \alpha_{32}\vec{b}' + \alpha_{33}\vec{c}', \end{aligned} \tag{A.39}$$

repeated use of the linearity property leads to the relation

$$[\vec{a}\,\vec{b}\,\vec{c}] = \begin{vmatrix} \alpha_{11} & \alpha_{12} & \alpha_{13} \\ \alpha_{21} & \alpha_{22} & \alpha_{23} \\ \alpha_{31} & \alpha_{32} & \alpha_{33} \end{vmatrix} [\vec{a}'\,\vec{b}'\,\vec{c}']. \tag{A.40}$$

We consider, next, differentiation of vector functions. Suppose that the end point of the vector $\vec{a}$ moves along a continuous space curve so that its coordinates depend on a single parameter u, specifying the position of the point on the curve. The situation may be indicated by the notation

$$\vec{a}\,(u) = a_1\,(u)\,\vec{\imath} + a_2\,(u)\,\vec{\jmath} + a_3\,(u)\,\vec{k}. \tag{A.41}$$

Giving the three functions $a_1\,(u)$, $a_2\,(u)$, $a_3\,(u)$ is equivalent to specifying the curve in question. If u and $u + \Delta u$ are two values of the parameter indicating two nearby points of the curve, the derivative of $\vec{a}\,(u)$ at the point u is defined as*

$$\frac{d\vec{a}}{du} = \lim_{\Delta u \to 0} \frac{\vec{a}\,(u + \Delta u) - \vec{a}\,(u)}{\Delta u} \tag{A.42}$$

provided the limit exists. The vector

$$\frac{\vec{a}\,(u + \Delta u) - \vec{a}(u)}{\Delta u} \tag{A.43}$$

is always parallel to the chord joining the points of the curve indicated by u and $u + u$. The limiting position, $d\vec{a}/du$, is therefore a vector parallel to the tangent of the curve at the point u. When any vector $\vec{a}$ moves into a limiting position, its three coordinates must assume corresponding limiting values. It follows that

$$d\vec{a}/dv = \vec{a}_1{}'(u)\vec{\imath} + \vec{a}_2{}'(u)\vec{\jmath} + \vec{a}_3{}'(u)\vec{k}, \tag{A.44}$$

the prime indicating differentiation with respect to u.

Using Formula (A.44) one readily proves the laws

$$\begin{aligned} \frac{d}{du}(\lambda\vec{a} + \mu\vec{b}) &= \lambda\frac{d\vec{a}}{du} + \mu\frac{d\vec{b}}{du} \\ \frac{d}{du}(\vec{a}\vec{b}) &= \vec{a}\frac{d\vec{b}}{du} + \vec{b}\frac{d\vec{a}}{du} \\ \frac{d}{du}(\vec{a} \times \vec{b}) &= \vec{a} \times \frac{d\vec{b}}{du} + \frac{d\vec{a}}{du} \times \vec{b}. \end{aligned} \tag{A.45}$$

* The division of a vector by a scalar (such as Δu) means multiplication by the reciprocal scalar.

In the same way, one defines the partial differentiation of a vector which is a function $\vec{b}(u, v)$ of two parameters. The end point of $\vec{b}$ is considered to move on a surface whose points are given by the three functions

$$b_1(u, v), \quad b_2(u, v), \quad b_3(u, v), \tag{A.46}$$

that is, the coordinates of the vector $\vec{b}$.

Considering a fixed reference point (fixed values of u, v), we can first assume $\vec{b}$ to move with v fixed and u varying along a curve lying in the surface and passing through the reference point. The derivative $\vec{b}_u = \partial\vec{b}/\partial u$ is defined as the derivative (A.42) relative to this curve. Correspondingly, holding u constant, we obtain $\vec{b}_v = \partial\vec{b}/\partial v$. It is evident that these derivatives are vectors parallel, in each case, to the tangent line of the curve used, so that the plane of $\vec{b}_u$ and $\vec{b}_v$ is parallel to the tangent plane of the surface at the reference point. At a given point (u, v), the normal to the surface is perpendicular to the tangent plane and so is parallel to the vector product $\vec{b}_u \times \vec{b}_v$. A unit vector $\vec{o}$ indicating the direction of the normal may be given by writing

$$\vec{o} = \pm (\vec{b}_u \times \vec{b}_v)/\sqrt{(\vec{b}_u \times \vec{b}_v)^2}. \tag{A.47}$$

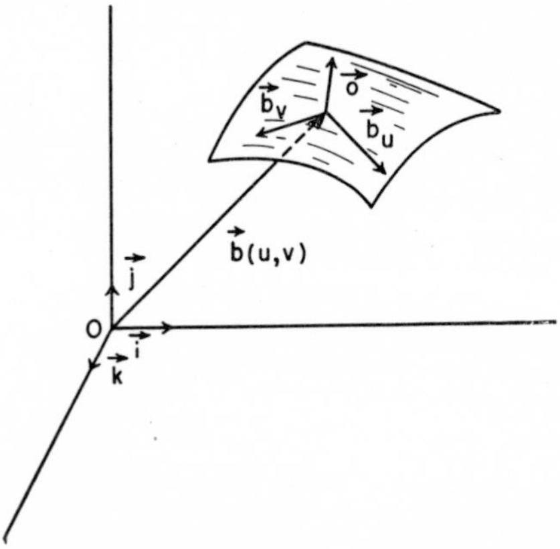

Fig. A.9. Normal to a surface, $\vec{o} = \pm (\vec{b}_u \times \vec{b}_v)/\sqrt{(\vec{b}_u \times \vec{b}_v)^2}$.

Actually two opposite directions are possible for the normal depending on which is considered to be the positive side of the surface. An exception arises at any point where $\vec{b}_u$ or $\vec{b}_v$ is undefined or where they are dependent. At such a point the surface does not have a unique tangent plane. When the equation of the surface is given in the form

$$f(b_1, b_2, b_3) = 0, \tag{A.48}$$

where the b_i are the ordinary Cartesian coordinates of the points of the surface, we derive an alternate formula for $\vec{o}$. If the ξ_i are considered to depend on two parameters u, v, we have on the one hand

$$\vec{b}_u = b_{1u}\vec{i} + b_{2u}\vec{j} + b_{3u}\vec{k}$$
$$\vec{b}_v = b_{1v}\vec{i} + b_{2v}\vec{j} + b_{3u}\vec{k}, \tag{A.49}$$

where b_{1u} indicates $\partial b_1/\partial u$ and correspondingly for b_{iu}, b_{iv}. This gives

$$\vec{b}_u \times \vec{b}_v = \begin{vmatrix} \vec{i} & \vec{j} & \vec{k} \\ b_{1u} & b_{2u} & b_{3u} \\ b_{1v} & b_{2v} & b_{3v} \end{vmatrix}, \tag{A.50}$$

whereas differentiation of (A.48) with respect to u and v gives (by the so-called *chain law of calculus*),

$$f_1 b_{1u} + f_2 b_{2u} + f_3 b_{3u} = 0$$
$$f_1 b_{1v} + f_2 b_{2v} + f_3 b_{3v} = 0, \tag{A.51}$$

where $f_i = \partial f/\partial b_i$. The solution of these equations is

$$\frac{f_1}{\begin{vmatrix} b_{2u} & b_{3u} \\ b_{2v} & b_{3v} \end{vmatrix}} = \frac{f_2}{\begin{vmatrix} b_{3u} & b_{1u} \\ b_{3v} & b_{1v} \end{vmatrix}} = \frac{f_3}{\begin{vmatrix} b_{1u} & b_{2u} \\ b_{1v} & b_{2v} \end{vmatrix}}. \tag{A.52}$$

Comparison with (A.50) shows that the coordinates of $\vec{b}_u \times \vec{b}_v$ and so of the vector $\vec{o}$ are proportional to f_1, f_2, f_3. Hence

$$\vec{o} = \pm \frac{f_1\vec{i} + f_2\vec{j} + f_3\vec{k}}{\sqrt{f_1^2 + f_2^2 + f_3^2}}. \tag{A.53}$$

In optical problems, the surface is usually assumed to have rotational symmetry with respect to the z-axis. In this case Equation (A.53) may be reduced to the form

$$F\,(u, v) = 0, \tag{A.54}$$

with

$$u = \tfrac{1}{2}\vec{b}^2 = \tfrac{1}{2}\,(b_1^2 + b_2^2 + b_3^2), \quad v = \vec{b}\vec{k} = b_3. \tag{A.55}$$

This gives

$$F_1 = F_u b_1, \quad F_2 = F_u b_2, \quad F_3 = F_u b_3 + F_v \tag{A.56}$$

and (A.53) gives the vector $\vec{\sigma}$ as

$$\vec{\sigma} = (1/\tau)\,[F_u b_1 \vec{\imath} + F_u b_2 \vec{\jmath} + (F_u b_3 + F_v)\,\vec{k}] \tag{A.57}$$

$$\tau = \pm\sqrt{2uF_u^2 + 2vF_uF_v + F_v^2}.$$

However, owing to the rotational symmetry, the vector $\vec{\sigma}$ must lie in the plane of $\vec{b}$ and $\vec{k}$ and so is expressible in the form

$$\vec{\sigma} = \alpha\vec{b} + \beta\vec{k} = \alpha b_1\vec{\imath} + \alpha b_2\vec{\jmath} + (\alpha b_3 + \beta)\,\vec{k}. \tag{A.58}$$

The expansion of $\vec{\sigma}$ in terms of $\vec{\imath}$, $\vec{\jmath}$, $\vec{k}$ must always have unique coefficients. Therefore comparison with (A.57) gives the values of α and β, and one obtains

$$\vec{\sigma} = \pm\,(F_u\vec{b} + F_v\vec{k})/\sqrt{2uF_u^2 + 2vF_uF_v + F_v^2}. \tag{A.59}$$

In this book it is assumed that the normal of a refracting or reflecting surface is always chosen so that its z-component, $\vec{\sigma}\vec{k}$, is positive. If this convention is adopted and if the equation of the surface is written in the form

$$b_3 - \psi\,(b_1, b_2) = 0 \tag{A.60}$$

(by solving Equation (A.48) for its z-coordinate), then Formula (A.53) for $\vec{\sigma}$ takes the unambiguous form

$$\vec{\sigma} = (-\,\psi_1\vec{\imath} - \psi_2\vec{\jmath} + \vec{k})/\sqrt{\psi_1^2 + \psi_2^2 + 1}, \tag{A.61}$$

which has a positive z-component.

CHAPTER B

Miscellaneous Mathematical Tools

This chapter will include four mathematical topics which are useful in optical problems: matrices, least squares, Gaussian brackets, and a certain method of solving problems by using polynomial approximations.

Matrices

Consider two linear transformations given by

$$\begin{aligned} z_1 &= a_{11}y_1 + a_{12}y_2 + a_{13}y_3 \\ z_2 &= a_{21}y_1 + a_{22}y_2 + a_{23}y_3 \\ z_3 &= a_{31}y_1 + a_{32}y_2 + a_{33}y_3 \end{aligned} \tag{B.1}$$

and

$$\begin{aligned} y_1 &= b_{11}x_1 + b_{12}x_2 + b_{13}x_3 \\ y_2 &= b_{21}x_1 + b_{22}x_2 + b_{23}x_3 \\ y_3 &= b_{31}x_1 + b_{32}x_2 + b_{33}x_3. \end{aligned} \tag{B.2}$$

By direct substitution of (B.2) into (B.1), one finds the quantities z_i as linear combinations of the x_i:

$$\begin{aligned} z_1 &= c_{11}x_1 + c_{12}x_2 + c_{13}x_3 \\ z_2 &= c_{21}x_1 + c_{22}x_2 + c_{23}x_3 \\ z_3 &= c_{31}x_1 + c_{32}x_2 + c_{33}x_3 \end{aligned} \tag{B.3}$$

with

$$\begin{aligned} c_{11} &= a_{11}b_{11} + a_{12}b_{21} + a_{12}b_{31} \\ c_{12} &= a_{11}b_{12} + a_{12}b_{22} + a_{12}b_{32} \\ &- - - - \end{aligned} \tag{B.4}$$

to nine terms.

Examination of these terms shows that they may be obtained by the following simple rule: the number c_{ik} is obtained by multiplying the ith row of coefficients a_{i1}, a_{i2}, a_{i3} in (B.1) respectively by the kth column of coefficients b_{1k}, b_{2k}, b_{3k} in (B.2) and summing. Thus the nine quantities in (B.4) may be described by writing

$$c_{ik} = a_{i1}b_{1k} + a_{i2}b_{2k} + a_{i3}b_{3k} = \sum_{j=1}^{3} a_{ij}b_{jk}, \qquad i = 1, 2, 3; \quad k = 1, 2, 3. \tag{B.5}$$

Problems of this type are simplified by the concept of a matrix. Each of the 3×3 arrays of coefficients (a_{ij}), (b_{ij}) and (c_{ij}) is called a *matrix*. Thus we write

$$A = \begin{bmatrix} a_{11} & a_{12} & a_{13} \\ a_{21} & a_{22} & a_{23} \\ a_{31} & a_{32} & a_{33} \end{bmatrix}, \quad B = \begin{bmatrix} b_{11} & b_{12} & b_{13} \\ b_{21} & b_{22} & b_{23} \\ b_{31} & b_{32} & b_{33} \end{bmatrix}, \quad C = \begin{bmatrix} c_{11} & c_{12} & c_{13} \\ c_{21} & c_{22} & c_{23} \\ c_{31} & c_{32} & c_{33} \end{bmatrix}. \tag{B.6}$$

The product of two matrices, such as A and B above, is defined as the matrix having in its ith row and kth column the number given by $\sum_{j=1}^{3} a_{ij}b_{jk}$; that is, the element in the ith row and kth column of the product is obtained by multiplying elements of the ith row of A by the corresponding elements of the kth column of B and summing. Thus the simple matrix equation

$$C = AB \tag{B.7}$$

is sufficient to describe the effect of the substitution since the resulting transformation can be written down by inspection once the matrix C is known.

At times it is convenient to deal with rectangular matrices (arrays) and also with larger square matrices. Matrix multiplication in these cases is defined the same as for square matrices, the element in the ith row and the kth column of AB being given by $\sum_{j} a_{ij}b_{jk}$. However, the matrices can only be multiplied provided their dimensions "fit," that is, if A is $n \times s$ (having n rows and s columns), B must be $s \times t$. The product will then be an

$n \times t$ matrix. A very useful special case is a matrix having only a single column. If we let

$$X = \begin{bmatrix} x_1 \\ x_2 \\ x_3 \end{bmatrix}, \qquad Y = \begin{bmatrix} y_1 \\ y_2 \\ y_3 \end{bmatrix}, \qquad Z = \begin{bmatrix} z_1 \\ z_2 \\ z_3 \end{bmatrix}, \tag{B.8}$$

we find that (B.1), (B.2), and (B.3) can be written in the simple matrix form

$$Z = AY, \quad Y = BX, \quad Z = CX. \tag{B.9}$$

It follows quickly, from the definition of the product of matrices, that matrix multiplication obeys the associative law

$$P\,(QR) = (PQ)\,R \tag{B.10}$$

for any three matrices which fit. Using this law one can deduce from the first two equations of (B.9) that

$$Z = AY = A\,(BX) = (AB)\,X. \tag{B.11}$$

The identical transformation

$$\begin{aligned} y_1 &= x_1 \\ y_2 &= \quad x_2 \\ y_3 &= \qquad x_3 \end{aligned} \tag{B.12}$$

may be written

$$Y = IX, \text{ where } I = \begin{bmatrix} 1 & 0 & 0 \\ 0 & 1 & 0 \\ 0 & 0 & 1 \end{bmatrix}. \tag{B.13}$$

The matrix I is known as the *identity matrix*. Whereas matrix multiplication in general is dependent on the order of A and B, (for example

$$\begin{bmatrix} 1 & 0 & 1 \\ 0 & 1 & 0 \\ 0 & 0 & 1 \end{bmatrix} \begin{bmatrix} 1 & 0 & 0 \\ 0 & 1 & 0 \\ 1 & 0 & 1 \end{bmatrix} = \begin{bmatrix} 2 & 0 & 1 \\ 0 & 1 & 0 \\ 1 & 0 & 1 \end{bmatrix}$$

but

$$\begin{bmatrix} 1 & 0 & 0 \\ 0 & 1 & 0 \\ 1 & 0 & 1 \end{bmatrix} \begin{bmatrix} 1 & 0 & 1 \\ 0 & 1 & 0 \\ 0 & 0 & 1 \end{bmatrix} = \begin{bmatrix} 1 & 0 & 1 \\ 0 & 1 & 0 \\ 1 & 0 & 2 \end{bmatrix} \tag{B.14}$$

so that $AB \neq BA$) on the other hand, the matrix I multiplied with any square matrix of the same size gives

$$IA = AI = A. \tag{B.15}$$

A matrix A is called *nonsingular* if there exists a second matrix (denoted by A^{-1} and called its *inverse*) having the property that

$$AA^{-1} = I = A^{-1}A. \tag{B.16}$$

The concept of nonsingularity is of importance in connection with linear transformations. A transformation of the form

$$Y = AX \tag{B.17}$$

can be solved provided A is nonsingular. For, if A^{-1} exists, multiplication on the left of each member gives

$$A^{-1}Y = A^{-1}(AX) = IX = X. \tag{B.18}$$

It is easily shown that, if a matrix has an inverse, this inverse is unique. For if both B and C have the property of being inverses of A, then

$$\begin{aligned} AB &= I = BA \\ AC &= I = CA, \end{aligned} \tag{B.19}$$

whence

$$\begin{aligned} BAC &= BI = B \\ BAC &= IC = C, \end{aligned} \tag{B.20}$$

proving that $B = C$.

The inverse of a product is given by the formula

$$(AB)^{-1} = B^{-1}A^{-1} \tag{B.21}$$

provided the inverses exist. The simple proof is

$$(B^{-1}A^{-1})(AB) = B^{-1}(A^{-1}A)B = B^{-1}IB = B^{-1}B = I,$$

with a similar proof for multiplication in the reverse order.

It can be shown that a square 3×3 matrix A is nonsingular if and only if the determinant (see the definition of second- and third-order determinants given in a footnote on page 435)

$$|A| = \begin{vmatrix} a_{11} & a_{12} & a_{13} \\ a_{21} & a_{22} & a_{23} \\ a_{31} & a_{32} & a_{33} \end{vmatrix} \tag{B.22}$$

is nonzero, and correspondingly for a square matrix of any size. However, we shall not give the proof here.

If A is any given matrix, its *transpose* A' is defined as the matrix obtained by replacing a_{ik} everywhere by a_{ki}, that is, interchanging each row with its corresponding column. Thus the transpose of A in (B.6) is given by

$$A' = \begin{bmatrix} a_{11} & a_{21} & a_{31} \\ a_{12} & a_{22} & a_{32} \\ a_{13} & a_{23} & a_{33} \end{bmatrix}. \tag{B.23}$$

The definition of matrix multiplication leads to the rule

$$(AB)' = B'A'. \tag{B.24}$$

A matrix A for which $A' = A$ is called *symmetric*. In this case, evidently, for all i, k, we have $a_{ik} = a_{ki}$.

If two matrices of the same dimensions are given, their sum is defined as indicated by the formula

$$c_{ik} = a_{ik} + b_{ik}, \tag{B.25}$$

that is, the (i, k) element of the sum matrix is the sum of the corresponding elements of the given matrices. Multiplication of a matrix by a number (scalar) is done by multiplying *all* the elements of the matrix by this number.

With these definitions, it is seen that matrices consisting of a single row (or those with a single column) behave like vectors (see the last chapter). However, to obtain a scalar product of two vectors by matrix methods, it is necessary to regard the first vector as a column matrix and the second as a row matrix. Thus

$$(a_1\ a_2\ a_3) \begin{bmatrix} b_1 \\ b_2 \\ b_3 \end{bmatrix} = (a_1 b_1 + a_2 b_2 + a_3 b_3), \tag{B.26}$$

the result being a 1×1 matrix whose single element is the scalar product of the vectors involved.

Only a few of the many properties and uses of matrices have been indicated here. For the purposes of optics, the most important application of matrix theory is in connection with linear transformations. Here it should be pointed out that the treatment outlined above depends only on the linearity properties of the transformations. The same results hold for transformations between sets of vectors provided the coefficients are scalars. For example, transformations of the form

$$\begin{aligned} \vec{y}_1 &= a_{11}\vec{x}_1 + a_{12}\vec{x}_2 + a_{13}\vec{x}_3 \\ \vec{y}_2 &= a_{21}\vec{x}_1 + a_{22}\vec{x}_2 + a_{23}\vec{x}_3 \\ \vec{y}_3 &= a_{31}\vec{x}_1 + a_{32}\vec{x}_2 + a_{33}\vec{x}_3 \end{aligned} \tag{B.27}$$

can be handled by the methods described above. Vector relations of this type frequently occur in optics. Actually many nonlinear problems can be "linearized" by an approximation method which is described in a later part of this chapter.

Least Squares*

The following type of problem arises in various scientific investigations. We describe the problem first in a simplified form to show the basic facts. Suppose that for n values of x, that is, $x_1, x_2, \ldots x_n$, corresponding values of y, namely $y_1, y_2, \ldots y_n$ are known (from measurements or otherwise). It is desired to determine a continuous function $y = f(x)$ which is approximately satisfied by the above data, that is, the differences $y_i - f(x_i)$ are to be small. A problem of this type is called *curve-fitting* since one can regard the pairs (x_i, y_i) as defining points of the (x, y) plane and try to determine the equation of a curve which will pass through these points (or sufficiently near them so that the errors involved are within a given size, based, for instance, on the experimental errors of the problem being considered).

* See also *M. Herzberger* and *R. H. Morris*, "A Contribution to the Method of Least Squares," Quart. Appl. Math., *5*, 354–357, (1947), and *M. Herzberger*, "The Normal Equations of the Method of Least Squares and Their Solution," Quart. Appl. Math., *7*, 217–223 (1949).

The method has great scientific value because it combines a large number of isolated data into a single mathematical formula. In fact, the equation of the curve obtained sometimes indicates a basic law which governs the relationship of the measured quantities (*cf.* Chapter 12, which treats the dispersion of optical glass). In other cases, where a basic law is known to exist, the method of curve-fitting serves to determine the special form it takes for the given set of data. The formula, once found, can then be used for interpolation. For example, after tracing a number of rays through an optical system, one can derive a function which gives the behavior of *all* the rays, at least approximately. The nature of the problem shows that, in general, the answer is not unique, since any number of curves can be found to approximate a given set of points to a given degree of precision.

In any curve-fitting problem, the first step is to decide on the general form of the function $y = f(x)$ to be selected. Examples are

$$ax + b, \quad ax^2 + bx + c, \quad ac^{bx}, \quad a \sin bx. \tag{B.28}$$

No general rule can be given for selecting the best form in cases in which there is no information as to a basic underlying law. The most common choice is a polynomial. However, here the degree chosen should be small enough to give a simple function but large enough to allow a good approximation.

To illustrate the method of least squares, let us suppose that a quadratic function of the form

$$y = f(x) = ax^2 + bx + c \tag{B.29}$$

is assumed. Substitution of the values x_i and comparison with the given or measured values y_i gives a set of differences

$$f(x_i) - y_i = (ax_i^2 + bx_i + c) - y_i, \tag{B.30}$$

which indicate how well the function approximates the given data. The basic problem is to select the coefficients a, b, c so that these differences are small. However, to minimize the differences *simultaneously*, some criterion is needed to indicate what is meant by a "minimum" set of differences. By the method of *least squares*, one means the selection of the undetermined coefficients of $f(x)$

so that the sum of the squares of the differences $f(x_i) - y_i$ is a minimum. Thus, in the example of a quadratic function,

$$\sum_{i=1}^{n} (ax_i^2 + bx_i + c - y_i)^2 = F(a, b, c) \tag{B.31}$$

is to be minimized. The reason for using this particular criterion will be shown presently by giving a geometrical picture of the problem.

In accordance with the usual rule of calculus, F can have a minimum only when

$$\partial F/\partial a = \partial F/\partial b = \partial F/\partial c = 0. \tag{B.32}$$

This leads to the relations

$$\begin{aligned} &\sum_{i=1}^{n} x_i^2 (ax_i^2 + bx_i + c - y_i) = 0 \\ &\sum_{i=1}^{n} x_i (ax_i^2 + bx_i + c - y_i) = 0 \\ &\sum_{i=1}^{n} (ax_i^2 + bx_i + c - y_i) = 0, \end{aligned} \tag{B.33}$$

which are three linear equations to be solved for a, b, and c. Equations (B.33) are called the *normal equations* of the least-square problem. If $f(x)$ has a higher (or lower) degree or if the given data require determination of a function of two or more variables, the procedure is essentially the same. In every case, the normal equations have the form of k linear equations in k unknowns. In the present example, $k = 3$.

The form of Equations (B.33) can be remembered easily by considering n-dimensional vectors (*cf.* the last chapter):

$$\begin{aligned} \vec{a}_1 &= (x_1^2, x_2^2, \ldots x_n^2) \\ \vec{a}_2 &= (x_1, x_2, \ldots x_n) \\ \vec{a}_3 &= (1, 1, \ldots 1) \\ \vec{y} &= (y_1, y_2, \ldots y_n). \end{aligned} \tag{B.34}$$

The normal equations (B.33) may then be written in the form

$$\begin{aligned} (\vec{a}_1^2)\, a + (\vec{a}_1\vec{a}_2)\, b + (\vec{a}_1\vec{a}_3)\, c &= \vec{a}_1\, \vec{y} \\ (\vec{a}_1\vec{a}_2)\, a + (\vec{a}_2^2)\, b + (\vec{a}_2\vec{a}_3)\, c &= \vec{a}_2\, \vec{y} \\ (\vec{a}_1\vec{a}_3)\, a + (\vec{a}_2\vec{a}_3)\, b + (\vec{a}_3^2)\, c &= \vec{a}_3\, \vec{y}. \end{aligned} \tag{B.35}$$

The matrix of coefficients (*cf.* the discussion of matrices above),

$$A = \begin{bmatrix} \vec{a}_1^2 & \vec{a}_1\vec{a}_2 & \vec{a}_1\vec{a}_3 \\ \vec{a}_1\vec{a}_2 & \vec{a}_2^2 & \vec{a}_2\vec{a}_3 \\ \vec{a}_1\vec{a}_3 & \vec{a}_2\vec{a}_3 & \vec{a}_3^2 \end{bmatrix}, \tag{B.36}$$

is seen to be symmetric. The problem of solving the normal equations in the general case is therefore equivalent to finding the inverse of a $k \times k$ symmetric matrix. When k is large, special methods are used to find the approximate solution of the equations (or the inverse of the matrix) as easily and systematically as possible.

The use of vectors gives a better insight into the nature of the least-square method since it makes possible a significant geometrical interpretation of the quantities involved. Consider in ordinary three-dimensional space the problem of projecting a vector $\vec{a}$ into the plane of two others, say $\vec{b}$ and $\vec{c}$. By this we mean to find a vector

$$\beta\vec{b} + \gamma\vec{c} \tag{B.37}$$

in the plane of $\vec{b}$ and $\vec{c}$ such that the difference vector

$$\beta\vec{b} + \gamma\vec{c} - \vec{a} \tag{B.38}$$

shall have a minimum length. To minimize

$$(\beta\vec{b} + \gamma\vec{c} - \vec{a})^2 = F(\beta,\gamma), \tag{B.39}$$

one must have

$$\partial F/\partial\beta = \partial F/\partial\gamma = 0. \tag{B.40}$$

Using the rules of vector differentiation described in the last chapter, we obtain

$$\begin{aligned} \vec{b}\,(\beta\vec{b} + \gamma\vec{c} - \vec{a}) &= 0 \\ \vec{c}\,(\beta\vec{b} + \gamma\vec{c} - \vec{a}) &= 0, \end{aligned} \tag{B.41}$$

showing that β and γ must be chosen so that the difference vector is perpendicular to $\vec{b}$ and to $\vec{c}$. This is in agreement with our geometrical picture of the problem in the three-dimensional case.

To find β and γ, observe that Equations (B.41) may be written

$$(\vec{b}^2)\,\beta + (\vec{b}\vec{c})\,\gamma = \vec{a}\vec{b}$$
$$(\vec{b}\vec{c})\,\beta + (\vec{c}^2)\,\gamma = \vec{a}\vec{c}, \qquad \text{(B.42)}$$

which are of the same form as (B.35) but with only two equations in two unknowns.

By thinking of n-dimensional vectors as line segments in n-dimensional space, one finds a complete geometrical analogy between the general least-square problem and the three-dimensional projection problem just described. The vectors $\vec{a}_1$, $\vec{a}_2$, $\vec{a}_3$ may be thought of as determining a subspace of the n-dimensional space in which they lie. This subspace consists of all points obtainable by linear combinations of the vectors $\vec{a}_1$, $\vec{a}_2$, $\vec{a}_3$; it is analogous to the plane in the preceding projection example. Equations (B.5) give the conditions for finding the projection of $\vec{y}$ in this subspace, that is, for finding a linear combination

$$\vec{p} = a\vec{a}_1 + b\vec{a}_2 + c\vec{a}_3 \qquad \text{(B.43)}$$

such that the length of the difference vector $\vec{p} - \vec{y}$ is a minimum or, what is equivalent, so that $\vec{p} - \vec{y}$ is perpendicular to each of the three vectors $\vec{a}_1$, $\vec{a}_2$, $\vec{a}_3$. This is possible when $n > 3$.)

When the values of a, b, c have been found, the calculation of the quantity $(\vec{p} - \vec{y})^2$ gives an indication of the "goodness of the fit." If its value is too large, this fact suggests using a polynomial of higher degree or perhaps even a different type of function for $f(x)$. The method of least squares can be used for non-polynomial type functions if $f(x)$ is assumed to be a linear combination

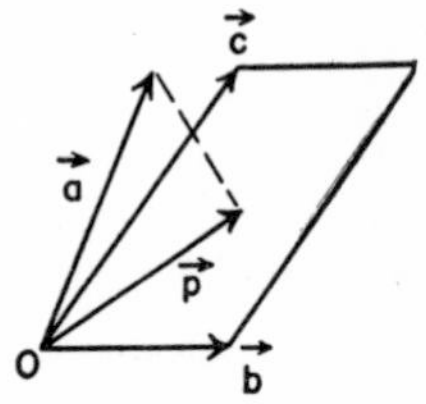

Fig. B.1. Projection p of a vector a in the plane of b and c.

$$f(x) = c_1 f_1(x) + c_2 f_2(x) + \ldots + c_k f_k(x), \qquad \text{(B.44)}$$

where the $f_i(x)$ are known functions and the c_i are the undetermined coefficients. The extension to functions of two or more variables is quite straightforward. In such cases, the term "curve-fitting" no longer describes the problem. Here one might coin the term "surface-fitting." In optics, when dealing with a congruence (two-dimensional family) of rays, one ordinarily assumes a function $f(x, y)$ which has the form of a polynomial in two variables, these being the two parameters of the congruence.

We consider now a method of solving the normal equations (B.35) for a, b, and c. This is easy for a small number of equations, but it increases very greatly in difficulty for larger systems. The method to be described is called the *square-root* method, and again it is found that the geometrical point of view is very helpful. Inspection of the normal equations (B.35) shows that, whenever the vectors involved happen to be orthogonal, the equations can be solved by inspection since then $\vec{a}_i\vec{a}_j = 0$ when $i \neq j$. We therefore look for three mutually orthogonal vectors $\vec{e}_1$, $\vec{e}_2$, $\vec{e}_3$ in the subspace determined by $\vec{a}_1$, $\vec{a}_2$, $\vec{a}_3$ and require for added convenience that the $\vec{e}_i$ be unit vectors.

We therefore write

$$\begin{aligned} \vec{a}_1 &= \alpha_{11}\vec{e}_1 \\ \vec{a}_2 &= \alpha_{21}\vec{e}_1 + \alpha_{22}\vec{e}_2 \\ \vec{a}_3 &= \alpha_{31}\vec{e}_1 + \alpha_{32}\vec{e}_2 + \alpha_{33}\vec{e}_3, \end{aligned} \tag{B.45}$$

where the matrix of coefficients

$$\Delta = \begin{bmatrix} \alpha_{11} & 0 & 0 \\ \alpha_{21} & \alpha_{22} & 0 \\ \alpha_{31} & \alpha_{32} & \alpha_{33} \end{bmatrix} \tag{B.46}$$

is to be determined so that the vectors $\vec{e}_i$ obtained by solving the equations satisfy the relations

$$\begin{aligned} \vec{e}_i^{\,2} &= 1 \\ \vec{e}_i\vec{e}_j &= 0 \qquad (i = 1, 2, 3;\, j = 1, 2, 3). \end{aligned} \tag{B.47}$$

Applying conditions (B.45) and (B.47), one finds that

$$\begin{aligned} \vec{a}_1^{\,2} &= \alpha_{11}^2 & \vec{a}_2^{\,2} &= \alpha_{21}^2 + \alpha_{22}^2 \\ \vec{a}_1\vec{a}_2 &= \alpha_{11}\alpha_{21} & \vec{a}_2\vec{a}_3 &= \alpha_{21}\alpha_{31} + \alpha_{22}\alpha_{32} \\ \vec{a}_1\vec{a}_3 &= \alpha_{11}\alpha_{31} & \vec{a}_3^{\,2} &= \alpha_{31}^2 + \alpha_{32}^2 + \alpha_{33}^2. \end{aligned} \tag{B.48}$$

These equations can be solved in turn for α_{11}, α_{21}, α_{31}, α_{22}, α_{32}, α_{33} since the quantities on the left are known. In each case where square roots occur, the positive root may be chosen, the negative root merely leading to a different possible choice of the orthogonal unit vectors $\vec{e}_i$. Equations (B.48) may be stated in the simple matrix form

$$\Delta\Delta' = A, \tag{B.49}$$

where Δ' is the transpose of Δ and A is the matrix (B.36).

Due to (B.49), the normal equations may be written in the matrix form

$$\Delta\Delta' \begin{bmatrix} a \\ b \\ c \end{bmatrix} = \begin{bmatrix} \vec{a}_1\vec{y} \\ \vec{a}_2\vec{y} \\ \vec{a}_3\vec{y} \end{bmatrix}, \tag{B.50}$$

the right-hand side, of course, being known. This may be solved in two steps indicated by

$$\begin{gathered} \Delta' \begin{bmatrix} a \\ b \\ c \end{bmatrix} = \Delta^{-1} \begin{bmatrix} \vec{a}_1\vec{y} \\ \vec{a}_2\vec{y} \\ \vec{a}_3\vec{y} \end{bmatrix} \\ \begin{bmatrix} a \\ b \\ c \end{bmatrix} = (\Delta')^{-1}\Delta^{-1} \begin{bmatrix} \vec{a}_1\vec{y} \\ \vec{a}_1\vec{y} \\ \vec{a}_3\vec{y} \end{bmatrix}. \end{gathered} \tag{B.51}$$

To indicate the computation in detail, let

$$\Delta^{-1} \begin{bmatrix} \vec{a}_1\vec{y} \\ \vec{a}_2\vec{y} \\ \vec{a}_3\vec{y} \end{bmatrix} = \begin{bmatrix} \varkappa_1 \\ \varkappa_2 \\ \varkappa_3 \end{bmatrix}, \quad \Delta \begin{bmatrix} \varkappa_1 \\ \varkappa_2 \\ \varkappa_3 \end{bmatrix} = \begin{bmatrix} \vec{a}_1\vec{y} \\ \vec{a}_2\vec{y} \\ \vec{a}_3\vec{y} \end{bmatrix}, \quad \Delta' \begin{bmatrix} a \\ b \\ c \end{bmatrix} = \begin{bmatrix} \varkappa_1 \\ \varkappa_2 \\ \varkappa_3 \end{bmatrix}. \tag{B.52}$$

In nonmatrix form, this means that the $\varkappa_i$ are determined by solving in turn the relations

$$\begin{aligned} \alpha_{11}\varkappa_1 &= \vec{a}_1\vec{y} \\ \alpha_{21}\varkappa_1 + \alpha_{22}\varkappa_2 &= \vec{a}_2\vec{y} \\ \alpha_{31}\varkappa_1 + \alpha_{32}\varkappa_2 + \alpha_{33}\varkappa_3 &= \vec{a}_3\vec{y}, \end{aligned} \tag{B.53}$$

and then the quantities c, b, a are found (in that order) from the equations

$$\begin{aligned} \alpha_{11}a + \alpha_{21}b + \alpha_{31}c &= \varkappa_1 \\ \alpha_{22}b + \alpha_{32}c &= \varkappa_2 \\ \alpha_{33}c &= \varkappa_3. \end{aligned} \tag{B.54}$$

The geometrical significance of the intermediate quantities appears if the projection vector $\vec{p}$ in (B.43) is expressed as a linear contribution of the $\vec{e}_i$. One can show that

$$\vec{p} = a\vec{a}_1 + b\vec{a}_2 + c\vec{a}_3 = \varkappa_1\vec{e}_1 + \varkappa_2\vec{e}_2 + \varkappa_3\vec{e}_3. \qquad \text{(B.55)}$$

Also it can be verified that

$$\vec{p}\vec{y} = \varkappa_1^2 + \varkappa_2^2 + \varkappa_3^2. \qquad \text{(B.56)}$$

Therefore the square of the length of the difference vector can be expressed (with the help of the above relation and the fact that $\vec{p}\,(\vec{p} - \vec{y}) = 0$) in the form

$$(\vec{p} - \vec{y})^2 = \vec{y}^2 - \vec{y}\vec{p} = \vec{y}^2 - \varkappa_1^2 - \varkappa_2^2 - \varkappa_3^2. \qquad \text{(B.57)}$$

The size of this quantity gives an indication of the "goodness of the fit," as mentioned before. The numerical computation can be arranged thus:

$$\begin{array}{cccc|cc}
 & \vec{a}_1^2 & \vec{a}_1\vec{a}_2 & \vec{a}_1\vec{a}_3 & \vec{a}_1\vec{y} & a = \\
 & \alpha_{11} & \vec{a}_2^2 & \vec{a}_2\vec{a}_3 & \vec{a}_2\vec{y} & b = \\
 & \alpha_{21} & \alpha_{22} & \vec{a}_3^2 & \vec{a}_3\vec{y} & c = \\
 & \alpha_{31} & \alpha_{32} & \alpha_{33} & & \\
\hline
 & \varkappa_1 & \varkappa_2 & \varkappa_3 & & \\
\vec{y}^2 & \beta_1 & \beta_2 & \beta_3 & &
\end{array} \qquad \text{(B.58)}$$

The quantities β_i are defined by

$$\begin{aligned}
\beta_1 &= \vec{y}^2 - \varkappa_1^2 \\
\beta_2 &= \vec{y}^2 - \varkappa_1^2 - \varkappa_2^2 \\
\beta_3 &= \vec{y}^2 - \varkappa_1^2 - \varkappa_2^2 - \varkappa_3^2 = (\vec{y} - \vec{p})^2.
\end{aligned} \qquad \text{(B.59)}$$

They are helpful in checking the computation at the intermediate stages. A numerical example is given in Table IX.

The method described above involves taking several square roots, which can be done readily with an ordinary calculating

TABLE IX

Sample Least-Square Calculation.

The example chosen illustrates, using different numerical values, the computation of $\overline{M}_o$, $\overline{M}_3$, $\overline{M}_{33}$ for 0° in Table VII of Chapter 34. A decimal point adjustment has been made to facilitate the machine calculation.)

Preliminary data		*Least-square data*		
y'	$10x'$	$100e_3$ $e_3 = \frac{1}{2}(x'^2 + y'^2)$	$\frac{1}{2}(100e_3)^2$	M
0	0.25759+	0.03317630+	0.00055033+	1.0303345−
0	0.77293+	0.29871039+	0.04461395+	1.0304615−
0	1.28876+	0.83045116+	0.34482456+	1.0306405−
0	1.80542+	1.62977069+	1.32807625+	1.0308662−
0	2.32206+	2.69598132+	3.63415764+	1.0310030−
0	2.84451+	4.04561857+	8.18351480+	1.0310240−

Least-square calculation, $\overline{M}_o + \overline{M}_3 e_3 + \overline{M}_{33}\frac{1}{2}(e_3^2) = M$				*Assumed function results*
6.0000000+	9.5337084+	13.535737+	6.1843298−	$\overline{M}_o$ = 1.0303316−
2.4494897+				$\overline{M}_3$ = .00042304
	27.071475+	45.369165+	9.8286590−	
				$\overline{M}_{33}$ = .00012507+
3.8921202+	3.4529517+			
		82.061697+	13.955227−	
5.5259416+	6.9104749+	1.9419071+		
2.5247421−	.00059638−	.00024289+		

machine. If an approximate value of $\sqrt{N}$ is a, then $\frac{1}{2}(a + N/a)$ gives a better approximation. By repetition one quickly obtains an accurate value for $\sqrt{N}$. If the vectors $\vec{a}_i$ are dependent, the method described above must be modified since the matrix A in the normal equations is found to be singular. What more often happens in practice is that the vectors $\vec{a}_1$ are "nearly" dependent, as indicated by the matrix A having a small determinant. This leads to difficulties in maintaining the accuracy of the numerical calculation. Special procedures to be used in this type of problem are suggested in the papers referred to on p. 448.

Gaussian Brackets

In his "Disquisitiones Arithmeticae," the mathematician *Karl Friedrich Gauss* introduced an algorithm for solving a linear diophantine equation. The symbols he defined there are now known as *Gaussian brackets* and have been found very useful in optics as well as in other fields.

Let $a_1, a_2, \ldots a_n$ be an ordered set of quantities (which for our purposes may be assumed to be real numbers or real functions) and let us define the symbol $[a_1, a_2, \ldots a_n]$, the Gaussian bracket, with the help of a recursion formula as follows. The empty bracket $[\quad]$ is defined as the value 1. A bracket with one element $[a_1]$ is the number a_1 itself. A bracket with n elements is defined in terms of brackets with one fewer and two fewer elements. Thus

$$[\quad] = 1, \quad [a_1] = a_1, \quad [a_1, a_2] = [a_1]\, a_2 + [\quad],$$
$$[a_1, a_2, \ldots a_n] = [a_1, a_2, \ldots a_{n-1}]\, a_n + [a_1, a_2, \ldots a_{n-2}]. \qquad \text{(B.60)}$$

It is easy to find the value of a typical bracket. Let us write the brackets having from 1 to 6 elements:

$$
\begin{aligned}
[a_1] &= a_1 \\
[a_1a_2] &= a_1a_2 + 1 \\
[a_1a_2a_3] &= a_1a_2a_3 + a_1 + a_3 \\
[a_1a_2a_3a_4] &= a_1a_2a_3a_4 + a_1a_2 + a_1a_4 + a_3a_4 + 1 \qquad \text{(B.61)} \\
[a_1a_2a_3a_4a_5] &= a_1a_2a_3a_4a_5 + a_1a_2a_3 + a_1a_2a_5 + a_1a_4a_5 \\
&\quad + a_3a_4a_5 + a_1 + a_3 + a_5
\end{aligned}
$$

$$[a_1a_2a_3a_4a_5a_6] = a_1a_2a_3a_4a_5a_6 + a_1a_2a_3a_4 + a_1a_2a_3a_6$$
$$+ a_1a_2a_5a_6 + a_1a_4a_5a_6 + a_3a_4a_5a_6$$
$$+ a_1a_2 + a_1a_4 + a_1a_6 + a_3a_4 + a_3a_6 + a_5a_6 + 1.$$

The bracket containing n elements is equal to the sum of (a) the product of all elements, (b) all products of $n - 2$ elements which can be formed with indices increasing from left to right starting with an odd index and with alternating odd and even indices, (c) all products of $n - 4$ elements under the same conditions, and so on. When n is even, a last term of 1 is included, whereas, when n is odd, the addition ends with the sum of the elements with odd indices.

Gaussian brackets have some interesting properties, which we enumerate in a series of theorems.

THEOREM I. A Gaussian bracket is a linear function of its last element. This is shown by the defining relation (B.60):

$$[a_1 \quad a_n] = [a_1 \quad a_{n-1}]a_n + [a_1 \quad a_{n-2}], \quad n > 1. \qquad \text{(B.62)}$$

THEOREM II. A Gaussian bracket is a linear function of its first element. In fact, for $n > 1$,

$$[a_1 \quad a_n] = a_1 [a_2 \quad a_n] + [a_3 \quad a_n]. \qquad \text{(B.63)}$$

The proof can be obtained by induction. Equation (B.63) holds for brackets with two or three elements since (B.61) shows that

$$[a_1a_2] = a_1a_2 + 1 = a_1 [a_2] + [\quad]$$
$$[a_1a_2a_3] = a_1[a_2a_3] + [a_3]. \qquad \text{(B.64)}$$

Let us assume it to hold for brackets with more than one but fewer than n elements and make use of (B.60). Thus

$$\begin{aligned} [a_1 \quad a_n] &= [a_1 \quad a_{n-1}]a_n + [a_1 \quad a_{n-2}] \\ &= a_1[a_2 \quad a_{n-1}]a_n + [a_3 \quad a_n]\, a_n \\ &+ a_1[a_2 \quad a_{n-2}] + [a_3 \quad a_{n-2}] \\ &= a_1[a_2 \quad a_n] + [a_3 \quad a_n]. \end{aligned} \qquad \text{(B.65)}$$

THEOREM III. A Gaussian bracket is symmetric. That is

$$[a_1, a_2, \ldots a_{n-1}, a_n] = [a_n, a_{n-1}, \ldots a_2, a_1], \; n > 1. \qquad \text{(B.66)}$$

Again this is seen to hold for brackets with two or three elements, and the proof for $n > 3$ can be obtained by induction:

$$
\begin{aligned}
[a_1 a_2] &= a_1 a_2 + 1 = [a_2 a_1] \\
[a_1 a_2 a_3] &= [a_3 a_2 a_1] \qquad (B.67) \\
[a_1 \ a_n] &= a_1[a_2 \ a_n] + [a_3 \ a_n] \\
&= [a_n \ a_2]a_1 + [a_n \ a_3] \\
&= [a_n \ a_1],\ n > 3.
\end{aligned}
$$

THEOREM IV. A Gaussian bracket is a linear function of any of its elements. In fact, if $n > 1$,

$$
\begin{aligned}
&[a_1 \ a_n] = C\, a_\varkappa + D \\
&C = [a_1 \ a_{\varkappa-1}]\,[a_{\varkappa+1} \ a_n] \qquad (B.68) \\
&D = [a_1,\ a_{\varkappa-1} + a_{\varkappa+1},\ a_n].
\end{aligned}
$$

Here C is the product of the brackets obtained by using the groups of elements before and after $a_\varkappa$, and D is the bracket obtained by replacing the three elements $a_{\varkappa-1}$, $a_\varkappa$, $a_{\varkappa+1}$ by the single element $a_{\varkappa-1} + a_{\varkappa+1}$. Again the proof can be obtained by induction, but it will not be given here.

As an important corollary, it should be observed that, if a bracket has one zero element, the bracket can be replaced by a bracket containing $n - 2$ elements, obtained by replacing the zero element and its two adjacent elements by a single element consisting of the sum of the adjacent elements, that is, the bracket D of (B.68). Thus

$$
[a_1,\ a_{\varkappa-1},\ 0,\ a_{\varkappa+1},\ a_n] = [a_1,\ a_{\varkappa-1} + a_{\varkappa+1},\ a_n]. \qquad (B.69)
$$

For cases where alternate zeros occur, observe that

$$
\begin{aligned}
&[a_1, 0, a_3, 0, \ldots 0, a_{2\varkappa+1}] = [a_1 + a_3 + \ldots + a_{2\varkappa+1}] \\
&\qquad\qquad\qquad\qquad = a_1 + a_3 + \ldots + a_{2\varkappa+1} \\
&[a_1, 0, a_3, 0, \ldots a_{2\varkappa-1}, 0] = [a_1 + a_3 + \ldots + a_{2\varkappa-1}, 0] = 1 \\
&[0, a_2, \ldots 0, a_{2\varkappa}] = [0, a_2 + a_4 + \ldots + a_{2\varkappa}] = 1 \\
&[0, a_2, \ldots, a_{2\varkappa-2}, 0] = [0, a_2 + a_4 + \ldots + a_{2\varkappa-2}, 0] = 0.
\end{aligned}
$$

Another important corollary of Theorem IV is that a bracket can easily be differentiated:

$$\frac{\partial}{\partial a_\varkappa}[a_1 \; a_n] = [a_1 \; a_{\varkappa-1}]\,[a_{\varkappa+1} \; a_n]. \qquad \text{(B.71)}$$

THEOREM V. A Gaussian bracket is a linear function of any partial bracket, the formula being

$$[a_1 \; a_n] = [a_1 \; a_\varkappa]\,[a_{\varkappa+1} \; a_n] + [a_1 \; a_{\varkappa-1}]\,[a_{\varkappa+2} \; a_n]. \qquad \text{(B.72)}$$

Again the proof is by induction on $\varkappa$. When $\varkappa = 1$, the formula holds, as (B.63) shows. Let us assume that it holds for a value $\varkappa - 1$ and prove that it holds for the next higher number, $\varkappa$.

$$\begin{aligned}
[a_1 \, a_n] &= [a_1 \; a_{\varkappa-1}]\,[a_\varkappa \; a_n] + [a_1 \; a_{\varkappa-2}]\,[a_{\varkappa+1} \; a_n] \\
&= [a_1 \; a_{\varkappa-1}]\,(a_\varkappa\,[a_{\varkappa+1} \; a_n] + [a_{\varkappa+2} \; a_n]) + [a_1 \; a_{\varkappa-2}]\,[a_{\varkappa+1} \, a_n] \\
&= [a_{\varkappa+1} \; a_n]\,([a_1 \; a_{\varkappa-1}]\,a_\varkappa + [a_1 \; a_{\varkappa-2}]) \\
&\quad + [a_1 \; a_{\varkappa-1}]\,[a_{\varkappa+2} \, a_n] \\
&= [a_1 \; a_\varkappa]\,[a_{\varkappa+1} \; a_n] + [a_1 \; a_{\varkappa-1}]\,[a_{\varkappa+2} \; a_n]. \qquad \text{(B.73)}
\end{aligned}$$

As special cases we have

$$\begin{aligned}
[a_1 \; a_n] &= [a_1 a_2]\,[a_3 \; a_n] + a_1\,[a_4 \; a_n] \\
[a_1 \; a_n] &= [a_1 \; a_{n-2}]\,[a_{n-1} \; a_n] + [a_1 \; a_{n-3}]\,a_n. \qquad \text{(B.74)}
\end{aligned}$$

THEOREM VI. The following determinant formula holds:

$$D_n = \begin{vmatrix} [a_1 \; a_n] & [a_2 \; a_n] \\ [a_1 \; a_{n-1}] & [a_2 \; a_{n-1}] \end{vmatrix} = (-1)^n, \quad n > 1. \qquad \text{(B.75)}$$

For $n = 2$, we have

$$D_2 = \begin{vmatrix} [a_1 a_2] & [a_2] \\ [a_1] & [\;] \end{vmatrix} = 1. \qquad \text{(B.76)}$$

In general the determinant D_n can be reduced by multiplying the second row by a_n and subtracting from the first. This gives [due to (B.62)]:

$$D_n = \begin{vmatrix} [a_1\ a_n] & [a_2\ a_n] \\ [a_1\ a_{n-1}] & [a_2\ a_{n-1}] \end{vmatrix} = \begin{vmatrix} [a_1\ a_{n-2}] & [a_2\ a_{n-2}] \\ [a_1\ a_{n-1}] & [a_2\ a_{n-1}] \end{vmatrix}$$

$$= \begin{vmatrix} [a_1\ a_{n-1}] & [a_2\ a_{n-1}] \\ [a_1\ a_{n-2}] & [a_2\ a_{n-2}] \end{vmatrix}. \tag{B.77}$$

Thus $D_n = -D_{n-1}$ so that, by virtue of (B.76), the desired result is proved.

Theorems I, III, and VI are to be found in Gauss's original paper. Theorem VI can be generalized as stated in the following theorem.

THEOREM VII.

$$\begin{vmatrix} [a_1\ a_\varkappa] & [a_2\ a_\varkappa] \\ [a_1\ a_\varrho] & [a_2\ a_\varrho] \end{vmatrix} = (-1)^{\varrho-1}[a_{\varrho+2}\ a_\varkappa], \quad 1 < \varrho < \varkappa. \tag{B.78}$$

The proof proceeds as follows: Multiplying the second column by a_1 and subtracting the product from the first, we obtain the same determinant with its sign changed and one less member in each bracket. Repeated $\varrho - 1$ times, this gives

$$\begin{vmatrix} [a_1\ a_\varkappa] & [a_2\ a_\varkappa] \\ [a_1\ a_\varrho] & [a_2\ a_\varrho] \end{vmatrix} = (-1)^{\varrho-1} \begin{vmatrix} [a_\varrho\ a_\varkappa] & [a_{\varrho+1}\ a_\varkappa] \\ [a_\varrho] & [\ ] \end{vmatrix} \tag{B.79}$$

$$= (-1)^{\varrho-1} \begin{vmatrix} [a_{\varrho+2}\ a_\varkappa] & [a_{\varrho+1}\ a_\varkappa] \\ 0 & 1 \end{vmatrix} = (-1)^{\varrho-1}[a_{\varrho+2}\ a_\varkappa].$$

Theorem VII gives all partial brackets of $[a_1\ \ a_n]$ when those starting with a_1 and a_2 are given.

One of the most common uses of Gaussian brackets is in connection with continued fractions. Observe that

$$\frac{1}{a_1} = \frac{[\ ]}{[a_1]}, \quad \frac{1}{a_1 + (1/a_2)} = \frac{a_2}{a_1 a_2 + 1} = \frac{[a_2]}{[a_1 a_2]}$$

$$\frac{1}{a_1 + \cfrac{1}{a_2 + (1/a_3)}} = \frac{1}{a_1 + \cfrac{[a_3]}{[a_2 a_3]}} = \frac{[a_2 a_3]}{[a_1 a_2 a_3]}. \tag{B.80}$$

It is evident that in the general case

$$\cfrac{1}{a_1 + \cfrac{1}{a_2 + \cfrac{1}{a_3 + \ddots + \cfrac{1}{a_n}}}} = \frac{[a_2 \quad a_n]}{[a_1 \quad a_n]}. \tag{B.81}$$

Polynomial Approximation Method

Consider a problem in which several functions of, let us say. two variables x and y occur and suppose that any terms of, say, the third degree in x and y can be neglected. It will ordinarily then be possible to approximate these functions by their Taylor expansions about the origin, that is,

$$f(x, y) = a_0 + a_1 x + a_2 y + \tfrac{1}{2} a_{11} x^2 + a_{12} xy + \tfrac{1}{2} a_{22} y^2$$
$$g(x, y) = b_o + b_1 x + b_2 y + \tfrac{1}{2} b_{11} x^2 + b_{12} xy + \tfrac{1}{2} b_{22} y^2, \tag{B.82}$$

where the a_i and b_i are constants. The sum $f + g$ is then, of course, obtained as a similar polynomial. The product fg can be found as a polynomial of the same degree due to the assumption that terms of the third and higher degrees may be neglected. Furthermore the derivatives $\partial f/\partial x = f_1$ and $\partial f/\partial y = f_2$ etc., are found as polynomials of lower degree. We may represent the polynomials as columns in a table:

	f	g	fg	f_1	f_2	g_1	g_2
1	a_0	b_o	$a_0 b_o$	a_1	a_2	b_1	b_2
x	a_1	b_1	$a_0 b_1 + a_1 b_o$	a_{11}	a_{12}	b_{11}	b_{12}
y	a_2	b_2	$a_0 b_2 + a_2 b_o$	a_{12}	a_{22}	b_{12}	b_{22}
$\frac{1}{2}x^2$	a_{11}	b_{11}	$a_0 b_{11} + 2a_1 b_1 + a_{11} b_o$				
xy	a_{12}	b_{12}	$a_0 b_{12} + a_1 b_2 + a_2 b_1 + a_{12} b_o$				
$\frac{1}{2}y^2$	a_{22}	b_{22}	$a_0 b_{22} + 2a_2 b_2 + a_{22} b_o$				

(B.83)

It may be noted that in the general case the coefficients of the derivative f_1 can be obtained by putting 1 on the index of f at each level and omitting terms of second degree. A corresponding rule applies to f_2.

Various types of implicit problems can be solved in terms of these polynomial approximations. To find the reciprocal of f, use the fg column of the table. Assume the coefficients a_i known and the b_i to be found so that the polynomial for fg is identically equal to unity. This leads to the relations

$$\begin{aligned}
&a_0 b_o = 1 \\
&a_0 b_1 + a_1 b_o = 0 \\
&a_0 b_2 + a_2 b_o = 0 \\
&a_0 b_{11} + 2a_1 b_1 + a_{11} b_o = 0 \\
&a_0 b_{12} + a_1 b_2 + a_2 b_1 + a_{11} b_o = 0 \\
&a_0 b_{22} + 2a_2 b_2 + a_{22} b_o = 0.
\end{aligned} \qquad (B.84)$$

Inspection of these equations shows that, if $a_0 \neq 0$, $b_o = 1/a_0$ and the successive values b_1, b_2, b_{11}, b_{12}, b_{22} can be found successively without any further divisions. The resulting polynomial for g is then the desired reciprocal of f. The result can be checked by multiplication to see if A satisfies the relation $fg = 1$ (provided third-degree terms are again neglected in the product).

Suppose it is desired to find the square root of a function h with coefficients given by constants c_o, c_1, c_2, c_{11}, c_{12}, c_{22}. Assume the unknown function to be indicated by the polynomial f of (B.83). Then the square of f is obtained from the fg column of the table assuming $g = f$, whereupon the identity $f^2 = h$ leads to the solution of the problem. We show the details in tabular form:

	h	f	f^2	$f^2 = h$	
1	c_o	a_0	a_0^2	$a_0^2 = c_o$	
x	c_1	a_1	$2a_0 a_1$	$2a_0 a_1 = c_1$	
y	c_2	a_2	$2a_0 a_2$	$2a_0 a_2 = c_2$	(B.85)
$\frac{1}{2}x^2$	c_{11}	a_{11}	$2(a_1^2 + a_0 a_{11})$	$2(a_1^2 + a_0 a_{11}) = c_{11}$	
xy	c_{12}	a_{12}	$2(a_0 a_{12} + a_1 a_2)$	$2(a_0 a_{12} + a_1 a_2) = c_{12}$	
$\frac{1}{2}y^2$	c_{22}	a_{22}	$2(a_2^2 + a_0 a_{22})$	$2(a_2^2 + a_0 a_{22}) = c_{22}$	

The first equation $a_0^2 = c_o$ gives two values of a_0 corresponding to the two possible branches of the square-root function. If one of these is selected, the following equations then have unique solutions provided $a_0 \neq 0$. The series for f, when obtained, can, of course, be checked by squaring it and comparing the square with the given polynomial for h.

Numerous other types of implicit problems can be solved by the above approximation method. These include many cases of simultaneous implicit equations where two or more unknown polynomial expansions must be substituted and the respective coefficients found by successive calculation.

A common problem occurring in optical and other fields is that of expressing a function $f(x, y)$ in terms of new variables $\bar{x}, \bar{y}$. Let us assume that f is approximated by a known polynomial as in (B.83) and that one has obtained (perhaps by the earlier use of our approximation method) relations of the form

$$\begin{aligned} \bar{x} &= \bar{x}_1 x + \bar{x}_2 y + \tfrac{1}{2}\bar{x}_{11}x^2 + \bar{x}_{12}xy + \tfrac{1}{2}\bar{x}_{22}y^2 \\ \bar{y} &= \bar{y}_1 x + \bar{y}_2 y + \tfrac{1}{2}\bar{y}_{11}x^2 + \bar{y}_{12}xy + \tfrac{1}{2}\bar{y}_{22}y^2, \end{aligned} \tag{B.86}$$

where the $\bar{x}_i$, $\bar{y}_i$ are constants. From these relations, it is clear that third-degree terms in $\bar{x}$, $\bar{y}$ can also be considered negligible. Using our approximation method we can determine the inverse relations

$$\begin{aligned} x &= x_1\bar{x} + x_2\bar{y} + \tfrac{1}{2}x_{11}\bar{x}^2 + x_{12}\bar{x}\bar{y} + \tfrac{1}{2}x_{22}\bar{y}^2 \\ y &= y_1\bar{x} + y_2\bar{y} + \tfrac{1}{2}y_{11}\bar{x}^2 + y_{12}\bar{x}\bar{y} + \tfrac{1}{2}y_{22}\bar{y}^2. \end{aligned} \tag{B.87}$$

We now use (B.87) to form the following table, which again is to be read by columns:

	1	x	y	$\frac{1}{2}x^2$	xy	$\frac{1}{2}y^2$
1	1					
$\bar{x}$		x_1	y_1			
$\bar{y}$		x_2	y_2			
$\frac{1}{2}\bar{x}^2$		x_{11}	y_{11}	x_1^2	x_1y_1	y_1^2
$\bar{x}\bar{y}$		x_{12}	y_{12}	x_1x_2	$x_1y_2 + x_2y_1$	y_1y_2
$\frac{1}{2}\bar{y}^2$		x_{22}	y_{22}	x_2^2	x_2y_2	y_2^2

(B.88)

The problem of transforming a known polynomial in x, y to the new variables is of course done by substituting the polynomials given in this table in place of the quantities 1, x, y, etc. and rearranging terms. However, it is easy to verify that the coefficients of the new polynomial can be obtained by a simple matrix multiplication. If one considers the matrix M of coefficients in the above table and multiplies this matrix on the right by the coefficients of the given polynomial (arranged as a column matrix), one obtains the coefficients of the new polynomial (arranged as a column matrix).

As a final example to illustrate the uses of the approximate polynomial method, consider the nonlinear partial differential equation $p^2 = q$, where $p = \partial z/\partial x$, $q = \partial z/\partial y$. Assume $z = f(x, y)$ to be analytic at the origin, that is, write it as a polynomial in x, y with undetermined coefficients, assuming again that third-degree terms may be neglected. Polynomial expansions can then be found for p, q, and p^2 involving the unknown coefficients a_i, and the identity $p^2 = q$ gives relations for finding the a_i. The work is again arranged as the columns of a table:

	z	p	q	p^2	$p^2 = q$	
1	a_o	a_1	a_2	$a_1{}^2$	$a_1{}^2 = a_2$	
x	a_1	a_{11}	a_{12}	$2a_1a_{11}$	$2a_1a_{11} = a_{12}$	
y	a_2	a_{12}	a_{22}	$2a_1a_{12}$	$2a_1a_{12} = a_{22}$	(B.89)
$\frac{1}{2}x^2$	a_{11}			$2a_{11}{}^2$		
xy	a_{12}			$2a_{11}a_{12}$		
$\frac{1}{2}y^2$	a_{22}			$2a_{12}{}^2$		

Thus one obtains a set of relations which the coefficients must satisfy. Now the general solution of a partial differential equation always involves one or more arbitrary functions. Here, if one knows the function z when $y = 0$, that is, if the coefficients a_o, a_1, a_{11} are known, then one finds the remaining coefficients consecutively:

$$a_2 = a_1{}^2, \quad a_{12} = 2a_1a_{11}, \quad a_{22} = 2a_1a_{12}. \tag{B.90}$$

Or, if the function z is given when $x = 0$, that is, a_o, a_2, a_{22} are assumed known, one finds the remaining coefficients by computing a_1, a_{12}, a_{11} in that order. It may be noted here that the first equation is nonlinear, so that one must choose one of two possible values of a_1 (which corresponds to selecting a certain branch of the solution). But after the first coefficient is determined, all the others can be found (provided $a_1 \neq 0$) with only a single division.

It should be observed that equations beyond the first degree in (B.89) cannot be used unless z and accordingly p and q are expanded to a higher degree. The reason for this fact is clear if one considers that the *exact* functions z, p, and q are given by infinite series.

The examples given here have involved functions of two variables. The same procedure may be used for functions of any finite number of variables, and also the degree of terms to be neglected can be chosen as large as we please.

CHAPTER C

Numerical Examples. Tracing of Skew Rays. Tracing of Astigmatism and Asymmetry

The most important ray-tracing problem in practice is that of an optical system having only plane and spherical refracting and reflecting surfaces, these surfaces being rotationally symmetric about a common axis. In this chapter, we give a numerical example to illustrate the trace of a skew ray through such a system.

The tracing formulae in Chapters 4 and 5 were developed in the so-called vertex-to-vertex form. This has two practical advantages. First, if one or more plane surfaces are present, the same formulae can be used at these surfaces as elsewhere in the system. One merely regards the plane as a sphere with zero curvature. This is especially convenient in connection with automatic computing machines since the same program can be used at all surfaces. Second, if some of the spherical surfaces have weak curvatures (nearly zero), some types of tracing formulae (such as the center-to-center method) lead to computational inaccuracies caused by rounding errors. The vertex-to-vertex method is free from this difficulty. It should be mentioned that the special case of meridional rays can be treated by very much simplified formulae. However, the skew-ray formulae can be applied in this case, too, a procedure which is usually preferable when automatic computing machines are used since one thus avoids changing the program.

In order to arrange Formulae (5.30) and (5.31) in coordinate form ready for actual computation, it will be necessary to adopt a suitable notation. Whereas, in the body of the book, the components of the direction vector $\vec{s}$ have been indicated by ξ, η, ζ, we shall here modify the notation to make the numerical results conform (in the case of meridional rays) to the classical convention in optics for the sign of the angle of inclination of a meridional ray with the optical axis. Therefore, in this chapter, we shall assume the components of $\vec{s}$ to be $(-\xi, -\eta, \zeta)$ and correspondingly for $\vec{s}'$. Thus $(-\xi, -\eta, \zeta)$ are the ordinary (mathematical) direction cosines of the ray each multiplied by the refractive index n of the medium.

The lateral intersection coordinates of the ray with the successive vertex planes will be indicated by (x_1, y_1), (x_2, y_2), etc., while $(x_1\zeta_1 = p_1,\ y_1\zeta_1 = q_1)$, $(x_2\zeta_2 = p_2,\ y_2\zeta_2 = q_2)$, etc. will indicate the modified intersection coordinates obtained by multiplying the ordinary coordinates at each vertex plane by the ζ-value of the entering ray for that surface. Thus the components of the vectors $\vec{P}$ and $\vec{S}$ appearing in Equations (5.30) are indicated by

$$\vec{P} = (p, q, 0), \quad \vec{S} = (-\xi, -\eta, 0). \tag{C.1}$$

The fundamental starting data for a ray trace, then, are the first two optical direction cosines ξ_1 and η_1 of the entering ray and the coordinates x_1, y_1 of the intersection of this ray with the first vertex plane. Frequently a short preliminary calculation is needed to determine these data. The first part of the ray-tracing computation consists of finding the third direction cosine ζ_1 and the modified quantities $p_1 = x_1\,\zeta_1$, $q_1 = y_1\,\zeta_1$.

In the course of the computation it is found that the modified intersection coordinates p and q suffice at each *interior* surface, the ordinary intersection coordinates (x, y) not being needed. However, at the end of the ray trace, it is necessary first to find ζ' from $\zeta' = \sqrt{n'^2 - \xi'^2 - \eta'^2}$ for the outgoing ray. Then, since the routine ray-tracing procedure gives the values of p and q for the intersection of the ray with any convenient terminal plane at a distance d from the last vertex, the ordinary intersection coordinates x', y' at this plane can be found by $x' = p'/\zeta'$, $y' = q'/\zeta'$.

With these facts in mind we arrange Formulae (5.30) and (5.31) in component form and insert a few obvious abbreviations in order to facilitate the computation. For simplicity we also write $\bar{q}$, $\bar{q}'$ and $\bar{\psi}$ as q, q' and ψ, respectively. The formulae for refraction then are written:

$$\begin{aligned} B &= 1/r, \quad p_1 = x_1\zeta_1, \quad q_1 = y_1\zeta_1 \\ A &= B(p_1^2 + q_1^2) \\ C &= n^2 - \xi_1^2 - \eta_1^2 = \zeta_1^2 \end{aligned}$$

$$
\begin{aligned}
D &= C + B\,(p_1\xi_1 + q_1\eta_1)\\
q^2 &= D^2 - ABn^2, \quad [q = +\sqrt{D^2 - ABn^2}]\\
q'^2 &= q^2 + C(n'^2 - n^2), \quad [q' = +\sqrt{q^2 + C(n'^2 - n^2)}]\\
z &= A/(D + q)\\
\psi &= (1/C)\,(q' - q)\\
\alpha &= \psi\,(p_1 - z\xi_1)\\
\beta &= \psi\,(q_1 - z\eta_1)\\
\xi_2 &= \xi_1 + B\alpha\\
\eta_2 &= \eta_1 + B\beta\\
p_2 &= p_1 + \alpha - d\xi_2\\
q_2 &= q_1 + \beta - d\eta_2.
\end{aligned}
\tag{C.2}
$$

If one or more reflecting surfaces are present, a slight modification of these formulae is necessary since ζ changes sign and $n' = n$ for any reflecting surface. For a reflecting surface, therefore, we have

$$q' = -q, \quad \psi = -2q/C.$$

Otherwise the tracing formulae (C.2) will yield the correct results for reflection provided the signs of the radii are properly defined (positive if convex against the light entering the system) and if d is considered negative in any space where the light is passing backwards in the system. We collect the tracing formulae for the case of a *reflecting* surface:

$$
\begin{aligned}
A &= B\,(p_1^2 + q_1^2)\\
C &= n^2 - \xi_1^2 - \eta_1^2 = \zeta_1^2\\
D &= C + B\,(p_1\xi_1 + q_1\eta_1)\\
q^2 &= D^2 - ABn^2, \quad [q = +\sqrt{D^2 - ABn^2}]\\
z &= A/(D + Q)\\
\psi &= -2q/C\\
\alpha &= \psi\,(p_1 - z\xi_1)\\
\beta &= \psi\,(q_1 - z\eta_1)\\
\xi_2 &= \xi_1 + B\alpha\\
\eta_2 &= \eta_1 + B\beta\\
p_2 &= p_1 + \alpha - d\xi_2\\
q_2 &= q_1 + \beta - d\eta_2.
\end{aligned}
\tag{C.2a}
$$

It should be emphasized that the above formulae, (C.2) and (C.2a), may be used at a plane surface by merely taking $B = 0$. In every case the ordinary intersection coordinates at the terminal plane are found by

$$\zeta' = \sqrt{n'^2 - \xi'^2 - \eta'^2}$$
$$x' = p'/\zeta', \quad y' = q'/\zeta'. \tag{C.3}$$

In the case of an odd number of reflections, the negative square root for ζ' must, of course, be taken since the terminal ray in this case is directed backwards in the system.

A convenient numerical check is obtained from Equation (4.25). The z-component of the vector $(\vec{P} \times \vec{S})$ represents a scalar invariant in any rotationally symmetric system. At interior surfaces, the ray-tracing formulae involve ζ^2 and not ζ, so the square of the scalar invariant is simpler to deal with in this case. Then the invariance of the quantity

$$[\vec{P}\vec{S}\vec{k}]^2/\zeta^2 = (p\eta - q\xi)^2/C \tag{C.4}$$

at all vertex planes, including the terminal plane, provides a check of the computation.

The numerical example to be presented here consists of the trace of a skew ray through a simple lens in air, the two radii of the lens being 1.15 and -0.85, the thickness being 0.5, and the index of refraction of the glass being 1.523.

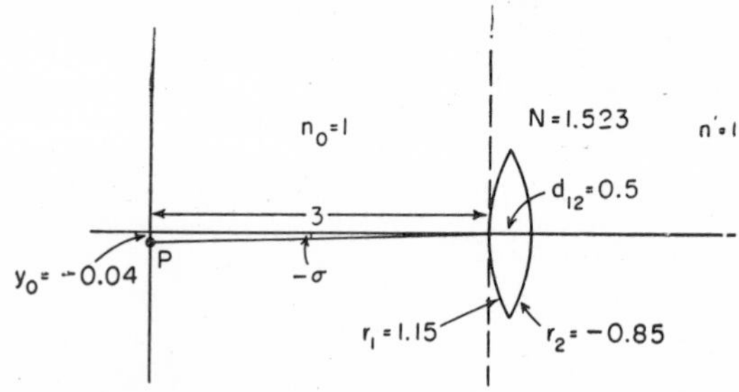

Fig. C.1. Simple lens used to illustrate trigonometric trace of meridional ray and also astigmatism and asymmetry.

Let it be required to trace a ray which is given by its intersection with two planes perpendicular to the axis, the first being at a distance 3.0 in from of the first vertex and the second being the first vertex plane itself. We assume the intersection coordinates in these two planes to be given as $x_o = 0$, $y_o = -0.04$, and $x_1 = 0.4$, $y_1 = 0$, respectively. Let it be required to find the intersection coordinates of the image ray in a plane at a distance 1.348 096 from the vertex of the second surface. The system is sketched in Figure C.1.

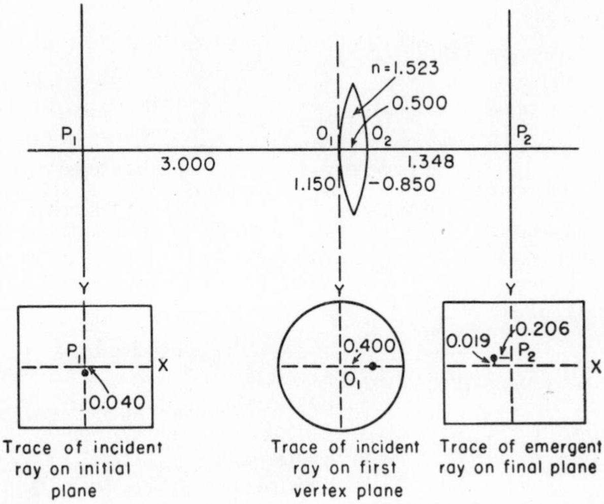

Fig. C.2. Geometrical description of ray-tracing example.

In this example a short preliminary calculation is required in order to obtain the basic starting data for the ray trace. By elementary analytical geometry, we obtain the distance t along the ray between the two specified points as well as the optical cosines of the entering ray. The formulae for those are

$$t = \sqrt{(x_o - x_1)^2 + (y_o - y_1)^2 + (z_o - z_1)^2}, \qquad \text{(C.5)}$$

$$\xi_1 = (x_o - x_1)/t, \quad \eta_1 = (y_o - y_1)/t, \quad \zeta_1 = (z_1 - z_o)/t,$$

where we have taken account of the special definition of ξ_1 and η_1 mentioned earlier. The modified intersection coordinates p_1 and q_1 are then obtained by multiplication of x_1 and y_1 each by ζ_1.

Skew-Ray Trace

The details of the calculation are given in Table X. The computations for ξ_2, η_2, p_2, and q_2 are repeated to make the format of the table show more clearly the similarities and dissimilarities between the computations for the two surfaces, but of course this would not be done in practice.

TABLE X

Sample Calculation of Skew Ray

Quantity	*Initial Medium*	*First Surface*	*Lens Medium*	*Second Surface*	*Final Medium*
d	3.0000000		0.5000000		1.348096
r		1.1500000+		0.8500000−	
n	1.0000000		1.5230000		1.0000000
$B = 1/r$		0.8695652+		1.1764706−	
n^2	1.0000000		2.319529		1.0000000

$x_0 = 0.000$ $y_0 = -0.040$ $z_0 = 0.000$

$x_1 = +0.400$ $y_1 = 0.000$ $z_1 = +3.000$

First Surface		*Second Surface*	
$t = \sqrt{(x_0 - x_1)^2 + (y_0 - y_1)^2 + (z_0 - z_1)^2}$	3.0268135+		
$\xi_1 = (x_0 - x_1)/t$	0.1321521−	$\xi_2 = \xi_1 + \beta\alpha$	0.0702111+
$\eta_1 = (y_0 - y_1)/t$	0.0132152−	$\eta_2 = \eta_1 + B\beta$	0.0127178−
$\zeta_1 = (z_1 - z_0)/t$	0.9911413+	$\zeta_2 = \sqrt{n^2 - \xi_2^2 - \eta_2^2}$	Not needed
$p_1 = x_1 \zeta_1$	0.3964565+	$p_2 = p_1 + \alpha - d\xi_2$	0.5940687+
$q_1 = y_1 \zeta_1$	0.0000000	$q_2 = q_1 + \beta - d\eta_2$	0.0069309+
$A = B(p_1^2 + q_1^2)$	0.1366763+	A	0.4152538−
$C = n^2 - \xi_1^2 - \eta_1^2 = \zeta_1^2$	0.9823612+	C	2.3144377+
$D = C + B(p_1\xi_1 + q_1\eta_1)$	0.9368024+	D	2.2654705+
$q^2 = D^2 - ABn^2$	0.7587498+	q^2	3.9991880+
q	0.8710624+	q	1.9997970+
$q'^2 = q^2 + C(n'^2 - n^2)$	2.0550039+	q'^2	0.9452203+
q'	1.4335285+	q'	0.9722244+
$z = A/(q + D)$	0.0756010+	z	0.0973570−
$\psi = (q' - q)/C$	0.5725654+	ψ	0.4439836−
$\alpha = \psi(p_1 - z\xi_1)$	0.2327177+	α	0.2667916−
$\beta = \psi(q_1 - z\eta_1)$	0.0005720+	β	0.0025275−
$\xi_2 = \xi_1 + B\alpha$	0.0702111+	ξ_3	0.3840836+
$\eta_2 = \eta_1 + B\beta$	0.0127178−	η_3	0.0097443−
$p_2 = p_1 + \alpha - d\xi_2$	0.5940687+	p_3	0.1905045−
$q_2 = q_1 + \beta - d\eta_2$	0.0069309+	q_3	0.0175400+
		$\zeta_3 = \sqrt{1 - \xi_3^2 - \eta_3^2}$	0.9232938+
		$x' = p_3/\zeta_3$	0.2063313−
		$y' = q_3/\zeta_3$	0.0189968+

The computation for the first surface shows that the direction cosines ξ_2 and η_2 of the emergent ray with the x- and y-axes are 0.070 211 1 and −0.012 717 8, respectively, which are also the direction cosines of the ray with the second surface at incidence. The x- and y-coordinates of the intersection of this ray with the vertex plane of the second surface are the values of p_2 and q_2, 0.594 068 7 and 0.006 930 9, respectively, divided by the third direction cosine ζ_2. However, this intersection itself is not essential to the computation so ζ_2 need not be found, the quantities ξ_2, η_2, p_2, and q_2 being the entering quantities for the second surface.

The subsequent calculation gives 0.384 083 6 and −0.009 744 3 for the first two direction cosines of the final emergent ray. The third direction cosine can be readily computed from the consideration that the sum of the squares of the three equals the square of the refractive index of the image space, and thus ζ_3 is found to be 0.923 293 8. The values of p_3 and q_3 are found to be −0.190 504 5 and 0.017 540 0, respectively, and division by ζ_3 shows the x- and y-coordinates of the intersection of the emergent ray with the plane 1.348 096 from the second vertex to be −0.206 331 3 and 0.018 996 8, respectively. (See Fig. C. 2.)

The values of the running check obtained from Equation (C.4) in the form

$$(p_1\eta_1 - q_1\xi_1)^2/\zeta_1^2 = (p_2\eta_2 - q_2\xi_2)^2/\zeta_2^2 \qquad \text{(C.6)}$$

are, in the present example, 0.000 027 942 64, 0.000 027 942 74, and 0.000 027 944 20.

Diapoints

Formulae (C.2) yield the intersection coordinates x' and y' of the emergent ray with any convenient terminal plane at a specified distance from the last vertex plane. However, it is frequently important to obtain the *diapoints* of a number of rays coming from a given object point. The reader is reminded that the diapoint of a given ray through a given object point is the intersection of the corresponding image ray with the meridional plane passing through the object point and the optical axis. In the case of a meridional ray, the definition must be slightly modified;

here the diapoint coincides with the so-called sagittal focus, which will be described presently.

To calculate the diapoints, one may assume, without loss of generality, that the object point lies in the plane $x = 0$. Let $\vec{A}'$ with coordinates $(x', y', 0)$ represent the intersection of the ray with an arbitrary terminal plane, the vector $\vec{A}'$ being known as a result of the standard trace by means of Equations (C.2). Then

$$\vec{A}' + \lambda'\vec{s}' = \vec{a}_D', \tag{C.7}$$

where λ' is some scalar to be determined immediately and $\vec{a}_D'$ is the vector from the axial point of the terminal plane to the diapoint. By the definition of diapoint, the x-coordinate of $\vec{a}_D'$ must be zero. Since $\vec{s}'$ has coordinates $(-\xi', -\eta', \zeta')$, we therefore obtain

$$x' - \lambda'\xi' = 0, \tag{C.8}$$

giving

$$\lambda' = x'/\xi'$$

and

$$\vec{A}' + (x'/\xi')\,\vec{s}' = \vec{a}_D'. \tag{C.9}$$

Taking y- and z-components of the above vector equation, we then obtain

$$y_D' = y' - (x'/\xi')\,\eta'$$

and

$$z_D' = (x'/\xi')\,\zeta' \tag{C.10}$$

as the two components of the diapoint, the distance z_D' being measured from the terminal plane.

In the case of a meridional ray, we have $\xi' = 0$ so that Equations (C.10) are meaningless. As mentioned above, the diapoint in this case is defined as the sagittal focus, which is the limiting position of the point as the ray varies from a skew position into a meridional position. The calculation of the diapoint for a meridional ray can be performed by replacing the ray by a neighboring ray, leaving all its starting data the same except that the value of ξ is taken to be some small quantity, for instance 0.0001, instead of zero. Trace this neighboring ray, which is a skew ray, through the system as usual and find its diapoint. This diapoint will coincide closely enough with the desired diapoint of the meridional ray.

Returning to the meridional example described above, we

recall that the first given point on the object ray had lateral coordinates $x_o = 0$, $y_o = -0.4$, that is, the meridional plane for this point is the plane $x = 0$. Therefore, regarding this point as the object point, we may use Equations (C.10) directly to compute its diapoint for the skew ray which was considered. We have

$$\begin{aligned} \xi' &= \xi_3 = 0.3840836 \\ \eta' &= \eta_3 = -\ 0.0097443 \\ \zeta' &= \zeta_3 = 0.9232938, \\ x' &= -\ 0.2063313 \\ y' &= 0.0189968. \end{aligned} \qquad (C.11)$$

The calculation by (C.10) then gives

$$\begin{aligned} y_D' &= 0.0137621 \\ z_D' &= -\ 0.4959972. \end{aligned} \qquad (C.12)$$

In other words, the diapoint is 0.0137621 above the axis and 0.4959972 to the left of the terminal plane.

Trigonometric Trace of a Meridional Ray

When tracing meridional rays with desk calculators, one usually adopts the simple trigonometric formulae given in Chapter 2. The refraction formulae for spheres are given in Equations (2.25), and transition, which involves a change of origin from the center of one sphere to the center of the next, is accomplished with the help of the simple formula

$$m = n\,(d_{12} + r_2 - r_1), \qquad (C.13)$$

where m is the optical distance from center to center and d_{12} is the distance between the vertices of the surfaces.

The formulae may be collected in the form

$$\begin{aligned} R &= 1/nr, \quad R' = 1/n'r, \quad -m = -n\,(d_{12} + r_2 - r_1) \\ p &= nz \sin \sigma \\ \sin i &= pR, \quad \sin i' = pR' \\ \sigma' &= \sigma + i - i' \\ p_2 &= \sin \sigma\,(-m) + p. \end{aligned} \qquad (C.14)$$

Here z is the distance from the center of the first sphere to the intersection point of the object ray with the axis. The angle σ is the angle of inclination of the object ray with the axis, the angle being considered positive if the slope is negative in accordance with the standard optical convention.

As a numerical illustration of these formulae, we consider the same simple two-surface lens which was described above. We trace a meridional ray passing through the point $x_o = 0$, $y_o = -0.04$ in the plane a distance 3.0 in front of the first vertex and passing through the center of the the first vertex plane (*cf.* Fig. C.2].

The calculation is straightforward and proceeds as follows:

$$
\begin{aligned}
\tan \sigma_1 &= -\ 0.04/3 = 0.0133333-, \quad \sigma_1 = 0.7639°- \\
\sin \sigma_1 &= 0.0133322- \\
R_1 &= \frac{1}{n_0 r_1} = \frac{1}{r_1} = 0.8695652, \quad R_1' = \frac{1}{N r_1} = 0.5709555+ \\
-m &= -n_0\,(d_{12} + r_2 - r_1) = 1.5+ \\
z &= -\ r_1 = 1.15-, \quad p_1 = n_0 z \sin \sigma_1 = 0.0153320+ \\
\sin i_1 &= p_1 R_1 = 0.0133322+, \quad i_1 = 0.7639°+ \\
\sin i_1' &= p_1 R_1' = 0.0087539+, \quad i_1' = 0.5016°+ \\
\sigma_2 &= \sigma_1' = \sigma_1 + i_1 - i_1' = 0.5016°- \\
p_2 &= \sin \sigma_1\,(-m) + p_1 = 0.0046663- \\
R_2 &= 1/N r_2 = 0.7724692- \\
R_2' &= 1/n' r_2 = 1/r_2 = 1.1764706- \\
\sin i_2 &= p_2 R_2 = 0.0036046+, \quad i_2 = 0.2065°+ \\
\sin i_2' &= p_2 R_2' = 0.0054898+, \quad i_2' = 0.3145°+ \\
\sigma_2' &= \sigma_2 + i_2 - i_2' = 0.6096°-, \quad \sin \sigma_2' = 0.0106394- \\
z' &= p_2/(n' \sin \sigma_2') = 0.4385868+. \qquad \text{(C.15)}
\end{aligned}
$$

Thus the inclination angle σ_2' of the emergent ray with the axis and the distance z' (from the second center) of the axial intersection point of the emergent ray are found.

In cases in which many surfaces are involved, a more convenient arrangement of the numerical entries is usually adopted.

Some of the values appearing in Formulae (C.15) will be used in the following paragraphs, which describe the numerical trace of astigmatism and asymmetry through an optical system.

Trace of Astigmatism

In Chapter 25 formulae were given for tracing astigmatism and asymmetry values through an optical system. These quantities are properties of a bundle of rays arising from a given object point, and the formulae developed were valid in the neighborhood of a principal ray lying in the meridional plane. For the special case of a spherical surface, Equations (25.29) and (25.30) are the required tracing formulae, whereas for the transition to the following surface, Equations (25.27) are used for astigmatism; the asymmetry values are invariant.

The quantity e appearing in (25.27) represents the distance along the ray from its incidence point with one surface to its incidence point with the next surface. Reference to Figure C.3

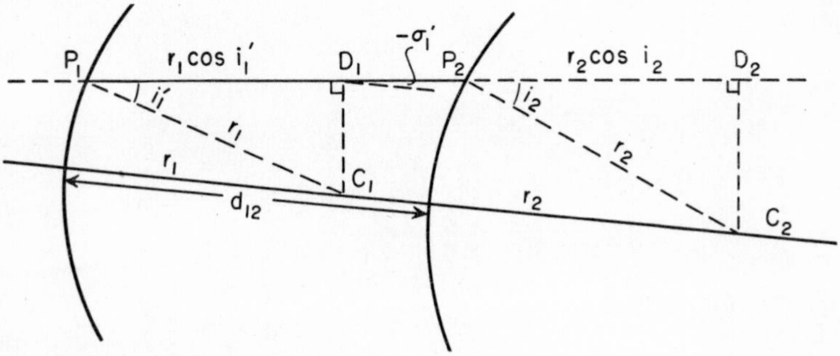

Fig. C.3. Generalized figure to show method of finding distance along ray between incidence points.

shows that, when the surfaces are spheres, e is easily expressed in terms of the data obtained from the trigonometric trace of the principal ray. Reference to the figure shows that

$$\begin{gathered} C_1C_2 = d_{12} + r_2 - r_1, \quad D_1D_2 = C_1C_2 \cos \sigma_1' \\ P_1D_1 = r_1 \cos i_1', \quad P_2D_2 = r_2 \cos i_2 \\ e = P_1P_2 = D_1D_2 + P_1D_1 - P_2D_2. \end{gathered} \tag{C.16}$$

This result and the expanded formulae obtained from Equations (25.29) may be collected, together with Equation (25.27), to give the tracing formulae for l_m and l_s, the meridional and the sagittal astigmatism. The resulting formulae are

TABLE XI

Numerical Trace of Astigmatism and Asymmetry for a Meridional Ray in a System Having Spherical Surfaces. The values in italics are the desired results.

	Astigmatism (1)	Astigmatism (2)
σ_1	0.7639°+	
$l_{m1} = -3/\cos\sigma_1$	3.0002667−	*12.0273311+
$l_{s1} = -3/\cos\sigma_1$	3.0002667−	*12.0344041+
i	0.7639°+	0.2065°+
i'	0.5016°+	0.3145°+
$c = \cos i$	0.9999111+	0.9999935+
$c' = \cos i'$	0.9999617+	0.9999849+
$1/r$	0.8695652+	1.1764706−
n	1.0000000+	1.5230000+
n'	1.5230000+	1.0000000+
$A = \frac{1}{r}(n'c' - nc)$	0.4548092+	0.6153002+
$\frac{n'}{l'_s} = \frac{n}{l_s} + A$	0.1215055+	0.7418540+
l_s'	12.5344121+	*1.3479741+*
$\frac{n'c'^2}{l_m'} = \frac{nc^2}{l_m} + A$	0.1215648+	0.7419268+
l_m'	12.5273390+	*1.3478011+*
$l_s' - l_m'$	0.0070731+	0.000173+
σ_1'	0.5016°−	
i_2	0.2065°+	
e	0.5000079+	

	Asymmetry (1)	Asymmetry (2)
C_m	0	23.9541698−
C_s	0	7.9934091−
c/l_m	0.3332740−	0.0831434+
c'/l_m'	0.0798223+	0.7419380+
$s = \sin i$	0.0133321+	0.0036058+
$3\,ns$	0.0399963+	0.164749+
$3\,ns$ [*]	0.01855549−	0.0217240+
$n\,(c/l_m)^3\,C_m$	0	0.209695−
$n'\,(c'/l_m')^3$	0.0007746+	0.4084161+
C_m'	23.9541698+	*0.0018470+*
$1/l_s'^2$	0.0063649+	0.5503474+
$1/l_s^2$	0.1110914+	0.0069048+
ns [†]	0.0061853−	0.0072406+
$(n/l_s^2)\,(c/l_m)C_s$	0	0.0069886−
$(n'/l_s'^2)\,(c'/l_m')$	0.0007738+	0.4083237+
C_s'	7.9934091−	*0.0006171+*

* At second surface $l_{m2} = l_{m1}' - e$; $l_{s2} = l_{s1}' - e$.

$$[*] = \left[\left(\frac{c'}{l_m'}\right)^2 - \frac{1}{r}\left(\frac{c'}{l_m'}\right) - \left(\frac{c}{l_m}\right)^2 + \frac{1}{r}\left(\frac{c}{l_m}\right)\right]$$

$$[\dagger] = \left[\frac{1}{l_s'^2} - \frac{1}{r}\left(\frac{c'}{l_m'}\right) - \frac{1}{l_s^2} + \frac{1}{r}\left(\frac{c}{l_m}\right)\right]$$

Refraction:

$$\frac{n'c'^2}{l_m'} = \frac{nc^2}{l_m} + \frac{1}{r}(n'c' - nc), \quad c = \cos i, \ \ c' = \cos i'$$

$$\frac{n'}{l_s'} = \frac{n}{l_s} + \frac{1}{r}(n'c' - nc). \tag{C. 17}$$

Transition:

$$e = (d_{12} + r_2 - r_1)\cos\sigma_1' + r_1c_1' - r_2c_2$$
$$l_{m2} = l_{m1}' - e$$
$$l_{s2} = l_{s1}' - e.$$

It is seen that the trace of astigmatism depends on the values of i and i', the angles of the principal ray with the normal at each surface, and on the inclination angle σ_1' of the principal ray with the axis in each intermediate space. These values for the present example are given in Formulae (C.15).

The numerical trace of the two astigmatism values l_m and l_s is given on the left-hand side of Table XI. The starting values of l_m and l_s are simply the distances along the principal ray from the incidence point at the first surface to the two focal points of the entering bundle. Since the rays of the entering bundle all pass through a common point, the object point, these distances are equal, and in the present case are found by $l_m = l_s = -3/\cos\sigma_1$ (see Fig. C.1). The rest of the calculation is then straightforward, the values obtained being $l_{s2}' = 1.347\,974+$ for the sagittal and $l_{m2}' = 1.347\,801+$ for the meridional astigmatism.

The difference $l_{s2}' - l_{m2}' = 0.000\,173+$ may be referred to as the *astigmatism*, meaning the distance along the principal ray between its sagittal and meridional foci (the two points where the principal ray is tangent to the caustic). Many lens designers prefer to define the astigmatism as the projection of this distance on the optical axis.

Trace of Asymmetry

Once the principal ray and the astigmatism values have been traced through the system, it is possible to trace the asymmetry values C_m and C_s. For this purpose Formulae (25.30) may be written in the expanded form

$$n'\left(\frac{c'}{l_m'}\right)^3 C_m' = n\left(\frac{c}{l_m}\right)^3 C_m + 3ns\left[\left(\frac{c'}{l_m'}\right)^2 - \frac{1}{r}\left(\frac{c'}{l_m'}\right) - \left(\frac{c}{l_m}\right)^2 + \frac{1}{r}\left(\frac{c}{l_m}\right)\right]$$

$$\frac{n'}{l_s'^2}\left(\frac{c'}{l_m'}\right)C_s' = \frac{n}{l_s^2}\left(\frac{c}{l_m}\right)C_s + ns\left[\frac{1}{l_s'^2} - \frac{1}{r}\left(\frac{c'}{l_m'}\right) - \frac{1}{l_s^2} + \frac{1}{r}\left(\frac{c}{l_m}\right)\right], \tag{C.18}$$

where $c = \cos i$, $c' = \cos i'$, $s = \sin i$.

These formulae, which serve to trace the two asymmetry values across a spherical refracting surface, require a knowledge of the astigmatism values l_m and l_s as well as the angles i and i' at each surface, that is, the intermediate data obtained from the trace of the principal ray [Formulae (C.15)] and the trace of astigmatism (the left-hand side of Table XI).

For the transition, we have simply the invariant relations

$$C_{m2} = C_{m1}', \quad C_{s2} = C_{s1}', \tag{C.19}$$

since the asymmetry values are geometrical properties of the bundle in any intermediate space of the system and are independent of the choice of origin.

The starting values of C_m and C_s are zero because all the rays of the initial bundle pass through the same point (the object point).

In these differential calculations, one must watch the number of significant digits. An analysis of the above computation shows that only four decimal places in the values of C_{m2}' and C_{s2}' are significant. Thus the results may be written

$$C_{m2}' = 0.0018$$
$$C_{s2}' = 0.0006$$

CHAPTER D

Historical Remarks

Since the purpose of this book has been to give a survey of some of the results obtained by the author, he has refrained from an extensive review of the history of the problems at the time. However, it seems fitting, on the one hand, to draw the reader's attention to the classical papers of optical literature, and, on the other hand, to note with satisfaction that during the last ten years a new interest in problems of geometrical optics has been demonstrated in many countries and that young and talented workers are finding new and promising approaches to the problems.

If one should attempt to list a handful of names of men who have built the science of geometrical optics, the author would suggest R. Descartes, I. Newton, C. Huygens, W. R. Hamilton, and A. Gullstrand. Let us therefore discuss, in some detail, the contributions of these men.

René Descartes (1596–1650), in his "Dioptrique," tried to give a theory based on elasticity, comparing light with a little ball traveling along the light ray, being deflected at the surface separating two media. He explained the correct law of refraction by the assumption that the ball has different velocities in different media. Descartes also derived the correct form of the refraction law, which had eluded the efforts of such eminent scientists as Kepler. (Whether or not the Frenchman Descartes or the Dutch scientist Snell was the first to formulate the refraction law is a difficult question to decide. The interested reader is referred to a paper by H. Boegehold, "Einiges aus der Geschichte des Brechungsgesetzes.")

Descartes applied the methods of analytical geometry (developed by him) to calculate the Cartesian surfaces, that is, the surfaces which refract or reflect the rays from a finite or infinite object point in such a way that the emergent rays come accurately to a focus (real or virtual). He even developed methods for grinding the aspheric surfaces required. His "Dioptrique," published in 1637, is the first modern textbook of optics. It contains beautiful illustrations which are instructive even to modern readers.

Christian Huygens (1629–1695) published two important books in the field of optics, "Traité de la Lumière" and "Dioptrica." The first of these (finished in 1678 but not published until 1690) contains his wave theory of light. Huygens compared light waves with water waves. When water waves meet an obstruction, their further progress can be predicted by assuming that each point of the obstruction is the center of a new set of wavelets whose envelope represents the new wave front. By applying the same principle to light waves, Huygens derived the laws of refraction and reflection, not only for ordinary media but also for Iceland spar, that is, for doubly refracting crystalline media. In addition, he treated inhomogeneous media, like the atmosphere, where the light rays are curved. An elegant theory of the caustic surfaces as evolutes of the wave surface is also found in this treatment.

The "Dioptrica" (finished in 1653, published in 1703) contains a wealth of geometrical optical ideas. Huygens discovered the aplanatic surfaces of the sphere and the aplanatic lenses discussed in Chapter 2 of this book. He discovered that a simple lens has a center of symmetry (the common image of the nodal points inside the lens) such that every ray passing through this point inside the lens has the property that its corresponding object and image rays are parallel to each other. The concept of a thin lens presupposes that the lens thickness can be neglected for the axial bundle. In this case we cannot reasonably assume the lens thickness at the margin to be zero. To avoid this dilemma, Huygens introduced the fiction of a *narrow* lens, introducing as *mathematical* thickness the mean between the axial and the marginal thickness. Using this concept, he derived approximation formulae for the spherical aberration of a lens as a function of its radii.

Isaac Newton (1642–1727) wrote two major works devoted to optical theory, "Opticks" (published in 1704) and the "Lectiones Opticae" (published posthumously in 1728).

Newton's "Opticks" gives the theory of dispersion of light by a prism, that is, Newton's discovery that the refractive index is a function of the color (the wavelength) of light. This is one of the most important discoveries in optics, second only to the discovery of the refraction law. Any student of optics should read the beautiful description and analysis Newton gave in deriving his thesis. In describing his experiments, he investigated the geometrical optical properties of prisms, finding the corresponding laws in all detail, and investigated the properties not only of colored lights but also of dyes. He applied his theory to explain the colors of the rainbow.

Comparing the dispersion of water and crown glass, he erroneously concluded that all matter has the same ν-value (see Chapter 12), which would imply that a refracting instrument could not be corrected for color. He therefore advocated the use of reflecting telescopes and discussed their properties, including their lateral spherical aberration.

In Newton's "Opticks" we find also the description of many experiments that are now explained by diffraction theory, for instance, the color of thin layers.

W. R. Hamilton (1805–1865), one of the greatest scientists of all time, has, by introducing the characteristic functions, given to geometrical optics its most powerful tool. If a ray in the object space is given by an initial point, vector $\vec{a}$, and the vector $\vec{s}$ (of length n) in its direction, and the corresponding image ray is given by a vector $\vec{a}'$ to a terminal point and the direction vector $\vec{s}'$ (of length n'), and if E is the light path between the initial and terminal points, we always have $dE = \vec{s}'\,d\vec{a}' - \vec{s}\,d\vec{a}$. This leads to a two-point function E from which, if the initial and terminal points are given, the directions of object and image rays can be computed. Whereas the characteristic function E depends on $\vec{a}$ and $\vec{a}'$, correspondingly we find other characteristic functions, depending in turn on $\vec{a}$ and $\vec{s}'$, $\vec{s}$ and $\vec{a}'$, and $\vec{s}$ and $\vec{s}'$. In each case, the coordinates of the remaining vectors can be found by differentiating the characteristic function.

Hamilton showed how one can derive from the form of the characteristic function the general laws of optical image formation, as well as how to determine the quality of the image of a point. He gave a method for computing the caustic surface and the density of the light distribution in an optical image. He recognized that a special definition is needed to describe the light density on the caustic surface.

But Hamilton's work goes far beyond the foundations of geometrical optics. He applied his ideas to the investigation of inhomogeneous and anisotropic media. He developed in great detail the optics of doubly refracting crystalline media. Hamilton demonstrated, moreover, that the characteristic function can also be applied in the study of other phenomena of physics, especially in classical mechanics, which can be regarded as optical phenomena in a space-time continuum. In this respect his ideas have not yet quite found the consideration they merit.

The understanding of the work of W. R. Hamilton and its impact on the development of geometrical optics was at first retarded by the fact that his major work was published in the Transactions of the Irish Academy of Sciences, which has a comparatively restricted circulation. The publication of the first volumes of his collected works by A. Conway and J. Synge has since made his deeply original ideas easily available to the present generation.

Allvar Gullstrand (1862–1929) is another lonesome giant in the development of optical theory. Although his work in the field of ophthalmology and optics has been crowned with the highest scientific honor, the Nobel prize, it is buried in the Acta of the Swedish Academy of Science and is seldom read by the young scientists of today, who frequently rediscover isolated results of his work. A critical edition of his works, containing a rederivation of his results by means of modern mathematical technique, would have the same importance as the edition of Hamilton's works. We shall enumerate here only a few of the most important results of Gullstrand's work. The reader will see that, in the present book, an attempt has been made to present many of his ideas and to coordinate them with the more common aspects of optical image theory.

Gullstrand discussed the general neighborhood of a ray in a normal system, that is, the normals of a general wave surface. He calculated the caustic surface and the curvatures of the two envelopes tangential to the principal ray of a bundle, tying up the coefficients associated with a wave surface of the normal system with certain well-defined geometrical quantities. He investigated especially the degeneration present in the caustic when the wave surface has no astigmatism or, in the language of mathematics, when it has an umbilical point.

By defining quantities that have a geometrical significance for the normal bundle, Gullstrand defined intrinsic quantities that can be computed from the coefficients of the equation of the wave surface but are independent of the arbitrarily chosen coordinates of the problem. He then computed these intrinsic quantities for a single surface and gave formulae which enable these quantities to be traced through an optical system. The reader will remember how, in Part VI of this book, it was possible to coordinate these intrinsic qualities of Gullstrand with the spot diagrams which show the actual light distribution due to the intersection of the rays with an image plane.

Again Gullstrand's work goes somewhat beyond the frame of this book. Since his first interest was the human eye, he investigated the optical qualities of inhomogeneous media, where the light rays are generally curved.

Gullstrand's work is especially recommended as reading for young scientists working in our field because he discusses, often in very emphatic language, many misconceptions about the laws of optical image-formation—misconceptions which usually have their origin in trying to interpret geometrically approximations that are insufficiently accurate to give the correct information.

To speak of the men of my own generation and of the many promising young scientists in our field, I shall first mention the two men with whom I was in the most intimate contact, *H. Boegehold* and *T. Smith.* Boegehold has made many contributions in the field of geometrical and instrumental optics, as well as in the field of historical investigations. I had the pleasure of working in close cooperation with him off and on from 1923 to 1935. Of the many problems which interested us both, some lay in the field of the differential qualities of optical systems and others dealt with the behavior of the characteristic function in the large, that is, the forms of the characteristic function for special types of imagery and the limitations optical laws impose on our desire for a perfect imagery. The study of concentric systems in Part IV of this book was undertaken in a common endeavor to give a complete mathematical survey of at least one special class of optical systems and their image formation. His selfless interest in bringing to the knowledge of his contemporaries the works of men like Kepler, Gullstrand, Schleiermacher, A. Kerber, Hamilton, and others gave me, in my youth, a better historic perspective.

T. Smith's work is of great originality and depth, and I hope that his retirement will give him an opportunity to order and collect in book form the manifold ideas which abound in his publications. We shall sketch here only a few of his ideas, which are recommended for further study.

T. Smith published no fewer than six papers on ray-tracing methods, discussing not only ordinary tracing formulae but also difference formulae, the purpose of which was to improve the exactitude of the results of approximate ray-tracing. The iteration methods he suggested have been found especially valuable by many scientists in connection with calculation by automatic machines. In an address as President of the Optical Society, he described uncultivated optical fields, gave a very simple introduction to Hamilton's ideas, and applied them, among other things, to the derivation of the characteristic function for a single refracting surface. (See Chapter 30 of this book.)

In his most profound paper entitled "The Changes in Aberration When the Object and Stop are Moved," he tried to generalize the results of Chapters 28 and 29 of this book to finite aperture and field. The special meaning of the Petzval error, as an error independent of object and stop position, has frequently aroused the question as to whether or not there exist higher order errors which have the same properties. We have proved in Chapter 26 that all the coefficients of the angle characteristic except one satisfy this condition. But the connections of the coefficients of the angle characteristic with the intrinsic image errors for a finite object are complex, and thus the division of image errors in groups according to the proposal of Smith has great theoretical value. Unfortunately the author has not yet been able to coordinate all of Smith's results with the methods employed in this book.

T. Smith wrote many papers in which he developed methods and charts for the practical designer, especially for computing achromatic doublets for telescope objectives in which spherical aberration and coma were corrected. The aberration coefficients for a lens with double symmetry in the neighborhood of a skew ray forms another interesting topic investigated by Smith, and still another is the effect on image formation of the constructional data of an optical system.

Analytical methods of design have been developed by Abbe and his school, Kerber, Taylor, Schwarzschild, Harting, and Conrady. The publication of the books of Chrétien in France and of Conrady in England and the new and interesting developments in instrument design during World Wars I and II, which brought leading mathematicians like Carathéodory and Synge and astronomers like Baker into the optical field, have furthered important research. The optical institutes in Paris, Florence, Rochester, Madrid, Leningrad, and Boston University, as well as the Bureau of Standards in Washington, and the National Physical Laboratory in Teddington, have produced many able scholars. Moreover, the optical industries in all countries have attracted many competent and ingenious optical scientists.

Outstanding work, which is only sketchily covered in this book, includes the work of Schade in the United States, Toraldo in Italy, Duffieux in France, and especially Ingelstam in Sweden and Linfoot and his group in England. These workers have attempted to apply the methods and concepts of information theory, so fruitful in radio and television, for determining the quality of the optical image. Great progress has been made in the diffraction theory of optical instruments under the influence of Zernike and Nijboer in Holland, of Maréchal in France, of Toraldo in Italy, and of H. H. Hopkins in Great Britain.

A few recent developments can be mentioned specifically. In lens design, the contribution of the individual surfaces of a system to image quality and its deterioration has been studied by T. Smith in England and by Cruickshank and Buchdahl in Australia. Third- and fifth-order aberration theory has been developed further by Slusareff and his pupils in the U.S.S.R. and by Slevogt, Marx, and Wachendorf in Germany.

In allied fields, a clever idea has been developed by Kapany, who uses thin, transparent fibers to transport light points. This procedure has numerous practical applications, as in transmitting light from a circular exit pupil to the slit of a spectroscopic instrument with little loss. Finally there may be mentioned an interesting approach to the entire science of optics by V. Ronchi, who proposes to treat optical problems as a whole without splitting them up into their constituent parts.

From the standpoint of practical computation, a revolution has been wrought by the high-speed electronic computer. In the past, much ingenuity has been spent in deriving algebraic formulae that would give as much information as possible about the performance of a system from data furnished by tracing the fewest possible rays. Because of the complexity of the formulae, skew rays were traced as rarely as possible. Now that the tracing of a large number of both skew and meridional rays is comparatively rapid, provided the program is unchanged, the more precise methods developed in this book, which give a clear picture of the light distribution at any image plane, are practical for even routine work.

The fifth-order interpolation method gives a sufficient, accurate, and mathematically simple model for an optical system. Moreover, it seems that the fifth-order approximation theory gives an accurate idea of the limitations of optical systems.

The author believes that the most valuable development in theoretical optics in the near future will consist of analyzing and simplifying fifth-order approximation formulae and studying fifth-order models of various types of optical systems.

BIBLIOGRAPHY

For a nearly complete bibliography up to about 1923, see the author index to the third edition of Czapski-Eppenstein's "Grundzüge der optischen Instrumente nach Abbe." Later works are cited in Boegehold's paper entitled "Über die Entwicklung der Theorie der optischen Instrumente seit Abbe." Additional references up to about 1932 will be found in the author's "Geschichtlicher Abriss der Strahlenoptik." The early history of optics, with excerpts from early writers, is to be found in Wilde's "Geschichte der Optik."

Abbe, E., Gesammelte Abhandlungen, Fischer, Jena, 1904–1906.

Alhazen (Ibn al-Haitham), Opticae thesaurus Alhazeni, etc., item Vitellonis... Libri X, etc., two volumes (Vol. I, Alhazen; Vol. II, Witelo), Ed. F. Risner, Basle, 1572.

Baker, J. G., Image structure and test data, Optical Image Evaluation, Nat. Bur. Standards Circ. 526, 117–160, 1954.

Berek, M., Grundlagen der praktischen Optik, W. de Gruyter, Berlin & Leipzig, 1930.

Boegehold, H., Über die Korrektion des Astigmatismus bei sphärotorischen Brillen, Z. ophthalm. Opt., *4*, 161–171, 1916.

Boegehold, H., Einiges aus der Geschichte des Brechungsgesetzes, Central-Ztg. Opt. u. Mech., *40*, 94–124, 1919.

Boegehold, H., Koma und natürliche Blende, Central-Ztg. Opt. u. Mech., *43*, 430–433, 1922.

Boegehold, H., Zur Behandlung der Strahlenbegrenzung in 17. und 18. Jahrhundert, Central-Ztg. Opt. u. Mech., *49*, 94–95, 105–109, 1928.

Boegehold, H., Über die Entwicklung der Theorie der optischen Instrumente seit Abbe, Ergeb. exact. Naturw., *8*, 69–130, 1929.

Boegehold, H., Keplers Gedanken über das Brechungsgesetz und ihre Einwirkung auf Snell und Descartes, Ber. naturw. Ver. Regensburg, *19*, 150–167, 1928/30. (Kepler-Festschrift, Part I, Ed. K. Stöckel, H. Schiele, Regensburg, 1930.)

Boegehold, H., Raumsymmetrische Abbildung, Z. Instrumentenk., *56*, 98–109, 1936.

Boegehold, H., Note on the Staeble and Lihotzky condition, Trans. Opt. Soc. London, *26*, 287–288, 1924–25.

Boegehold, H., and Herzberger, M., Die optische Abbildung eines endlichen Ebenenstückes durch eine Umdrehungsfolge, Z. Physik, *61*, 15–36, 1930.

Boegehold, H., and Herzberger, M., Über die nahfeldscharfe Abbildung durch eine achsensymmetrische Folge bei endlicher Öffnung des abbildenden Bündels, Z. angew. Math. u. Mech., *10*, 585–596, 1930.

Boegehold, H., and Herzberger, M., Kann man zwei verschiedene Flächen ... scharf abbilden ? Compositio Mathematica, *1*, 448–476, 1935.

Boegehold, H., and Herzberger, M., Kugelsymmetrische Systeme, Z. angew. Math. u. Mech., *15*, 157–178, 1935.

Brauckhoff, H., Brechzahl und Dispersion optischer Glassorten im photographierbaren Ultrarot, Z. Instrumentenk., *59*, 154–162, 1939.

Bruns, H., Das Eikonal, Leipziger Sitz. ber., *21*, 321–436, 1895 (also published by S. Hirzel, Leipzig, 1895).

Buchdahl, H. A., Optical Aberration Coefficients, Oxford Univ. Press, London, 1954.

Carathéodory, C., Geometrische Optik, J. Springer, Berlin, 1937.

Carathéodory, C., Elementare Theorie des Spiegelteleskops von B. Schmidt, B. G. Teubner, Leipzig u. Berlin, 1940.

Chrétien, H., Cours de Calcul des Combinaisons Optiques, 3rd ed., Paris, Revue d'Optique, 1938.

Coddington, H., A System of Optics, Simpkin and Marshall, London, 1829 (Part I), 1830 (Part II).

Conrady, A. E., Applied Optics and Optical Design, Part I, Oxford Univ. Press, London, 1929.

Conrady, A. E., On the chromatic correction of object-glasses, Monthly Notices Roy. Astron. Soc., *64*, 182–188, 458–460, 1904.

Conrady, A. E., The optical sine-condition, Monthly Notices Roy. Astron. Soc., *65*, 501–509, 1905.

Conrady, A. E., Decentred lens-systems, Monthly Notices Roy. Astron. Soc., *79*, 384–390, 1919.

Cruickshank, F. D., A system of transfer coefficients for use in the design of lens systems, Proc. Phys. Soc., London, *57*, 350–361, 362–367, 419–429, 1945.

Cruickshank, F. D., The paraxial transfer coefficients of a lens system, J. Opt. Soc. Amer., *36*, 13–19, 1946.

Czapski, S., and Eppenstein, O., Grundzüge der Theorie der optischen Instrumente nach Abbe, Leipzig, J. A. Barth, 1924, 3rd ed.

Descartes, R., La dioptrique, See Œuvres de Descartes, *6*, 79–228, Ed. C. Adam and P. Tannery, Leopold Cerf, Paris, 1902.

[Descartes, R.] See Boegehold, Keplers Gedanken, etc., above.

Duffieux, P., L'intégrale de Fourier et ses applications à l'optique, Rennes, privately printed, 1946.

Duffieux, P., and Lansraux, G., Les facteurs de transmission et la lumière diffractée, Rev. opt., *24*, 65–230, 1945.

Dupin, C., Les routes suivies par la lumière dans les phénomènes de la réflexion, A. L. Cauchy's Bericht Ann. chim. et phys, (2) *5*, 85–88, 1817.

Euclid, Catoptrica, in Opera omnia, 6th ed., Ed. L. I. Heiberg, B. G. Teubner, Leipzig, 1895.

Fraunhofer, J., Bestimmung des Brechungs- und Farbenzerstreuungsvermögens verschiedener Glasarten, etc., Münchn. Denkschr., *5*, 193–226, 1814–15. Also republished in Ostwald's Klassiker, No. 150, W. Engelmann, Leipzig, 1905.

Gardner, I. C., Validity of the cosine-fourth power law of illumination, J. Research Nat. Bur. Standards, *39*, 213–219, 1947.

Gauss, K. F., Disquisitiones Arithmeticae, 1801. German trans., H. Maser, Springer, Berlin, 1889.

Gullstrand, A., Allgemeine Theorie der monochromatischen aberrationen, etc., Nova Acta Reg. Soc. Sci. Upsala, *3*, 1900.

Gullstrand, A., Die reelle optische Abbildung, Svenska Vetensk. Handl., *41*, 1–119, 1906.

Gullstrand, A., Tatsachen und Fiktionen in der Lehre von der optischen Abbildung, Arch. Optik, *1*, 1–41, 81–97, 1907.

Gullstrand, A., Das allgemeine optische Abbildungssystem, Svenska Vetensk. Handl., *55*, 1–139, 1915.

[Hall, C. M.] See Court, T. H., and von Rohr, M., A history of the development of the telescope from about 1675 to 1830 based on documents in the Court Collection (third paper), Trans. Opt. Soc. London, *30*, 207–260, 1928–29, pp. 228–235. See also King, H. C., The Telescope, Ch. VIII, Sky Publishing Corp., Cambridge, Mass., 1955.

Hamilton, Sir W. R., The Mathematical Papers of Sir William Rowan Hamilton, Vol. I. Geometrical Optics, Cambridge Univ. Press, Cambridge, 1931. Also German edition by George Prange, Abhandlung zur Strahlenoptik, Akademische Verlagsges., Leipzig, 1933.

Harting, H., Zur Theorie der zweitheiligen verkitteten Fernrohrobjektive, Z. Instrumentenk., *18*, 357–380, 1898.

Harting, H., Zur Berechnung von Fernrohrobjektiven, Z. Instrumentenk., *29*, 365–368, 1909.

Hero of Alexandria, Opera quae supersunt omnia, 303–365, Ed. Nix & Schmidt, B. G. Teubner, Leipzig, 1900. See also E. Wilde, Geschichte der Optik, Rücker and Püchler, Berlin, 1838.

Herzberger, M., Die Gesetze zweiter Ordnung in einfach-symmetrischen Systemen, Z. Physik., *74*, 88-109, 1932.

Herzberger, M., Über Sinusbedingung, Kosinusrelation, Isoplanasie- und Homöoplanasiebedingung, ihren Zusammenhang mit energetischen Überlegungen und ihre Ableitung aus dem Fermatschen Gesetz, Z. Instrumentenk., *48*, 313–327, 465–490, 524–540, 1928.

Herzberger, M., Über die Gesetze zweiter Ordnung längs einem Meridianstrahl in Rotationssystemen, Z. Instrumentenk., *48*, 384–386, 1928.

Herzberger, M., Über nahfeldscharfe Abbildung, Physik. Z., *31*, 805–806, 1930.

Herzberger, M., Strahlenoptik, J. Springer, Berlin, 1931.

Herzberger, M., Geschichtlicher Abriss der Strahlenoptik, Z. Instrumentenk., *52*, 429–435, 485–493, 534–542, 1932.

Herzberger, M., Zur Optik inhomogener Mittel, Z. Instrumentenk., *53*, 436–443, 1933.

Herzberger, M., Die Hauptsätze der Abbildung der Umgebung eines Strahls in allgemeinen optischen Systemen, Z. Instrumentenk., *54*, 337–350, 381–392, 429–441, 1934.

Herzberger, M., On the fundamental optical invariant, the optical tetrality principle, and on the new development of Gaussian optics based on this law, J. Opt. Soc. Amer., *25*, 295–304, 1935.

Herzberger, M., A simplified theory of the image errors according to L. Seidel, J. Opt. Soc. Amer., *26*, 35–51, 1936.

Herzberger, M., First-order laws in asymmetrical optical systems. Part I. The image of a given congruence: Fundamental conceptions, J. Opt. Soc. Amer., *26*, 354–359, 1936. Part II. The image congruences belonging to the rays emerging from a point in object and image space: Fundamental forms, J. Opt. Soc. Amer., *26*, 389–406, 1936.

Herzberger, M., Theory of microscope vision, J. Opt. Soc. Amer., *26*, 52–62, 1936.

Herzberger, M., Normal systems with two caustic lines, J. Opt. Soc. Amer., *29*, 392-394, 1939; *30*, 307-308, 1940.

Herzberger, M., Theory of image errors of the fifth order in rotationally symmetrical systems. I., J. Opt. Soc. Amer., *29*, 395–406, 1939.

Herzberger, M., The dispersion of optical glass, J. Opt. Soc. Amer., *32*, 70–77, 1942.

Herzberger, M., Gaussian optics and Gaussian brackets, J. Opt. Soc. Amer., *33*, 651–655, 1943.

Herzberger, M., and Hoadley, H., The calculation of aspherical correcting surfaces, J. Opt. Soc. Amer., *36*, 334–340, 1946.

Herzberger, M., The limitations of optical image formation, Ann. N. Y. Acad. Sci., *48*, 1–30, 1946.

Herzberger, M., and Morris, R., A contribution to the method of least squares, Quart. Appl. Math., *5*, 354–357, 1947.

Herzberger, M., Light distribution in the optical image, J. Opt. Soc. Amer., *37*, 485–493, 1947.

Herzberger, M., Performance of an optical system as the sum of the contributions of its construction elements, J. Opt. Soc. Amer., *38*, 324–328, 1948.

Herzberger, M., and Jenkins, H., Color correction in optical systems and types of glass, J. Opt. Soc. Amer., *39*, 984–989, 1949.

Herzberger, M., The normal equations of the method of least squares and their solution, Quart. Appl. Math., *7*, 217–223, 1949.

Herzberger, M., Some remarks on ray tracing, J. Opt. Soc. Amer., *41*, 805–807, 1951.

Herzberger, M., and Marchand, E., Image error theory for finite aperture and field, J. Opt. Soc. Amer., *42*, 306–321, 1952.

Herzberger, M., Precalculation of optical systems, J. Opt. Soc. Amer., *42*, 637–640, 1952.

Herzberger, M., The contributions of the single surfaces to the diapoint coordinates, J. Opt. Soc. Amer., *42*, 544–546, 1952.

Herzberger, M., Approximate methods in mathematics, Proc. Nat. Acad. Sci., *39*, 853–860, 1953.

Herzberger, M., and Marchand, E., Tracing a normal congruence through an optical system, J. Opt. Soc. Amer., *44*, 146–154, 1954.

Herzberger, M., A mathematical model of an optical system, Optical Image Evaluation, Nat. Bur. Standards Circ. 526, 73–80, 1954.

Herzberger, M., Image errors and diapoint errors, Studies in Mathematics and Mechanics presented to Richard von Mises, Academic Press, New York, 1954.

Herzberger, M., A new method of designing lenses, International Projectionist, *31*, 7–8, 1956.

Herzberger, M., Analysis of spot diagrams, J. Opt. Soc. Amer., *47*, 584–594, 1957.

Herzberger, M., Automatic ray tracing, J. Opt. Soc. Amer., *47*, 736–739, 1957.

Hopkins, H. H., Wave Theory of Aberrations, Clarendon Press, Oxford, 1950.

Huygens, C., Œuvres complètes, Soc. hol. d. sci., M. Nijhoff, the Hague, 1888–1950. Eng. trans., S. P. Thompson, Macmillan and Co., Ltd., London, 1912.

Huygens, C., Dioptrica, C. Boutesteyn, Leiden, 1703. Reprinted in Opera reliqua, *2*, 1–202, Jansson-Waesberg, Amsterdam, 1728.

Huygens, C., Traité de la lumière, van der Aa, Leiden, 1690. Reprinted by Gressner u. Schramm. Leipzig, 1885. Latin trans. in Opera reliqua *1*, 1–92, Jansson-Waesberg, Amsterdam, 1728.

Ingelstam, E., and Lindberg, P. J., Apparatus and procedure for the examination of cameras and photographic lenses, especially of long focal length, Reports from the Laboratory of Optics, No. 9, Royal Institute of Technology, Stockholm, 1950.

Ingelstam, E., and Lindberg, P. J., A combined test procedure for camera lenses, and photoelectric examination of intensity distribution in line images, Optical Image. Evaluation, Nat. Bur. Standards Circ. 526, 171–182, 1954.

Kapany, N. S., Fiber optics. Part I. Optical properties of certain dielectric cylinders, J. Opt. Soc. Amer., *47*, 413–422, 1957.

Kapany, N. S., Eyer, J. A., and Keim, R. E., Fiber optics. Part II. Image transfer on static and dynamic scanning with fiber bundles, J. Opt. Soc. Amer., *47*, 423–427, 1957.

Kapany, N. S., and Hopkins, R. E., Fiber optics. Part III. Field flatteners, J. Opt. Soc. Amer., *47*, 594–598, 1957.

[Kepler, J.] Bibliographica Kepleriana, Ed. M. Caspar, Munich, 1936.

Kepler, J., Dioptrice, etc., Franc, Augsburg, 1611. Reprinted in Opera omnia, 2, Ed. C. Frisch, Heyden und Zimmer, Frankfurt, 1859. German trans., Ostwald's Klassiker, No. 144, W. Engelmann, Leipzig, 1904.

Kepler, J., Gesammelte Werke, Bay. Akad. d. Wiss., Ed. W. van Dyck and M. Caspar, Beck, Munich, 1937–1955.

[Kepler, J.] Kepler-Festschrift, Ed. K. Stöckel, H. Schiele, Regensburg, Vol. I, 1930; Vol. II (bibliography), 1931, being Vols. 19 and 20 of Ber. naturw. Ver. Regensburg, 1928/30 and 1931.

Kepler, J., Ad Vitellionem paralipomena, etc., Ed. Marnium and Aubrii, Frankfurt, 1604. Reprinted in Opera omnia, *2*, Ed. C. Frisch, Heyden und Zimmer, Frankfurt, 1859. German trans., Ostwald's Klassiker, No. 198, W. Engelmann, Leipzig, 1922.

[Kepler, J.] A Tercentenary Commemoration, etc. (bibliography), Hist. Sci. Soc., Williams and Wilkins Co., Baltimore, 1931.

Kerber, A. Über die Korrektur von Systemen grösserer Öffnung, Central-Ztg. Opt. u. Mech., *8*, 145–146, 1887.

Kerber, A., Beiträge zur Dioptrik, Vols. II–V, G. Fock, Leipzig, 1896, 1897, 1898, 1899.

Kerber, A,. Ein Taylor-Objektiv für astronomische Zwecke, Z. Instrumentenk., *35*, 23–31, 1915.

Kingslake, R., and Kingslake, H., A refractometer for the near infrared, J. Opt. Soc. Amer., *27*, 257–262, 1937.

Kohlschütter, A., Die Bildfehler fünfter Ordnung optischer Systeme, etc., Kaestner, Inaugural Dissertation, Göttingen, 1908.

Linfoot, E. H., Recent Advances in Optics, Clarendon Press, Oxford, 1955.

Linfoot, E., and Fellgett, P., On the assessment of optical images, Phil. Trans. Roy. Soc. London, *247*, 369–407, 1955.

Luboshez, B., U. S. Patent 1,910,115, 1933.

Malus, E. L., Optique, J. école polytech., *7*, 1–44, 84–129, 1808.

Maréchal, A., Influence des aberrations géométriques sur la tache de diffraction, Cahiers Phys., No. 26, 1–15, 1944.

Maréchal, A., Étude des effets combinés de la diffraction et des aberrations géométriques sur l'image d'un point lumineux, Thesis, Revue d'Optique, Paris, 1948.

Maréchal, A., Propriétés générales des faibles aberrations, Rev. opt., *27*, 649–656, 1948.

Maréchal, A., The contrast of optical images and the influence of aberrations, Optical Image Evaluation, Nat. Bur. Standards Circ. 526, 9–22, Washington, 1954.

Marx, H., Linearisierung der Durchrechnungsformeln für windschiefe Strahlen, Optica Acta, *1*, 127–140, 1954.

Maxwell, J. C., On the application of Hamilton's characteristic function, etc., Proc. London Math. Soc., *6*, 117–122, 1874–1875.

Newton, I., A new theory about light and colours, Phil. Trans., *6*, 3075 et alia, 1672.

Newton, I., Opticks, first ed., Smith and Walford, London, 1704; fourth ed., Innys, London, 1730. Fourth ed. reprinted by Dover Publications, New York, 1952. German trans., Ostwald's Klassiker, Nos. 96–97, W. Engelmann, Leipzig, 1898.

Newton, I., Lectiones Opticae, etc., London, 1728. Republished by J. Manfré, Padua, 1773.

Nijboer, R. A., The diffraction theory of optical aberrations, Physica, *13*, 605–620, 1947.

Petzval, J., Bericht über dioptrische Untersuchungen, Wiener Sitz. ber., *26*, 33–90, 1857.

Ptolemy, L'ottica di Claudio Tolomeo, etc., Ed. G. Govi, G. B. Paravia, Turin, 1885.

Reiss, M., The cos⁴ law of illumination, J. Opt. Soc. Amer., *35*, 283–288, 1945.

Reiss, M., Notes on the cos⁴ law of illumination, J. Opt. Soc. Amer., *38*, 980–986, 1948.

Ronchi, V., Optics, The Science of Vision, Eng. trans., E. Rosen, University Press, New York, 1957.

Schade, O., A new system of measuring and specifying image definition, Optical Image Evaluation, Nat. Bur. Standards Circ. 526, 231–249, 1954.

Schade, O., Image gradation, graininess, and sharpness in television and motion-picture systems, J. Soc. Motion Picture Television Engrs., *64*, 593–617, 1955.

Schade, W., and Frederick, C.W., U. S. Patent 2, 165, 365, 1939.

Schleiermacher, L., Über den Gebrauch der analytischen Optik, etc., Pogg. Ann., *14*, 1828.

Schleiermacher, L., Analytische Optik, Z. Physik u. Math., *9*, 1831. 1–35, 161–178, 454–474, 1831; *10*, 171–200 329–357, 1832.

Schleiermacher, L., Analytische Optik, Jonghaus, Darmstadt, 1842.

Schwarzschild, K., Untersuchungen zur geometrischen Optik, Abhandl. Ges. Wiss. Göttingen, N. F. *4*, Nos. 1–3, 1905.

Schwarzschild, K., Über Spektrographenobjektive, Sitzber. preuss. Akad. Wiss. Berlin, *53*, 1220–1239, 1912.

Seidel, L., Zur Dioptrik. Über die Entwicklung der Glieder 3ter Ordnung, etc., Astron. Nachr., *43*, 289–332, 1856.

Slevogt, H., Über eine Gruppe von aplanatischen Spiegelsystemen, Z. Instrumentenk., *62*, 312–327, 1942.

Slevogt, H., and Drodofsky, M., Zur Theorie des anallaktischen Punktes, Optik, *7*, 23–26, 1950.

Slevogt, H., Die Verzeichnung als Funktion der Bildlage, Optik, *6*, 321–326, 1950.

Slevogt, H., Über die Seidelschen Formeln bei Elimination des Objektstrahls, Optik, *8*, 180–186, 1951.

Slevogt, H., Zur Auswertung Seidelscher Rechnungen: Vergleich mit Fehlerdarstellungen nach v. Rohr und mit reduzierten Aberrationen, Optik, *8*, 537–541, 1951.

Slusareff, G., Methods of Calculation of Optical Systems (in Russian), United Scientific and Technical Publishing Houses, Moscow, 1937.

Slusareff, G., Geometrical Optics (in Russian), Moscow, Akad. Nauk., 1946.

Smith, T., The changes in aberrations when the object and stop are moved, Trans, Opt. Soc. London, *23*, 311–322, 1921–22.

Smith, T., Presidential Address: Some uncultivated optical fields, Trans. Opt. Soc. London, *28*, 225–284, 1926–1927.

Smith, T., On tracing rays through an optical system, Proc. Phys. Soc. London, *27*, 502–510, 1915; *30*, 221–233, 1917; *32*, 252–264, 1920; *33*, 174–178, 1921; *57*, 286–293, 1945.

[Snell, W.] See Boegehold, Keplers Gedanken, etc., above.

[Snell, W.] Risneri opticam cum annotationibus Willibrordi Snellii, Pars prima, librum primum continens, Ed. I. A. Vollgraff, Plantini, Ghent, 1918. (Werken, uitg. von d. Rijksuniversiteit Gent, No. 3.)

Synge, J. L., Geometrical Optics, Cambridge Univ. Press, London, 1937.
Taylor, H. D., A System of Applied Optics, Macmillan and Co., Ltd., London, 1906.
Tillyer, F. D., Optics and the glass industry, J. Opt. Soc. Amer., *28*, 1–4, 1938.
Toraldo di Francia, G., Le onde evanescenti nella diffrazione, Ottica, (2) *7*, 3–11, 1942.
Toraldo di Francia, G., Introduzione alla teoria geometrica e interferenziale delle onde aberranti, Atti Fondazione "Giorgio Ronchi", *2*, 1–45, 1947.
Toraldo di Francia, G., Utilisation des résultats du calcul de la marche des rayons dans un système optique, Rev. opt., *31*, 381–392, 1952.
Toraldo di Francia, G., Electromagnetic Waves, Interscience Publishers, New York and London, 1953.
Toraldo di Francia, G., On the image sharpness in the central field of a system presenting third- and fifth-order spherical aberration, J. Opt. Soc. Amer., *43*, 827–835, 1953.
Toraldo di Francia, G., Geometrical and interferential aspects of the Ronchi test, Optical Image Evaluation, Nat. Bur. Standards Circ. 526, 161–169, Washington, 1954.
Toraldo di Francia, G., Resolving power and information, J. Opt. Soc. Amer., *45*, 497–501, 1955.
Wachendorf, F., Bestimmung der Bildfehler 5. Ordnung in zentrierten optischen Systemen, Optik, *5*, 80–122, 1949.
Wandersleb, E., Tücken der Cosinuspotenzen, etc., Z. wiss. Phot., *46*, 16–60, 1951.
Wandersleb, E., Die Lichtverteilung im Grossen in der Brennebene des photographischen Objektivs, Akademie-Verlag, Berlin, 1952.
Wilde, E., Geschichte der Optik, Rücker and Püchler, Berlin, 1838.
Witelo, see Alhazen, Opticae thesaurus, etc., Vol. II, above.
Zernike, F., Beugungstheorie des Schneidenverfahrens und seiner verbesserten Form, der Phasenkontrastmethode, Physica, *1*, 689–704, 1934.

INDEX

This index includes subjects and persons mentioned in the text, exclusive of the bibliography. Names of persons are in small capitals. References are to pages, and extensive treatments are indicated by italics.

* Recent investigations by O. Neugebauer have drawn attention to an eclipse seen by Hero which took place in 68 B.C. This gives a definite time for his life, which in the literature has been set as early as 250 B.C. and as late as A.D. 250.

S

T

U

V

W

Z